17126

£12-50

Hawker Aircraft

since 1920

British Aerospace Hawk T. Mark 1 XX238 of the Central Flying School in 1987.

Hawker Aircraft

since 1920

Francis K Mason

© Francis K Mason 1961, 1971 and 1991

Third revised edition 1991
Reprinted 1993

Published in Great Britain 1991 by
Putnam Aeronautical Books, an imprint of
Conway Maritime Press Ltd,
101 Fleet Street,
London EC4Y 1DE

British Library Cataloguing in Publication Data
Mason, Francis K. (Francis Kenneth) 1928–
Hawker Aircraft since 1920. – 3rd ed.
1. Hawker aeroplanes, history
I. Title
623.746
ISBN 0 85177 839 9

Typeset by Inforum Typesetting, Portsmouth, Hants
Printed in Great Britain at the Alden Press, Oxford

CONTENTS

ACKNOWLEDGEMENTS

THE views expressed in this book are those of the author and should not be construed as being those necessarily held by the Directors of the Companies about whose work the book is written. The author, however, acknowledges with gratitude the permission of the Directors, Hawker Aircraft Ltd, granted him to prepare this work and to record the fact that full access has been allowed to countless company records and historical documents.

The name of the late Sir Sydney Camm, CBE, FRAES, should be recorded in particular, as without constant reference to records of his superlative achievements this book could not have been written.

Members of the industry who have contributed much useful information are Sir W G Armstrong Whitworth Aircraft Ltd, The Austin Motor Co, Ltd, A V Roe & Co, Ltd, The Bristol Aeroplane Co, Ltd, Boulton-Paul Aircraft Ltd, Bristol Siddeley Engines Ltd, General Aircraft Ltd, Gloster Aircraft Company Ltd, D Napier and Sons, Ltd, Rolls-Royce Ltd, Vickers-Armstrong (Aircraft) Ltd, and Westland Aircraft Ltd.

Other useful information and material has been furnished from time to time by R Cross, C Peckham, R H Shaw (of Hawker Aircraft Ltd) and R Sturtivant, and the author expresses his gratitude to Owen Thetford, author of the companion volumes, *Aircraft of the Royal Air Force, 1918–1959* and *British Naval Aircraft, 1912–1959*, and to A J Jackson, author of *British Civil Aircraft, 1919–1959*, for their advice and assistance during the compilation of this work, to Bruce Robertson for the benefit of his wide knowledge of individual aircraft histories, to A Lumsden, ARAES, a driving force behind aviation historical research in the Royal Aeronautical Society, to the Staffs of the Air Historical Branch, Air Ministry, and Imperial War Museum, and particularly to the late L E Bradford, who applied his customary thoroughness in the preparation of the line drawings.

Finally acknowledgement is due, though cannot adequately be expressed, to the many Royal Air Force Officers who have, during the past thirty years, made loans of personal records, log books and so on, which have formed the basis on which the notes on individual aircraft have been compiled.

INTRODUCTION TO THIS EDITION

WHEN this book was first published, almost thirty years ago, the Hawker company, then Hawker Aircraft Limited, was about forty years old. Sir Sydney Camm was still Chief Designer. The awe-inspiring P.1127 vertical take-off prototype had just achieved its first successful hover in the hands of Bill Bedford, then the company's Chief Test Pilot. Elsewhere, TSR-2 was still the gleam in many an Air Staff eye. Concorde was still a paper dart. The Duncan Sandys Defence White Paper, stating confidently that the Lightning would be the last manned fighter, still overshadowed the aircraft industry; America and the Soviet Union, it seems, had not bothered to read it.

I was employed in the Hawker Project Office, having been invited by Sir Sydney to join the company after eight years in the Royal Air Force. Among my extra-mural jobs was that of collecting together a detailed history of the company, principally, I suspected, for Camm's own satisfaction. One day I took it to his office to announce that it was finished up to date — only to meet with the characteristically Camm-like reply: 'So what? I assume you'll continue to keep it up to date . . .'.

In due course my old friend, the late John Huntington wrote to me asking if I would like Putnams to publish the Hawker history in roughly the same format as Owen Thetford's *Aircraft of the Royal Air Force*. If it proved successful, it was suggested that it might be followed by other books on the products of single manufacturers. This book, with the kind sanction of Sir Sydney, thus became my first published work (I fear it showed), but was indeed the first member of a veritable bookshelf of 'Putnam histories' that gained an enviable reputation, not only for authority and accuracy, but on account of their many illustrious authors.

I parted company with Hawker when a certain — perhaps I should say uncertain — Government decided that Britain did not need to produce her own excellent aeroplanes and, at a stroke, cancelled, *inter alia*, the Hawker P.1154, thereby effectively cutting the ground from under the Project Office in Kingston, and, conveniently forgotten by the politicians of the same shade, making 70,000 people unemployed throughout the industry over a period of six months.

The Wilson administration staggered from blunder to blunder. First it ordered the American F-111, then changed its mind and had to forfeit a penalty of hundreds of millions of pounds by way of cancellation costs. It then ordered the Phantom — already ten-year-old technology — specifying a British engine which, it transpired, was good but fundamentally unsuitable.

For Hawker at Kingston the gloom and despondency were shortlived,

vii

for there arose, Phoenix-like from the ashes of cancellation, the Harrier project. Sir Sydney Camm lived just long enough to see this manifestation of his enthusiasm for the vertical take-off principle justified, for in 1966 the great man died — in harness.

I do not believe that Sir Sydney had the slightest premonition of his death, yet, about six weeks earlier, he had written to me asking if I would consider writing his autobiography, and when I visited his office he handed over a vast quantity of old records, correspondence and other material which, he said, I should sift through and use or dispose of as I thought fit.

Alas, I was never able to talk to Sir Sydney again, and what would then have been a biography remained stillborn. Although my own life had moved away from the aircraft industry into writing and publishing, I always maintained a close interest in the fortunes of the company, marvelling in the exploits of the superlative Harrier, and keeping in touch with former colleagues in the Project Office, some of whom reached the highest echelons of their profession.

The year 1989 brought with it the death of Hawker's venerated Chairman for so many years, and latterly President of the Hawker Siddeley Group. Sir Thomas Sopwith, at the age of 100 years, was unquestionably the greatest man in British aviation — a fact so unreservedly acknowledged by today's captains of industry on the occasion of his 100th birthday. Yet in all those unqualified tributes, and those of his obituaries soon after, scarce mention was made of the true debt owed by the nation to Sir Thomas. Much was made, and rightly so, of his Board's decision, in 1936, to go ahead with production of the Hurricane in advance of a Government order, yet overlooked was the fact that for three years he had been working to save Britain's aircraft industry from extinction. The creation of the giant Hawker Siddeley Group — not by the modern method of predatory acquisition of reluctant and healthy companies — placed great manufacturers such as A V Roe & Co, Sir W G Armstrong Whitworth Aircraft, Gloster Aircraft and Armstrong Siddeley, then facing difficult times, on a firm footing. Subcontracts to build Hawker aeroplanes, moreover, were not confined to his Group, but were also awarded to Vickers-Armstrong, Westland, General Aircraft, Boulton-Paul and Bristols. Almost every one of those companies was facing the alternative of laying off large numbers of their workforces, and would have unquestionably had to do so had not Sopwith forcefully advocated the distribution of subcontracts *throughout* the industry. Moreover, of course, every one of those subcontracted aeroplanes originated at Kingston under the design leadership of Sydney Camm.

The past two decades have been traumatic years for Britain's aircraft industry, although, at a superficial glance, the affairs of the old Hawker company appear to have proceeded with less crisis than elsewhere. The unique ability to boast that Britain's air forces have never been without a Kingston-designed and built aeroplane still holds as good today as it did thirty years ago, thanks to the Harrier, Sea Harrier and Hawk, but many names have gone forever, not simply swallowed up through amalgamation, but shut down and their incomparable workforces dispersed. The Hawker Siddeley Group continued to grow, embracing such companies as de Havilland, Blackburn and Folland. Gradually, in the 1960s, the industry moved into an era of rationalisation, the creation of three large groups of adequate size and resources to meet foreign competition on an equal footing. As well as the Hawker Siddeley Group, there was the British Aircraft Corporation, which combined the aviation interests of Vickers, English Electric, Bristol Aeroplanes and Hunting-Percival, while Rolls-Royce created an aero-engine group embracing Bristol Engines and Armstrong Siddeley. Those companies which preferred to maintain their independence, such as Handley Page, withered and died, and the names of Hawker and Siddeley, the one a young Australian who saved the Kingston factory in 1920, and the other a trust established by Sopwith in 1934 to save other companies from bankruptcy, lived on.

Yet apparently the voluntary rationalisation of the 1960s did not satisfy socialist dogma, besotted with state ownership and preferring as an alternative to private enterprise (the industry has always thrived on the genius of individualists) control by politicians and ministries — men whom Camm referred to as 'busybodies and professional amateurs'. Accordingly, in 1977, the entire aircraft industry, defined as those companies possessing, or aspiring to acquire government contracts, was nationalised. The name Hawker Siddeley, though no longer alive in the aircraft industry itself, survived through its diversified interests, for Sir Thomas Sopwith, having seen the writing on the wall, encouraged his fellow directors to diversify into other fields in order to survive. The Kingston and Dunsfold factories became divisions within the giant semimonopolistic, state-owned British Aerospace conglomerate.

Tycoons and industrialists, some of them less than adequately versed in the particular character of the aircraft industry, were appointed to positions of considerable responsibility, their earnings being equated with other state corporation executives rather than with their suitability to administer the nation's best interests in matters of defence.

Alas, many of the most gifted and important figures in the industry who preferred, metaphorically, to touch their forelock to a boss in the next office with whom they had worked over a lifetime of learning, left to offer their services elsewhere. Anything, they argued, was better than being wholly beholden to an anonymous cipher in a Whitehall office.

Now the wheel has turned full circle. The aircraft industry is once more a private enterprise, albeit virtually monopolistic through financial necessity. Thanks largely to a legacy of nationalisation, however, the character of the industry has undergone a subtle, some would say an ominous change. Individual elements of the industry have lost their identity in the American-style corporate philosophy. The eagerness to make money first, and aeroplanes second, is an endemic feature of

British Aerospace management today, and is entirely justifiable just so long as the company can continue to produce the aeroplanes that the market needs and can afford. If, however, the policy is carried too far, and the company fails to retain its greatest assets — the highly experienced design teams, qualified technicians and shop-floor workforces — the company itself will be neither a money-maker nor a plane-maker.

The centre of gravity of the industry shows signs of edging northwards, a situation that is viewed with some alarm at Kingston, for it is feared that concentration of all aircraft design and production could, in the foreseeable future, take place in the 'industrial north'. After all, it is pointed out, the established basis of collaboration which was created between the old Hawker Siddeley Group and McDonnell-Douglas almost twenty years ago, and which has since resulted in the shared production of the Harrier and Hawk, and their derivatives, now exists with British Aerospace as a whole, not simply with a Kingston factory.

Alas, the subject of history is not advocated reading among the captains of industry. This is a pity, for all too often such men of undoubted talents would do well to understand how their predecessors managed to satisfy their shareholders *and* serve their country best, and avoid the pitfalls of personal prestige. Alas, when these whizzkids of the company balance sheet fall, they take their company with them.

* * *

THE advent of new aircraft does not constitute the only change in this edition of *Hawker Aircraft* from those published previously. Constant research has enabled more light to be thrown on the events of earlier days, and this is particularly so in the instance of the Hornbill fighter. Records available to me in 1960 suggested that this aeroplane was first flown in mid-1926, and Camm's correspondence mentions that 'it was his first British interceptor design'. In fact this reference was almost certainly intended to imply that it was the first such aeroplane *in the design of which* he was involved at Hawkers. It is now clear, as a result of research by Mr Philip Jarrett (*Aeroplane Monthly*, September and October 1985), that the Hornbill first flew in mid-1925, and that therefore it was certainly designed under the leadership of W G Carter before he left for the Gloucestershire Aircraft Company that year. Camm was thus probably responsible for the extensive modifications that took place thereafter.

This is of great significance in the early history of British fighter design, for it throws an entirely new light upon Carter's ability to match, and indeed surpass by a considerable margin, the performance of the Fairey Fox light bomber which, with a speed of over 150 miles per hour, had first flown early in 1925. It does also, incidentally, tend to corroborate many anecdotes — previously judged to be apocryphal — relating to numerous covert escapades by both Hawker and Fairey to penetrate each other's security to learn the other's design secrets (what today would be termed 'industrial espionage')! Each company, believing that its product represented a fundamental breakthrough in technology, went to extraordinary lengths to protect those secrets. With a maximum speed approaching 200 miles per hour, the Hornbill in 1925 was certainly more than a match for the Fox, although, as told in this book, it failed to meet with the RAF's approval.

Interest in aviation history has, during the past thirty years, steadily increased, particularly among former serving members of the Royal Air Force and the Fleet Air Arm, who have gone out of their way, either privately or through the great museums, to make available countless personal photographs. The emphasis in this edition of the Hawker history has therefore shifted perceptibly to include more 'in-service' photographs and, in particular, those taken at Martlesham Heath and Felixstowe during evaluation by the RAF. This, I think, redresses the balance, for I was always aware that the earlier editions laid too much emphasis on my own close association with Hawker Aircraft, with an all-too-obvious dependence upon 'company' pictures. This was a reflection of the work's origin, referred to above.

Little further needs to be said here about the modern products of the Kingston factories. Unlike the aeroplanes of former years, whose span of service seldom reached a decade, the Hunter served for a quarter-century in Britain's air forces, and this will be matched ere long by the Harrier. This longevity, as well as their constant development and improvement, is reflected in the much-increased space devoted to these superlative aeroplanes. It should never be forgotten that, as recently as eight years ago, Britain would have been wholly incapable of mounting the operation to repossess the Falkland Islands had it not been for her ability to deploy Harriers and Sea Harriers to the South Atlantic. Their presence, and the skill and gallantry of their pilots, were the dominant factors of the entire operation.

The Sopwith legacy. A view of the Richmond Road factory in December 1918 showing Sopwith Snipes, Dolphins and Salamanders in production. Known officially as Aircraft Factory No. 1, these premises were leased by the H G Hawker Engineering Company to the Leyland Motor Company between 1928 and 1948, but today they accommodate the main Harrier production lines. Compare with pictures on page 74.

HAWKER AIRCRAFT SINCE 1920

FORMATION OF THE COMPANY

One day, late in 1920, the following Company Notice appeared in the Press:

'H. G. Hawker Engineering Co. Ltd. (171,409) — Private Company. Registered Nov. 15th. Capital £20,000 in £1 shares. To acquire from F. I. Bennett all the patents, rights, etc., relating to the manufacture of motor cycles, and to carry on the business of manufacturers of and dealers in cycles of all kinds, infernal [*sic*] combustion engines and steam engines, motor cars, aircraft, etc. The first directors are: F. I. Bennett, 19 Cadogan Road, Surbiton, engineer; H. G. Hawker, "Ennerdale", Hook Road, Surbiton, aeroplane pilot; T. O. M. Sopwith, Horsley Towers, Surrey, engineer; F. Sigrist, Torrington House, Wolsey Road, East Molesey, engineer; V. W. Eyre, Honeyhanger, Hindhead, Surrey, engineer. Qualification £500. Sec.: F. I. Bennett. Registered Office: Canbury Park Road, Kingston-upon-Thames.'

Behind this austere announcement lay a web of financial intricacies. Due largely to a lack of any coherent Government policy towards aviation in general, and military aviation in particular, the years following the First World War were lean indeed where the aircraft industry was concerned. Squadron after squadron of the newly-born Royal Air Force disbanded, until the fighter defence of Great Britain rested upon but a single squadron of Sopwith Snipes. Nor was the slightest incentive in evidence to support and invigorate the industry — an industry that had scarcely existed half-a-dozen years earlier. The emphasis lay in making do with the countless war-surplus aircraft, with the result that many companies were obliged to eke out an existence on 'hospital' contracts. T O M Sopwith had courageously advocated the growth of commercial aviation and had striven to place on the market a fairly wide range of civil aircraft until, through lack of adequate support and orders, the company was forced to seek continued existence in the manufacture of motor cycles and car bodies. However, successful though these products undoubtedly proved, the Sopwith company could scarcely pay its way, and when, in 1920, the Treasury for Excess War Profits Duty lodged an enormous claim against the firm, the day of reckoning arrived. The year had witnessed heavy trading losses by the Sopwith company, yet, had it been possible to write these off against the Excess Profits Duty claim, the firm might have been in a position to continue its activities.

1

The Sopwith legacy. The old Canbury Park Road offices taken over by H G Hawker Engineering Co Ltd, in 1920 and only vacated in 1959 with the building of the administrative block in Richmond Road.

Unfortunately the claim could not be written off immediately and so, in order to protect the interests of the creditors, it was deemed wise to put the affairs of the company in the hands of a receiver.

To effect the necessary extreme measures of economy, the joint managing director, R O Carey, and the secretary, Musgrave, voluntarily relinquished their posts and left them vacant. Other savings were achieved by increasing the mortgages on the company premises, with the result that not only was the Treasury claim met in full, but the company was able to pay twenty shillings in the pound to every creditor.

Before the Sopwith Aviation Company was declared solvent once more, however, the new firm of H G Hawker Engineering Co Ltd was announced. Indeed Harry Hawker, on learning of Sopwith's difficulties, had been among the first to offer assistance, only to meet with Sopwith's determination to put his own house in order before making any plans to join in the creation of a new company. Hawker did, nevertheless, suggest that he should take over the mortgage of the Canbury Park Road premises, and by the time the formation notice was published his company already occupied a large part of the Sopwith premises in Kingston.

Despite the stated intention to continue the manufacture of motor cycles, it needs little imagination, having regard for the names of the new company's directors, to understand the yearning to re-enter the world of aviation. It is therefore not surprising to find that almost

2

A Hawker motor car of 1921 photographed in Canbury Park Road.

The late Harry Hawker.

immediately contracts were accepted by Hawker to recondition large numbers of war-surplus aircraft — mostly Sopwith Snipes and various de Havilland aircraft.

Then, on 12 July 1921, came the saddest blow suffered in the history of the two companies. Harry Hawker, who was due to compete in the Aerial Derby in ten days time, died at the controls of a Nieuport Goshawk, which he was testing in preparation for the race. For some considerable time it had been known that this gallant pilot had been suffering from a tubercular disease of the spine, but such was his persevering character that he had not considered this to be a handicap to his sporting activities. It appears that, while executing a tight turn near the ground under relatively high g-loading, he suffered a haemorrhage and died before the aircraft crashed. It is unlikely that any airman has ever been more widely mourned than Harry Hawker, for his many exploits had been performed in a rapidly shrinking world — shrinking by reason of the air travel to which he had already contributed so much during the ten embryonic years of aviation. Thus passed the man whose name has been carried by his company and immortalised in the title of the enormous Hawker Siddeley Group of more recent times.

By the time of Hawker's death his company had reached firmer ground, with plenty of work in hand. More of the old Sopwith factory was occupied and, as motor car and motor cycle manufacture was gradually tailed off, more and more Snipes were returned to the factory for reconditioning.

Lest the term 'reconditioning' should imply a superficial inspection and new coat of dope, it should be said that such a course was entirely alien to a man like Fred Sigrist. In fact it entailed dismantling each aircraft down to the smallest component. Every rib, frame and spar was minutely examined for cracks and warping of the wood; every metal fitting was sandblasted, examined and painted. Any faulty part was scrapped and replaced, the wooden members being of the best and most seasoned timber. The Bentley rotary engines were top-overhauled and thoroughly tested at Brooklands — much to the consternation of local residents, judging by the repeated complaints to the Weybridge Urban District Council.

Fred Sigrist, formerly Sopwith's works director, was now, in 1922, Hawkers' managing director, the other directors being T O M Sopwith, Maj V W Eyre, F I Bennett (also works manager) and Capt L F Peaty, brother-in-law of the late Harry Hawker. That the company intended to re-enter the aircraft manufacturing industry with designs of its own was evidenced by the appointment of a Chief Designer, Capt B Thomson.

EARLY HAWKER DESIGNS

Already the design office was filling with draughtsmen and, while the Government continued with its shortsighted policy of making do with war-surplus aeroplanes, faint rustlings of Specification papers could be heard in Whitehall offices as the true inadequacy of the Royal Air Force as a fighting Service was fully appreciated by the farsighted. Notwithstanding the illogical 'Ten Year Rule', whose tenets came to be reviled increasingly, until it was almost too late, by those whose responsibility it was to defend Britain, small concessions were made in the form of invitations to the aircraft industry for the production of a small number of prototypes. There was precious little evidence of constructive thought behind the formulation of these Specifications, rather the basic function of the aircraft was stipulated. In many instances the influence of army officers, with their entrenched ignorance of aviation matters, was all too apparent. The aircraft designer was therefore left to choose his powerplant and place what emphasis he deemed appropriate on the various aspects of design.

The result was a collection of prototypes, few of which could be considered to be realistic approaches to Service requirements — even if the Service knew what it wanted, and could afford what it was offered. Moreover, there still existed a prevailing atmosphere of deep-seated resentment between the three Services, each of which considered it had prior claims on the limited resources of the industry. Sir Hugh Trenchard, in his consuming efforts to safeguard the future of the Royal Air Force as an autonomous Service, gave scant thought to its equipment. When, in 1922, he began to realise the importance of providing the RAF with new aeroplanes, the interceptor fighter came to be placed near the bottom of the list of priorities. The bombing aeroplane, the Royal Air-Force's *raison d'être* according to Trenchard, came first.

It was against this uneasy background that Thomson, having reluctantly shelved a promising racing aircraft early in 1922, submitted two

The drawing offices in 1927.

5

designs to the Air Ministry in answer to Specifications, and both projects were accepted and ordered in prototype form.

The first was a two- or three-seat corps reconnaissance monoplane with a parasol wing and either a Siddeley Jaguar or Bristol Jupiter engine. Following the custom of the company, construction was entirely of wood, although later a fabric-covered metal wing was planned. The Duiker, for such was the highly inappropriate name bestowed on this machine, proved to be something of a disaster and, despite repeated attempts to rectify at least some of its unpleasant tendencies, the aircraft was firmly rejected by the Service evaluation establishment at Martlesham Heath. Among the pilots entrusted with the assessment of the Duiker was a Flt Lt A H Orlebar, a name to achieve worldwide fame in the final glorious years of the Schneider Trophy.

The other design submitted in 1922 was that of a small single-seat 'day and night interceptor' named the Woodcock and powered by a Siddeley Jaguar engine. Preliminary design was Thomson's responsibility, drawing extensively on the Sopwith Snipe, which, when faced with any uncertainty, the chief designer could simply examine in the factory shops. In other words the Woodcock, as it originally appeared, was to all intents and purposes little more than a 1918-vintage aircraft with a new signature on the drawings.

The first prototype Woodcock featured two-bay wings (as had the Snipe), and was completed in mid-1923, when it was flown by the company's retained pilot, F P Raynham. It then went to Martlesham for Service evaluation, where it was criticised on account of its lack of manoeuvrability. However, the Hawker company was encouraged to persevere with the design as the aircraft was considered to represent the basis of a promising interceptor.

By the time the Woodcock returned to Brooklands (where the Hawker company had taken over Sopwith's flight sheds and was to continue flying for another quarter century), Thomson had left Kingston, his place being taken by Wilfred George Carter, formerly Sopwith's chief draughtsman since 1916. Carter it was who now undertook an extensive redesign of the Woodcock.

By now the Hawker company had occupied the entire premises of the old Sopwith firm in Canbury Park Road in Kingston, including the famous skating rink next to the cinema, while progressive modernisation of plant was being undertaken. Sopwith Camels were now under reconstruction for the Royal Navy, Snipes were being converted into two-seaters, and a subcontract had been received to manufacture the landing gear of Fairey Fawns. A total of twenty-two draughtsmen was employed, these being engaged in no fewer than eight new designs, of which four came to be built.

To begin with, Carter revised the Woodcock, producing in the space of six weeks the drawings for a new set of single-bay wings and a new engine installation for the more powerful Bristol Jupiter radial. A new

Woodcocks under construction in Canbury Park Road.

This Woodcock, G-EBMA, was entered by the Company in the 1925 King's Cup Race, but suffered a forced landing due to bad weather.

prototype was built, its handling characteristics transformed and, following favourable comments at Martlesham Heath, the company was rewarded by a small production contract for ten aircraft, designated the Woodcock Mark II. As such it was destined to become the Royal Air Force's first Hawker fighter.

Mention should be made here of the company test pilots. During the early 1920s test flying was being developed into something approaching a science. However, the small number of what might be regarded as 'professional test pilots' were almost exclusively employed by the Royal Aircraft Establishment at Farnborough. Others, widely regarded as being pilots of long experience in checking out newly built aircraft, were retained *ad hoc* by manufacturers, as and when the necessity arose to fly a new product. Men like Fred Raynham, George Bulman and even

Harry Hawker had been retained to undertake preliminary flying of new aeroplanes by different manufacturers as the need arose, the bulk of development flying being carried out either at Farnborough or Martlesham Heath. Gradually, however, the pattern was changing as the number of new post-war aircraft designs increased. It was George Bulman who advocated the training at Farnborough of specialist test pilots who, once they were deemed proficient, might offer their services on a more permanent basis for exclusive employment by a manufacturer.

After Harry Hawker's death in 1921 the company frequently secured the services of Fred Raynham, who had attempted to fly the Atlantic in a Martinsyde at about the same time that Hawker had made his attempt. It is, however, for his sporting flying that Raynham is best remembered, having taken second place in the 1922 King's Cup Race (flying a Martinsyde), second in the Grosvenor Challenge Cup in 1923 in an Avro, and fourth position in the 1923 Aerial Derby. He had undertaken test flying in the Sopwith Antelope in 1922, and on coming to Hawker Engineering the following year, on a two-year contract, carried out all initial flying of the Duiker and Woodcock.

With the slow expansion of the aircraft industry and its struggle to exist in a buyer's market, it became all too obvious that the company test pilot must inevitably combine his powers of acute technical observation with an equally important ability to demonstrate the finer flying qualities of an aircraft to potential customers on the ground. As the salesman of an aircraft, apart from being the technician who accompanies it through the most exacting part of its early life, the test pilot has perhaps seldom received his true recognition. Throughout the years the Hawker company never lacked the services of test pilots of the very highest qualities; names like Raynham, Bulman, Sayer, Lucas, Wade, Duke, Bedford and Simpson became synonymous with British test flying, for these men, in their respective days, reached the pinnacle of their profession.

It was Raynham who demonstrated Hawkers' successful, though isolated, deviation into the realms of private flying in 1924, flying the ultralight Cygnet. The significance of this aircraft lay in two attributes, on the one hand in its remarkable design characteristics and on the other in its designer.

At about the same time that Raynham joined the H G Hawker Engineering Company the firm was also able to secure the services of a young draughtsman who had been with Martinsydes for some seven years, and who had considerable experience in the design and construction of wooden aircraft. His name was Sydney Camm. At once he joined Carter in the design of the military aircraft then in hand and, having displayed exceptional talent, was put in charge of the Cygnet design.

Camm's contribution to aviation had always been entirely practical and constructive. Before the war he had founded the Windsor Model Aeroplane Club, and had built a number of successful model aircraft,

SIR THOMAS SOPWITH, CBE, HON FRAeS. Aviator's Certificate No. 31 (1910) winner of various flying competitions in America, 1911. Founded Sopwith Aviation Co Ltd, 1913. Chairman and Joint Managing Director of Hawker companies from 1920. Chairman of SBAC, 1925–7. Chairman of Hawker Siddeley Group since 1936. Knighted, 1953, for services to aviation. Died 27 January 1989.

SIR SYDNEY CAMM, CBE, FRAeS. Joined Martinsydes, 1914. Joined G H Handasyde, 1921. Joined H G Hawker Engineering Co Ltd, 1923. Appointed Chief Designer, 1925. Director, 1935. Awarded British Gold medal for Aeronautics, 1949. Chairman, Technical Board of SBAC, 1951–53. Knighted, 1953, for services to Aviation. President, Royal Aeronautical Society, 1954–55. Appointed Chief Engineer, Hawker Aircraft Ltd, 1959. Died 12 March 1966.

and also a man-carrying glider. He then entered Martinsydes', gaining the essential background of factory shop techniques before eventually joining the design staff. In 1922 he and Fred Raynham together reconditioned a Martinsyde F.3 aircraft and gained second place in the first King's Cup Race ever held. In the same year a glider designed — and largely built — by Camm achieved a commendable performance in the International Gliding Meeting at Itford Hill.

The responsibility for the design of the Cygnet late in 1923 and 1924 was handed over to Camm by Carter because, as the latter confessed, he 'simply couldn't get used to thinking in terms of ounces instead of pounds'. The result was an achievement seldom equalled since, for the aeroplane weighed no more than 375 pounds — considerably lighter than the smallest drop tank carried under the wing of a modern fighter.

The RAE Aero Club's Hawker Cygnet, G-EBJH, passing the gate test in the 1926 Lympne Light Aeroplane Competition.

Two Cygnets were built and were entered for the Air Ministry Light Aeroplane Competition at Lympne in 1924. Flown by Raynham and Longton, they narrowly missed the second prize owing to engine trouble. Raynham, however, secured a £100 prize for the best take-off and pull-up, while Longton achieved the best landing performance. Nothing daunted, the Cygnet was entered for and won the 100-mile International Handicap Race at Lympne in 1925, piloted by Flt Lt P W S Bulman, of whom much will be related in due course. The following year the two Cygnets took first and second places in the *Daily Mail* competition for two-seat light aircraft.

The company was thus established with an aircraft (the Woodcock) in production for the Royal Air Force and a healthy number of projects under consideration. The latter included aircraft that were to

10

become known as the Danecock, Horsley, Hedgehog, Heron and Hornbill.

Until very recently it was always thought that the Hornbill was the first Hawker aircraft to be designed exclusively from the outset under the leadership of Sydney Camm, all company records stating that the aircraft first flew during May 1926. Recent research, however, has established that the prototype flew as early as July 1925, thus placing the aircraft firmly in the Carter regime. There is also evidence to suggest that Raynham, not Bulman, first flew the Hornbill.

Although Camm undoubtedly was involved in the design of the Hornbill — albeit under Carter's leadershp — the first Hawker fighter aircraft for which Camm assumed principal authority was the Danecock, a re-engined adaptation of the Woodcock for Denmark. Powered by the Armstrong-Siddeley Jaguar engine, three Danecocks were produced and exported to Denmark, the first of hundreds of Hawker aircraft to be chosen to equip the air forces of the world and contribute in ever-increasing value to the prestige of Britain's aircraft industry. Danecocks were subsequently built under licence at the Royal Danish Naval Dock-yard factory, remaining in service until 1937.

The saga of the Hedgehog remains somewhat obscure, and the reason for perseverance with the prototype remains unknown. It is, however, now known that the very first Hawker project, known as the Humpback, was the first design undertaken in the drawing office when the company began its shift back to aviation in 1920, and was probably a continuation of a Sopwith design scheme for a three-seat fleet spotter/reconnaissance aircraft whose general arrangement drawings carried the number A.1. As far is known, Thomson took no interest in pursuing the design, and it was not until Carter took over that interest returned to the fleet spotter requirement, and the Hedgehog was evolved and a prototype constructed. Featuring folding wings, the aeroplane was commented upon very favourably by the Service pilots who flew it but, with the Avro Bison, Blackburn Blackburn and Parnall Panther already in service, no contract was awarded for the Hedgehog. Further work was, however, officially sponsored on the prototype for development of a wheel/float amphibian undercarriage by the Marine Aircraft Experimental Establishment at Felixstowe in 1925.

Another important Hawker aircraft designed during the latter half of Carter's period of design leadership was the Horsley, although in its original configuration it failed to impress the Service. The two proto-types, being built before the Hawker shops had been equipped to cope with metal construction, were necessarily built entirely of wood, the first aircraft being flown at Brooklands before the end of 1924 (not in 1925 as stated in all surviving Hawker records).

Originally named the Kingston, but soon redesignated the Horsley (after Sopwith's home, Horsley Towers), the aircraft's design had been severely compromised from the outset by confused requirements

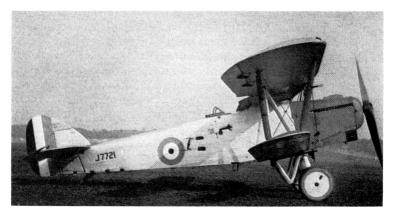

The second wooden Horsley prototype.

issued by the Air Ministry in 1923, where, faced with their customary financial limitations, the requirements department had attempted to combine the RAF's need for a 'medium' bomber with those of the Royal Navy for a torpedo bomber. Difficulties in arriving at a satisfactory compromise that allowed for the carriage of two 230 lb and two 112 lb bombs or a single 18-inch torpedo resulted in the Horsley being found to be too big for carrier operations and too heavy to carry adequate fuel to satisfy the RAF.

In 1925, however, when the Air Ministry tidied up its two requirements, Camm realised that a switch to metal construction in the Horsley would enable the aircraft to carry much more fuel, thereby satisfying the RAF's demands, while the requirement for the torpedo aircraft to be carrier-borne was dropped. On the strength of this attainable dual-rôle ability, the Horsley was ordered into production in 1926 and joined the Royal Air Force in 1927 as a 'medium' bomber, and as a torpedo bomber in 1928.

Despite the Horsley's long service both at home and overseas (the torpedo bombers served at Singapore until 1935), it is perhaps for the long-distance flights of 1927 that it will be best remembered. In that year a proposal was put foward (it is believed to have been originated by Trenchard himself) that the Royal Air Force should attempt a non-stop flight to India, a distance of some 5,000 miles. Such an achievement, apart from establishing a new world distance record, would undoubtedly bring the young Service considerable prestige.

Owing to the lack of a suitable machine capable in its normal configuration of anything approaching the necessary range, the project might have remained stillborn, but such were the potentialities of the Horsley, not yet fully tried, that Sopwith suggested that the

12

aircraft might be modified to accommodate the necessary fuel. An aircraft was duly taken from the production line and a series of range checks carried out from Brooklands. After strengthening of the undercarriage, stress calculations showed that the Horsley's take-off weight could be increased from 9,000 to over 14,000 pounds (it weighed less than 5,000 pounds empty), and the fuel capacity was increased from 230 to 1,100 gallons by the introduction of extra fuselage and wing tanks. The substitution of a larger fuselage tank resulted in the cockpit being moved further aft, while provision of a camp bed constituted the rather austere sleeping quarters!

The South Field at Cranwell, being one of the longest flying fields in the country, was chosen as the point of departure and, by May 1927, the aircraft was ready with its selected crew, Flt Lt C R Carr (later Air Marshal Sir Roderick, KBE, CB, DFC, AFC) and Flt Lt L E M Gillman. On 20 May, after some anxious moments when the heavily laden Horsley burst a tyre while being wheeled from the hangar, the record attempt started. The big machine executed a particulary exciting take-off run for some 800 yards across the undulating field (during which the wind suddenly backed round to port), narrowly missed a stone wall, and slowly climbed away to the south-east. After having been seen the same day passing over Ostend and Wiesbaden, nothing further was heard for two days.

Then on 22 May news arrived that Carr and Gillman had been forced down in the Persian Gulf (due, it was subsequently deduced, to fuel starvation), but that both occupants had been rescued after spending a night on their ditched aircraft. The empty wing tanks had no doubt served as useful buoyancy chambers. The aircraft had nevertheless covered a distance of 3,420 miles, just sufficient to beat the recently established figure (3,390 miles covered by Costes and Rignot in 1926 flying a Breguet 19 from Paris to Jask, Persia), and although Carr's achievement was recognised as a new record it was only to stand for a few hours. That same day Charles Lindbergh landed safely at Paris, having covered the 3,590 miles from New York.

Encouraged rather than dismayed, Carr made two further attempts to fly non-stop to India, both within a month of the first. Unfortunately neither achieved even the limited success of the first, for the second ended with a force landing on the Danube and the last, on 18 June, resulted in a stupendous landing of the overloaded Horsley on Martlesham Heath aerodrome. Bulman, now Hawkers' chief test pilot, who had been accompanying Carr in another machine for the opening stages of the flight, noticed a thin stream of spray issuing from the Horsley's radiator and, in view of overheating which would inevitably follow the loss of even a small quantity of coolant, Carr decided to land. In the event of trouble he had been advised to take to his parachute, but preferred to save the aeroplane.

No further record attempts were made by Horsleys, but several notable survey flights were performed by the RAF later. In January 1931 No.36 Squadron, stationed at Singapore with metal Horsley torpedo bombers, carried out a 4,300-mile survey to Calcutta and back, while in January 1933 the same unit flew to Peshawar, North-West Frontier — a return flight of 7,100 miles.

METAL CONSTRUCTION

Before dealing with the all-metal Heron design, it is necessary to return once more to the Hornbill fighter of 1925. As already mentioned, it is now known that this design emerged in prototype form a year earlier than had previously been thought, and therefore constituted an extremely advanced fighter design, possessing a maximum speed in the region of 190 miles per hour, almost 25 per cent higher than that of the Woodcock. The Hornbill employed a mixed wood and metal structure, the front fuselage and engine bearers comprising a duralumin-covered welded tubular steel frame, and the wooden rear fuselage and tail unit being fabric covered. The wings, of A.D.1 high-speed section, were built up using high quality spruce ribs and spars. It is undoubtedly significant to note that it was on account of Fred Sigrist's experience and qualification as a master welder that the choice of a welded steel structure was adopted, and it was originally the provision of a welding shop at Canbury Park Road that encouraged Carter to incorporate this structure. The lightweight nose frame proved perfectly strong enough to accommodate the heavy but very powerful Rolls-Royce Condor in what was, after all, a very small aeroplane.

The technical ingenuity, however, in close-cowling the big engine resulted in a very cramped cockpit and, on this account, the aeroplane was criticised by Service pilots who flew it. But it was for the marked lack of directional stability at speeds above 150 miles per hour that the Hornbill was ultimately rejected, and although considerable remedial work continued to be carried out on the prototype it never proceeded beyond the prototype stage. Even so, the Hornbill went on flying until May 1933.

After Carter left Hawkers to join the Gloucestershire (later Gloster) Aircraft Company in 1925, Camm questioned the benefits of the welded steel structure in the Hornbill, pointing to the shortage of men in the metal-working trades in the Royal Air Force. Instead he advocated the use of a much simpler form of metal tubular structure employing endplate joints bolted or riveted together to form prefabricated trusses and box sections to which stringers and formers could be attached for covering with ply or fabric.

Despite his own predilection for welded structures, Sigrist saw the immediate production advantages of Camm's proposal: airframe structures could be assembled almost anywhere in the factory without having to rely on a special welding shop. The repair of damaged airframes by the Service would also be simpler, and capable of being undertaken by field units rather than necessitating return to aircraft parks and depots. In Sigrist's own oft-quoted words, 'Find me a chippy with a spanner and we'll mend the aeroplane'.

The famous Hawker metal construction, developed by Camm and Sigrist during 1925, was so successful that it came to be employed on all Hawker aeroplanes up to 1943. The system incorporated round steel or duralumin tubes swaged to a rectangular section at their ends. To form joints, flat steel plates were riveted on to the tubes to which other tubes of either round or square section could be bolted. A cupped bolt was passed through the longeron to mount the lugs for the cross-bracing wires, which included turnbuckles for tensioning.

While the Hornbill was rejected mainly on account of handling shortcomings (and some difficulty in engine cooling), the all-metal Heron fighter on the other hand was unfortunate in not being ordered by the Royal Air Force. It was unquestionably a masterpiece without any vices. Every report that has been traced enthuses on the handling, manoeuvrability, control balance, pilot's field of view, and overall performance. The fact that it arrived after other fighters, possessing more pedestrian capabilities but ordered into production, and the swift perfection of the construction employed in the fighters that led to the Hawker Fury, prevented more interest being taken in the Heron.

Construction of the Heron had originally started as an all-metal version of the Woodcock II, but was completed as an entirely new design employing the fuselage structure described above. In 1926 it underwent change with the alteration of the wing design to incorporate a new Hawker innovation, the so-called dumbbell spar. This was conceived, and later patented, by a young new arrival in the Hawker design office, Roland Henry ('Roy') Chaplin, in 1926. The spar comprised two relatively light-gauge steel strips, rolled to polygonal sections and connected by a single plate web riveted to the boom flanges. The wing ribs were of pressed aluminium.

With Horsleys and Woodcocks filling the production shops in Canbury Park Road in 1926, Camm examined the various Air Ministry Specifications to find another suitable aircraft in which the new steel construction might be applied, and selected F.9/26. The new prototype, the Hawfinch, was completed and ready to fly early the following year, fitted initially with a Bristol Jupiter VI radial engine. This Specification had been drawn up by the Air Ministry to

A typical joint in the patent Hawker aircraft primary structure.

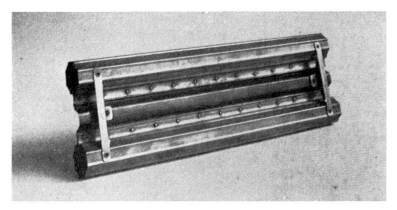

A section of the Hawker dumb-bell spar.

Part of the Heron's fuselage primary structure showing the Hawker system of tubular assembly.

The system adopted to move Horsleys the eight miles from Kingston to Brooklands. Too large to be carried by the standard Leyland lorry, the aircraft were towed backwards on a jury undercarriage.

produce an aircraft that, it was hoped, would be ready to replace the Gloster Grebe and Gamecock with the RAF in 1928. A total of nine contenders was produced by various manufacturers to compete in the trials at Martlesham Heath. Of these, the Hawfinch was the first to fly and, on being aware of the extent of the competition, Camm decided to change the engine to a Jupiter VII to be sure of competing on the best possible terms.

Originally built with two-bay wings, the Hawfinch gave an excellent account of itself and, once more, the Service pilots were highly complimentary in their assessment. Indeed, the aircraft was said to be superior in most respects to all the other aircraft, being quicker off the ground, more manoeuvrable and simpler to land. In the end the choice lay between the Bristol Bulldog and the Hawfinch, and, on account of Hawker already possessing production contracts for the Woodcock and Horsley, the Bulldog was declared the winner. In due course the Hawfinch returned to Brooklands, where it underwent considerable development, being fitted with a number of alternative engines, as well as single-bay wings. It was also flown with a float undercarriage as well as high-lift wings of various designs; at one time it was flying with wings incorporating pronounced camber forward of the ailerons as a means of improving lateral control at very low speed, a design evolved by the RAE.

By mid-1927 Camm's design office was staffed by thirty-three draughtsmen, three stressmen and three project designers, apart from Camm and Chaplin. It is not widely known that Camm's department embarked on the design of a large twin-engine heavy bomber to the Specification which ultimately brought forth the Handley Page Heyford and Fairey Hendon. To have been powered by a pair of Jupiter X engines, the Hawker B.19/27 design was somewhat similar to the

17

Heyford, though of less radical appearance (see Appendix). Camm always encouraged his design staff to try its hand at designing aircraft other than fighters when time permitted, and it is likely that the B.19/27 essay was no more than an attempt to establish at first hand the parameters of large aircraft then under consideration. Certainly there could never have been any possibility of Hawker producing such an aircraft, simply on account of the confined limits of the production shops in Canbury Park Road. Even the Horsley, with its more modest proportions, had to be towed by road the eight miles between Kingston and Brooklands before final assembly of its wings and tail.

Rather smaller than the Horsley was the next Hawker aircraft, the Harrier, a private venture to embody the load-carrying capabilities of the Horsley in a smaller airframe in an attempt to improve the overall performance. This was an interesting design which might have been outstanding in its day had British aircraft designers not been so severely restricted in their choice of engines. As it was, the experimentally-geared Jupiter VIII air-cooled radial chosen for the Harrier proved to be hopelessly inadequate. Nevertheless, some features of the design attracted favourable response from the RAF, not least the prone position for the bomb aimer (later adopted in the Hawker Hart and Hind). As was usual, even for aircraft undertaken as private ventures, the Harrier went to Martlesham to obtain the air force's general assessment. This was uncompromising, to say the least. It is on record that the take-off performance somewhat frightened the Martlesham pilots, so much so that, in order to carry aloft the stipulated torpedo at all, the fuel load had to be reduced by thirty per cent. Sarcasm crept into one of the reports sent to Camm: 'It is a pity that it has been found necessary to leave the observer/bomb aimer on the ground when bombs are being carried'. Yet the Harrier was used to good purpose, for it served the company for the development of bombing equipment used in the Hart, and was later delivered to Bristols for use as an engine test bed, the Hydra radial being among the engines flown.

THE TOMTIT

It is convenient to digress at this point from the strict chronological sequence of events to mention a Hawker design which itself diverged from the pattern already, in 1927, evolving those famous aeroplanes, the Hart and the Fury.

By that year the Avro 504 basic trainer had, in its various forms, been in service for some fourteen years, and the Air Ministry now sponsored an order for a replacement. The Specification laid emphasis on the powerplant, which was to be an Armstrong Siddeley Mongoose five-cylinder air-cooled radial engine, and the construction, which, owing to the gradual disappearance of the woodworking trades in the Royal Air Force, was to be all-metal. The latter condition suited Hawker

Engineering as, by 1928, the entire works in Canbury Park Road had been re-equipped for metal construction.

The Hawker design staff thus contributed the Tomtit, and the prototype, built as a private venture, was first flown in November 1928. For four years the RAF conducted trials at its flying training units to decide whether the Tomtit or the Avro (Mongoose) Trainer should be ordered in quantity and, although about thirty Tomtits were subsequently built for the Service, no large order was placed for either. Instead, the Avro Tutor (powered by a seven-cylinder Armstrong Siddeley Lynx radial) finally replaced the Avro 504N.

Tomtits served in the Royal Air Force with No.3 Flying Training School at Grantham, the Central Flying School, Wittering, and with No. 24 (Communications) Squadron at Northolt.

Several of those aircraft which served at Wittering became redundant in 1933 and were eventually disposed of to private owners. Another aircraft was fitted with a Cirrus Hermes in-line engine in 1930, being intended to attract the sporting pilot, but the lack of power deprived the Tomtit of its precise handling characteristics and only one such aircraft was built.

As a trainer the little Tomtit had delightful handling characteristics, possessing a speed range of 45–124 miles per hour and, of course, being fully aerobatic. Marked improvements over earlier trainers included the positioning of both cockpits well clear of the wings, thereby facilitating emergency departure as well as providing a wide field of view. Another significant feature was the Reid and Sigrist blind-flying panel, which included the new turn-and-bank indicator.

The Tomtit was always a great favourite at prewar (as well as some post-war) displays for, in the hands of such Hawker pilots as Bulman and Sayer, the sight of a 'falling leaf' brought many a crowd to its feet.

Flight Lieutenant P W S Bulman (universally known as 'George' on

The first blind-flying instrument panel developed by Reid and Sigrist and fitted in the Tomtit.

19

account of his famous inability to remember other persons' names, who were therefore similarly addressed) had been seconded to Hawker Engineering as test pilot from the Royal Aircraft Establishment when Fred Raynham's employment contract expired in 1925, and remained with the company until 1945. There could be few who remained impassive when George Bulman was demonstrating an aircraft for, not only did he possess the technical understanding essential in his profession, but he combined that brilliant showmanship memorable to so many.

In 1929 Bulman was joined by P E G ('Gerry') Sayer, and two years later by Philip Lucas. Together these three pilots formed one of the most famous test-flying partnerships of all time. On the other hand, there was seldom a period when one of them was not abroad demonstrating a Hart or Fury to some potential customer. Gerry Sayer was to lose his life while flying a Typhoon during the Second World War (probably the victim of a collision), while Lucas, as Chief Experimental Test Pilot, was awarded the George Medal in 1940 for saving the prototype Typhoon from destruction at considerable personal risk.

DEVELOPMENT OF THE HART

There appeared at Olympia in July 1929 two new aircraft which created something of a sensation with their striking lines and clean aerodynamic profiles. While both machines, the Hart and the Hornet, were products of the Hawker company, the former was a day bomber and the latter — soon to be renamed the Fury — was an interceptor fighter.

The Hart owed its conception to Air Ministry Specification No. 12 of 1926, which had called for a Rolls-Royce Falcon-powered day bomber to replace the veteran D.H.9As and Fairey Fawns.

The preliminary design study was tendered in December 1926 and featured a split-axle undercarriage with pneumatic shock absorbers. However, on acceptance of the tender in the following June a wooden mock-up was commenced, incorporating various alterations. The foremost of these was the engine, which was now the new Rolls-Royce F.XI, a direct descendant of the Falcon but employing cylinder blocks cast as single banks instead of individual cylinders. This engine was the first significant step on the path which led ultimately to the Merlin of Second World War fame. Other changes to the Hart included the landing gear, which now employed Vickers oleo-pneumatic shock absorbers and a cross-axle, and a pump-operated fuel system in place of the former gravity feed (prompted by doubts which followed experience with the long-distance Horsley).

Construction of the first prototype, J9052, commenced during the autumn of 1927, and in the following June it was taken to Brooklands for its first flight by George Bulman. Thereafter, in the hands of Royal Air Force pilots at Martlesham Heath as well as with a number of operational squadrons, J9052 was evaluated in competition with the Fairey

Fox II and the Avro Antelope. Although both the Hart and the Fox drew much appreciative support, only the Hart was ordered into production, and initially constituted the equipment of No.33 Squadron at Eastchurch early in 1930.

Such was the considerable advance in performance possessed by the Harts that in their first air exercise over the United Kingdom the defending Siskin fighters were unable to catch the new bombers (the top speeds of the Hart and Siskin being 184 and 154 miles per hour respectively).

An historic aeroplane. The original prototype Hawker Hart, J9052.

An early batch of Harts in the Brooklands erecting shop.

21

The pilot's cockpit of the Hart bomber.

Already contracts were being placed for large numbers of Harts and, by 1933, six Regular home-based light bomber squadrons had been re-equipped; that year also saw Harts enter service with Auxiliary Air Force squadrons. Moreover, with the not inconsiderable responsibilities of the Royal Air Force in India and the Middle East during the mid-1930s, special versions of the Hart were shipped out, equipped for desert operation with the four squadrons engaged in territorial policing duties, and in 1935, during the Abyssinian crisis, three home-based Hart squadrons were sent to the Mediterranean to reinforce the RAF in that theatre. The last Hart bombers were withdrawn from active service in the North-West Frontier Province of India in 1939, being replaced by Bristol Blenheims.

Hawker Harts flying over the inhospitable North West Frontier Province of India during the 1930s.

In common with many other widely-used military aircraft, several Harts were used by the manufacturers and the engine companies for testing new powerplants. Few were the engines, later to achieve fame in other aircraft, that were not at some time flown in Harts: Dagger, Perseus, Mercury, Pegasus, Jupiter and Merlin — these and others logged hundreds of hours on their way to give Britain such a choice of engines when the call for military expansion came in the mid-1930s.

Prompted by the remarkable ascendancy achieved at a stroke by the Hart over contemporary interceptors in 1930, Hawkers tendered a fighter version to meet an Air Ministry requirement for a two-seat fighter — in effect a continuation of the formula largely pioneered by the Bristol F2.B Fighter a dozen years earlier. Not for another ten years would modern air warfare demonstrate how badly flawed that formula was.

Known as the Demon, the new fighter adaptation was almost identical structurally (the prototype was a modified Hart), but, in addition to the Lewis gun on the rear cockpit, twin Vickers machine guns were mounted in the sides of the nose. Due principally to the greater installed weight and slightly less powerful Kestrel engine, the Demon's speed was fractionally lower than that of the Hart — particularly in exercises for which the Hart was not required to carry bombs, but still provided a marked superiority over the Siskin and Bulldog. The chance to prove this advantage arrived when the new aircraft (known initially as the Hart Fighter) was issued to one flight of No. 23 Squadron at Kenley, the other two flights temporarily retaining their Bulldogs. Two years later the Squadron's Bulldogs were also exchanged for Demons.

The Frazer-Nash 'lobster-back' gun turret fitted on late-series Demon fighters.

Famous pilot, famous 'plane, famous place. P W S Bulman flying an Audax
over the banking at Brooklands.

Demons continued to be built by Hawkers at Kingston until sheer
weight of new orders forced production to be subcontracted. In 1935
their manufacture was transferred to Boulton-Paul Aircraft Ltd at
Wolverhampton.

As with the Hart, Demon squadrons were despatched to the Middle
East at the time of Italy's assault on Abyssinia in October 1935, while
other squadrons on Malta and at Heliopolis were also equipped with the
aircraft. Home-based Auxiliary Air Force fighter squadrons continued
to fly their Demons until 1939, when they were replaced by such aircraft
as Blenheim fighters.

After introduction of the Demon into service in 1931 came the
Audax. Once again the somewhat embarrassing performance superiority of the Hart bomber encouraged the Air Ministry to seek replacement in the army co-operation rôle of the cumbersome Westland Wapiti
on the North-West Frontier and the elderly Armstrong Whitworth Atlas
at home. With a thirty-mile-an-hour speed improvement over the older
machines, yet fully equipped with all the accoutrements of its duties, the
Audax was placed in service in 1932, and within three years had reached
nine squadrons, five of them in Britain, two in India, one in Egypt and
one in the Sudan. The latter unit, No.237 (Rhodesia) Squadron, retained
its Audaxes until well into the Second World War, and together with its
Hawker Hardy aircraft (of which more anon) these flew with much

24

verve in the East African campaign and at Habbaniya during the Iraqi revolt of May 1941.

Almost simultaneous with the 1932 Service début of the Audax, the Hawker Osprey appeared. In extending the policy of standardisation as being the most cost-effective means of keeping Royal Air Force aircraft abreast of the times during the period of the Depression — having regard to the Hart's convenient adaptability — the Fleet Air Arm was able to adopt the Osprey as a fast 'fighter reconnaissance' aircraft for operation from its three aircraft carriers, HMS *Furious, Glorious* and *Courageous*.

The Specification foreshadowing this requirement had been issued as long ago as 1926, but the conditions laid down had been too severe for compliance by the few design tenders submitted. The main performance facets of the Specification, however, approximated to the Hart's abilities as it appeared in 1927, and by 1929 sufficient experience had been gained by Hawker Engineering in the sphere of naval requirements to enable the design staff to approach the problem with more confidence. The prototype Hart, J9052, having successfully completed its RAF evaluation as a light bomber, was back at Brooklands and was available for fairly extensive alteration to the required naval configuration. The wings were modified to incorporate folding mechanism on the trailing edges, while additional struts were included to provide the necessary wing stiffness at the lines of fold. Various twin-float undercarriage

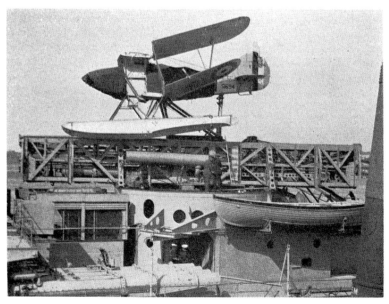

A Hawker Osprey on HMS *Leander's* catapult.

25

assemblies were evaluated, produced by Sir W G Armstrong Whitworth Aircraft Ltd and by Short Bros, Ltd, but only the latter were found suitable for production.

In 1930 a Specification was written around the naval Hart and production contracts for the Osprey followed. During the next year J9052, equipped with floats, accompanied No.407 Flight of a Fleet Air Arm contingent visiting the British Empire Trade Exhibition at Buenos Aires aboard HMS *Eagle*, but a mishap during hoisting operations resulted in the aircraft being dismantled and shipped home for return to Company charge. This famous aeroplane was finally written off on 9 May 1931 after an accident at Brooklands, suffered while taking off with crossed control cables.

Since the Osprey featured universal attachments for either wheel or float undercarriage, the Fleet Air Arm operated several composite Flights, partly shore-based and partly embarked. As well as equipping carrier-based units, Ospreys were embarked in a number of capital ships and cruisers of the Royal Navy, some of which served as far from home as the China Station. Though the aircraft was declared obsolete on the outbreak of war in 1939, at least four were still on establishment charge in the Far East in February 1940.

Of all the aircraft developed on the Hart formula, perhaps none saw more combat service than the least known variant, the Hardy, of which fewer than fifty were produced. After the prototype's first flight in 1934 production was transferred to T O M Sopwith's new acquisition, Gloster Aircraft Co Ltd, Brockworth. During 1935 about twenty examples were delivered to No. 30 Squadron, based at Habbaniya in Iraq. Despite numerous minor incidents involving marauding Arab tribesmen, most of these aircraft survived to be transferred to No. 6 Squadron in Palestine during 1938, while other Hardys were delivered to No.237 (Rhodesia) Squadron in British East Africa, joining forces with the Squadron's Audaxes. During the campaign against the Italian forces in Abyssinia Hardys were flown on operations in the presence of Italian aircraft of much later vintage and, although losses among the old biplanes were heavy, it is known that their guns claimed several victims. After others had been destroyed at Kassala, their swan song sounded at the Battle of Keren. The two sole survivors were flown to Habbaniya for training duties in 1941.

One other Hart derivative saw action in Africa. This was the Hartbees (usually referred to by its anglicised name, Hartebeest), of which only four were constructed by Hawker Aircraft for the South African Air Force in 1935. A much greater number, however, was built under licence at the Artillery and Aircraft Depot, Zwartkop, during 1936 and 1937, many of them being on the first-line strength of the South African Air Force at the outbreak of war in 1939. The Hartbees was intended for close ground support, and featured additional armour for crew protection from small-arms fire. Most aircraft were also equipped with desert survival kits.

The penultimate Hart variant was the Hind. Embodying all the lessons and refinements of the standard Hart bomber, the Hind was introduced into service with the Royal Air Force in large numbers as an interim light day bomber in 1935 to accommodate demands for the accelerated expansion of the Service. Production was undertaken solely by Hawker Aircraft Ltd, no fewer than 527 aircraft being delivered to the RAF between 1935 and 1938. Twenty-five home-based Regular bomber squadrons were equipped with Hinds, together with eleven of the Auxiliary Air Force. Others were delivered overseas to Switzerland, Yugoslavia, Portugal, Afghanistan, Iran and Latvia and, when finally replaced in the RAF in 1938 (mostly by Blenheims and Battles), many were supplied to Kenya, New Zealand, South Africa, India and Eire.

The Hawker Hector was the final Hart variant, adopted by the Air Ministry in 1936 for use in the army co-operation rôle. Superseding the Audax, the Hector was intended as no more than a stopgap until the Westland Lysander could be introduced. Such were the demands being made on Rolls-Royce for Kestrel engines that the Napier Dagger was selected for the Hector (this engine having completed considerable flying in a Hart test bed).

The Hector was unique among the Hart Variants in being fitted with a top wing that featured no sweep-back. Production was undertaken by Westland Aircraft Ltd, Yeovil, and, although that company's Lysander started delivery to the army co-operation squadrons in 1938, Hectors were still in front-line service as late as 1940, being sent into action over Calais during the dark days of the Dunkirk evacuation. Later still they were employed as glider tugs, towing Hotspur training gliders.

The passing of the Hector, though outlived in isolated instances by other variants, marked the end of the Hart era. In ten years over 2,800 aircraft had stemmed from designs created in the Canbury Park Road offices, had been built by eight major companies in the British aircraft industry as well as two overseas, and had been delivered to twenty air forces of the world, in addition to the Royal Air Force and Royal Navy. It is not too fanciful to attribute the survival of Britain's aircraft industry during the early 1930s to the Hart and its many derivatives. Certainly no other British aircraft had achieved such widespread employment, and the revenue from its production placed the Hawker company on firmer financial ground than any other — with the exception of Rolls-Royce Ltd. Just how T O M Sopwith and the Hawker board of directors employed this new-found wealth will be told in due course. That Britain's aircraft industry was able to meet the demands for enormously increased output when the need arose was evidence of Sopwith's wisdom and integrity.

THE FURY BIPLANES

Having regard to the relatively small size of the H G Hawker Engineering Company and its modest premises during the mid-1920s, and the well-deserved success attending the Hart bomber, it is perhaps surprising that the company was able simultaneously to pursue the development of an interceptor. The truth was that Sydney Camm always regarded the development of fighter aircraft as the most technically rewarding means of advancing aeronautical science. The search for speed and the creation of aeroplanes that were pleasing to the eye were always his consuming passion, even if the interpretation of design style occasionally offended his peers. Few people could, however, criticise the Fury biplane on any count. That this beautiful little fighter, as it eventually evolved, also achieved considerable success, at a time when production contracts were relatively difficult to come by, provides ample testimomy to the farsightedness of Camm and the extraordinary organising abilities of Sopwith and Sigrist.

The discovery, as recently as March 1960, of a project drawing (reproduced in the Appendix) bearing Camm's signature and dated January 1925, portraying a monoplane interceptor fighter, provides further evidence of the Hawker philosophy, which was to engage in the design of all types of high-performance military aircraft.

Development of the Woodcock had been followed by the Hornbill and Heron, both interesting fighter designs and each constituting significant advances in the evolution of Hawker design and construction techniques. The introduction of the simple, relatively inexpensive and lightweight metal primary structures made possible the design of high-performance aircraft whose strength became the renowned hallmark of Hawker aeroplanes down the years.

It was, furthermore, Camm's belief that naval fighter requirements need not differ fundamentally from those of the land-based interceptor, only specific equipment and local strengthening necessarily being incorporated. Such features, he contended, should not dictate the fundamental design but be subordinate to it. (Sad to relate, Camm did not live long enough to witness the most outstanding manifestation of this philosophy, for the Sea Harrier has been the perfect example of maritime adaptation of an RAF fighter.)

Two Specifications, N.21/26 and F.20/27, were therefore studied by the Hawker design staff in 1927 and, though the requirements appeared quantitatively unrelated, it seemed likely that a single basic design might satisfy both. The naval insistence on a radial engine appeared to negate this approach and the resulting fleet fighter, so handicapped, produced little advance over the Fairey Flycatchers then in service, since it featured two-bay wings and a Mercury radial engine.

The Hoopoe, prepared for evaluation in the N.21/26 context, was first flown by Bulman in 1928, and delivered to Martlesham Heath with a wheel undercarriage. Later, in 1929, fitted with a twin-float undercarriage, the aircraft was severely criticised for its sluggish controls and poor take-off characteristics, having, as a Felixstowe pilot put it, 'a marked desire to hop from one float to the other rather than to get into the air'. It was returned to Brooklands where it was fitted with a powerful Armstrong Siddeley Jaguar engine and single-bay wings, whereupon all pilots reported that the aeroplane's handling had been transformed. Much useful flying was carried out with the Hoopoe with Jaguar and Panther engines during 1930–32, and aircraft contributed much to the development of the Nimrod fleet fighter.

At about the same time that the Hoopoe first flew, the Hawker F.20/27 Interceptor was also completed. This aircraft, never properly named, was, however, promising from the start. Both the Mercury and Jupiter radial engines were fitted in turn, and the aeroplane met with favourable comment at Martlesham. Nevertheless, in view of the superiority of the in-line Rolls-Royce F.XI engine being demonstrated in the Hart prototype, it is hardly surprising that both the Hoopoe and the F.20/27 should be redesigned to accommodate the new engine.

Thus were born the two most significant prototypes in the Hawker single-seat biplane fighter line, and it was at this point that the two hitherto parallel RAF and naval fighter designs converged. The RAF

Typical of interceptor fighter design in the late 1920s, the Hawker F.20/27 featured radial engine, twin Vickers guns with cocking handles just in front of the pilot's face and main fuel tank immediately forward of the cockpit.

aeroplane, named by the Company the Hornet, appeared in 1929, and shortly afterwards the naval counterpart, the Norn (a name contracted, again unofficially, from Naval Hornet, *not* from Scandinavian mythology as often related), emerged.

The Hornet was the third member of that remarkable trio which was presented on the H G Hawker Engineering stand at the 1929 Olympia Aero Show, the others being the Hart and Tomtit, and although this was the first public showing of the new fighter, evaluation of the aircraft as an RAF interceptor was already under way.

Employing a supercharged Rolls-Royce F.XIS, the Hornet was a single-bay biplane with many features and valuable experience derived from the earlier experimental fighters, but with greatly reduced drag from the closely-cowled 480 hp in-line engine it achieved a top speed slightly over 200 miles per hour fully armed and loaded.

Later in 1929 the new machine was purchased by the Air Ministry (for the sum of £5,920) and, in pursuance of the current system of nomenclature, which required that fighters of the RAF should bear names implying ferocity, the name Hornet was dropped and, from a short list submitted to the Hawker company, the name Fury was adopted.

While in general terms the Aeroplane and Armament Experimental Establishment expressed itself well satisfied with the new Fury design, the aircraft could not immediately be introduced into the RAF. Comprehensive trials were not completed until 1930, for the heavy demand on Rolls-Royce engine production delayed development of the Kestrel IIS, while the production Specification, drafted in February 1930, was not finalised and issued until August that year.

Of domestic significance, moreover, the H G Hawker Engineering Company had parted, in 1928, with a twenty-year lease on the extensive Richmond Road factory facilities near Ham Common (the freehold of which had been acquired by T O M Sopwith after the First World War, but which had remained almost empty and unproductive ever since) to the Leyland Motor Company, with the result that all Hart, Tomtit and Horsley production was carried out in the extremely cramped premises in Canbury Park Road and at Brooklands. While Horsley production was tailing off in 1930 and Tomtit orders occupied relatively little space on the shop floor, the follow-up Hart orders stretched the existing facilities to capacity. For this reason the initial Fury order was for only twenty-one aeroplanes until the Brooklands sheds could be extended.

It was now that the Hawker company embarked on its memorable campaign to bring its aircraft to the attention of foreign air forces, and in this respect there existed no better sales team than the three company test pilots, Bulman, Sayer and Lucas. In addition to their routine testing of Harts and Furies the three pilots engaged in countless demonstrations both in the United Kingdom and abroad. The Yugoslavs and Norwegians expressed interest in the Fury some months before even the first RAF machines had been flown, Bulman visiting Yugoslavia with the old

The first batch of Furies being assembled in the Canbury Park Road shops early in 1931.

Hornet prototype early in 1931, thereby initiating an association with that country that was to last for six years. The Furies sold to Yugoslavia were flown with great skill, and were to distinguish themselves in many international events during the coming years.

The first RAF Furies passed through the shops early in 1931 and were issued to that famous fighter Squadron, No. 43 ('The Fighting Cocks') at Tangmere, while aircraft of subsequent batches were flown by No.1 (Fighter) Squadron, also at Tangmere, and No. 25 (Fighter) Squadron at Hawkinge. As had been shown with their previous aircraft (Armstrong Whitworth Siskins), these squadrons were past masters in the skills of demonstrating formation aerobatics and air drill, and their reputation was further enhanced during their many appearances in those years of air pageants and Hendon air displays. There can surely be few who do not recall with nostalgia those surpassingly beautiful little biplanes with their polished cowlings and colourful insignia, trailing smoke as they performed their tied-together formation aerobatics or carried out air drill manoeuvres at radioed requests from members of the crowd on the ground.

By mid-1932 the three Fury squadrons were fully operational and together they constituted the *force élite* of Britain's air defences; they

31

Hawker Furies of No. 1 (Fighter) Squadron formate in characteristic fashion. (*Photograph by courtesy of 'Flight'.*)

were the only interceptors with a performance superior to that of the Hart bombers. Immediately there sprang up fierce competition between the Fury squadrons in the annual Fighting Area gunnery and flying contests, time and again these units taking the three top places and No.25 Squadron winning the Air Defence Trophy outright. Among all the names associated with the Fury that were to achieve fame in later years was No.25 Squadron's Commanding Officer in 1935, Sqn Ldr W Dickson (later Marshal of the RAF Sir William, GCB, KBE, DSO, AFC, Chief of the Air Staff from 1953 and Chairman of the Chiefs of Staff Committee from 1955). Another pilot, this time a sergeant pilot on No. 43 Squadron, was Sammy Wroath who, after four years on Furies, was posted as a test pilot to Martlesham, where he was given the exclusive responsibility for the RAF's evaluation of the first Hawker Hurricane. Later commissioned, he became the first Commandant of the Empire Test Pilots' School, an appointment he uniquely occupied twice.

While Furies set the pace for the fighter defences at home, others were being delivered abroad. The Norwegian variant was not so successful, the Armstrong Siddeley Panther radial engine installation proving disappointing, and only a single evaluation example was flown in Norway. Nor were the American Pratt & Whitney Hornet engines in the aircraft ordered by Persia any more popular, and, although sixteen aircraft were delivered with these engines, further Furies for Persia were ordered to be fitted with Bristol Mercury radials, a combination found to be eminently satisfactory.

By 1936 an improved version, the Fury Mark II with Kestrel VI, had been ordered for the RAF, and this type entered service with five home-based fighter squadrons. That year, however, brought massive orders for the Hawker Hurricane with the result that, after a small batch of Fury IIs had been built at Kingston, further production of the aircraft was undertaken by General Aircraft Ltd at Hanworth. A number of ex-RAF Fury IIs was later shipped to the South African Air Force.

Though not, strictly speaking, a variant of the Fury, but rather developed in parallel, the Nimrod fleet fighter possessed many characteristics common to both. Again the Air Ministry had insisted on a change in name and Nimrod was adopted in place of Norn. Again the successful Kestrel was employed, the first prototype naval fighter being flown towards the end of 1930. Production got under way the following year, and the Nimrod entered service in 1932 with Nos. 402, 408 and 409 Fleet Fighter Flights on H M Aircraft Carriers *Courageous* and *Glorious*.

An improved version, the Nimrod II with slightly swept-back wings, was introduced in 1934 and issued to Nos. 800, 801 and 802 Squadrons of the Fleet Air Arm. By reason of naval requirements for such equipment as arrester hook and flotation gear, the Nimrod's performance never quite matched that of the Fury. A small number was, nevertheless,

A batch of Hornet-powered Furies and Audaxes destined for Persia.

shipped abroad to Japan and Denmark, though plans for their licence production in the former country never materialised.

Before turning away from the families of biplanes which had served to bring the Hawker company to the forefront of the British aircraft industry, mention should be made of two of Camm's designs which, though in all probability representing the ultimate in their class, were rendered entirely obsolete by the monoplane as soon as they appeared. These were the private-venture F.7/30 (P.V.3) and G.4/31 (P.V.4), the former fundamentally derived from the Fury, and developed from it by way of an aircraft known as the High-Speed Fury. The P.V.3, stemming from the 1930 requirement for a four-gun high-performance day and night interceptor and of which more will be said later on, appeared in the summer of 1934. Unfortunately, like all the other companies' designs tendered to F.7/30, the P.V.3 was compromised and delayed by the Air Ministry's determination to insist on the use of the steam-cooled Rolls-Royce Goshawk engine — an engine which, on account of the need to incorporate large evaporative cooling radiators, penalised the entire design owing to their weight and drag. Although Camm produced by far the neatest solution to the problem, the arrival of the monoplane fighter designs compromised the future of the F.7/30 concept. Ironically, the Air Ministry held to its original demands, and so was born the Gloster Gladiator.

The P.V.4 was an enlarged derivative of the Hart series, and this aeroplane, first flown in December 1934, was also doomed by the advent of the monoplane. As with the fighter, an interim bomber requirement was manifest, but it was decided that to order a fundamentally new design into production would be too lengthy a process. The Specification was upgraded and a monoplane, the Vickers Wellesley, came to be adopted. In this instance, however, the P.V.4 afforded Hawkers useful experience in evolving the Hind, and, as already recorded, this aeroplane was the subject of huge orders during 1936–37 — far in excess of those for the Wellesley!

So ended not only a chapter in the life of Hawker Aircraft Ltd, but one that many came to regard as the golden age of flying. Hawker biplanes continued to serve in many countries until well into the Second World War, it being on record that some were even committed to battle five years after they had been officially declared obsolete.

THE BIRTH OF THE HURRICANE

Having followed the fortunes of the ubiquitous Hawker biplanes during the 1920s and 1930s up to the outbreak of the Second World War, it is necessary to return once more to 1930 to trace the events which led ultimately to the introduction of one of the most famous fighting aeroplanes of all time — the Hurricane.

The year 1930 saw the imaginative F.7/30 Specification issued, calling for a high-performance fighter armed with four machine guns in place of the traditional twin-gun armament; the aircraft was also required to possess a maximum speed of 250 miles per hour. When one considers that the Bristol Bulldog had only just entered service with a two-gun armament and a top speed of 174 mph, the radical nature of the new demands may well be appreciated. Implicit in the new Specification was Air Staff recognition of the current deficiency of fighter armament in view of the high performance of bombers thought to be under development abroad. Because of the disappearance of any speed advantage possessed by the interceptor fighter over an attacking bomber, it was becoming increasingly difficult to bring the fighter's guns to bear for a sufficient length of time to prove lethal. The armament problem was compounded by the traditional unreliability of the Vickers machine gun, which demanded that the gun breeches be located within reach of the pilot so that jams could be cleared 'manually'. At Gloster W G Carter, on the other hand, determined on another course and adopted the more reliable Lewis gun, of which he mounted no fewer than six on the wings of an experimental aircraft, the S.S.18 (later to become the Gauntlet, though with armament conventionally reduced to a pair of Vickers guns in the nose).

As recorded above, the F.7/30 requirement produced a number of ingenious designs, of which Camm's P.V.3 was the most orthodox. Those submitted by Westland, Blackburn and Supermarine were all compromised by their designers' misinterpretation of the salient demands being made. Reginald Mitchell, at Supermarine, alone took the bold step of attempting to capitalise on his experience in the design of the successful Schneider Trophy seaplanes by adopting a monoplane configuration, only to find that a world of difference existed between the wing design of a racing seaplane that, apart from being externally wire-braced, was effectively required to fly in a straight line, and that of a nimble interceptor fighter in which manoeuvrability was of paramount importance. As a result his Type 224 design to F.7/30 possessed a disappointing performance — and one that was little better than Camm's biplane.

Nor, for that matter, was the Air Ministry inclined to offer encouragement to the aircraft companies to pursue monoplane design. There was, after all, a deeply entrenched prejudice among some of the senior RAF staffs against the monoplane — an ill-informed prejudice that had persisted since before the Kaiser's War.

The stimulus to overcome the prejudice could only come from the industry itself, and the success of Mitchell's racing seaplanes had certainly begun the process. In 1933 Camm directed his thoughts towards the development of a monoplane fighter and, with the Fury biplane well established and popular in service with the Royal Air Force, and production contracts for this aircraft in hand for foreign governments, it was not surprising that the Fury was adopted as the starting point for the new monoplane design.

In August that year preliminary discussions were held between Camm and the Directorate of Technical Development at the Air Ministry regarding the potential afforded by a monoplane fighter and, as a result, certain well-defined ideas took shape in Camm's mind. Under his direction a radical redesign of the Fury started. The configuration of the aircraft was altered to feature a low cantilever wing with tapered leading and trailing edges culminating in rounded tips. A Rolls-Royce Goshawk steam-cooled engine was chosen (still regarded with favour by the Air Ministry), and a fixed, spatted undercarriage and enclosed cockpit with sliding hood incorporated. The rear fuselage and tail unit remained unchanged.

The new design was strictly a private venture, and in the absence of official support or requirements it was decided to adopt the latest known specified armament of four machine guns — two mounted on the sides of the fuselage and two in the wing roots. Standard Hawker metal construction was proposed, with fabric covering throughout except on the fuselage forward of the cockpit, which was metal-clad. Such a structure was well within the production capabilities of the company. Many years later Camm was to confess that he felt uneasy about the armament layout then being proposed for the Fury Monoplane. Two of the Vickers guns — those in the wing roots — were out of physical reach of the pilot, and all four guns, being mounted to fire through the propeller arc, would still demand interrupter gear — often regarded as one of the causes for the Vickers gun's predilection for jamming.

That this radical design immediately interested the Air Staff and Ministries alike is naturally of great credit to Camm's initiative, but it should be remembered that the political atmosphere in Europe, while not galvanising the Government into a state of positive activity, stirred Ministers into a painful awareness of the dangerous results of the now-defunct Ten Year Rule.

It is well known how unaware Great Britain was of the German military resurgence in 1933. Even so, it was towards the end of that year, when the Fury Monoplane was in its early project stages, that the Government called on the aircraft industry to reorganise itself into fewer, but technically and financially more powerful units. Men such as Lord Weir and Viscount Swinton accepted the principle that to gain military ascendancy in the air the nation must accelerate technical progress with an industry backed by sound financial support. With the economic depression so recently past, the necessary financial backing was unlikely to be forthcoming from the Treasury for some years, and it was decided to call upon the industry itself to shoulder this responsibility.

Thus the political background to the Fury Monoplane project amounted to academic enthusiasm without financial support, but with an international situation developing which suggested that it was only a matter of time before growing Government awareness would bring about action in the form of Contract cover.

Unfettered by industrial motives and political apathy, Camm was now imbued with an urgency to bring his monoplane fighter to reality and, by December 1933, he was in a position to discuss the proposed design with the Air Ministry.

In January 1934, however, detailed performance forecasts were made available by Rolls-Royce Ltd for the new P.V.12 liquid-cooled twelve-cylinder engine which had been undergoing extensive preliminary tests at Derby. The figures suggested that the new engine, at a very early stage in its development, was producing more power than almost any existing powerplant in service, without the complexity and weight associated with the steam-cooled Goshawk with which the Air Ministry still seemed besotted. Furthermore, Rolls-Royce confidently forecast a ten per cent increase in power from the P.V.12 by the time any Service prototype could be made ready for its installation. These figures encouraged Camm to substitute the P.V.12 engine for the Goshawk in the Fury Monoplane, and with this fundamental change the ancestry of the design became so obscure as to warrant a departure from association with the Fury. Instead the sobriquet 'Interceptor Monoplane' was adopted as a temporary expedient.

Detailed design of the new fighter was started in the Experimental Drawing Office — now staffed by seventeen draughtsmen — in May 1934, and the following month a one-tenth-scale model was completed for extensive tests in the National Physical Laboratory's windtunnel at Teddington, not half-a-dozen miles from the design's birthplace. By now some idea of the weight of the aeroplane could be predicted, and the initial estimate of 4,600 pounds, loaded, was about the same as that of the Hawker P.V.3 biplane interceptor, also armed with four guns. On account of demands for more and more equipment and armament, this estimate was inevitably to be increased during the next few years. The maximum speed, however, was expected to be about 80 miles per hour higher than that of the biplane — such were the rewards of an efficient monoplane design.

Discussions also took place with the Air Ministry upon the matter of armament, as Camm expressed his doubts and asked whether the Air Ministry harboured any plans to replace the age-old Vickers gun with a more efficient weapon. At this point it was disclosed that the newly-formed Armament Branch was examining the results of a competitive evaluation of the rifle-calibre Colt, Darne, Hispano, Kiraleji, Lewis, Madsen, Spandau (Mauser) and Vickers machine guns and, depending on the result of this evaluation, a decision would be taken on the armament requirements of future RAF fighters. In the meantime Camm was advised to persist with the four-Vickers arrangement in the proposed design. A draft requirement, Specification F.5/34, was drawn up to cover the Hawker design proposal, with a promise that a full Specification would be issued before the end of 1934.

By August that year the design of the Interceptor Monoplane had

The prototype Hurricane under construction. Note the Vickers machine gun on the side of the fuselage, as originally proposed.

been completed and was submitted to the Air Ministry, and on 4 September the full Specification, F.36/34, was issued to Hawkers. The mock-up was examined by Air Staff members during the next two months, and on 21 February 1935 the company received a contract for 'one High Speed Monoplane, K5083, to design submitted 4 September 1934, known as F.36/34 Single Seat Fighter'.

This contract covered the proposed four-gun armament, but in the meantime Camm had been pursuing his argument in favour of heavier fighter armament, and found ready sympathy with Sqn Ldr R S Sorley (later Air Marshal Sir Ralph, KCB, OBE, DSC, DFC) of the Air Ministry Armament Research Establishment, who was also an enthusiastic advocate of heavier fighter armament. It transpired that the American Colt had been shown to be the best all-round machine gun under evaluation, although it existed only in 0.300-inch calibre. Plans were afoot to examine the possibility of adapting the gun to 0.303 inch calibre and, if successful, it was proposed to negotiate a production licence in Britain. Camm explained that, with the compactness and light weight of the Colt gun, it should be possible to mount up to four such guns in a single gun bay inside each of the Hawker fighter's wings *outboard* of the propeller arc, thereby obviating the need for gun synchronisation. It has never been disclosed whether Sorley passed this information on to Mitchell at Supermarines, or whether the Spitfire designer had reached an independent decision to mount the eight-gun battery. What is quite evident is that the structure of the Hurricane's relatively thick wing enabled the guns to be located in a single, compact bay, allowing for much quicker replenishing of ammunition, whereas the Spitfire's thinner, and aerodynamically more efficient wing, required the guns to be widely distributed, so that each gun required a separate access panel. Gun harmonisation was also a quicker and simpler undertaking in the Hurricane.

Provision was therefore made for the eight guns in the Hawker prototype, and the original Vickers gun installation was removed. No guns were installed initially as the Air Ministry refused to believe that it would be safe to fly the aircraft and fire eight machine guns with fabric-covered wings. The Hawker board pointed out that to change to an all-metal wing would delay completion of the prototype, and agreed that the aircraft would be produced initially with ballast in lieu of guns for general assessment of the aircraft by the Service.

Construction of K5083 continued apace and, during September 1935, the Rolls-Royce engine, now officially named the Merlin, was received and installed in the airframe. This Merlin 'C' engine delivered 1,029 horsepower to a Watts two-blade wooden propeller at the remarkably low installed weight of 1,180 pounds, and thereby amply fulfilled the early promises of its illustrious makers. By 23 October the aeroplane had been completed and was taken by lorry from Canbury Park Road to Brooklands for final assembly, weighing and engine tests.

A fortnight later, on 6 November, the prototype was ready and, with George Bulman at the controls, made its maiden flight. In the short space of two years the entire scope of interceptor fighter design had undergone fundamental change — probably one of the most radical advances achieved in the history of aviation.

A very early in-flight picture of the prototype Hurricane being flown by P W S Bulman.

39

A view of the Gloster factory at Hucclecote at about the time of Hawker's take-over.

REORGANISATION AND EXPANSION

Those two years had witnessed the realisation of the inadequacy of Britain's Royal Air Force. This reaction owed its origins to a far-sighted though ill-pursued Government policy conceived in 1933, which prompted a few industrial leaders to think in terms of closer collaboration within the aircraft industry. The fact of, and reasons for the probable temporary absence of Government support for research, already mentioned, did not escape the attention of the Hawker directors, Sopwith and Spriggs (later Sir Frank Spriggs, KT, KBE), who sought to expand their production facilities in good time to meet the demand for military aircraft, which to them appeared inevitable.

Also in 1933, the outstanding success of Hawker designs had prompted Sopwith to seek additional capital by formation of a public company, and since any pretence at general engineering had long disappeared, the name Hawker Aircraft Ltd was adopted. Reasonable assets already existed, though the company still possessed inadequate production facilities to undertake large orders for its aircraft.

The first step to expand and strengthen their resources was taken in February 1934, when Hawker Aircraft purchased outright the Gloster Aircraft Company, which concern owned one of the largest aircraft factories in the country in addition to its aerodrome at Brockworth on the outskirts of Gloucester. Already Glosters had started quantity production of the Gauntlet fighter, while the Gladiator prototype was displaying such promise that orders could well follow shortly. The first Hawker contract to be transferred to Brockworth was one for Audaxes in 1934, and this was to be followed the next year by the Hardy production order. In subsequent years, Henleys, Hurricanes and Typhoons —

40

amounting in all to several thousand aircraft — were to be built in that factory.

Sopwith was able to face his shareholders with confidence at the First Annual General Meeting of Hawker Aircraft Ltd in July 1934. Backed by capital of two million pounds he could announce the investment of over £180,000 share capital resulting from the Gloster takeover. Regarding aircraft sales, he announced that Hawker aeroplanes were in service in India, Egypt, Canada, New Zealand, Norway, Sweden, Denmark, Estonia, Yugoslavia, Japan and Greece, as well as with the Royal Air Force and the Royal Navy the world over, and that during the past year not one fatality had occurred as a result of failure of any part of these aircraft.

In 1935, with the disappearance of any pretence at pursuing international disarmament, the Under-Secretary of State for Air, Sir Philip Sassoon, presented his first significantly increased Air Estimates. These forecast an increase in spending on aircraft and other RAF equipment from seven to eleven million pounds over the previous year. A considerable proportion of this expenditure was expected to be expressed in terms of contracts placed with Hawker Aircraft Ltd, with the result that further reorganisation within the company was being studied. Spriggs became Chairman of Glosters, while Sydney Camm (Chief Designer), George Bulman (Chief Test Pilot), H Chandler (Secretary), H K Jones and R W Sutton were appointed directors of the Hawker company in June 1935.

In the following month Sopwith announced the formation of a Trust to acquire all the shares of the Armstrong Siddeley Development Company Ltd, and the formation of a public holding company to be known as the Hawker-Siddeley Aircraft Company Ltd. At the same time the Hawker-Gloster combine subscribed half its share capital to the new company, but maintained a large degree of autonomy by virtue of retaining one million pounds capital as a private company in its own right. Thus, at a stroke, a powerful group of companies had been brought together such as could not be found elsewhere in the industry. It included Sir W G Armstrong Whitworth Aircraft Ltd, Armstrong Siddeley Motors Ltd, Air Service Training Ltd, and A V Roe & Co Ltd, in addition to Hawkers and Glosters. (In due course it would also embrace de Havilland, Blackburn, Folland and other companies.) Four directors were appointed, T O M Sopwith, F Sigrist, F S Spriggs (all from Hawkers), and P E Hill from Armstrong Siddeley Development Co Ltd.

By 1936 large orders were flowing into all the Hawker factories, yet Hawker Aircraft desperately required greater production facilities and space, with the result that a loan of £30,000 was made available by the capital holding company for the construction of a factory and aerodrome on Parlaunt Park Farm at Langley in Buckinghamshire. Moreover, the capital of the Group, already standing at two million pounds, was doubled in November that year, while in 1937 almost all the

An aerial view of the Hawker factory at Langley, built shortly before the Second World War. It was occupied by the Ford Motor Company in 1959.

remaining Hawker Aircraft shares were bought out by the Group. A further issue of two million pounds capital (heavily over-subscribed within the first week) was authorised, as was payment of a 42 per cent gross dividend. With a capital of six million pounds the Group was ready and able to face the nation's call at the time of the Munich crisis.

This was the financial expansion that enabled the relatively small Hawker company to undertake development of the Hurricane simultaneously with the quantity production of the numerous biplane designs. Even so, the expansion proved insufficient to permit accelerated development of other aircraft related to the Hurricane. Such was the singlemindedness associated with the Hurricane venture that two other promising designs were delayed somewhat, resulting in the relegation of one to secondary duties and the non-acceptance of the other. The aircraft, the Henley and Hotspur respectively, were not to fly until two years after the Hurricane's maiden flight.

THE HURRICANE GOES AHEAD

Returning to that historic day in November 1935 when the Hurricane first lifted from the grass at Brooklands, Bulman contented himself with a report on the general handling qualities in the simplest terms. The aircraft flew and flew comfortably, and only two months were to elapse before K5083 was considered ready for delivery to the A & AEE at Martlesham Heath for the Service's initial evaluation. The preliminary report issued after completion of these trials paid glowing

42

tribute to the simplicity and ease with which the aircraft could be flown.

Against a background of rumours that the Air Ministry had recommended production of the Hurricane, K5083 was demonstrated to an enthusiastic public at the Hendon Air Pageant in July 1936. Behind the scenes at Canbury Park Road, however, a decision unique in aviation history had been taken in April which may well have influenced events in the skies over southern England some four years later. Without waiting for receipt of the rumoured Government contract, the Hawker Board authorised design responsibility for the Hurricane to be taken over by the Production Drawing Office, and instructions were issued for the production planning, jigging and tooling for 1,000 airframes. Such was the degree of confidence held in the aircraft.

Government support quickly materialised, however, and on 3 June the Hawker Board received a contract for 600 Hurricanes and, by reason of the company's anticipation, the issue of production drawings to the shops was completed only one week later. There is even evidence in Air Ministry records, made available to the public in recent years, that news of the Hawker Board's precipitate decision acted as a spur to the flanks of bureaucracy, for, on the same day that Hawker received its contract, an order was sent to Supermarine for 310 Spitfires (the prototype of which had flown only on 5 March, five months after K5083). This has led to some confusion as to the reason behind the fact that so many more Hurricanes than Spitfires were available to the RAF throughout 1939 and 1940. It was *not* related to the comparative numbers of aircraft ordered from each company in 1936, but rather it reflected the ease with which production of the Hurricane got under way, employing as it did a structure with which the Hawker workforce was entirely familiar. By comparison, the Spitfire employed what was, after all, an extremely advanced monocoque structure, and one that did pose problems in achieving a fast accelerating production rate. There could have been no question of Camm adopting a similar monocoque structure, even if he had wished to do so. The Hawker factory was simply not yet equipped to produce an aeroplane like the Spitfire. Indeed, had a decision been taken to build the Hurricane in monocoque, it is most unlikely that more than a handful of such aircraft would have been in Royal Air Force hands by mid-1940. As it was, despite being marginally inferior in performance to the Spitfire during the Battle of Britain, the Hurricane displayed its own aspects of superiority — ability to withstand battle damage, ease of repair, better ability to operate from poor quality aerodromes and comparative ease of flying training. It also proved much simpler to fly at night.

Moreover, had not a setback occurred in the development of the Hurricane — which had little to do with the airframe in any case — it is likely that the aircraft would have reached the first operational squadrons six months earlier than it did. This difficulty arose towards the end of 1936, when it was decided to discontinue the Merlin Mark I engine in the Hurricane and to confine this version to the Fairey Battle light bomber. The decision to concentrate all production of the Merlin II (which featured inclined valve rocker boxes over the cylinders) on the Hurricane and Spitfire necessitated considerable alteration to the Hurricane's nose profile, and a new design of engine cowling panels. Production tooling was delayed about four months, as was delivery of the first production Merlin IIs. Nevertheless, the first production Hurricane was flown on 12 October 1937 by P G Lucas at Brooklands.

Thereafter the Hawker pilots, Bulman, Lucas, Hindmarsh (who had joined Hawkers in 1935 soon after he had won the classic Le Mans twenty-four-hour motor race in a Lagonda car), R C Reynell and K G Seth-Smith, were kept busy testing the fast-increasing flow of Hurricanes and Hinds. In the remarkably short period of two months the first Squadron, No.111, under the command of Sqn Ldr John Gillan at Northolt, was receiving its aircraft. On 10 February 1938 this officer was to bring the Hurricane to the forefront of public attention by performing a spectacular dash from Turnhouse, Edinburgh, to his base at Northolt, a distance of some 400 miles, at an average ground speed of 408 miles per hour. It has to be said, of course, that his Hurricane benefited from a strong tailwind (the early Hurricane's maximum speed being in the

Pilots of No.111 (Fighter) Squadron, the first to receive Hurricanes, being briefed by their CO, Sqn Ldr John Gillan.

Photograph taken in 1937 at Brooklands of the Henley prototype, K5115, with the Hurricane prototype, K5083.

region of 325 miles per hour), a fact which the national Press was careful not to emphasise. Nevertheless, the flight, at 17,000 feet, was not without its difficulties, being performed in semi-darkness, above cloud and without oxygen.

The year 1938 was one of transformation for the Royal Air Force. The process of introducing into service Hurricanes, Spitfires, Blenheims, Wellingtons and the rest of the new generation of modern monoplanes was accelerated by the grim portents of the Munich Crisis. The flow of Hurricanes quickly increased, even though production had not yet started at the new Langley factory. By the end of that year no fewer than eleven squadrons of Fighter Command had received Hurricanes, namely Nos. 1, 3, 32, 43, 56, 73, 79, 85, 87, 111 and 151 — although not all were yet fully operational on their new aircraft.

Digressing briefly, it is necessary here to turn to the other two Hawker designs which, though closely related to the Hurricane, had fared rather differently. The Henley had been developed from a misconceived requirement issued in 1934 for an ultimate replacement for the Fairey Battle. When it became evident that little advance in performance would result, it had been decided to suit the aircraft to perform the rôle of dive bomber, and in this it seems likely that, fitted with a constant-speed propeller, it would have excelled. Opinion, both military and public however, was inclined to discount the dive bomber's merits having regard for the vulnerability of such aircraft experienced during the Spanish Civil War. Moreover, the strictly limited supplies of Rotol constant-speed propellers, which became available late in 1939, were scheduled exclusively for the Hurricane. So the Henley was doomed to relegation; a subcontract for 350 aircraft (later reduced to 200) was placed with the Gloster Aircraft Company, the aircraft being destined to spend their lives performing the inglorious but essential task of target towing.

The other aircraft, the Hotspur, also used many Hurricane components and jigs, but was a two-seat turret fighter intended to replace the Hawker Demon. Designed to the same Specification as the Boulton Paul Defiant, the Hotspur suffered subordinate priority to the Hurricane and was so delayed that it was too late to be considered, with the result that the Defiant had already been ordered into production by the time it flew. Whether this requirement was comprehensively flawed, or whether the Defiant was a thoroughly bad design, has always been a matter for conjecture. It was certainly ill-fated for, after a brief moment of glory over Dunkirk, the Defiant suffered catastrophically in the opening weeks of the Battle of Britain. Despite the fact that it was almost impossible for the gunner to abandon the aircraft in an emergency, and that it possessed no forward-firing armament, the Defiant was later re-introduced into service as a night fighter, a rôle in which it fared little better than by day owing to its thoroughly pedestrian performance.

It can now be seen to have been providential that more importance was not attached to the Henley and Hotspur, for Hawkers were able to devote their undivided attention to the all-important Hurricane during 1936 and 1937 (although, as related anon, the normal practice of pursuing project studies in other directions late in 1937 led to the development of the Typhoon fighter). Such was the considerable effort capable of being channelled into the Hurricane's production, that Hawker Aircraft Ltd was granted licence to pursue its lucrative export business in the new aircraft, so that during 1938 and 1939 significant numbers of the new fighter were exported to Yugoslavia, Belgium, Romania and Turkey. A number was also sold to Poland, but only one evaluation aircraft is known to have arrived before the swiftly moving events of September 1939 prevented other Hurricanes from reaching their destination. Another contract was signed with the Persian Government in 1939 and, although two of the fighters had been delivered by 1940, the remainder was withheld until a more propitious opportunity — indeed, the contract could not be completed until after the war.

Small numbers of Hurricanes were shipped out to the South African Air Force in 1939, but more significant were those delivered to Canada, for, mindful of the vulnerability of aircraft factories in Britain to air attack, Hawkers were urged to negotiate a licence contract with Canadian Car and Foundry Corporation for the production of Hurricanes in Canada. The aircraft sent from England were early Mark Is, and were used as manufacturing patterns and to obtain pilot training. Simultaneously every factory drawing of Hurricane components was committed to microfilm at Kingston and copies shipped and flown across the Atlantic. Such was the high degree of efficiency achieved that only eleven months were to elapse from the date of the contract to the first flight by a Canadian-built Hurricane early in 1940. Rolls-Royce Merlins shipped from the United Kingdom powered the early aircraft; later, however, Packard-built Merlin engines were used.

THE SECOND WORLD WAR

At the outbreak of war on 3 September 1939 the Hawker factories at Kingston, Brooklands and Langley, between them employing just over 4,000 men and women, were almost exclusively engaged in building Hurricanes, about 500 of which had already been delivered to the Royal Air Force. Production was also under way in the Gloster factory at Brockworth.

With the uneasy peace now in the past, and war a reality, Air Marshal Sir Hugh Dowding's worst fears seemed to have been justified. According to a pre-arranged plan it was proposed to despatch Hurricane squadrons from his Metropolitan Air Force to France in defence of the Allied Expeditionary Force as, by their own admission, the French Air Force was scarcely able to cover its own army and bases, let alone those of the British army.

Within days of the outbreak of war, four Hurricane Squadrons of Fighter Command flew to France, Nos.1 and 73 being given the task of covering the British Blenheim and Battle bases of the Advanced Air Striking Force (AASF), and Nos.85 and 87 accompanying the Air Component of the British Expeditionary Force. It was to the guns of a No.1 Squadron Hurricane, flown by Plt Off Peter Mould, that the first German to be shot down by the RAF in France fell when, on 30 October 1939, this pilot shot down a Dornier Do 17P over Toul. Nevertheless, although all the Hurricane squadrons drew blood during the period of 'Phoney War' of that first winter, it was not until the Germans opened their big offensive in the West on 10 May 1940 that the British pilots and their Hurricanes were really put to the test.

In the meantime, however, the German invasion of Norway had resulted in the despatch of No.46 Squadron with Hurricanes to defend the northern port of Narvik, a task undertaken with great gallantry, although the inevitable withdrawal of British forces cost the loss of the aircraft carrier HMS *Glorious*, and with her all but two of the pilots and all the Hurricanes being brought home.

Up to the date of the German offensive in the West, almost all Hurricanes issued to Fighter Command had been of the early configuration, that is to say fitted with fabric-covered wings. Most of the early aircraft with two-blade propellers had, however, been withdrawn to the training units, and aircraft with Merlin III engines driving three-blade de Havilland two-pitch propellers were serving in France. Replacement aircraft being delivered to France in May included some of the early Gloster-built Hurricane Is fitted with the latest Rotol constant-speed propellers, these providing a marked improvement in performance.

The Battle of France involved a total of fourteen Hurricane squadrons, all of which came to be based on French soil at some period in the fighting. In protecting the withdrawal of the BEF, these Hurricane pilots shouldered by far the greatest responsibility for providing air cover, and

In an attempt to provide the Royal Air Force with a fighter capable of operations in the Norwegian campaign of 1940, these floats were intended for a Hurricane. The scheme was, however, abandoned.

suffered accordingly. More serious than the loss of aircraft, including 386 Hurricanes in less than a month, was that of almost 200 pilots, killed or seriously wounded, of whom 29 were squadron or flight commanders.

While Dowding had done all in his power to argue against the despatch of fighter squadrons to France, when it became clear that the losses suffered could fatally weaken his home defences, it transpired that Hurricane production was running at sufficient rate to make good the losses in France without delaying the formation of new squadrons. The Spitfires, by contrast, had been committed to battle in far smaller numbers — mainly in defence of Dunkirk in the closing stages — and the wisdom of this was quickly apparent owing to the time taken to replace Spitfire losses.

As it was, when the Battle of Britain opened in July 1940, Hurricanes still outnumbered Spitfires by five to three, while the Hurricane squadrons, with much greater battle experience, were widely regarded as providing the main strength of Fighter Command. Moreover, with experience of operating from ill-equipped French aerodromes, often with inadequate drainage, the Hurricane squadrons showed themselves capable of much wider deployment. Indeed, in the early stages of the Battle of Britain, as Hurricanes proved capable of being repaired at most of the forward aerodromes, the Spitfires were largely dependent upon the facilities at a handful of aerodromes with specialist metal-working repair facilities, such as Hornchurch, Biggin Hill and Middle Wallop.

Thus it was that Hurricanes outnumbered all other British fighters

(Spitfires, Blenheims, Defiants and Gladiators) combined, their share of enemy aircraft destroyed being in roughly the same proportion.

With three production lines turning out Hurricanes (Brooklands, Langley and Brockworth), Fighter Command was receiving new aircraft at the rate of about 120 aircraft per month at the beginning of the Battle, and when the Canadian deliveries began to build up in August the figure had grown to almost 200.

Another organisation responsible for the flow of Hurricanes to the Service was the elaborate and highly efficient Hurricane Repair Network. As this organisation was to return more than 4,000 repaired aircraft to the Royal Air Force during the war, it is perhaps worth outlining the principles on which the scheme operated. Based on the parent company at Kingston, the Hurricane repair complex was spread throughout the country, embracing aircraft factories, maintenance units, small general engineering works, and the furnishing and light engineering industries. When news of a damaged Hurricane was received, the RAF would deliver the aircraft to the nearest Repair Depot, where it would be subjected to the minutest damage inspection. The extent of the damage was notified to Hawkers, where the necessary manufacturing drawings would be taken from stock, together with any proprietary equipment necessary, and sent to the Repair Depot. Such was the importance attached to this organisation that when, towards the end of the Battle of Britain, the *Luftwaffe* began its attacks against the aircraft industry, not only were the major aircraft factories listed as primary targets but

A formation of Hurricanes flying over Southern England in 1940.

This Hurricane of No. 615 Squadron, Royal Auxiliary Air Force, was hit by an explosive shell in the rear fuselage, but was flown back and landed safely at base.

seemingly small and otherwise unimportant factories received a share of the enemy's attention. One such firm, Rollasons of Hanworth, maintained a particularly creditable record for Hurricanes repaired, but suffered considerable damage in a raid late in the Battle.

Hawkers itself was to feel the weight of enemy bombs although, compared with many aircraft manufacturers, its premises escaped lightly. Most of the staff of the design department were moved to Claremont, a large mansion near Esher, for it was thought that the prominent building which had accommodated the offices between Canbury Park Road and the parallel railway line would remain easily identifiable from the air and be a natural target for enemy bombs. In the event only one bomb might have had serious consequences, falling as it did close to the Experimental Shop in which the prototype Typhoon was undergoing final assembly. Fortunately the aircraft was not damaged.

After a heavy attack on Brooklands and Byfleet, in which a lot of damage was done and casualties caused in the Vickers factory on 4 September, the Germans returned a couple of days later, evidently intent on hitting the Hawker sheds, but relatively little damage resulted. Indeed, the delivery of Hurricanes from Brooklands increased by ten per cent that month!

Several bombs fell on and near the new factory at Langley, but at no time were the production facilities affected. The aerodrome was provided with a number of barrage balloons, and these were usually flown even when Hawker aircraft were flying on test. Later a Hurricane was set aside for the defence of Langley, but there is no record of its guns having been fired in anger. On the other hand, one of the wartime Hawker test pilots, T B Fitzgerald, airborne in the old Hurricane prototype — by then fully armed with eight machine guns — came across a lone Dornier Do 17 over Surrey and shot it down.

It was during the Battle of Britain that Dick Reynell, who had joined Hawker Aircraft in 1938 and had performed a large share of the Hurricane's development flying, was killed in action over the Thames Estuary on the evening of 7 September. Flying with No.43 Squadron from Tangmere, whom he was visiting to gain combat experience, he was ordered up against the big German raids that day. At the time of his death he was about to join in the development flying of the Typhoon and Tornado.

By the end of the Battle the rate of Hurricane production at Hawker Aircraft factories was running at around 150 aircraft each month, this despite the fact that a new version of the Merlin, the Mark XX, had been

The Langley Defence Hurricane of 1941.

51

introduced, requiring minor alterations to the nose cowlings of the aircraft.

On account of a twenty per cent power increase from the new engine, the Merlin XX enabled the armament of the Hurricane to be substantially increased, and by mid-1941 the Hurricane IIB, with twelve Browning machine guns, and the IIC, with four 20 mm cannon, were joining the squadrons of Fighter Command. In August that year the first Hurricane IIs were also being supplied to Russia by means of the North Cape convoys to Murmansk. It is perhaps a little-known fact that about 3,000 Hurricanes were sent to Russia as aid, representing almost a quarter of all Hurricanes produced.

Hurricanes also started arriving in North Africa in mid-1940, and later pioneered the long trans-African supply route from Takoradi. They were flown off carriers in the Mediterranean to relieve the slender defences of Malta at an early stage in the war against Italy.

While the Battle of Britain was being fought and won, the Battle of the Atlantic was beginning to take its ominous toll of Allied shipping. Losses attributed to U-boats and French-based enemy long-range aircraft mounted steadily, and it was to help combat the depredations of the latter that the first Sea Hurricanes were produced. Flown by many ex-Battle of Britain volunteer pilots and those of the Fleet Air Arm, these Hurricanes were flown off catapult-equipped merchant vessels to engage Focke-Wulf Fw 200 Condors which were used to shadow British convoys. Performing one of the most arduous flying tasks undertaken during the war, their pilots seldom possessed adequate fuel to enable them to reach land after combat, and usually had to ditch or bale out near the convoy in the hope that some ship would be able to stop and recover them from the sea.

Development of the Sea Hurricane continued throughout 1941 and 1942, eventually enabling the Royal Navy to launch Hurricanes at least as heavily armed as their land-based opponents, though possessing a rather inferior performance because of their maritime accoutrements. Many Hurricanes were converted for use by the Royal Navy — much of this work being carried out by General Aircraft Ltd — being flown into action in every part of the world almost until the end of the war in the Pacific.

While Hurricanes fought over Northern Europe, Russia, North Africa, the Balkans and the high seas, a small number was hurriedly diverted from the Middle East in January 1942 in order to meet the Japanese attack in Malaya. Owing to the shortcomings of such American aircraft as the Brewster Buffalo (with its absence of worthwile armament), faith was pinned on the Hurricane's attempts to wrest air superiority from the Japanese air forces. After an initial success against unescorted bombers over Singapore, the Hurricanes were, however, to be heavily punished by the Mitsubishi A6M2 Zeke naval fighters in later air battles, severely handicapped as they were by the desert air intakes, relics of their deployment in the Middle East; on this account the Hurricanes were no match for the Japanese fighters below 10,000 feet.

Notwithstanding these early setbacks, the Hurricane Mark II began arriving in India in 1942 and, from then until the end of the war, this and later versions continued to operate in the fighter-bomber and reconnaissance rôles with considerable success.

By the end of 1942 the Hurricane had been replaced in almost every other land-battle theatre as an interceptor fighter, but continued to serve in the ground-attack rôle until 1945. It was in 1942 that the Hurricane was first fitted with rocket projectiles, thereby becoming the first Allied fighter-bomber to employ these deadly weapons. Another effective weapon was the 40 mm anti-tank gun, two of which were mounted under the wings. Used mainly in the Western Desert, but also supplied in small numbers to Russia and flown by a single squadron of the RAF over Northern France, these Hurricanes were soon to claim the destruction of many of Rommel's armoured fighting vehicles. Their operational début was in the defence of the Free French Brigade at Bir Hakim in June 1942, and they were used to good effect at El Alamein. Thereafter they accompanied the Allied armies throughout the campaigns in Cyrenaica, Tripolitania, Tunisia, Sicily and Italy.

The peak Hurricane production rate was reached by the Kingston factories in March 1942, when 77 aircraft were completed in a single week, although the maximum monthly average of 279 was achieved in March 1943. By the latter date the number of workers employed by Hawker Aircraft Ltd exceeded 12,500, many of whom were women.

Hurricane IICs on the Langley production line in 1943.

'George' Bulman steps down after his demonstration of the Hurricane *Last of the Many!* in 1944.

Hurricanes remained in production until July 1944, although deliveries to the RAF and to Russia continued for some months thereafter from the large stocks being held at Maintenance Units.

So it was that the final Hurricane, suitably inscribed *The Last of the Many*, was purchased by the parent company in mid-1944 and to this day has been preserved in flying condition, an ever-present reminder of the 15,000-odd Hurricanes which flew and fought in more parts of the world than any other fighter. Not only did this classic fighter destroy more German aircraft in the Battle of Britain than all other defences combined, but recent extensive research has disclosed the astonishing fact that, in the entire war, RAF and Fleet Air Arm Hurricane pilots destroyed 55 per cent of all enemy aircraft claimed by the fighter pilots of those Services (compared with 33 per cent by those of Spitfires and 12 per cent by those of other fighters). If claims by bomber crews are taken into account, the figures are modified to become 51.5, 30.5 and 11.0 respectively, with approximately seven per cent claimed by the bomber crews. This achievement is clearly explained by the fact that it was the Hurricane that, apart from its preponderance during the Battle of Britain, was the first modern RAF fighter to reach overseas theatres, usually at times when the enemy air forces were most active in offence. For example, the Hurricane was fighting in North Africa almost two years before the arrival of the first Spitfire fighters, and nearly as long in the Far East. Sea Hurricanes were in action almost two years before the first Seafires.

After the war many surplus Hurricanes were sold to Eire, Portugal and Persia, the latter being in settlement of the contract interrupted six years earlier. Such was the sentimental regard held by the Royal Air Force for the old fighter that a single Hurricane was selected to lead the annual Battle of Britain Commemoration Fly-Past over London for several years. As these words were written there were just four surviving airworthy Hurricanes flying in the world, two flown by the Royal Air Force Battle of Britain Memorial Flight at public air displays (one of them *The Last of the Many*), and there are signs that the number may slowly increase as painstaking restoration bears fruit.

THE TYPHOON

Returning once more to the time when preparations were being made to place the Hurricane in production for the RAF in 1936, Camm's attention was already turning to a possible replacement, likely to be required some five years hence. That year preliminary information was given to Hawkers concerning two new engines being developed by Rolls-Royce Ltd and by D Napier & Sons Ltd. Both were twenty-four-cylinder liquid-cooled engines, and both were expected to develop about twice the power of the twelve-cylinder Merlin — then also just entering production in its early form.

Although both engines were expected to be a good deal larger and heavier than the Merlin, their power-to-weight ratio was expected to be somewhat greater, and Camm realised that it might still be possible to accommodate them in an aircraft not much bigger than the Hurricane. After discussing the preliminary findings of his Project Office staff with the Air Ministry at the end of 1936, Camm received a draft of Specification F.18/37, written largely around his own proposals, for a single-seat interceptor capable of 400 miles per hour and with an armament of four 20 mm cannon.

Although official policy seemed to favour the Napier engine (on account of Rolls-Royce's heavy commitment to Merlin development, as well as the slightly greater power output of what was to become the Napier Sabre), Camm decided to go ahead with alternative designs in case either engine failed to materialise, the two designs being referred to initially as the N-type (Napier) and R-type (Rolls-Royce). Because of some scepticism harboured by the Air Ministry, however, as to the practicality of employing such big engines in a single-seat interceptor, it should be explained that both engines were regarded as being more relevant to heavy bombers, and it was for such aircraft that their development was primarily sanctioned.

Be that as it may, Camm's design staff persevered and succeeded in producing designs during 1938 for two fighters, later to become the Typhoon (with Napier Sabre) and Tornado (with Rolls-Royce Vulture). It proved possible, moreover, to incorporate a single gun bay in each wing capable of accommodating three Oerlikon 20 mm cannon, such was the thickness of the wing section evolved. On the strength of performance calculations which promised a maximum speed of slightly over 400 miles per hour at 20,000 feet, two prototypes of each aircraft were accordingly ordered from Hawker.

Apart from the considerable performance increase over that of the Hurricane, the significance of the new designs lay in their all-metal monocoque construction — the first Hawker designs to be so built. Their wing span was to be no more than nineteen inches greater than that of the Hurricane (a consideration largely dictated by Hawker's existing production facilities, although it was intended that manufacture of the new fighter would take place at the Langley factory, yet to be completed).

The repercussions of the Munich Crisis in the autumn of 1938, however, were to have a profound effect on the priorities forced upon the aircraft industry. Absolute priority was to be afforded to the production of the Merlin engine and of Hurricanes and Spitfires, with the result that essential development work on the Vulture (in particular) slowed appreciably during 1939 so that, when the first flight engine was delivered to Hawker that year, much work still required to be done to ensure reliability. This lack of urgency continued throughout the dark days of 1940, with the result that, when it was decided to switch production of the Manchester — the only heavy bomber to persist with the Vulture engine — to a four-Merlin version (that became the Lancaster), work on the Vulture was brought to a virtual standstill. Thus the Hawker Tornado, which it must be said experienced relatively little trouble from its engine, was discontinued after only four examples had been completed in 1941.

The Napier Sabre-powered Typhoon also suffered its share of problems, again resulting from diminished priority during the early months of the war. Indeed, realisation that this fighter could not possibly reach Fighter Command during 1940 only contributed to a feeling that, if Britain did not survive the Battle of Britain, the Typhoon would be superfluous in any case. That is not to say that Hawkers did not pursue flight trials energetically during 1940 whenever possible. When, on 9 May that year, a failure occurred in the fuselage monocoque of the first prototype, it was only the courage and skill displayed by Philip Lucas that enabled the aircraft to be landed safely (when he would have been entirely justified in abandoning by parachute), for which he was awarded the George Medal. And this was the only Typhoon prototype to be flown in 1940.

The second prototype was flown early in 1941, by which time, with manufacturing space becoming available at Brockworth, production had been switched to the Gloster Aircraft Company. A small batch of production Typhoons was, however, built at Langley but, with all development of the aircraft centred at the aerodrome, these were in the nature of a pre-production batch on which most experimental flying was conducted.

By 1941, however, with the appearance in *Luftwaffe* service, first of the Messerschmitt Bf 109F, and soon afterwards of the Focke-Wulf Fw 190A (both of which were superior in performance to the Spitfire II and V, by then adopted as Fighter Command's standard single-seat fighter), pressure was being exerted on Hawker to accelerate the Typhoon into

The prototype Typhoon in which Philip Lucas suffered failure of the rear fuselage monocoque structure during an early test flight.

One of many accidents, this Typhoon IA suffered engine failure while approaching to land at Matlask, Norfolk.

service. Early aircraft were armed with twelve Browning machine guns, but the Air Ministry decided against the six-cannon armament in favour of four Hispano 20 mm guns in the interests of increased performance.

Typhoons first entered service at Duxford in September 1941 but, still being plagued by problems with the Sabre engine, and later by a spate of accidents caused by structural failure of the rear-fuselage transport joint (which in turn resulted from fatigue failure of a small bracket in the elevators), it was not until well into the following year that the first Typhoon Wing of three Squadrons was formed. In August 1942 this Wing participated in its first major cross-Channel operation, covering the Dieppe landings. Intended to represent the RAF's answer to the Fw 190, the Typhoon failed to meet expectations, being both badly committed to combat and possessing inadequate performance at heights above 20,000 feet.

The latter shortcoming had been known for some time, and moves were already afoot to change the Typhoon's operational rôle to that of ground attack, and it was in this duty that the aircraft came to excel. Armed with bombs or rockets in addition to the four cannon, Typhoons went on to equip numerous squadrons of Fighter Command, and in the operations before, during and immediately after the Normandy landings in 1944, they came to be accepted as the scourge of enemy radar stations, road and rail transport, aerodromes and other tactical targets behind the invasion front.

Among the pilots who were engaged in development flying of the Typhoon was Sqn Ldr R P Beamont DSO, DFC, who not only commanded one of the first Typhoon squadrons in the RAF (No.609), but also joined the Hawker pilots at Langley for test work on both the Typhoon and its successor, the Tempest. He it was who first flew the Typhoon on a series of ground-attack operations in 1942, the results of which encouraged Fighter Command to look more closely at this type of operation. Development of the Typhoon was costly in terms of lives, and both P E G Sayer (then Chief Test Pilot at Glosters) and Kenneth Seth-Smith of Hawkers were to lose their lives in Typhoons — although the former was almost certainly killed in an air collision.

In the final months of the war in Europe the Typhoon Wings of the Second Tactical Air Force represented a major element in the forces supporting the advancing Allied armies. Numerous 'set-piece' attacks were carried out on enemy headquarters and other pin-point targets, using cannon, bombs and rockets. Other Typhoons were also employed in the fighter-reconnaissance rôle. One of their widely-used tactics was that of the 'cab-rank', a standing patrol over the land battle, their pilots in contact with an observer accompanying the leading troops on the ground. On encountering an enemy strongpoint, the ground forces were able to mark the obstacle with smoke shells and then call-down a strike by a formation of Typhoons armed with rockets or bombs.

At the end of the war the Typhoon was already being replaced in service by the Tempest and, by September 1945, it had all but disappeared from the Royal Air Force. A total of 3,330 had been produced — all but a tiny handful by the Gloster Aircraft Co Ltd.

THE LAST GENERATION OF PISTON-ENGINED FIGHTERS

Numerous circumstances conspired to hamper the development of the Typhoon, of which the immediate effects of the Munich crisis and the

A rocket-equipped Typhoon dispersed in the outfield of an emergency landing strip in Normandy during 1944. The explosion in the background was caused by a mine disposal unit. (*Photo: Imperial War Museum.*)

The cockpit of the Tempest V.

subsequent diminution of priorities have already been cited. To these should be added a failure to look far enough ahead to appreciate the altitudes at which air combat was likely to take place, and a reluctance to authorise the provision of an adequate number of prototypes on which development could be carried out. The decision to adopt a cannon armament was bold indeed, but it did conspire to compromise the provision of a relatively thin wing; indeed, it was this thick but extremely robust structure that so severely restricted the Typhoon's altitude performance. In long retrospect it can be seen that none of these shortcomings represented any dereliction either at Hawker or the Air Ministry. On the one hand the nation was facing extreme peril, and the singleminded determination to pursue the development and production of the Hurricane and Spitfire was vital to its survival. On the other, the Hawker design staff possessed scarcely any experience in designing a monocoque aircraft, while the production facilities available in Canbury Park Road and Brooklands could not be enhanced in time to meet an earlier production schedule without compromising that of the Hurricane.

It was for these reasons that, at the very time the Typhoon was encountering its most serious problems, Camm put forward a proposal to incorporate a thin elliptical wing and an improved version of the Sabre engine, then being investigated by Napiers. Known first as the Typhoon Mark II, and later to become the Tempest, the proposal was accepted by the Air Ministry, together with alternative engine installations — namely the Bristol Centaurus eighteen-cylinder radial and the twelve-

60

cylinder Rolls-Royce Griffon liquid-cooled in-line — as insurance against continuing trouble with the Sabre.

By the end of 1942 the Sabre was over the worst of its difficulties, and the following year the Tempest Mark V entered production at Langley. Following more slowly, the Centaurus-powered Tempest Mark II also achieved production status both at Langley and at the Bristol Aeroplane Company's 'shadow' factory at Weston-super-Mare, though it was too late to see service during the war.

The Tempest retained much of the Typhoon's character of power and weight, though it was more aerodynamically refined with its much thinner elliptical wing and improved controls. It possessed excellent performance at all altitudes up to around 25,000 feet, and particularly at low and medium heights such that when, in 1944, the Germans launched their flying bomb attacks against southern England, the Tempest V formed the spearhead of the fighter defences, one Wing alone destroying more than 600 bombs. This Wing was commanded by Wg Cdr Beamont, mentioned above, who was also to lead it to the Tempests' first bases on the continent of Europe before the end of 1944, but alas was to be shot down and taken prisoner.

(It is worth recording here that, shortly before he was shot down, Beamont had been approached by Hawkers with an offer of appointment as the Company's Chief Test Pilot, Bulman having long

About forty Tempest V front fuselage sections are visible in this corner of the Langley factory. A photograph taken in 1946.

since retired from active experimental flying, and Lucas having expressed a desire to do so. Beamont decided to remain with his Wing at least until he had completed his 100th operational sortie on Tempests but, unfortunately, he was to be shot down. On his return from captivity he was immediately offered the command of the first Tempest II Wing, in mid-1945 planned for redeployment in the Far East to continue the war against Japan. When these plans came to naught following the end of the Pacific War, Beamont left the Service and, after a short spell with the Gloster Aircraft Company, joined the English Electric Company, with which he undertook the early development flying of the Canberra jet bomber, followed by that of the Lightning supersonic fighter. More recently he was appointed Director of Flight Operations with Panavia, being charged with overall responsibility for the flight development of the tri-national Tornado multi-rôle combat aircraft. It would be difficult to find an equal anywhere in the history of aviation of such a span of service (which also embraced the Battle of France in 1940 and the Battle of Britain) and experience in test flying over thirty years.)

The Tempest V was among the fastest of all Allied piston-engine fighters during the war, possessing a top speed of 442 mph at 20,500 feet, and was one of the few aircraft to destroy Messerschmitt Me 262 jet fighters.

The Tempest II had progressed more slowly, having entered production in 1944 and encountered some problems with its Bristol Centaurus eighteen-cylinder sleeve-valve radial engine, associated in the main with a breakdown of crankshaft lubrication and excessive vibration. This engine was, however, the most powerful available in production at the end of the war, and the ever-present demand for increased power lent urgency to eventual rectification of the faults, and the Tempest II finally entered service in the autumn of 1945. Squadrons served with the RAF in India and the Far East, as well as with the Second Tactical Air Force in Germany. In 1948 surplus RAF Tempest IIs were supplied to the air forces of India and Pakistan.

Development of the Tempest led to one other family of fighters whose life-span was to last until the early 1960s. This was the Fury monoplane, whose genesis came about during the course of discussions between Camm and the Air Ministry towards the end of 1942, when the former put forward proposals for a lightened version of the Tempest. Camm realised that, fast though the Tempest would ultimately be, there still remained scope to reduce the size of the airframe, and this he proposed doing by almost eliminating the Tempest's wing centresection, thereby reducing the wing span from forty-one to around thirty-eight feet. The following year an Air Ministry Specification was drafted around these ideas and several prototypes were ordered. By the end of 1943 the Admiralty had also become interested in the design and had issued a similar requirement, with the result that two parallel designs materialised, later known as the Fury and Sea Fury.

Langley aerodrome shortly after the end of the Second World War in 1945.

Hawker Aircraft Ltd was now so fully committed to Hurricane and Tempest production that development of the Fury extended over many months. To complicate matters, the Air Ministry required that the Fury prototypes be powered by three alternative engines, namely the Centaurus, the Sabre and the Griffon (the latter driving contra-rotating propellers).

The end of the war in Europe, however, brought with it an end to the Air Ministry's interest in the Fury, the decision to terminate the development contracts clearly being taken on account of the appearance and early success of such jet fighters as the Gloster Meteor and de Havilland Vampire.

Nevertheless, the Sea Fury continued to command support from the Naval Staff, and production orders which had been placed during 1944 survived without cancellation. Difficulties with the Centaurus, which had so delayed the Tempest II, had by 1946 been largely overcome, with the result that the first production Sea Furies were completed that year. After only minor alterations had been made, found necessary during deck landing trials, the new aircraft entered service with the Royal Navy in 1947. The following year a new version, equipped as a fighter-bomber, also joined the fleet.

Thus it was that, at a time when the major air forces of the world were fully committed to the jet fighter, the Royal Navy was to participate in the Korean war, which began in 1950, armed with propeller-driven Fairey Fireflies and Hawker Sea Furies. Equally remarkable was the fact that, although they were completely outpaced by the enemy land-based MiG-15 jet fighters, the carrier-borne Sea Furies performed their duties with spectacular success, being used principally for ground attack and

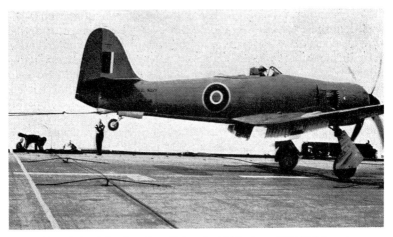
Carrier trials of the Sea Fury X late in 1946, aboard HMS *Victorious*.

thereby operating at such low level as to render interception difficult. Moreover, on those rare occasions when they were committed to fighting the MiG-15s, the Sea Fury pilots acquitted themselves well, claiming several victories and providing convincing testimony to their manoeuvrability and firepower.

This singular aptitude for low-level support duties was undoubtedly responsible for the Sea Fury's long service, for, apart from the Royal Navy and the Royal Canadian Navy, the air forces of Holland, Iraq, Egypt and Pakistan all placed sizeable orders for the aircraft between 1946 and 1955. On being declared surplus to requirements after the Korean war, many Sea Furies (among them a number of two-seat trainers) were re-purchased by Hawker Aircraft Ltd, refurbished and sold between 1957 and 1962 to Burma, Cuba and West Germany. Furthermore, during the past twenty years, American owners have acquired ex-RCN Sea Furies for racing, some of the resulting 'conversions' achieving some extraordinary speeds in the National Air Races.

EARLY HAWKER JET AIRCRAFT

While preoccupation with the family of piston-engine fighters undoubtedly absorbed much of the Hawker Design Staff's efforts up to 1946, it should not be thought that the project staff had remained unaware of the great potential offered by the turbojet engine. Jet-powered projects had been studied at Hawkers as early as 1941, when schemes were evolved to install experimental Power Jets W.2B engines in the P.1055 twin-engine high-speed bomber design, which had been prepared to Specification B.11/41 and which featured a pair of Napier Sabre engines. Further schemes continued to appear in 1942 and 1943, and much useful design experience was gained. These projects were little more than design exercises, for the power output of the early turobjets was considered inadequate to warrant serious consideration. (It should be remembered that the early Gloster Meteors, which entered limited service against the flying bombs in 1944, were in fact scarcely faster than the Tempest V, and a good deal less reliable.)

Nevertheless when, in 1943, preliminary details of the Rolls-Royce B.41 jet engine were made available, it was at once realised that here was a powerplant of relatively low diameter, low installed weight and giving promise of moderate power output. Thus a preliminary study was initiated to adapt an existing design, the Fury, to take this engine, mounted amidships behind the pilot, whose cockpit was moved forward about five feet. Designated the P.1035, this scheme was developed until, by early 1944, several novel features had been introduced to overcome the apparent difficulties. The engine air intakes had been moved from the nose to the wing root leading edges and, to reduce thrust losses, the tailpipe was shortened considerably by bifurcation to exhaust on either side of the fuselage immediately aft of the trailing edge. This split tailpipe was patented by the company.

The design, which was renumbered P.1040, was tendered in 1944 together with performance estimates, and by the following year sufficient interest had been generated in the Air Ministry to encourage the Hawker Design Staff to proceed with limited detail design. Later in 1945 the design assumed such promise that the Naval Staff, already mindful of the approaching obsolescence of the Fury — even though it was not yet in service — took active note of the progress being made. This was fortunate indeed, for when, in 1946, the Air Staff, undoubtedly

A twin-engine Hawker design which reached advanced mock-up stage. The P.1005, which was prepared to meet Spec. B.11/41 and on which much project work was later done to investigate the possible installation of Power Jets engines.

The bifurcated jet pipe scheme, patented by Hawker Aircraft Ltd and applied so successfully in the Sea Hawk naval jet fighter.

influenced by the speed record performance of the Meteor IV, decided that the P.1040 represented insufficient advance and announced that it no longer supported the project as a future RAF fighter, all subsequent interest stemmed from the Admiralty.

A naval fighter Specification, N.7/46, was prepared and, after acceptance of the P.1040, contracts were raised to cover manufacture of three prototypes (though the P.1040 had already begun manufacture as a private venture).

Later in 1946, following discussions with the Royal Aircraft Establishment at Farnborough, a research Specification, E.38/46, was issued for the application of a swept wing to the P.1040 design, and a contract was received for the manufacture of two prototypes under the designation P.1052.

So it was in 1947, when public speculation as to whether Hawker Aircraft would enter the field of jet aircraft design was being expressed, that the company was actively engaged in the manufacture of five prototypes, each of which — unlike other, almost worthless prototypes of the day — was to contribute much to the development of high-speed operational aircraft.

Progress on the P.1040 continued throughout 1947, and on 2 September the prototype was flown by Bill Humble at Boscombe Down, this being followed in 1948 by the first of the fully-navalised prototypes. Two months later, the first swept-wing P.1052 was also flown.

The P.1052 research aircraft being assembled in the new Richmond Road experimental department in 1948.

At this point, with production contracts for the N.7/46 naval fighter imminent, a brief survey of the company is necessary. After Brooklands had been vacated early in the war, production facilities were concentrated at Canbury Park Road, Kingston, and at the now-enlarged factory and aerodrome at Langley, a dozen miles away. The twenty-year lease on the extensive factory premises in Richmond Road (Government Aircraft Factory No. 1, which Sopwith had acquired for the production of aircraft during the First World War), held by Leyland Motors since 1928, now expired, and Hawker Aircraft Ltd lost no time in re-occupying the thirty-four-year-old buildings, although the administrative offices, Design Department and some machine shops remained in Canbury Park Road for a further ten years.

The flight test facilities at Langley were, however, fast becoming unsatisfactory. The post-war growth of London Airport, a bare six miles distant, the increasing flow of airliner traffic across the approaches to Langley and the lack of hard runway surfaces severely hampered Sea Fury testing, while flights by the new jet prototypes were performed almost exclusively from Farnborough, where Hawker Aircraft occupied a single hangar. These arrangements were clearly inconvenient owing to the dispersion of labour and plant, and Hawkers were fortunate to acquire tenancy in 1950 of Dunsfold aerodrome, about twenty miles from Kingston. Here, relatively free from industrial haze and commercial air traffic, final-assembly shops and experimental-flight facilities were established and remain in use to this day.

Responsibility for experimental flight testing in 1949 rested on the Chief Test Pilot, Sqn Ldr T S ('Wimpey') Wade, DFC, AFC, a veteran of the Battle of Britain, and for something like a year he was the sole Hawker pilot engaged in flying the P.1040, N.7/46 and P.1052 prototypes (although Humble had performed the initial flights of the P.1040). In 1949 Wade was joined by Sqn Ldr Neville Duke, DSO, OBE, DFC, AFC, who had spent several months with Hawkers in 1945, seconded from the RAF, and by 1950 this pair performed the greater share of experimental flying. In terms of flying time, however, most work fell to the production test pilots, Sqn Ldr Frank Murphy, DFC, and E S Morrell (soon to be joined by Frank Bullen).

Sqn Ldr T S Wade in the P.1040.

Sqn Ldr N F Duke standing by the Sea Fury which in 1949 he flew to Cairo in record time to establish a new Point-to-Point record.

The Armstrong Siddeley Snarler liquid-fuel rocket motor being ground run in the tail of the Hawker P.1072.

By January 1949 the original P.1040 prototype's share in the development programme for the Royal Navy was complete, and the aircraft was returned to Kingston for installation of the Armstrong Siddeley Snarler liquid-fuel rocket engine in the aircraft's tail. For the past three years various studies of rocket-powered fighters had been carried out by the Project Team at Kingston, and the new installation in the P.1040 (now redesignated the P.1072) produced Britain's first high-performance, manned rocket-powered aircraft — apart from being Hawker Aircraft's first twin-engine aircraft to fly. Never intended as anything other than a research experiment, the machine flew under rocket power only half-a-dozen times before a minor explosion brought flight trials to an end.

On the other hand, the P.1052s were to perform many hours of flying both for Hawker Aircraft and for the Royal Aircraft Establishment at Farnborough. By 1950 the first of the two prototypes had been handed over for various naval research programmes (during which it carried out the first deck landings by a British swept-wing aircraft), while the other aircraft was returned to company charge for conversion into the P.1081. This design retained the P.1052's swept wing but introduced a straight-through tailpipe, exhausting through the rear fuselage, as well as all-swept tail surfaces. At the time the Australian Government was expressing considerable interest in this project (powered by a Rolls-Royce Tay) but, although preliminary plans were made to put the aircraft into production, nothing came of the scheme. First flown in June 1950 by Wade, the P.1081 was shown at the Brussels and Farnborough Air Displays and underwent much flight testing in preparation for the forthcoming Hunter fighter. However, disaster overtook the aeroplane on 3 April

1951, when it was destroyed in a flying accident involving the death of Sqn Ldr Wade.

Meanwhile, the N.7/46 prototypes, now officially named Sea Hawks, continued their development programmes, and in November 1949 a production contract for 151 aircraft was issued to the company. Transfer of the design responsibility to the Production Drawing Office had been anticipated by several months, with the result that the first production machine was flown just two years later. As will become evident shortly, however, Hawker Aircraft was again to be embarrassed by the simultaneous production demands of two successful service aircraft types, and the size of the orders which, by 1951, had been placed for the Hunter, made it necessary to transfer Sea Hawk production elsewhere. Thus, starting in the autumn of that year, all Sea Hawk drawings, jigs and tools were despatched to Sir W G Armstrong Whitworth Aircraft Ltd at Coventry and, after only thirty-five production Sea Hawks had left the Kingston factory, all development of the aircraft henceforth became the responsibility of Armstrong Whitworth.

By 1953 Sea Hawk production was under way at Coventry, and follow-up design work, originally started at Kingston, resulted in the aircraft soon appearing with underwing external stores for ground-attack duties. From 1955 onwards the Sea Hawk assumed the Fleet Air Arm's dual responsibilities of interception and tactical strike. Replacing the Sea Fury and Supermarine Attacker, the Sea Hawk became the principal naval fighter between 1955 and 1960, equipping Nos. 800, 801, 802, 803, 804, 806, 810, 892, 897, 898 and 899 Squadrons, as well as three squadrons of the RNVR and two training squadrons.

Six Sea Hawk squadrons were flown on tactical strike operations from the carriers HMS *Albion, Eagle* and *Bulwark* in support of the Anglo-French landings during the Suez campaign in November 1956, this being the only occasion that the aircraft could prove its worth in combat.

As with the Hunter, the Sea Hawk gained immense popularity with its pilots for its pleasant control characteristics, evidenced by the appearance of formation aerobatic teams, and during 1956–58 several scintillating displays were given by Sea Hawk units.

Production at Coventry for the Fleet Air Arm came to an end in 1956, but, undeterred by the prospects of lengthy delays, the West German and Netherlands governments placed sizeable orders for Sea Hawks even after the assembly lines had been dismantled, and in 1959 further Sea Hawks were ordered by India.

'THE MOST BEAUTIFUL FIGHTER EVER'

The delegation of development and production responsibility for the Sea Hawk to Sir W G Armstrong Whitworth Aircraft Ltd had been brought about simply because Hawker Aircraft Ltd had not the factory area necessary to accommodate the large-scale production facilities required for both the Sea Hawk and the Hunter. Both aircraft were, in 1951, made subjects of Winston Churchill's 'Super Priority' administrative programme deemed necessary to redress the harm done to the Royal Air Force during the six years of Socialist government following the Second World War. During those years Britain's air forces stood still, forfeiting world leadership in technology. Good aeroplanes were on the horizon, but the miasma of beaucratic inertia threatened to render them obsolete before they ever saw the light of day. The 'SP' scheme embraced a small number of selected military aircraft which were considered to be of great importance for the re-equipment of the Services, and were to benefit from priority distribution of materials and proprietary components. All contracts raised under the scheme were prefixed with the letters SP, and were to be processed 'today rather than tomorrow'. There is no doubt that the selected aircraft did benefit to a considerable extent, although chaos continued to reign among companies less fortunate in not possessing favoured designs, such was the lethargy spawned by governmental incompetence.

The origin of the Hunter may be traced back as far as 1946, when the Air Staff, following the pattern set by the twin-engine Meteor, issued a pair of Specifications, F.43/46 and F.44/46, for single-seat day and two-seat night twin-engine fighters respectively, and Hawker Aircraft Ltd was invited to tender design proposals. Neither Specification was, however, considered a realistic approach to RAF requirements, largely owing to a lack of fundamental knowledge of high speed flight problems, a situation that was allowed to continue owing to an almost total lack of government funding for research. This was particularly apparent in the severe financial restrictions placed on the experimental establishments, to such an extent that, for example, Farnborough was starved of funds adequate to pursue in-depth examinations of captured German aircraft, such as the Messerschmitt Me 262 — found by the Americans to represent a priceless short-cut to transonic aerodynamic technology. Instead, British aerodynamicists were obliged to play with ballistic models in their development of high-speed aerofoils, on the basis of 'suck it and see'. The result was that the 'clipped and clapped' Meteor, excellent by the standards of 1946, was kept in front-line service until the mid-1950s. It also underwent two-seat adaptation to provide an even less auspicious night fighter for the RAF over the same period. Little wonder that Britain did not feel inclined to send RAF fighters to Korea to face the Communist MiG-15s (which, incidentally, had benefited immeasurably from the British government-sponsored export of Rolls-Royce turbojet engines in 1947).

Sydney Camm — not a politically-minded man in any sense — was careful to confine his discusions with the Air Ministry to an examination of what was capable of being produced with the slender research facilities available, pointing to the aerodynamic advances that might be achieved by progressive adaptation of the P.1040, first with a swept wing

The installation mock-up of the F.3/48 Hunter. This picture, taken early in 1949, shows the high-set tailplane originally proposed.

and later with swept tail surfaces as well. Thus were the P.1052 and P.1081 conceived in the context of limited research. Stemming from these discussions, the Air Ministry evolved a new Specification, F.3/48, and this was issued in draft form in Feburary 1948.

In the meantime, however, Hawkers had received preliminary details of the new axial-flow Rolls-Royce A.J.65 turbojet, which, at an initial rating of 6,500 pounds thrust, represented approximately the same power as two of the latest Derwent engines in the Meteor. Accordingly a project design was begun as a private venture of an aircraft conforming in broad outline to the performance capabilities of the F.43/46 Specification. This design underwent progressive alteration when F.3/48 was received, and was to be designated the Hawker P.1067.

The P.1067 was a swept-wing, single-engine single-seat day fighter whose A.J.65 engine (soon to become the Avon) was enclosed in the centre fuselage. As first conceived, a high-set tailplane and nose air intake were envisaged; however, because of increasing demands for cockpit accommodation of additional equipment, and the general inefficiency of nose ducts and the restrictions they imposed, twin air intakes were incorporated (Sea Hawk fashion) in the wing roots. Furthermore, operating requirements of the nose-mounted radar-ranging gunsight confirmed the wisdom of this change. Later still, the tailplane was re-positioned some three feet lower on the fin.

Perhaps the most significant operational design feature was the inclusion of four 30 mm Aden guns, certainly an advanced armament for a single-seat fighter (although the Messerschmitt Me 262 twin-jet fighter had, five years earlier, been similarly armed).

As with all interceptor fighters, the importance of a quick turn-round between sorties cannot be overstressed, and Hawkers' proposal for a completely detachable gun pack met with immediate approval. This pack, which contained all four gun bodies and ammunition, could be winched down from the nose of the aircraft after a sortie and replaced by another already loaded with ammunition. Combined with a single refuelling point, this feature enabled the aircraft to be refuelled and rearmed in something like five minutes between flights.

A mock-up of the new aircraft was started in September 1948, and in the following year three prototypes were ordered, the first two scheduled for Avon engines and the third for a Sapphire for, apart from providing insurance against delays or troubles with the Avon, it should be remembered that this excellent engine was to have heavy demands made upon its production by English Electric Canberras and several other aircraft nearing the flight stage.

Construction of the first prototype jigs began in December 1949 in the Richmond Road experimental department and, by the following April, the fuselage nose was ready for skinning. A temporary setback occurred in May 1950, when the Ministry of Supply decided to abandon the 30 mm Avon gun installation, but the decision was revoked shortly afterwards and, in July 1951, the first prototype was completed. The P.1067 made its maiden flight at Boscombe Down on 20 July in the hands of Sqn Ldr Neville Duke, newly appointed as the company's Chief Test Pilot — and whose name will always be synonymous with that of the Hunter, the name now bestowed on the new Hawker fighter.

The first prototype Hunter nearing completion at Kingston in 1951.

Super priority — Hunter production in full swing in the middle 1950s.

A view of the Hunter wing bay. Compare the picture on this page with that of the same shop in 1918 (page xii).

As had so often been Camm's practice in the past, his thoughts now turned to a successor to the Hunter, and work started on a development employing a 50-degree swept swing of reduced thickness/chord and a reheated Avon of greatly increased power. Known as the P.1083, this was proposed as being the first truly supersonic RAF fighter but, as will be told shortly, the aircraft was to suffer changed official policies and was never completed.

On the other hand, the Hunter's own devleopment went ahead and, by the time the first prototype flew, orders for 350 aircraft had been signed for the Royal Air Force, of which 200 were to be Avon-powered, built at Kingston, and the remainder (Mark 2s) with Sapphire engines by Armstrong Whitworth at Baginton, Coventry, as Sea Hawk production began to run out. (These totals came to be progressively changed — for instance, the 150 Sapphire Hunters eventually produced comprised 45 Mark 2s and 105 Mark 5s).

Large-scale tooling-up for Hunter production continued throughout 1952 at Kingston and Coventry, while arrangements were made for sub-component assembly elsewhere — nose sections by the Gloster Aircraft Company and tailplanes by Folland Aircraft Ltd.

The first flight by a production Hunter took place from Dunsfold on 16 May 1953, but this event tended to be overshadowed by the cancellation of the P.1083 project. There is no doubt but that the appearance of the North American F-100 Super Sabre, capable of supersonic speed in level flight, had a profound effect on the Air Staff's outlook for, all too painfully, it highlighted RAF Fighter Command's inferiority in first-line aircraft. The F-86 Sabre, a genuinely transonic fighter, had not only been in service for four years but had fought with great distinction over Korea, while the RAF could still boast of nothing better than first-generation subsonic Meteors and Vampires. Behind the Air Ministry's decision to cancel the P.1083 was the fear that, once such an aircraft had been accepted for the RAF, it would soldier on in service to the exclusion of aircraft of comparable performance to the F-100 (and the F-104, soon to materialise). Time has shown that, in all likelihood, the decision was probably correct, even though it prevented Hawker Aircraft Ltd from acquiring first-hand experience of designing, building and flying a supersonic fighter. As it was, the Hunter — eventually given a more appropriate task, that of ground attack — remained in service almost as long as the English Electric Lightning, a third-generation jet fighter capable of Mach 2 performance.

The P.1083 prototype had been under construction for almost a year, and it had been hoped to have the aircraft ready for the 1953 SBAC Display at Farnborough, but it was becoming increasingly evident that Air Staff interest was shifting from the reheated turbojet to the new generation of large 'dry' engines foreshadowed by the 10,000-pound-thrust Avon 200-series, and in June 1953 official support for the P.1083 was withdrawn. Instead, proposals for a new version of the Hunter with the Avon 200-series engine were accepted, and found final form in the Hunter Mark 6. Unfortunately the wing of the standard Hunter was such that it could never be more than a transonic aeroplane, and it was the greatly increased power of the engine that permitted a good load-carrying ability and suited the aircraft perfectly to the ground-attack rôle.

Meanwhile, orders for Hunters, totalling over 600 aircraft, had been issued by the end of 1953, and in the following year Hunter 1s and 2s entered service with RAF Fighter Command, based in the United Kingdom. An alteration to the combat deceleration requirement (hitherto based on the Meteor's performance) caused some delay while a powerful airbrake was introduced under the Hunter's rear fuselage, but thereafter production continued scarcely checked for half a decade.

The Hunter's cockpit (a Swiss Mk. 58). Compare with those on pages 19, 60 and 97.

The year 1953 was significant for the Hunter in other respects, for in September — shortly after Sydney Camm had received a knighthood in the Coronation Honours List for his services to aviation — the Hunter, flown by Neville Duke, established a new World Absolute Speed Record at 727.6 miles per hour, as well as the record for the 100-kilometre Closed Circuit course at 709.2 miles per hour. Ironically, the aircraft involved was the original Hunter prototype, modified by the installation of an Avon with reheat.

Hawkers had, moreover, been engaged in developing the aircraft in the ground-attack rôle, though in a curiously circuitous manner. Soon after the early Hunter 1s had entered service, it was quickly found that firing the guns at altitudes above about 30,000 feet caused surging in the early RA7-series Avons, followed by flame-out, and the aircraft themselves were found to be prone to a new problem, that of pitch-up.The introduction of the Avon Series 21 engines, less prone to surging, led to a change to the Hunter Mark 4 on the production line, as well as wing-leading-edge 'saw-tooth' extensions to alleviate pitch-up. The wing modifications, as well as an increase in the internal fuel capacity (early Hunters had a very bad name for exceptionally short endurance), marked the change from Mark 2 to Mark 5 in the Sapphire-powered version. It was generally considered among Hunter pilots that the Mark 4 was the most pleasant of all to fly.

These two versions underwent a good deal of development to enable

76

This picture gives some idea of the diversity of stores carried by the Hunter. From front to rear: Practice bombs, 230 gallon drop tanks, 1,000 lb bombs, 500 lb bombs, 100 gallon drop tanks and Napalm bombs, 5 inch HVAR missiles, 3 inch RPs (left) and 2 inch RPs (right), 2 and 3 inch RP launchers, Fairey Fireflash and DH Firestreak missiles.

them to carry external stores under the wings, ranging from 1,000 lb and 100 gallon drop tanks to three-inch rockets and 20 lb practice bombs. This resulting ability to perform the two principal duties required of a tactical air force not only led to the introduction of the Hunter 4 into service with the RAF's Second Tactical Air Force in Germany, but attracted widespread attention among foreign governments, in the best Hawker tradition, and the aircraft was sold in large numbers to Sweden, Denmark and Peru, while licence agreements were drawn up with manufacturers in Holland and Belgium for service with the NATO air forces. At home, production continued at Hawkers and Armstrong Whitworth, and by the end of 1956 a total of 860 Mark 4s and 5s (including foreign variants) had been completed.

After the discontinuation of the P.1083 project in 1953 the company had gone ahead with the P.1099 (the Hunter 6), in which the new 10,000 lb thrust Avon 203 was combined with the store-carrying abilities of the Mark 4. By 1955 production Mark 6s were beginning to come off the production lines, and heavy RAF ordering resulted in this version also being set up at a Hawker factory at Blackpool; Mark 6s also superseded the Mark 5s at Coventry. Eventually the Belgian and Dutch factories also switched to the later version.

This Hunter survived a mid-air collision during a low-level mock dog-fight and despite the loss of tail cone and starboard tailplane, the pilot (an American serving with the RAF), brought his machine safely back to base.

If, as remarked above, the Hunter 4 gained popularity among its pilots on account of its pleasant handling characteristics, the big Avon-powered Mark 6, and its principal derivative, the Mark 9, were undoubtedly widely regarded as one of the world's finest all-round fighters. It was argued in support of its subsonic performance that, in the ground-attack rôle, supersonic speed was superfluous; accurate navigation equipment, capable of being accommodated in a relatively small aircraft, was not available and, in the absence of terrain-avoidance radar, low-level attack operations had to be carried out in fairly good weather conditions and at speeds not much in excess of 500 knots. This situation did not change materially for another dozen years anywhere in the world. The greater power from the engine enabled greater loads to be carried without detriment to the already excellent short-field performance of the Hunter, while the development of 230-gallon drop tanks enabled the aircraft to undertake reinforcement operations to the Middle East and elsewhere. In due course these big tanks were stressed for limited combat manoeuvres.

THE ECHOES OF THE SANDYS WHITE PAPER

The year 1957 witnessed a shift in the British government's policy on defence. This came about largely as the result of disillusionment following the abortive Suez operations of the previous year, when ill-advised long-range political interference by America proved to be more decisive in the short term than long-range military action. The Conservative government, facing pressure all round for a rationalisation of the armed forces, believed it was not possible to match the technology of the two Super Powers and, in its Defence White Paper of 1957, put forward proposals suggesting that the future air defence of Britain should be dependent upon ground-to-air missiles. It stated that the Lightning fighter, soon to enter service, would in all likelihood be the last manned fighter, and that Britain's policy in the air would centre on deterrence — the build-up of a nuclear-armed force of strategic bombers. Already the determination to avoid all military involvement 'east of Suez' had been decided upon, but the domestic defence policy took no account of Britain's worldwide responsibilities as an integral part of Western defence.

Although it was quickly seen that the arguments behind the White Paper were fundamentally flawed, its immediate effect could have been disastrous for aircraft manufacturers such as Hawker Aircraft Ltd. The last 100 Hunters for the Royal Air Force were summarily cancelled and, had it not been for the tremendous export potential of this aeroplane, Hawkers might well have faced the possibility of closure. After all, it had no new aircraft scheduled for production in the foreseeable future.

The situation was, as in the 1930s, saved by the receipt of large export orders, both India and Switzerland taking advantage of the possibility of quick delivery of Hunters. Indeed, production of the cancelled RAF

Two-seat Hunter trainers for the RAF and foreign air forces awaiting delivery from Dunsfold.

Hunters went ahead without any interruption — only the customers had changed. The RAF cancellation did, however, result in the closure of the Blackpool factory, production of the Hunter T.7 trainer, which had been scheduled for that factory, being undertaken at Kingston so that little delay in the delivery of this version to the RAF resulted. The Royal Air Force was to rue the day that those last 100 aircraft were cancelled and, as far ahead as 1966, there arose an uncomfortable shortage of Hunters in the Service (resulting in the purchase back from abroad of aircraft for delivery to the RAF!).

Notwithstanding the tenets of the 1957 White Paper, by mid-1958 all home-based day fighter squadrons of the Royal Air Force had been equipped with the Hunter 6 (most units also receiving at least one Mark 7 for instrument and other training), and two such squadrons moved to the Middle East and the Mediterranean. In foreign service Hunter 6s also served in the air forces of Holland, Belgium, India, Switzerland, Iraq, Jordan and the Lebanon, while trainers were on order for Denmark, Holland, India, Peru and Jordan. The list would continue to grow over the next decade.

Thus the Hunter — to many people the most graceful fighter ever produced — had become established as one of the principal fighters of the Western world for, by 1960, almost 2,000 aircraft had been built. It has carried the name of Hawker far and wide, earning itself a reputation worthy of its tradition. Adaptability, manoeuvrability, fine controls and great strength were all features inbred by experience with an unbroken line of great aircraft that had gone before. Indeed, there are indications that Hunters may continue to serve almost to the end of the century.

TOWARDS NEW HORIZONS

In 1954, with the transfer of most Hunter work to the Kingston Production Drawing Office, the Project Office had begun work as a private venture on a large supersonic fighter, the Hawker P.1103, powered by a single de Havilland Gyron turbojet with reheat. The design was submitted in detail to the Air Ministry in response to a draft Requirement, and more than passing interest encouraged Camm to persevere with the project. By 1956, however, the emphasis in operational requirements was beginning to shift, and the need for an ability to undertake both interception and strike operations was being expressed by the Air Staff. The old draft Requirement was abandoned, but Hawker was encouraged to continue its work as a private venture in the light of a new Requirement, OR.339, about to be issued in draft form.

Extensive redesign was carried out and a new prototype, now designated the P.1121, was started. By the end of 1957 much of the structure was complete, and alternative proposals were made to use either the Gyron, Bristol Olympus or Rolls-Royce Conway turbojets. A speed of Mach 2.5 was to be achieved with the use of reheat at altitude, and strike

A full-size mock-up of the Hawker P.1121 air superiority strike aircraft.

weapons would be carried under the wings. Gradually, however, the Air Staff began to change its mind once more (taking account of the likely difficulty of being able to interest the Treasury in anything that perpetuated the 'stigma' of a manned interceptor fighter, whose demise had been recommended by the 1957 Defence White Paper). The dual-rôle capability was abandoned and exclusive emphasis was laid upon the development of sophisticated equipment to enable the aircraft to perform a specific strike function, that of delivering nuclear weapons at very low level against Warsaw Pact countries from bases in western France in the event of an outbreak of war in Europe. By mid-1958 it had become apparent that the P.1121 came nowhere near meeting the new Requirement, and that further adaptation would be pointless. The Hawker project was therefore terminated. Requirement OR.339 was to become central to Air Staff policy for the next six years, being changed to GOR.343 and ultimately bringing into existence the British Aircraft Corporation's ill-fated TSR-2, but not without bitter in-fighting between several manufacturers who anticipated massive political interference, and possibly catastrophic cancellation, in the event of a change in the political climate of Britain. In the event, these apprehensions proved justified and, although the TSR-2's ultimate cancellation did not spell final disaster for the British aircraft industry, it did change for ever the character and outlook of the industry. As Sir Sydney Camm so prophetically remarked in the early 1960s: 'Aircraft of the future will have to possess a fourth dimension — politics'.

Despite the gloom that pervaded Hawkers during 1957-58, Camm was convinced that time was on the side of the company, with orders for Hunters from overseas seeming likely to occupy the factory for at least five years. It will have by now become apparent how important he regarded the Project Office, it having always been his policy to encourage the investigation of new ideas, and it was in conjunction with Dr S G Hooker, technical director of the Bristol Engine Company, that the radical P.1127 vertical-take-off aircraft came into being.

The concept of vertical take-off, as old as aviation itself, had until recently centred wholly on the helicopter, and had come nowhere near the spheres of aviation pursued by the manufacturers of high performance military aeroplanes such as Hawker Aircraft Ltd. The principle of 'jet-lift' — whereby vehicles could be lifted off the ground and sustained in a hover by balancing the weight of the vehicle against the thrust of jet engines mounted vertically — was beginning to be investigated by companies in Britain and America, and several prototype 'tail-sitters' were under test in the USA.

At Hawkers it was a young Project Engineer, Ralph Hooper, who, on acquiring information from Bristols on a new axial-flow turbojet in which rotatable nozzles could direct 'cold' air from the compressor vertically downwards, schemed up a preliminary design for a two-seat battlefield surveillance aircraft, given the designation P.1127 in mid-1957. In due course Hooper developed the design, gradually arriving at a viable single-seat high-performance aircraft in which the hot gas exhaust from the engine was also passed through rotatable nozzles, so that four such nozzles could direct the turbojet's entire thrust vertically downwards for take-off, and then, by progressively rotating them aftwards, accelerate the aircraft into horizontal, wing-borne flight.

The new design offices in Richmond Road. Compare with the picture on page 5.

Ralph Hooper, the Hawker project designer who was responsible to Sir Sydney Camm for the design development of the original P.1127 vertical take-off aircraft, as well as its illustrious successor, the Harrier.

Elsewhere, notably at Short Bros Ltd, and in France, an alternative scheme employing batteries of small vertically-mounted 'jet-lift' turbojets accomplished the vertical take-off, while a separate 'cruise' engine accelerated the aircraft into horizontal flight. Although this scheme was examined by the Hawker Project Office, it was concluded that to carry around redundant engines, used only for take-off and landing, imposed an unnecessary weight penalty on a high-performance aeroplane. Better, Hooper argued, to use a single engine for both vertical and horizontal flight.

Unfortunately, at just about the time that design calculations were beginning to confirm the feasibility of Hooper's brilliant concept, neither the Air Staff nor the Treasury could find any basis for support of the project, while their preoccupation with OR.339 threatened to swallow all available funds for research and development.

Impressed by Hooper's design calculations, Camm gave the P.1127 project his full support, and in due course Robert Marsh (Head of Projects) and Hooper were encouraged to seek support from technical advisors to NATO, among whom Americans appeared to hold a number of key positions. This proved fortuitous for, in expressing considerable interest in the concept, they were instrumental in obtaining contact with NASA in America, and in due course some useful round-the-pole model testing was undertaken at Langley. Considerable testing of ground-effect models was conducted in the Experimental Department at Richmond Road, and even in the low-speed tunnel facilities at the Kingston Technical College.

Gradually a great quantity of data was amassed relating to control of an aircraft in the hover and at low forward speed, and numerous rigs were set up at private expense to investigate the behaviour of an aircraft in transition from the hover to horizontal flight. A response simulator (in effect a crude flight simulator) was installed in the Project Office by conversion of a large analogue computer. One of the objects of these efforts was to develop an aircraft that did not rely on a complex three-channel autopilot to achieve flight transition, as had been deemed necessary in the other jet-lift test vehicles.

Fairly confident that in due course the Ministry of Defence would have to take note of the work being done — and the important results being achieved — at Kingston, Hawkers took the decision to go ahead with the building of two prototypes at private expense, and the first of these was approaching completion in 1960 when eventually the Company was awarded a contract to cover these two aircraft. By that time, however, Hawker had decided on the necessity to build four additional prototypes to examine alternative wing planforms, as well as to contribute to the enormous amount of flight data required. It must also be said that it was Camm's determination to restrict the P.1127's 'sophistication' to the bare minimum that appealed to the Ministry of Defence — now beginning to appreciate just what its GOR.343 aircraft was likely to cost before it could enter service.

In 1961 an ironic situation began to develop as the result of the Hawker project engineers having involved the good offices of American advisors to the Mutual Weapons Defence Programme, whose job it was to advise on the suitability of future NATO equipment. It now transpired that, such was the high esteem in which the P.1127 concept was held on the continent (not forgetting, it must be said, work also being done by Marcel Dassault on the alternative jet-lift concept in the Mirage III-V vertical take-off aircraft), that NATO began working on a new Requirement for a highly sophisticated supersonic vertical/short take-off air-superiority fighter, termed the NATO Basic Military Requirement No. 3 (NBMR.3). By now having acquired a huge quantity of data and flight test experience with the first two P.1127 prototypes (the first of which had achieved untethered hovering flight on 19 November 1960 in the hands of Bill Bedford, the company's Chief Test Pilot), Hawker set

The new era of flight. The Hawker P.1127 prototype in untethered hovering flight for the first time on 19 November 1960.

about entering the NBMR.3 competition with a new project, the supersonic V/STOL P.1150. Despite being unofficially declared the winner of the NATO contest, the P.1150 was destined to be shortlived.

In fact the entries for the 'competition' were, by now predictably, to be judged both on technical and political grounds and, realising that France might hold all the aces in that the Dassault entry was proposed as being bi-national in employing a French airframe with British (Rolls-Royce) engines, Hawker Siddeley set about negotiating a powerful multi-national consortium of major manufacturers (in Belgium, Holland, Germany, France and the United States) who would participate in the P.1154 project if it was declared the winner. The result was stalemate. France — then still a component nation of NATO — insisted that she would go ahead with the Dassault project whatever the outcome, with the result that the contest was abandoned.

At last the British Ministry of Defence awoke to the enormous potential of the P.1154 (especially as there were the beginnings of rumblings regarding the future of TSR-2, whose development had not run entirely smoothly), and in 1953 two Requirements were drafted around the Hawker project, one a single-seat supersonic V/STOL strike aircraft with Mach 2 performance for the RAF, and the other a two-seat supersonic V/STOL carrier-borne interceptor with Mach 2.5 performance for the Royal Navy. The latter aircraft was to have been powered by a single 30,000 lb thrust Bristol Siddeley BS.100 turbofan with plenum chamber burning. Both were versions of the P.1154.

All might have gone ahead smoothly had the political climate in Britain been more settled. Development costs of all the new projects destined for the RAF had begun to rise sharply towards the end of 1963, and the domestic affairs of the Conservative government were by no means conducive to political stability in the future. First, the Admiralty discontinued its interest in the naval P.1154, of which a prototype had been begun at the beginning of 1964, on the grounds of high cost. Later that year a general election returned a socialist government, which, having declared it would severely reduce the spending on defence, promptly cancelled the remaining RAF P.1154 project, as well as TSR-2 and the AW.681 STOL transport.

This action by the Labour Government had far-reaching results, not only in British military aviation but in the defence structure of NATO. The ground was cut from under the British aircraft industry's feet, thereby eliminating any chance of it participating in European competition to supply military aircraft to the air forces of NATO (advanced development of vectored-thrust turbojets and turbofans was discontinued), so Britain could no longer support or subsidise the development of the whole spectrum of aircraft deemed necessary for her own air forces. This resulted in a far greater dependence upon American supply of aircraft — aircraft which, until the arrival of the Panavia Tornado, had little relevance to European requirements.

A W (Bill) Bedford, Hawker Chief Test Pilot, disembarks from the P.1127 prototype during its trials at the Royal Aircraft Establishment, Bedford, in March 1961.

To replace the now-defunct TSR-2, the Wilson government endorsed the purchase of the American F-111, an aircraft designed to meet particular USAF requirements, but shortly afterwards reversed its decision and cancelled the order, resulting in the payment of huge cancellation costs. Instead, it opted to buy the McDonnell F-4 Phantom and specified the Rolls-Royce Spey turbofan as the powerplant. Intended as a means of retaining British employment and participation in the aircraft's production, this was an unfortunate choice, as the adaptation of the airframe was costly in the extreme, and the engine itself proved unsuitable when it came into service with the RAF and Royal Navy. The result was that, by the time Britain had paid for the Wilson government's expensive and doctrinal blunders, the nation had paid far more than it would have done had it gone ahead with the TSR-2 and the P.1154 — aircraft that had been specifically developed to British and European requirements (and of which most development costs had been paid by the time they were cancelled). The P.1154 had, after all, a performance at least comparable with that of the F-4 Phantom, as well as possessing V/STOL capability; there is no reason to believe that it would not also have been attractive to some of the nations who later purchased the Phantom, not least West Germany.

RATIONALISATION, NATIONALISATION AND CENTRALISATION?

Despite the disappointment caused by the socialists' cancellation of the British military projects during 1964 and 1965, Hawkers at Kingston again weathered the storm, this despite fairly heavy laying-off of workers in Kingston. Elsewhere in the industry the labour forces were harder hit.

The P.1127 had gone from strength to strength, although, as yet, only a token production order had been received for a derivative. The year 1962 had brought an announcement that, following American participation in the project (the Mutual Weapons Defence Programme had provided a large share of the funds necessary for the development of the vectored-thrust Pegasus engine in the P.1127), and interest displayed by West Germany, a 'tri-partite' evaluation squadron would be formed two years hence to assess the P.1127 under fairly realistic operational conditions. The nine aircraft, to be named the Kestrel, ordered for the squadron were issued to the unit which formed at West Raynham in Norfolk during 1965, and it was the success achieved by this evaluation of the Kestrel that, in conjunction with the recent cancellation of defence projects, prompted the Ministry of Defence to adopt the aircraft for future service with the Royal Air Force. It should, however, be pointed out that, compared with the Kestrel, the P.1154 was in a different category altogether for, apart from high supersonic performance, the P.1154 was designed to accommodate all manner of sophisticated operational equipment, necessarily miniaturised and therefore relatively costly. It was estimated that the production version of the P.1154 for the RAF would have reached a unit cost of between £4m and £5m (compared with around £900,000 for a Kestrel and about £4m for a Spey-powered F-4 Phantom).

Before 1965 was out, Hawker had received a Contract to produce a developent batch of six pre-production examples of the new aircraft (to be named the Harrier), to be followed by an initial production order for sixty aircraft, for which authority was given to procure long-lead items.

Alas, Sir Sydney Camm was to die on 12 March 1966 as the shops in Kingston began to tool up to start production of those early Harriers. Yet he must have derived great satisfaction from the knowledge that once more an aircraft that emanated from his design team would serve with the Royal Air Force and maintain, unbroken, the forty-year-old line of Hawker aeroplanes. As far as is known, such a record of achievement is not matched by any other aircraft manufacturer in the world.

The first development-batch (or 'DB') Harrier made its maiden flight on 31 August that year, and during the next eleven months was joined by the other five, as well as the first five production aircraft, in an extensive programme of trials to ensure that the aircraft satisfied Air Staff

Harrier G.R. Mark 1 production in progress for the Royal Air Force at Kingston upon Thames in 1969.

Requirement No.384. Power was provided by a 19,000 lb thrust Bristol Siddeley Pegasus 6 (Mark 101) turbofan with water injection.

By now the Hawker Siddeley Group had embarked upon a programme to enhance its corporate image, believing that, to fall into line with major aircraft manufacturers abroad, it would simplify administration and reduce administrative overheads if a centralised parent organisation, Hawker Siddeley Aviation Ltd, co-ordinated all matters of finance, manufacturing policies, sales, public relations and so on. This process had started before the end of the 1950s and by the end of the 1960s was complete. Hawker Aircraft Ltd continued to exist as such, and some members of its board of directors were co-opted to sit on the board of Hawker Siddeley Aviation Ltd to represent the interests of Kingston. However, just as, strictly speaking, the P.1154 was submitted to tender as the Hawker Siddeley P.1154, now the new aircraft was known correctly as the Hawker Siddeley Harrier.

The Harrier GR Mark 1 entered RAF service at Wittering with No.1 Squadron of Strike Command in April 1968, this station being selected as the single base for all such aircraft in the United Kingdom. Early the following year the Harrier Operational Conversion Unit was also formed at Wittering, and in 1970 first-tour pilots, having completed their training with No. 233 OCU, joined No.1 Squadron, thereby releasing second- and third-tour pilots who would now become squadron and flight commanders on new squadrons to be formed in RAF Germany. The first of these was No. 4 Squadron, followed by No. 20, both of which received Harriers before the end of 1970, being based at Wildenrath.

As with the Hunter before it, the Harrier soon appeared in a two-seat trainer version, this being designated the T. Mark 2. Most examples were delivered to No. 233 OCU, but each of the operational squadrons received at least one such aircraft. As the RAF embarked on a number of updating progammes (resulting in the GR. Mark 3 and T. Mark 4) involving uprating the Pegasus engines, and installing the Ferranti laser ranging and marked target seeking (LRMTS) equipment as well as a radar warning receiver (RWR) in the aircraft's fin, Hawker succeeded in securing an export order for Harriers to be supplied to the United States Marine Corps. As is customary in the US Forces, procurement was arranged on an annual budgetary basis, and it was originally thought likely that Kingston would only build the first thirty aircraft and that the Americans would insist on negotiating a licence to manufacture any future Harriers. However, after batches of twelve and eighteen aircraft (designated AV-8A) had been delivered in 1971 and 1972 respectively, the Americans decided that the cost of setting up a new production facility at McDonnell-Douglas' plant at Saint Louis would exceed the amortised cost of aircraft delivered from Britain, with the result that

A Spanish Hawker Siddley AV-8S Matador (Harrier Mark 55) with a Royal Navy Sea Harrier F.R.S. Mark 1 of No. 899 Squadron during a visit by the Spanish *Escuadrilla* 008 to Yeovilton in 1988, where its pilots carried out ski-jump training. Later these pilots embarked in the new ski deck-equipped carrier *Principe de Asturias*.

AV-8As continued to be delivered to the US Marine Corps from Duns-fold until 1975, by which time a total of 102 aircraft had been supplied. A two-seat training version, the Harrier T. Mark 54 or TAV-8A, was also supplied.

The other export order for Harriers was negotiated with Spain (where they would be known as Matadors) and, although the aircraft were built at Kingston, it was initially a condition that they should be delivered from America, where the first six aircraft were used to train the Spanish pilots. The last five aircraft, however, were delivered direct from Britain. Two-seaters were also supplied.

Meanwhile, of course, the up-grading of the Harrier to become first-line equipment of the RAF, after the success of the Kestrel evaluation, was followed by promotions and reorganisation of the Kingston design staff as well as the flight staff at Dunsfold. Ralph Hooper, who had been the Project Engineer in charge of P.1127 development until 1963, be-came Assistant Chief Designer (Projects) until in 1968 he was appointed Executive Director and Chief Engineer, Hawker Siddeley Aviation (and later British Aerospace Corporation), Kingston and Brough, an ap-pointment he held until his retirement in the 1980s. John Fozard, who was a Senior Project Designer with Hawker Aircraft Ltd between 1955 and 1960, became Deputy Head of the Project Office in the latter year and Chief Designer (P.1154) until 1964; after three years as Chief De-signer (Harrier) he was appointed Deputy Chief Engineer at Kingston.

At Dunsfold, Bill Bedford remained Chief Test Pilot until 1965 and was appointed Sales Manager (Harrier) two years later; he still serves with British Aerospace in an advisory capacity in matters relating to V/STOL operations. Duncan Simpson, who had been Chief Production Test Pilot with Hawker Aircraft Ltd until 1966, was then appointed Chief Test Pilot, Hawker Siddeley Aviation (Dunsfold), a position he held until 1970, when John Farley was appointed to succeed him.

HARRIERS WITH THE ROYAL NAVY

For many years the Royal Navy had expressed more than passing inter-est in the Hawker vertical/short-take off aircraft. This was first manifest in February 1963, when Bill Bedford and Hugh Merewether conducted a brief series of trials from the deck of HMS *Ark Royal* in the first P.1127 prototype. However, as told above, the cancellation of work on a naval interceptor version of the P.1154 brought an end, for the time being, to efforts to introduce a V/STOL combat aircraft into service with the Royal Navy.

Interest was reawakened with the successful introduction of the Har-rier into RAF service at the end of the 1960s, and Hawker once more prepared designs for a naval version. However, although the company was encouraged to pursue the design up to manufacturing drawings in the early 1970s, restraints on naval spending delayed a final decision. It was clear, moreover, that with the two fleet carriers, HMS *Ark Royal* and *Eagle*, due to end their useful sea life in the 1970s, the class of commando carrier with which the Royal Navy would be equipped would probably be unsuitable for fixed-wing aircraft.

It was, however, in 1972 that a Royal Navy engineering officer, Lt-Cdr D R Taylor, evolved the system of ramp-launching the Harrier. It was shown that, by incorporating a sharply curved-up deck and launching the aircraft into a ballistic trajectory, and then rotating the thrust nozzles to the fully-aft position, the Harrier would quickly accelerate to wing-borne flight. This would enable the aircraft not only to be launched from a relatively short deck, but also to carry a worthwhile load of ordnance — be it bombs or air-to-air missiles. (The US Marine Corps had for some years been operating the AV-8As from carriers in the vertical take-off mode, but only in short-range, lightly-loaded configuration.)

In 1977 Hawker gained contract cover to build an adjustable steel ramp, and towards the end of that year a series of 'ski-jump' trials began, using both single- and two-seat Harriers. These proved conclusively that the scheme worked, and worked well. By then the company had received a contract to build three development Sea Harriers, and the first of these was flown by M H B Snelling at the end of 1978. They were followed by thirty-one Sea Harrier FRS Mark 1 production aircraft, the first of which joined No. 700A Squadron of the Fleet Air Arm at Yeovilton in August 1979, and later equipped Nos. 800, 801 and 899 Squadrons embarked in HMS *Hermes* and *Invincible* (the latter the first of a new class of 'Command Cruiser', so euphemistically named as to avoid the politically dangerous term 'aircraft carrier').

The events that constituted Operations Paraquat and Corporate —

A new generation of naval fixed-wing aircraft emerged at the end of the 1970s with the arrival of the British Aerospace Sea Harrier. Seen here is a single-seat F.R.S. Mark 1 of 899 Squadron, Fleet Air Arm, flanked by a Harrier T.4N naval trainer and, nearest the camera, a Hunter T.8M — employed to train naval pilots in the use of the Sea Harrier's Blue Fox radar.

the recovery of South Georgia and the Falkland Islands after their illegal seizure by Argentine forces in 1982 — are so well known as not to warrant lengthy commentary here. Nevertheless, a number of salient points do bear emphasis, not least of which is the fact that, had not the Royal Air Force and Royal Navy possessed the Harrier and Sea Harrier, and been able to deploy them to the South Atlantic when called on to do so, the entire operation would have been impossible. Secondly, the despatch of such a relatively small component of naval fixed-wing fighter/ground-attack aircraft to face an entire land-based air force equipped with modern aircraft — including supersonic fighters — was not only unprecedented but was attended with outstanding success. The figures relating to the campaign speak for themselves, and show that twenty-eight Sea Harriers and ten Harriers (of No.1 Squadron, RAF) flew more than 2,000 combat sorties, destroyed at least twenty-eight enemy aircraft in air combat, and achieved an overall serviceability rate of more than ninety per cent. Not one Harrier or Sea Harrier was lost in air combat, although six Sea Harriers and four Harriers were lost to ground fire or in accidents. Two of the Sea Harriers were lost when their pilots baled out from damaged aircraft rather than risk fouling their carrier's deck. The skill and courage of the small number of pilots involved in the operations were in the best traditions of the two Services.

The Falkland Islands campaign confirmed without question the correctness of the V/STOL philosophy, and ensured the continuation of service by the Harrier and Sea Harrier in the RAF and Royal Navy. It also prompted the Admiralty to press for development of a new version of the Sea Harrier, the Mark 2 with advanced electronics and enhanced look-down/shoot-down capability and, at the time of writing, aircraft are undergoing conversion to the new standard.

THE HARRIER II

It will be recalled that, partway through the manufacture of AV-8As for the United States Marines, the US government decided to allow manufacture to continue in the United Kingdom, rather than switch to a production line in the United States. This decision was conditional upon the negotiation of a fifteen-year agreement between Hawker Siddeley Aviation and the McDonnell-Douglas Corporation in America for the sharing of information and work relating to the development of V/STOL aircraft.

The success with which the AV-8A served with the US Marines encouraged the American company to pursue the development of this version. While Rolls-Royce (Bristol) developed a new and enlarged version of the Pegasus (the Mark 15, which returned a thrust of 25,500 lb), the two airframe companies returned to the old supersonic theme and began work on an aircraft, the AV-16-S6. This, however, proceeded no further than the project stage and was abandoned on the grounds of high cost.

The first Sea Harrier F.R.S. Mark 2 undergoing conversion at the BAe Dunsfold factory in 1988. Note the distinguishing Blue Vixen nose radome.

Instead, determined to increase the load-carrying capacity of the Harrier, McDonnell-Douglas continued to develop a new, 'super-critical' wing constructed largely of carbonfibre composite. This wing, of increased span, incorporated a total of six external store stations and internal fuel capacity increased by 2,000 lb. In due course the new aircraft, the AV-8B Harrier II, was flown and demonstrated outstanding load-carrying capabilities. Indeed, the new Harrier *doubled* the payload-radius of the AV-8A. This extraordinary improvement was, moreover, achieved with only modest development of the original Pegasus to produce a thrust of 21,600 lb.

In due course the US Marine Corps stated a requirement for no fewer than 340 AV-8Bs, including a number of TAV-8B trainers. This was to be of considerable benefit to the Kingston factory for, under the terms of the agreement mentioned above, roughly half the total AV-8B manufacture is being undertaken in Britain — forty per cent of the airframe and sixty per cent of the engine.

Meanwhile the Royal Air Force had, during the 1970s, been evolving a requirement, Air Staff Target 403 (AST 403), for an aircraft ultimately to replace the SEPECAT Jaguar and the Harrier GR Mark 3. Owing to the impossibly high costs of combining a replacement for both aircraft (the Jaguar was supersonic, the Harrier subsonic), a new requirement, ASR409, was issued for a replacement of the Harrier alone, the in-service target date being 1990. In parallel with the American development of the super-critical wing, the Kingston design staff had been investigating a new 'big wing' incorporating large leading-edge root extensions (LERX), but, with the announcement of the US Marine

Corps requirement, it was decided to combine the technological advances by both companies and order sixty aircraft based on the American AV-8B for the Royal Air Force. In this way, not only has the new Harrier, designated the GR Mark 5, exceeded the provisions of ASR409 in almost every respect and entered RAF service almost two years earlier than anticipated, but it has benefited from substantial cost amortisation resulting from the very large American participation.

The Harrier GR5 entered service with No.1 Squadron and No.233 OCU at Wittering early in 1989, and will go on to re-equip other Harrier squadrons in Germany in 1990. Already work is under way to incorporate new equipment to further enhance this remarkable aeroplane's capabilities. This equipment includes a GEC Avionics forward-looking infra-red (FLIR) system, a new Smiths Industries head-up head-down display and cockpit displays compatible with Night Vision Goggles (NVG); these modifications will result in the arrival in service of the Harrier GR Mark 7.

The latest version of the Harrier to be announced at the time of writing is the T. Mark 10, an anglicised version of the TAV-8B for the Royal Air Force.

In accordance with more than one Labour Government's election manifesto, the British aircraft industry passed into 'public ownership' in 1977. Nationalisation was, in effect, a means of appointing at a single stroke close on 100,000 new civil servants, each of whom became accountable to a number of government ministries for every action taken. The process of nationalisation itself was fairly painless until it gradually dawned upon the many highly-qualified designers, engineers and other workers that their working lives were to be accountable to Whitehall, and that personal initiative was not to be encouraged. This ran counter to the academic and technological instincts of some of the industry's most gifted men and women, with the result that many of them decided to leave the industry for good.

Two famous Kingston demonstrators, the two-seat Harrier T.52, ZA250/G-VTOL, and the Hawk Mark 50 ZA101/G-HAWK, in 1970 — during the period in which British Aerospace was a state-owned conglomerate.

Fortunately for the Kingston and Dunsfold elements of British Aerospace, the factories and other departments were fully employed with Harrier, Sea Harrier and Hawk production and development, and little impact of nationalisation was apparent, other than the trappings of bureaucracy — such as a new lick of paint here and there — and new scales and names of appointments.

With a return to a Conservative government two years later, no time was lost in announcing that privatisation would be undertaken at the earliest possible opportunity, by implication before any lasting damage could result from further losses of highly skilled members. In 1981 the British government anounced that, as a first step, it was to offer a large proportion of its shares in the industry to the public once more, and this process was completed on 10 September 1985, when the last block of government shares returned to the private sector.

THE HAWK

It was in 1968, at the time that the Harrier was first entering service with the Royal Air Force, that, under the direction of John Fozard (then Deputy Chief Engineer), the Kingston project office began studies of a new two-seat jet trainer and, after detailed analysis of about a score of aircraft configurations (including both tandem and side-by-side seating) and a dozen different engines, the P.1182 design project was evolved with an unreheated version of the Rolls-Royce Adour turbojet and submitted to the Ministry of Defence.

This was followed by the preparation of Air Staff Requirement 397 for an aircraft to replace the Hunter and Gnat in service with the RAF in the advanced-flying and weapon-training rôles. This included a 6,000-flying-hour fatigue life encompassing a fatigue cycle of unprecedented severity. Constant discussion followed between HSA and the Ministry of Defence during the next two years and, on 12 March 1972, the company received a contract to produce 175 aircraft, to be called the Hawk. There was to be no requirement for a prototype — almost unique in the acquisition of an entirely new aircraft being ordered for the RAF.

The first Hawk, referred to simply as the pre-production aircraft, made its maiden flight on 21 August 1974, and on 1 April 1976 the first production aircraft was delivered to No.4 Flying Training School at RAF Valley.

This remarkable little aeroplane was a bold step into a fast-expanding market and, from the start, faced strong competition from a number of foreign designs whose manufacturers had been intent on satisfying a dual rôle (training/combat) requirement of many of the world's smaller air forces. To take account of increasing demands by potential customers, the Hawk was designed from the outset with considerable 'growth potential', and the first major variant was referred to as the Series-50, powered by an Adour 851 which enabled the aircraft to carry

Hawks of the famous Red Arrows formation aerobatic team, during their tour of the Middle and Far East in 1986. This was the longest tour the team had made, covering over 12,000 miles, visiting seventeen countries and giving twenty-two displays. Arrival at each destination was timed to the second, and serviceability for every display was 100 per cent.

As part of the work-sharing agreement with McDonnell Douglas, British Aerospace builds the centre fuselage of the T-45A Goshawk for the US Navy. Seen here is the second aircraft at Kingston in 1987.

The Hawk 100 (left) and 200 demonstrators at BAe's Dunsfold aerodrome in 1988.

a seventy per cent greater disposable load than the basic version originally supplied to the RAF. This version attracted Finland, Kenya and Indonesia, whose air forces between them acquired eighty-two aircraft.

The next variant, the Series-60, followed in 1981 with an uprated Adour 861 turbojet which permitted a further thirty-three per cent increase in the load capable of being carried. A total of ninety-four of this version was sold to Zimbabwe, Dubai, Abu Dhabi, Kuwait, Saudi Arabia and Switzerland.

It was also in 1981 that the Hawk's greatest coup was achieved, when the United States Navy announced that it had been selected in a

Cockpit of the single-seat Hawk 200.

97

competitive evaluation with seven other contenders to form the aircraft element in its future jet flight training programme. Known as the T-45A Goshawk, the first of what may eventually amount to several hundred aircraft was rolled out at the Douglas Aircraft Company's factory at Long Beach, California, on 18 March 1988, and was first flown thirty-one days later. Hundreds of millions of dollars have already been set aside to cover the initial stages of the production and development programme, in which British Aerospace is the major subcontractor, in partnership with McDonnell-Douglas, a substantial proportion of the airframe being built in the old Hawker factory.

In 1984 the Hawk first appeared in a new guise when the single-seat Hawk 200-series was publicly launched at that year's SBAC Farnborough Air Show. The prototype of this version first flew on 19 May 1986.

The relatively brief sojourn in state ownership went a long way to changing the character of the British aircraft industry, for, with the creation of a single giant conglomerate and a single all-powerful administrative board of directors, all possibility of competitive working within the industry has disappeared. It can be argued that, by grouping all the former resources (financial and technical) of independent elements, the industry is in a better position to compete in the international market. It does, however, make possible the abuse of administrative power for partisan motives, and there is suspicion that, in the interests of realisation of capital assets, a move might conceivably be considered to dispose of industrial property in the south of England for lucrative redevelopment, and subsequently centre the entire aircraft industry further north. Leaving aside the sentimental aspects, such as Kingston's eighty-year-old association with aviation (not to mention more tangible considerations, such as ease of access to the numerous research establishments in the south), loyalty to a tradition has nevertheless been particularly strong, and it might prove disastrous to the industry if many of the key personnel in the Weybridge, Kingston and Dunsfold areas simply chose to find alternative work in other spheres rather than uproot their lives to move northwards. It is to be hoped that full consideration will be given to the real needs of the nation before equating the short-term benefits to the industry's shareholders.

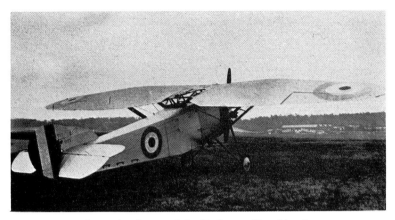

An early picture of the Duiker at Brooklands.

The Hawker Duiker

Among the very earliest Specifications issued by the Air Ministry after the First World War was a series calling for various reconnaissance aircraft. One of these, referred to as 'D of R Type 3A', brought forth the de Havilland D.H.30 Denbigh — which was not built, the Short Springbok, the Armstrong Whitworth Wolf and the Sopwith-Hawker Duiker. All of the manufacturers declared the Specification unsatisfactory, and its terms contradictory, with the result that after some consultation with the designers it was reissued as 10/21 (in the new numbering system) and later as 7/22. This outlined the general requirements for an aircraft capable of performing field operations, such as gunnery spotting, 'terrain surveillance' and unit liaison, generically termed Corps Reconnaissance Duties.

The design tendered by the Hawker Design Staff, under its newly appointed Chief Designer, Capt Thomson, was accepted and construction of a number of prototypes commenced. Only one Duiker, as the machine was called, was completed after numerous alterations had been made to the basic configuration and this aircraft, later registered J6918, was flown a number of times at Brooklands during July 1923, by F P Raynham.

The Duiker was of all-wood construction, featuring a swept-back parasol wing and was powered first by an Armstrong Siddeley Jaguar, and later by a Bristol Jupiter IV engine. A feature of this, the first new aircraft built by the H G Hawker Engineering Co Ltd, was the relatively large number of proprietary items of equipment manufactured by Vickers Ltd — another occupant of Brooklands aerodrome — for apart from the Vickers gun fitted on the nose, the wind-driven generator,

The Duiker J6918 at Martlesham Heath in December 1923. Note deletion of spinner, the enlarged wheels and modified rudder.

undercarriage oleos (*sic*), stick and rudder controls, rear gun mounting and tail skid were all of Vickers' stock.

J6918 was delivered to Martlesham Heath for assessment late in 1923, but only eighteen hours flying proved sufficient to indicate that the Duiker was not suitable as a military aircraft. Apart from displaying severe aileron flutter (which resulted in a tendency for the wing to part company with the rear cabane struts) the aircraft was directionally unstable throughout the entire speed range; moreover, undamped pitching oscillations resulted when the throttle was closed. It is true that a metal wing, presumably intended to give

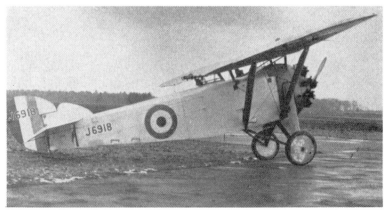

Another view of J6918 at Martlesham Heath. (*Photographs on this page: Crown Copyright.*)

greater torsional stiffness, was designed for the Duiker, but as far as is known it was never completed.

J6918 was delivered to the RAE at Farnborough on 15 April 1924, but no more than a guess can be made at the nature of the comments made. Three further Duikers, J6919, J6995 and J6996, had been ordereed, but manufacture of only one of these had been started, and tradition has it that this was taken out and quietly buried in a corner of Brooklands!

TECHNICAL DATA FOR DUIKER (JUPITER IV)*

TYPE: Two-seat Corps Reconnaissance parasol monoplane.
STRUCTURE: Wooden construction with fabric covering.
MANUFACTURERS: H G Hawker Engineering Co Ltd, Kingston.
POWERPLANT: 389 hp Bristol Jupiter IV radial engine driving 2-blade wooden propeller.

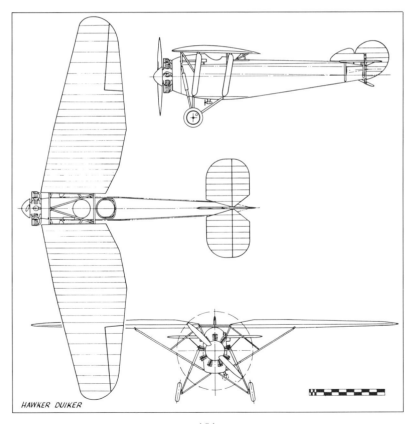

HAWKER DUIKER

DIMENSIONS: Span, 48 ft 5 in. Length, 31 ft 5 in. Height, 10 ft 7 in. Wing Area, 390 sq ft.

WEIGHTS: Empty, 3,956 lb. Loaded, 4,700 lb. (Note: The design loaded weight of 4,940 lb was considered unsafe during flight tests and 240 lb of equipment was deleted.)

PERFORMANCE: Max. speed, 125 mph at sea level. Cruising speed, 99 mph. Climb, 20 min 25 sec to 10,000 ft. Range 340 miles at 95 mph. Endurance (max), 3¾ hrs. Service ceiling (rate of climb, 100 ft/min), 14,500 ft.

OTHER DATA: Fuel capacity, 94½ gallons. Fuel, Petrol Benzol (Sp G 0.76). Armament, one Vickers gun on nose cowling and provision for one Lewis gun, but both removed owing to weight restriction. Undercarriage, Vickers oleo with 1,000 × 150 mm wheels.

---

* Ref. A & AEE Report M364/24–7/22.

The Woodcock I, J6987, as originally fitted with Armstrong Siddeley Jaguar engine.

The Hawker Woodcock

Designed towards the end of 1922 to meet the Air Ministry night fighter Specification 25/22, the Woodcock was initially the work of Capt Thomson, then Chief Designer of H G Hawker Engineering Company, but shortly before the first prototype flew he was replaced by W G Carter in this appointment.

Bearing many signs of its Sopwith ancestry the first Woodcock, J6987 (later referred to as the Mark I version), was powered by an Armstrong Siddeley Jaguar AS117A engine and featured two-bay wings. When flown by F P Raynham in 1923, J6987 proved disappointing, displaying an alarming degree of wing flutter even for those days. Moreover, the rudder proved almost entirely ineffective and, for this reason, spinning was never permitted on this aircraft. When, later in 1923, J6987 was delivered to Martlesham Heath for Service evaluation it was criticised and finally rejected on account of its lack of manoeuvrability, yet it found favour on other counts, possessing a reasonable field of view and being simple to maintain.

On his appointment in 1923 as Chief Designer, Carter at once began a redesign of the Woodcock, replacing the Jaguar with a Bristol Jupiter

The two-bay Woodcock I, J6987, with Bristol Jupiter engine.

The prototype Woodcock II, J6988, with single-bay wings and engine cylinder helmets.

An early series Woodcock II, J7517, with ring gun sight attached to wing centre section.

A fully-equipped Woodcock night fighter, J7971, of No. 17 (Fighter) Squadron.

engine and incorporating single-bay wings. A new prototype, J6988, the Woodcock II, was built with these features and flown in August 1923, and immediately showed itself to be much improved. The wing flutter, though still in evidence, was considerably reduced and positive directional control was now at least possible throughout most of the speed range. Unfortunately, the Jupiter IV engine gave trouble, the exposed valve gear being particularly vulnerable to icing-up (also experienced to a lesser extent by other uncowled radials), with the result that when J6988 appeared at the 1924 Hendon Display (as Experimental

A dramatic view of a late series Woodcock, J7962, being demonstrated by
Flt Lt P W S Bulman at Brooklands in 1926.

Aircraft No. 2) it featured a series of individual cylinder helmets, each
equipped with manually operated shutters to regulate the cooling airflow. Soon after, however, minor modifications to the valve gear and the
fitting of an exhaust collector shroud in front of the cylinders reduced
the risk of icing and the helmets were discarded.

Further assessment of the Woodcock followed towards the end of
1924, and after the tail surfaces had yet again been improved the Royal
Air Force pronounced it acceptable for service. A contract for ten aircraft was placed with the Hawker company and production commenced
at Canbury Park Road.

The first six aircraft, not fitted initially with night flying equipment,
were issued to Martlesham Heath and some subsequently served with
No.17 (Fighter) Squadron based at Hawkinge, Kent. It was, however,

No.3 (Fighter) Squadron at Upavon which received Woodcock IIs first, receiving eight new night fighters direct from Brooklands in May 1925, replacing its seven-year-old Sopwith Snipes.

In their early days Woodcocks suffered a number of accidents, those of a more serious nature resulting from main spar failures and others, usually attributable to the poor field surface at Hawkinge, caused by collapse of undercarriage struts.

Only Nos.3 and 17 Squadrons were equipped with Woodcocks, 61 Mark IIs being delivered to the Royal Air Force. One of the aircraft scheduled for delivery to the RAF was purchased by Hawker Engineering as a demonstration aircraft and registered G-EBMA. it was entered by Sopwith in the King's Cup Race of July 1925 but, flown by Bulman, it was forced down at Luton by bad weather in the opening stages of the race and badly damaged.

By the end of 1925 the structural weaknesses of the aircraft had been cured and the Woodcock became well liked as a night fighter. Armed with two synchronised Vickers machine guns mounted on brackets on each side of the fuselage, the machine displayed a somewhat untidy appearance, an effect heightened by a conglomeration of identification and navigation lights on the wings, not to mention the zig-zag markings of No.17 Squadron!

Two experimental Woodcocks are worthy of mention. J8312 was used by Hawkers for further tests with cylinder helmets in 1927 (joining J6988, similarly re-equipped), though these were of rather more advanced design than those tried in 1924. The other trial Woodcock, J7974, was flown at Brooklands and the RAE with slotted upper and lower wings. Their effect was to reduce the landing speed of the machine from about 53 to 45 mph.

In 1928 RAF Woodcocks were replaced on the two operational squadrons by Gloster Gamecocks, though several of the Hawker machines were still flying in 1936.

One of the RAE's trials Woodcocks, J7974, with slotted wings.

TECHNICAL DATA FOR WOODCOCK MKS I AND II*

TYPE: Single-seat night interceptor fighter (Mk I, single-bay; Mk II, two-bay biplane).
STRUCTURE: Wooden construction with fabric covering.

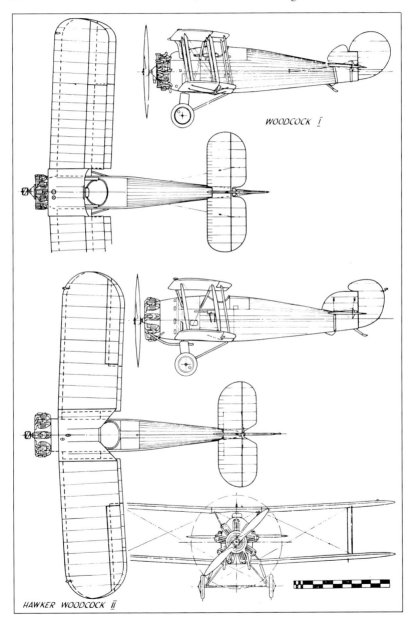

WOODCOCK I

HAWKER WOODCOCK II

MANUFACTURERS: H G Hawker Engineering Co Ltd, Kingston.

POWERPLANT: Mk I, 358 hp Armstrong Siddeley Jaguar II driving 2-blade wooden propeller.

Mk II, 380 hp Bristol Jupiter IV driving 2-blade wooden propeller. (Also fitted with a 416 hp Jupiter with variable timing.)

DIMENSIONS: Mk I. Span, 34 ft 8 in. Height, 9 ft 0 in. Length, 25 ft 7 in. Wing area, 356 sq ft.

Mk II. Span, 32 ft 6 in. Length, 26 ft 2 in. Height, 9 ft 11 in. Wing area, 346 sq ft.

WEIGHTS: Mk I. Empty, 2,083 lb. Loaded, 3,023 lb.

Mark II. Empty, 2,014 lb. Loaded, 2,979 lb.

PERFORMANCE: Mk I. Max speed, 143 mph at sea level. Cruising speed, 105 mph. Climb, 8 min 25 sec to 10,000 ft. Endurance, 2½ hours approx. Service ceiling (rate of climb, 100 ft/min) 20,550 ft.

Mk II. Max speed, 141 mph at sea level. Cruising speed, 103 mph. Climb, 8 min 18 sec to 10,000 ft. Endurance, 2¾ hrs approx. Service Ceiling (rate of climb, 100 ft/min) 22,500 ft.

OTHER DATA: Fuel capacity (both versions), 50 gallons. Fuel, Petrol Benzol (Sp G 0.76). Armament, two synchronised Vickers guns on sides of nose, with 750 rounds per gun. Provision for six 3.45 in reconnaissance flares. Wheel track, 6 ft 10½ in, 700 x 100 mm wheels.

---

* Ref. (Mk I): A & AEE Report M344/23–25/22. (Mk II): A & AEE Report M390/24–25/22.

The H G Hawker Engineering Company's Cygnet, G-EBMB, shortly after installation of the Bristol Cherub engine in 1926.

The Hawker Cygnet

The announcement early in 1924 of a Light Aeroplane Competition, organised by the Royal Aero Club, for which the Air Ministry was

G-EBMB in flight over Langley aerodrome in 1949. The pilot is Mr Frank Murphy.

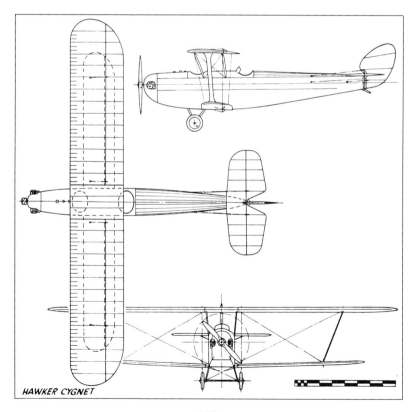

HAWKER CYGNET

G-EBMB fitted with the Anzani vee-twin engine.

offering £3,000 in prizes, resulted in designs from many companies large and small. The Hawker entry was the Cygnet, Sydney Camm's first design since joining the company in the previous year.

The aircraft was a remarkable achievement of minute attention to detail and was the lightest machine in the contest, weighing only 373 lb empty. The airframe, weighing no more than 270 lb, was of all-wood construction, fabric-covered. The fuselage consisted of four spruce longerons spindled out to X-section and braced in the form of a Warren truss by diagonal struts of the same section. The sides and bottom were flat while the domed decking was formed by wedge-section stringers. The wings were built upon fabric-wrapped box spars with Warren truss spruce ribs. Though the top centre wing section was attached to the fuslage by four spruce-faired steel struts, a minimum of metal fittings was employed, this undoubtedly contributing greatly to the low airframe weight. Full-span drooping ailerons were fitted.

Two machines were entered by T O M Sopwith and F Sigrist for the Competition held at Lympne in September 1924. Though not carrying their registration letters at the time, the machines were G-EBMB, flown by Longton and powered by a British Anzani engine, and G-EBJH, flown by Raynham with an ABC Scorpion. Both survived the eliminating heats and gained 4th and 3rd places respectively in the final. Cygnet 'BMB gained first place in the trials for best take-off and pull-up and also won the short landing competition and, had not valve trouble intervened on the last day, the aircraft would almost certainly have won the Air Ministry prize.

In 1925 'BJH was disposed of to the RAE Aero Club but 'BMB was entered, again by Sopwith and Sigrist, in the Royal Aero Club's Meeting at Lympne that year. Still powered by the Anzani engine, but now flown by P W S Bulman, 'BMB won the 100-mile International Handicap Race at 75.58 mph and came second in the 50-mile Light Aeroplane Scratch Race at 65.95 mph.

The Lympne Light Plane Competition of 1926 once more attracted both Cygnets, the first prize of £3,000 being sponsored by the *Daily Mail*. 'BMB was entered by Fred Sigrist and again flown by Bulman, the aircraft carrying the competition number 6. No. 4 was 'BJH, entered by the RAE Aero Club and flown by Fg Off Ragg. Both machines had by now been fitted with Bristol Cherub III two-cylinder engines. Ragg won the Lympne Open Handicap Race, Bulman finishing sixth, but it was Bulman who finally won the principal Competition on 26 September and carried off the *Daily Mail* prize. Ragg was second in 'BJH.

Shortly after this triumph 'BMB was displayed at the massive Croydon demonstration of British aircraft before senior Dominion representatives.

In 1927 both Cygnets were entered for the Bournemouth Easter Meeting and 'BMB for a number of other events during the rest of the year. It was later stored on Hawker premises and apparently forgotten. However, after the Second World War it was taken down from storage, stripped and painstakingly rebuilt by the Company. It subsequently appeared at numerous meetings and became a familiar sight at the RAeS Garden Parties of the mid-fifties. It was then kept at the Hawker aerodrome at Dunsfold and was proudly wheeled out in company with Hart G-ABMR and Hurricane G-AMAU as a nostalgic reminder that flying had undergone some fundamental changes since those early days at Lympne.

In 1972 the Cygnet went on permanent display in the Royal Air Force Museum at Hendon, alongside other famous Hawker aircraft designed by Sir Sydney Camm.

TECHNICAL DATA FOR CYGNET

TYPE: Two-seat light sporting aircraft.
STRUCTURE: All-wooden construction with fabric covering. Rectangular fuselage section with domed fairing. Folding wings with full-span camber-changing flaps and drooping ailerons. Cantilever tail unit.
MANUFACTURERS: H G Hawker Engineering Co Ltd, Kingston.
POWERPLANT: 34 hp 1,100 cc British Anzani 2-cylinder engine. 34 hp ABC Scorpion 2-cylinder engine. 34 hp Bristol Cherub III 2-cylinder engine.
DIMENSIONS: Span, 28 ft 0 in. Length, 20 ft 5 in. Height, 5 ft 10 in. Wing area, 165 sq ft. Width (folded), 8 ft 0 in.
WEIGHTS:(Cherub engine) Empty, 373 lb. Loaded, 950 lb.
PERFORMANCE: (Cherub engine) Max speed, 82 mph at sea level. Climb, 11 min 20 sec to 5,000 ft. Ceiling (absolute), 8,900 ft.

The Hawker Hedgehog, N187, in its initial form. A picture taken in 1924 before modifications were made to undercarriage and wing centre section.

The Hawker Hedgehog

Designed to Air Ministry Specification 37/22 during 1923 and first appearing in February 1924 under the company registration T.2, the Hawker Hedgehog was a three-seat fleet reconnaissance biplane of fabric-covered wooden construction. Powered by the widely-used Bristol Jupiter IV nine-cylinder air-cooled radial engine, the Hedgehog employed several quite novel features for its day, not the least of which was the use of landing flaps on both upper and lower wings. Both wings also featured 'drooping' ailerons. The pilot sat well forward under the top centresection with the observer immediately behind him. The gunner was just clear of the wing trailing edge, which was generously cut away to improve the field of view.

In September 1924, on leaving Brooklands where it had undergone all initial flight testing in the hands of F P Raynham, the Hedgehog was delivered to Martlesham Heath for the customary Service evaluation. Here, exhaustively flown by Fg Offs King, Battle and Hesketh, the machine's handling qualities met with unqualified approval, their report stating it to be 'exceptionally light and pleasant to handle in the air . . . it does not stall suddenly, nor dive after the stall . . .'

However, by the time the Hedgehog had completed these trials the Air Ministry cancelled the requirement, for it was not considered that the performance of the machine represented sufficient advance over such aircraft as the Avro Bison, Blackburn Blackburn and Parnall Panther, all of which had yet to complete their first year of service. Nevertheless, the prototype was purchased from the manufacturers, being serialled N187 and flown back to Martlesham on Air Ministry Experimental Charge in February 1925 for further tests with the drooping ailerons.

The Hedgehog with wings folded.

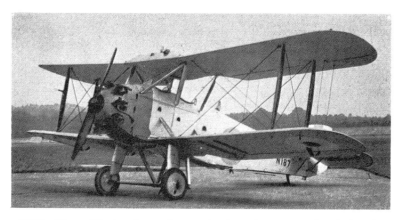

N187 with modified undercarriage and enlarged centre section fuel tank.

During June 1925 floats were substituted for the wheel undercarriage and N187 spent a short period at Felixstowe. While at the Marine Aircraft Establishment an amphibian landing gear was incorporated, and it is believed that it was during tests on this that the aircraft was wrecked and subsequently written off.

TECHNICAL DATA FOR HEDGEHOG*

TYPE: Three-seat Fleet Reconnaissance biplane.
STRUCTURE: Wooden construction with fabric covering.

113

MANUFACTURERS: H G Hawker Engineering Co Ltd, Kingston.
POWERPLANT: 398 hp Bristol Jupiter IV driving 2-blade wooden propeller.
DIMENSIONS: Span, 40 ft 0½ in. Length, 30 ft 8¾ in. Height, 12 ft 6 in. Width
   (wings folded), 16 ft 7½ in. Wing area, 480.7 sq ft.
WEIGHTS: Empty, 2,995 lb. Loaded, 4,791 lb. Overload, 4,800 lb.
PERFORMANCE: Max speed, 120.5 mph at sea level. Cruising speed, 89 mph.
   Climb, 23 min 59 secs to 10,000 ft. Endurance, approximately 2½ hrs. Service
   ceiling (rate of climb, 100 ft/min), 13,500 ft. Take-off ground run,

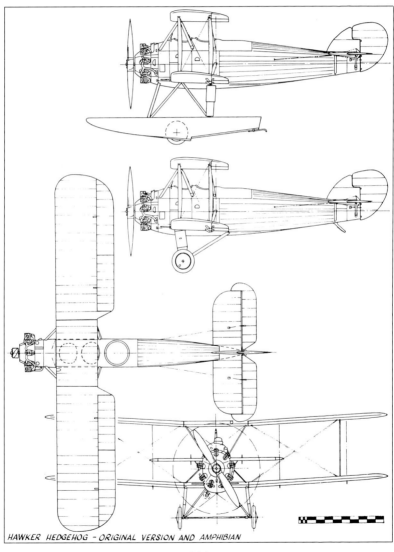

HAWKER HEDGEHOG - ORIGINAL VERSION AND AMPHIBIAN

114

155 yards (with full military load and 9 mph headwind). Landing ground run, 180 yards (light load and 9 mph headwind). Stalling speed (with flaps), 45 mph.

OTHER DATA: Fuel capacity, 134 gallons. Oil, 15 gallons. Fuel, Petrol Benzol (Sp G = 0.76). Armament, one forward-firing Vickers gun with 600 rounds, and one Lewis gun on observer's No. 2 Scarff ring, with five 97-round drums of ammunition. Wheel track, 9 ft 0½ in, 800 × 150 mm wheels.

---

* Ref. A & AEE Report M395/24–37/22.

The Hornbill as it originally appeared in July 1925, with twin underwing radiators, closely-cowled cylinder banks and Fairey Reed propeller.

The Hawker Hornbill

Now known to have flown around July 1925, the Hornbill fighter was W G Carter's answer to Air Ministry Specification 4/24 (the same that produced the Gloucestershire Gorcock), which called for a single-seat fighter to be powered by the new boosted, ungeared Rolls-Royce Condor III engine, and to possess a maximum sea level speed of no less than 208 miles per hour and a service ceiling of 29,000 feet. A single Vickers Mark II machine gun was to be provided, together with 1,000 rounds of ammunition.

Carter recognised in the terms of this requirement an attempt by the Air Ministry to break away from the traditional use of untidy radial engines and thereby acquire a fighter with a truly advanced performance. Accordingly he paid particular attention to close-cowling of the big engine as well as reducing the drag of the vee interplane and cabane struts. The result was a small and exceptionally clean single-bay biplane. Construction was of mixed wood and metal, the engine bearers being of

Two views of Hornbill J7782 in August 1925 after changing to a Watts wooden propeller.

steel tube with duralumin sheet panels formed to enclose the separate banks of cylinders with a prominent central cleft.

The first flight of Hornbill J7782, around July 1925, was almost certainly carried out by Fred Raynham, although on July 1 Flt Lt P W S ('George') Bulman joined the company as Chief Test Pilot. When first flown, the aircraft featured twin underwing radiators and flew without a spinner over the fine-pitch Watts wooden propeller to enable a Hucks starter to be used. Although provision was made for a Vickers gun, it was not fitted because the Condor III had no provision for synchronising gear.

Later reports by Bulman suggested some disappointment with the Hornbill's performance, and a Fairey Reed metal propeller was fitted temporarily, but this gave no appreciable improvement. The aircraft was flown to Farnborough in October 1925 to be inspected by Air Staff officers, and in December J7782 paid its first visit to Martlesham Heath for its initial assessment by the A&AEE. During the course of this it was found that the Condor tended to suffer from over-cooling, with the result that the outer segments of the radiators were permanently blanked off.

After being returned to Brooklands in February 1926 the Hornbill

Bearing the 'New Type' number 5 for the 1926 Hendon Air Display, the Hornbill J7782 is seen here with the new engine cowling and central, under-fuselage Serck radiator.

was dismantled and returned to Kingston, where it underwent extensive modification. A 698 hp Condor IV was fitted, its longer crankcase requiring new engine panels which were now raked back and faired flat across the top of the engine. A single semicircular-section Serck radiator, located between the landing gear struts, replaced the wing radiators, and the fin and rudder profile were both altered to provide slightly greater area, the fin being slightly cambered. All of these modifications were carried out to drawings prepared by Sydney Camm.

When the Hornbill returned to Brooklands, Bulman carried out a short series of performance and handling flights, reporting a maximum speed of 194 miles per hour (with ballast in lieu of the Vickers gun). In a ceiling climb, he reported that power from the Condor seemed to diminish rapidly above about 16,000 ft, and that the greatest height he was able to attain was slightly under 24,000 feet. Low-speed handling he reported as 'excellent', with view for landing 'good'.

On 3 July 1926 J7782, carrying New Type number 5, was shown to the public for the first time at the annual RAF Display at Hendon, where it was flown by Flt Lt Howard Saint.

After a short time back at Brooklands, when the camber on the fin was increased, the Hornbill was delivered to Martlesham for its full Service assessment, as well as comparative evaluation with the Armstrong Whitworth Siskin IIIA. These trials confirmed that the Hornbill was appreciably faster than the Siskin at all altitudes up to 21,000 ft, but the Siskin possessed a much superior ceiling. The latter finding destroyed any chance that the Hornbill might have had of earning a production contract.

The Hornbill was, however, to be criticised on many other counts. Engine *overheating* had been encountered, suggesting that the single radiator was now inadequate (although it transpired that normal Service fuel was unsuitable for the Condor when flown at full throttle for extended periods). Directional stability and control was lacking to such an extent that it was impossible to maintain height in steep turns above 150 mph without use of full top rudder. Worst of all, it was stated that the cockpit was so cramped for the average-sized pilot (owing to the fine blending of the engine with the fuselage contours) that it was impossible to reach the cocking handle of the Vickers gun, and that a larger-than-average pilot would find it impossible to abandon the cockpit by parachute in an emergency. Despite strengthening, the aircraft had a tendency to break its sternpost, although it was pointed out that while testing the handling during precautionary landings it was normal for the tail skid to strike the ground before the mainwheels.

For all these serious shortcomings, the Air Ministry suggested to Hawker that the Hornbill should be transferred to experimental charge at the RAE as 'the aeroplane displays certain outstanding handling

Flying view of J7782 being demonstrated by Bulman in July 1926; note the increased fin area.

Another 1926 view of the Hornbill, showing the 'smoothed-out' upper contours of the engine cowling.

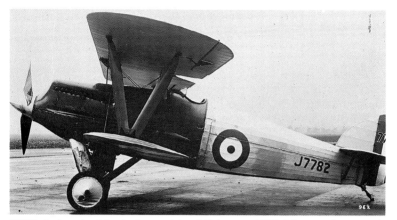

J7782 during the Martlesham trials of February 1927. The previous year's Hendon '5' on the rear fuselage has been obliterated — rather untidily. Note the Fairey Reed propeller.

qualities at low flying speeds and is, in many respects, of an advanced concept in high-speed design'.

The company gained permission to enter J7782 in the 1927 Aerial Derby, but this event was cancelled, and its entry in the King's Cup Race that year was withdrawn.

Thereafter, extensive trials were carried out both at Brooklands and at Farnborough to study the effect of automatic wing slats on the low-speed handling, and the RAE expressed some surprise that their effect was minimal, suggesting that the AD.1 aerofoil section possessed some characteristics that had not previously been fully understood.

Whatever difficulties were experienced by the Hornbill at the upper

The Hornbill at Farnborough in October 1928, fitted with high-speed slotted wings.

119

end of its speed range, it unquestionably possessed very fine low-speed characteristics for, as shown by RAE reports issued in 1931, the aircraft displayed remarkable stability near the stall, whether or not fitted with wing slats.

The aircraft was officially struck off Air Ministry charge in February 1932, by which time it had amassed 1,080 flying hours, but continued to undergo limited flight trials at Farnborough until 18 May the following year (possibly having been returned to company charge).

There is no doubt but that the Hornbill was a bitter disappointment to Sopwith and Camm in its early days, but if they felt in any way that the Service's judgement had been too harsh, Bulman's verdict was unequivocal: 'The Hornbill was too clever by half, and the designer almost forgot that the pilot *is* an important part of the design . . .'

Camm was never to forget that verdict.

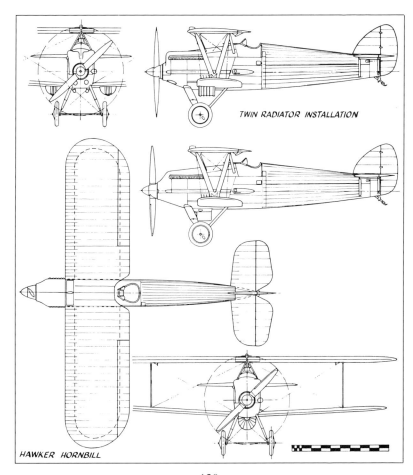

TWIN RADIATOR INSTALLATION

HAWKER HORNBILL

TECHNICAL DATA FOR HORNBILL (CONDOR IV)*

TYPE: Experimental single-seat interceptor biplane fighter.

STRUCTURE: Mixed wood/metal. The fuselage forward of cockpit of steel tubular construction with aluminium covering. Rear fuselage, tail and wings of wood with fabric covering.

MANUFACTURERS: H G Hawker Engineering Co Ltd, Kingston.

POWERPLANT: 698 hp Rolls-Royce Condor IV driving either Watts 2-blade walnut or Fairey Reed 2-blade metal propeller.

DIMENSIONS: Span, 31 ft 0 in. Length, 26 ft 7¼ in. Height 9 ft 8 in. Wing area, 317.4 sq ft.

WEIGHTS: Empty, 2,975 lb. Loaded, 3,769 lb. Overload, 3,820 lb.

PERFORMANCE: Max speed, 187 mph at sea level. Cruising speed, approx 140 mph. Climb, 6.5 min to 10,000 ft. Range, about 200 miles. Service ceiling (rate of climb, 100 ft/min 22,700 ft.

OTHER DATA: Stalling speed, 64 mph. Take-off ground run, 180 yards (5 kt headwind). Fuel capacity, 57 gallons. Fuel, Petrol Benzol (Sp G 0.76). Armament, one forward-firing Vickers Mk 2 gun with 1,000 rounds. Wheel track, 5 ft 0 in, 750 × 125 mm wheels.

---

* Ref. A & AEE Report M.449/26–7/24.

One of three Hawker-built Danecocks at Brooklands before delivery to Denmark in 1926.

The Hawker Danecock

Following evaluation of a Woodcock II demonstration aircraft in 1925, the Danish Government placed an order for three similar machines to be powered by Armstrong Siddeley Jaguar engines, and commenced negotiations to acquire a licence for production of a further small number.

Under the direction of Sydney Camm a limited redesign of the Woodcock II was carried out, the fuselage being lengthened slightly in the vicinity of the cockpit and minor improvements being incorporated in the wings (the span of the upper plane was fractionally increased and the lower plane reduced).

An Armstrong Siddeley Jaguar IV was installed driving a 9 ft 8 in diameter Watts wooden propeller. The first Danecock, No. 151, was flown by Bulman on 15 December 1925, at Brooklands, being followed by 152 and 153 within a month. All three aircraft cleared Customs for

Another view of the Hawker-built Danecock.

Danecock 158 was magnificently restored and preserved in Denmark. This photograph, taken in 1960, shows the cartridge chutes added below the Madsen guns, and the slightly modified exhaust manifolds. The large-section tyres were acquired shortly before the Second World War.
(*Photo: Royal Danish Air Force*).

Denmark in February 1926 (though at least one returned to the UK later for engine adjustments).

Production of the licence version (known as the L.B II, Dankok) got under way at the Danish Royal Navy Dockyard factory in 1927, a further twelve machines (Nos. 154–165) being built in that and the following year. In January 1927 one of the Hawker-built Danecocks set a Scandinavian Altitude Record of 28,208 ft, a record that was to stand for some eight years. This aircraft was displayed at the Copenhagen Aero Show in August 1927, while in 1934 Dankoks of the Danish Army Air Service were entered in the Scandinavian Military Aircraft Competition of that year, gaining fifth place in a sizeable field of more modern entries.

One Army Air Service Squadron and No.2 Naval Squadron were equipped with Dankoks, and due to the failure of the Nimrod to achieve full production status in Denmark in 1934, the Dankok remained in service until 1937. Machine No. 158 survived the Second World War and now reposes in the Copenhagen Museum, its log book bearing testimony to 704 hours 5 minutes flying time.

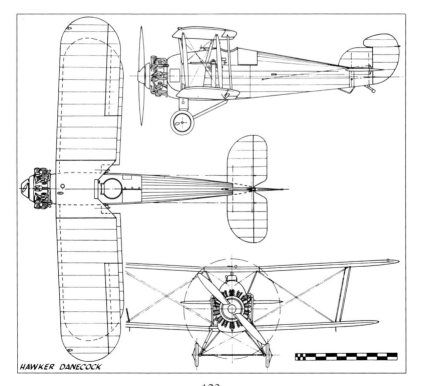

HAWKER DANECOCK

123

TYPE: Single-seat interceptor fighter.

STRUCTURE: Wooden construction with fabric covering.

MANUFACTURERS: H G Hawker Engineering Co Ltd, Kingston (3 aircraft); licence production at the Danish Royal Naval Dockyard factory (12 aircraft).

POWERPLANT: 385 hp Armstrong Siddeley Jaguar IV 14-cylinder 2-row radial engine driving 9 ft 8 in diameter Watts 2-blade wooden propeller.

DIMENSIONS: Span, 32 ft 7in. Length, 26 ft 1¼ in. Height, 10 ft 1 in. Wing area, 340 sq ft.

WEIGHTS: Empty, 2,128 lb. Loaded, 3,045 lb.

PERFORMANCE: Max speed, 145 mph at sea level. Cruising speed, 105 mph. Climb, 8 min 15 sec to 10,000 ft. Endurance, 2½ hrs approx. Service ceiling with full military load (rate of climb, 100 ft/min): 22,800 ft.

OTHER DATA: Fuel capacity, 52 gallons. Fuel, Petrol Benzol (Sp G 0.76). Armament, two synchronised 7.7 mm Madsen machine guns, with 720 rounds per gun. Wheel track, 6 ft 11 in, 700 × 100 mm wheels.

The Heron fighter, J6989.

The Hawker Heron

The Heron fighter represented an important landmark in the early history of the H G Hawker Engineering Company, in that it was the first aircraft to be completed employing a predominantly metal structure. Limited modernisation of the machine shops, with provision for metalworking, had started in Canbury Park Road in 1923.

The aircraft had been started as the third Woodcock (the second with single-bay wings), but Sopwith had obtained the Air Ministry's permission to complete it as a 'metal Woodcock' early in 1924, undertaking the project as a private venture. Carter assigned the redesign to Camm, who quickly discovered that, owing to changed weight distribution of the structure, a rather different aircraft would result. It was to be renamed the Heron.

The structure was built up using round steel and aluminium tubes swaged to rectangular section at their extremities and bolted together using fishplates and bolts to form a simple box, cross-baced with tensioning wires. The parallel-chord wing, without sweepback, employed twin spars of light-gauge steel tube (not of dumbbell section, as introduced later) to which were attached wooden ribs. The nose of the fuselage immediately aft of the Jupiter VI engine was covered with sheet duralumin, but in the region of the cockpit sheet ply was used; the remainder of the structure was fabric-covered. Unlike the Woodcock II, the Heron had straight wings of unequal span and increased stagger, with pronounced dihedral on the lower wings. A smooth-contoured fin and horn-balanced rudder replaced the Woodcock's untidy tail surfaces. Although the Heron's weight was marginally greater than that of the Woodcock II, its maximum speed was some 15 mph higher. Provision was made for a pair of Vickers guns with CC gear and 600 rounds per gun.

When first flown by Raynham, in mid-1925, the Heron, J6989, featured the customary fine-pitch Watts walnut two-blade propeller and, when displayed at the 1925 Royal Air Force Display (as New Type No.2) on 27 June that year, this propeller was still in use. When, the

The Heron in flight at Brooklands. The pilot is said to be Howard Saint.

aircraft was delivered to Martlesham Heath in December, however, comparative trials were carried out using a Fairey Reed metal propeller but, on account of the greater weight this did not materially improve the performance. Subsequent gun trials were carried out by No.15 Squadron (which was then the Armament Squadron of the A&AEE).

Heron J6989 remained at Martlesham for most of 1927, being transferred to No. 22 Squadron for handling and performance reports and attracting considerable praise for the pleasant handling and ease of servicing bestowed by the metal primary structure.

In later years Camm referred to the Heron with considerable affection, suggesting that, for him at least, it marked the transition from the outdated fighter formula (characterised by such aircraft as the Snipe, Woodcock and Grebe). The wing layout and tail surface profile of the Heron could easily be recognised in the beautiful Fury biplane that was to emerge in 1929.

The Heron was struck off Air Ministry charge in May 1928 and returned to Brooklands where, with armament removed, it was re-registered G-EBYC (C of A No. 1433) for entry in the King's Cup Race at Hendon on 27 July. However, while being taxied to the starting line by Bulman, it struck a parked car and was fairly badly damaged. The aircraft was later repaired, but the C of A was allowed to lapse and it was struck off the civil register in January 1930. It is said to have been stored in the corner of Hawkers' flight shed at Brooklands until the outbreak of the Second World War.

A picture of the Heron taken shortly before the 1928 King's Cup Race.

TECHNICAL DATA FOR HERON

TYPE: Experimental single-seat interceptor fighter.

STRUCTURE: All-metal construction with fabric covering.

MANUFACTURERS: H G Hawker Engineering Co Ltd, Kingston.

POWERPLANT: 455 hp Bristol Jupiter VI 9-cylinder radial engine driving 2-blade Watts wooden propeller; also fitted with Fairey Reed metal propeller.

DIMENSIONS: Span, 31 ft 10 in. Length, 22 ft 3 in. Height, 9 ft 9 in. Wing area, 291 sq ft.

WEIGHTS: Empty, 2,120 lb. Loaded, 3,126 lb.

PERFORMANCE: Max speed, 156 mph at 9,800 ft. Climb, 5 min 30 sec to 10,000 ft. Duration, approx 3 hr 30 min. Service ceiling (rate of climb, 100 ft/min), 23,300 ft.

OTHER DATA: Fuel capacity, 60 gallons. Armament, two fixed forward-firing Vickers guns with 600 rounds per gun. Wheel track, 5 ft 0 in.

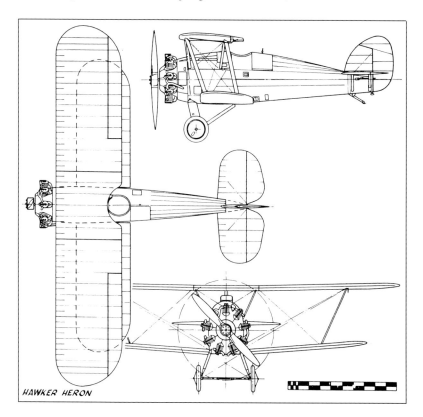

HAWKER HERON

The first prototype Horsley, J7511, as it originally appeared with radiators mounted on the sides of the fuselage.

The Hawker Horsley

The Hawker Horsley was notable in that it was the last wooden aircraft built by Hawker Engineering, entering quantity production in 1926 before the Kingston factory facilities for metal construction had been completed. By 1927 the now-famous Hawker system of metal construction had been adopted and was incorporated to a limited extent in the Horsley II, while the Horsley III (a designation not officially used) possessed an all-metal structure.

Originally designed by Sydney Camm under the direction of W G Carter in 1924, the Horsley (initially named the Kingston) was a large single-engine, two-bay biplane designed to Air Ministry Specification 26/23, which purported to lay down standard medium bomber load requirements. The first prototype, J7511, was nearing completion at Brooklands in December 1924 when it suffered damage in an accident which delayed its first flight until about March the following year, when it was taken aloft by Fred Raynham. At this stage the aircraft was powered by a Rolls-Royce Condor III engine (the same as in the Hornbill fighter), and featured radiators on the sides of the fuselage some six feet behind the engine, but these were found to be unsatisfactory and were soon replaced by a single radiator in the more orthodox 'chin' position. On 4 May J7511 was delivered to No.22 Squadron at Martlesham for performance assessment by the A&AEE and comparative evaluation with the other tenders to Specification 26/23, namely the Bristol Berkeley, Handley Page Handcross and Westland Yeovil. Initial reactions tended to favour the Horsley, although final judgement was withheld owing to none of the competitors being able to meet the load requirements. At the end of July J7511 embarked on its Service evaluation with No. 11 Squadron, but once more judgement was reserved; the Horsley was, however, criticised on account of poor engine accessibility.

The prototype was then returned to Brooklands for a number of improvements to be made, including a redesigned landing gear. Unfortunately, during the first flight with the new undercarriage a tyre burst on landing, causing the gear on one side to collapse and damaging one wing (this was the only occasion on which Camm ever flew in an aircraft of his own design).

In the meantime, however, the shortcomings of the 1923 Specification had been recognised and a new set of bomb load standards were laid down in Specification 23/25. Quite fortuitously, moreover, the following Specification, 24/25, also laid down load requirements, this time for torpedo-bombers. The maximum bomb load was to consist of either two 520-pound, two 550-pound, one 1,100-pound or one 1,500-pound bomb, though the last type had not been produced since 1918. The torpedo called for was the standard naval ordnance type, weighing 2,150 pounds. (An amendment issued later covered carriage of a torpedo weighing over 2,800 pounds.)

A second prototype Horsley, J7721, had been ordered late in 1924, but construction had not begun until the load requirements, outlined above, had been received at Kingston, so that Camm was able to make greater use of metal structure in the top wing centresection and inboard sections of the lower wing. This aircraft was first flown by Bulman on 6 December 1925, and was inspected at Brooklands by armament officers from Martlesham.

The ease with which the Horsley could now be adapted to carry these loads impressed the evaluation authorities sufficiently to prompt the Air Ministry to order thirty Horsleys in March 1926, the first ten aircraft being termed Mark Is and based largley on the first, predominantly wooden prototype, and the remainder Mark IIs based on J7721. The first production aircraft was completed in August that year, and as subsequent aircraft were checked out by Bulman they were delivered to the Home Aircraft Depot to await delivery to Service squadrons.

First Royal Air Force Squadron to receive the Horsley was No.11 (Bomber) Squadron, commanded by Wg Cdr J H A Landon, DSO, OBE, at Netheravon. During January 1927 this unit received the first of its Horsley IIs and by April the last of the old Fairey Fawns had been replaced; the Squadron then set off on a demonstration tour round the cities in the north of England. Shortly afterwards No.100 (Bomber) Squadron, at Grantham, also received Horsleys — again replacing Fawns. The Horsleys were a considerable advance over the earlier machines, capable of carrying three times the bomb-load over greater distances. Powered by a Rolls-Royce Condor IIIA the two-seat bomber featured a Mark IIB bomb-sight operated by the observer, who adopted

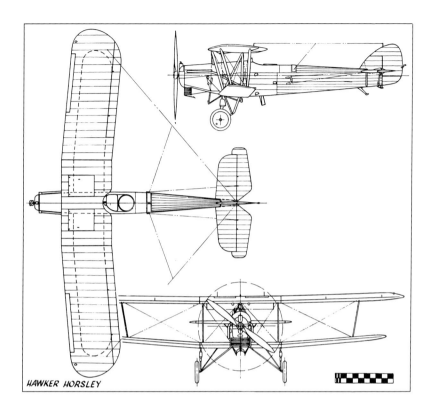

HAWKER HORSLEY

a prone position under the pilot's seat for bomb-aiming. Another feature of the Horsley, repeated on several later Hawker machines, was the ground-adjustable variable-incidence tailplane, incorporated principally to cater for the widely varying load dispositions anticipated.

May 1927 saw the first of three attempts to fly non-stop from Cranwell to India by Flt Lt C R Carr (later Air Marshal Sir Roderick Carr, KBE, CB, DFC, AFC), two Horsleys, J8607 and J8608, being prepared. As related on page 13 only the first of the attempts came near to success and both machines were severely damaged (though both were salvaged and returned to this country). Nevertheless the first flight beat the previous world long distance record by a small margin, though the feat was immediately eclipsed by Lindbergh's transatlantic flight to Paris.

Horsleys were to feature at several public gatherings in 1927. At the beginning of July Nos. 11 and 100 (Bomber) Squadrons performed formation flying demonstrations at the Eighth RAF Display at Hendon and, at the end of the same month, Horsley J8606 was entered in the King's Cup Race by T O M Sopwith and flown by Bulman. Based on Hucknall, Notts, the race attracted twenty-six entries of which Bulman finished sixth at an average speed of 121.5 mph.

The first long-distance Horsley, J8607 at Brooklands before delivery to Cranwell.

By 1928 four bomber squadrons had received Horsleys; they were Nos.11 and 33 (at Netheravon), No.15 (at Martlesham Heath) and No. 100 (at Grantham). In January that year the Night-flying Flight — later renamed the Anti-aircraft Co-operation Flight — at Biggin Hill received Horsleys in place of its Vickers Vimys.

The prototype Horsley torpedo bomber, J8006, was in fact the tenth

A standard Horsley I bomber (the third production aircraft, J7989) at Brooklands; it later served with No. 100 Squadron at Spittlegate.

The all-metal Horsley, J8932, undergoing evaluation at Martlesham as a bomber in 1927. It was later fitted with an experimental Rolls-Royce H.10 engine and was evaluated as a dual-rôle bomber/torpedo bomber during 1930.

The Horsley II torpedo-bomber, S1236, which was also evaluated at Martlesham Heath.

production aircraft in the original order for twenty Mark IIs; it had flown in August 1926 and been delivered the same month to Martlesham for preliminary assessment. In January 1927 J8006 was transferred to the Torpedo Development Flight at Gosport for several

A Greek Horsley.

months, being shown at the 1927 Hendon Air Display (as new Type No. 7) in July.

At the end of that year an initial production order for twelve torpedo bombers, powered by Condor IIIAs, was placed (S1236-S1247), the first Service deliveries being made to the Coast Defence Torpedo Flight in August 1928 at Donibristle in Scotland. On 1 October this unit was renamed No.36 (Torpedo Bomber) Squadron. Follow-up orders for further torpedo bombers — all metal aircraft, sometimes but incorrectly referred to as Mark IIIs — were placed (for eighteen in 1929 and eighteen in 1931, all with Condor IIIBs). Many of these Horsleys served with No.36 Squadron when it was redeployed to Singapore in 1930, remaining in service until July 1935. Others joined No.100 Squadron when it transferred to the torpedo bombing rôle in November 1930. (When this

One of the small number or Horsleys used for target towing, S1452.

133

Squadron also moved to Singapore in December 1933 it had been re-equipped with Vickers Vildebeests.)

In April 1929 the Hawker Company secured an order for six complete Horsley IIs to be built for the Greek Naval Air Service, and these aircraft were delivered to Greece by December. Five were used as torpedo-bombers, while the remaining aircraft became regarded as the Greek VIP transport; all were based at Tatoi.

Horsleys continued to serve the home-based bomber squadrons for several years, participating each year in the annual air exercises, though among day bombers of their era their performance was not exceptional (their highest position in the annual Bomber Command Competitions was fifth). They also appeared at all RAF Hendon Displays between 1927 and 1931. In 1932, however, replacement of home-based Horsley bombers by Vickers Vildebeests commenced, other aircraft having been issued to No. 504 Squadron of the Special Reserve at Hucknall in 1931; it was a Horsley of No. 504 Squadron (J8025) which accidentally landed on a hangar at Hawkinge on 7 August 1933, setting it on fire and destroying six Hawker Fury fighters of No. 25 Squadron inside. By February 1934 all Horsleys had been replaced in the United Kingdom.

One other service version of the Horsley should be mentioned. As early as 1930 design work commenced to adapt the Horsley for target-towing duties, and in January 1931 a trial installation was flown on an all-metal Horsley, S1452. The installation consisted of a fuselage-mounted target cable drum and wind-driven winch on the side of the rear cockpit. During 1931 and 1932 about a dozen target-towing conversions were carried out, mostly on the all-metal torpedo-bombers — the torpedo and bomb gear being retained.

THE HORSLEY TEST BEDS

From 1926 onwards the Horsley was widely used as an engine test bed, possessing on the one hand ample fuel capacity (bestowing a worthwhile test flight endurance) and on the other a remarkable degree of manoeuvrability over a wide speed range.

With the introduction of the fully representative second prototype, J7721, the original machine, J7511, was delivered to Rolls-Royce early in 1926 for development flying of the Condor, and in preparation for the forthcoming production orders much certification work was carried out on Condor IIAs, IIIAs and IIIBs. Later, this aircraft was flown with a Rolls-Royce Eagle VIII and the 810 hp Rolls-Royce H.10 before being transferred to D Napier and Sons Ltd for development flying with late-series Lion engines.

Another early Horsley, a Mark II J8003, was converted to mount a Rolls-Royce Condor C.1 compression-ignition engine (a development of the Condor III), producing about 480 bhp. This aircraft was handed over to the RAE in 1931 and at Farnborough extensive flight programmes

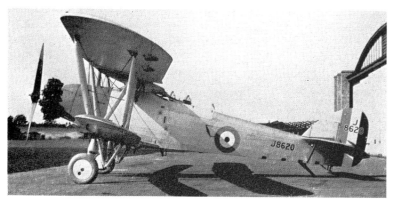

The Horsley test bed, J8620, with Armstrong Siddeley Leopard I engine.

J8620 with Leopard II engine.

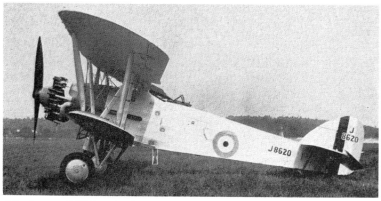

The Leopard III installation in J8620, similar to that used in the Dantorp.

135

were conducted until 1933. In that year it was demonstrated as a 'New and Experimental' aircraft at the RAF Hendon Display.

Also at Farnborough, it was while testing another Horsley, the all-metal prototype J8932, fitted with an 812 hp Rolls-Royce H.10 engine, that Flt Lt H R D Waghorn, AFC (winner of the 1929 Schneider Trophy contest) was killed on 4 May 1931.

In 1927 a design to Specification 17/27 was evolved to suit the Horsley to take an Armstrong Siddeley Leopard 14-cylinder radial engine and in January 1928 a Leopard I was flown in Horsley II J8620. This installation was evaluated by the A&AEE — the aircraft carrying full bomb-load — during that year and, such was the margin by which the original Specification was now exceeded, the Hawker Company was encouraged to proceed with the scheme. Accordingly, during the following two years Leopard IIs, IIIs, and IIIAs were flown in J8620. In 1933, after the aircraft had been in use at Farnborough for some time, a Junkers Jumo engine was installed and, so fitted, performed some fifty hours' flying. Another engine test bed was the Horsley II J8001, used for certification of the Rolls-Royce Buzzard III in 1931 and subsequently for further development of this engine.

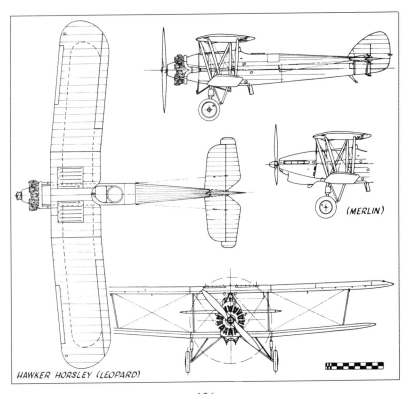

HAWKER HORSLEY (LEOPARD)

The Junkers Jumo installation in J8620.

Perhaps the most significant of all engines tested on the Horsley was the Rolls-Royce P.V.12. Two aircraft, J8611 and S1436, were used between 1934 and 1937 to gain certification of the Merlin 'C','E', 'F', and 'G' engines, driving many different types of two-, three- and four-blade propellers. The 1,145 hp Merlin X, later produced in large numbers for the Whitley V bomber, made its first flight in the Horsley S1436 on 7 September 1937.

Other engine test bed Horsleys included installations of the Rolls-Royce H.10, Napier Lion (in addition to J7511) and the Buzzard III in 1933.

SPECIAL HORSLEYS

A small number of Horsleys was used from time to time for trial installations and other *ad hoc* conversions for the Service. The first prototype, J7511, after it had completed its work as an engine test bed, was fitted with a float undercarriage in 1929 and spent a short period at the Marine Aircraft Experimental Establishment at Felixstowe, although no specific requirement existed for a Horsley seaplane in the Fleet Air Arm. In 1933, however, the Horsley II J8612 was fitted with a float undercarriage under contract to the Air Ministry and underwent formal assessment at Felixstowe. The figures issued with the report were used for comparison with those for the Dantorp seaplane (see below), which had visited the MAEE the previous year.

Another aircraft, J8606, known as the Horsley (Special Service), was developed against Air Ministry Contract in 1932 for the Special Duties Flight; it was fitted with a third seat for a passenger, and was equipped with smoke-laying generator. Trials were carried out at the RAE in May 1933.

In common with most other Service aircraft, a Horsley (J8019) was fitted with slatted wings in 1929–30 for comparison with the standard

The first Horsley Merlin test bed, S1436.

aircraft, but failed to generate any interest at either Martlesham or Farnborough.

An interesting 'private venture' involved the conversion of a Horsley, J7995, for target-towing duties. The aircraft was on No.25 (Fighter) Squadron's charge early in 1927, and the work was carried out at Brooklands, although there is no trace of a contract having been raised.

THE DANTORP

The undoubted success of the experimental Armstrong Siddeley Leopard installation in J8620 prompted the Danish Government in 1930 to place an order for two such aircraft, and to negotiate licence production of the type at the Danish Naval Dockyard factory at Copenhagen. Two machines were completed, 201 and 202, the undercarriages on both being interchangeable for wheels and floats. Known as the Dantorp, this

Horsley J8611 with Merlin 'G' installation.

138

design featured composite metal and wood construction and differed slightly in the disposition of the cockpits, for a third crew member was accommodated between pilot and observer/gunner. Dantorp 201, with a wheel undercarriage, was first flown from Brooklands by Sayer on 19 September 1932, 202 following shortly afterwards. The latter also underwent trials with floats at Felixstowe in November 1932. Although much flying was carried out on these two machines in Denmark from 1933 onwards, it is believed that the licence concession was not taken up and no further production followed.

TECHNICAL DATA FOR HORSLEY

TYPE: Two-seat day-bomber or torpedo-bomber (also target tug).

STRUCTURE: Initial aircraft were of all-wood construction (Mk I); composite wood and metal construction adopted in 1926–27 (Mk II). One batch of late series Horsleys employed all-metal structure.

MANUFACTURERS: H G Hawker Engineering Co Ltd, Kingston.

POWERPLANT: Standard RAF and Greek aircraft, 665 hp Rolls-Royce Condor IIIA engine driving 14 ft 6 in diameter Watts two-blade wooden propeller. Experimental seaplane version featured 13 ft 10 in four-blade wooden propeller. Test beds flown with the following: 670 hp Rolls-Royce Condor III, 665 hp Condor IIIA, 690 hp Condor IIIB, 480 hp Condor C.1 (compression-ignition); 810 hp Rolls-Royce Buzzard I, 880 hp Buzzard III; 810 hp Rolls-Royce H.10; 580 hp Napier Lion V; 765 hp Armstrong Siddeley Leopard I, 800 hp Leopard II, 805 hp Leopard III, 800 hp Leopard IIIA; 930–1,025 hp Rolls-Royce P.V.12 (Merlins C, E, F and G).

DIMENSIONS: Span (Mk II), 56 ft 5¾ in. Length (Mk II landplane), 38 ft 10 in. Length (experimental seaplane), 46 ft 4 in. Height (Mk II landplane, propeller horizontal), 13 ft 8 in. Height (experimental seaplane, overall), 17 ft 6 in. Wing area (Mk II), 693 sq ft.

WEIGHTS: (Mk II Day-bomber) Empty, 4,760 lb. Loaded, 7,800 lb. (Mk II Torpedo-bomber) Empty, 4,958 lb. Loaded, 9,270 lb. Overload (as for long-distance record attempt), 14,240 lb.

PERFORMANCE: (Mk II Day-bomber) Max speed, 125 mph at 6,000 ft. Climb, 14 min 20 sec. to 10,000 ft. Endurance, approx 10 hours. Service ceiling (rate of climb, 100 ft/min), 14,000 ft. (Mk II Torpedo-bomber) Max speed, 118 mph at 5,000 ft. Climb, 12 min 30 sec to 5,000 ft. Service ceiling (rate of climb 100 ft/sec), 11,200 ft. (Leopard III test bed) Max speed, 128.5 mph at 3,000 ft. Climb, 12 min 28 sec to 10,000 ft. Service ceiling (rate of climb, 100 ft/min), 17,750 ft. Absolute ceiling, 20,000 ft.

OTHER DATA: Fuel capacity, 230 gallons. Oil capacity, 127 gallons. Armament, one forward-firing Vickers gun with 500 rounds and one Lewis gun mounted on observer's cockpit with seven 97-round ammunition drums. Bomb load: (a) One Admiralty Type VI or VIII torpedo, (b) Either one 1,500, one 1,100 or two 550 lb bombs on Mk II carriers, or (c) combinations of light bombs (20, 112, 230 or 250lb) carried on No. I Mk III F skeleton tubular bomb racks. Wheel track, 15 ft.

The first Dantorp, 201, with wheel undercarriage.

The second Dantorp, 202, with twin floats.

TECHNICAL DATA FOR DANTORP

TYPE: Three-seat torpedo-bomber for Royal Danish Naval Air Service.
STRUCTURE: Composite wood and metal construction with wood and fabric covering.
MANUFACTURERS: H G Hawker Engineering Co Ltd, Kingston.
POWERPLANT: Fitted initially with 800 hp Armstrong Siddeley Leopard II but delivered with 805 hp Armstrong Siddeley Leopard IIIA driving 2-blade Watts wooden propeller.
DIMENSIONS: Span, 56 ft 5¾ in. Length (landplane), 38 ft 4½ in. Length (seaplane), 45 ft 11½ in. Height (landplane, propeller horizontal), 14 ft 1 in. Height (seaplane, overall), 18 ft 1 in. Wing area, 693 sq ft.

140

WEIGHTS: Empty (landplane, 5,360 lb. Empty (seaplane), 6,450 lb. Loaded (landplane), 8,230 lb. Loaded (seaplane), 9,420 lb.

PERFORMANCE: (Landplane) Max speed. 126.2 mph at 3,200 ft. Climb, 12 min 50 sec to 10,000 ft. Endurance, approximately 8½ hrs. Service ceiling (rate of climb, 100 ft/min), 17,450 ft.

(Seaplane) Max speed, 104.5 mph at 2,200 ft. Climb, 22 min 30 sec to 10,000 ft. Endurance, approximately 7½ hrs. Service ceiling (rate of climb, 100 ft/min), 12,800 ft.

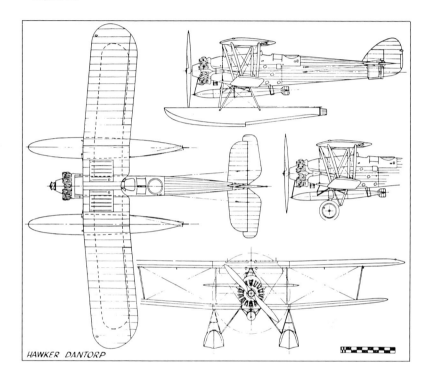

HAWKER DANTORP

The Hawker Hawfinch fighter, J8776, being demonstrated by Flt Lt Bulman at Brooklands.

The Hawker Hawfinch

The Hawfinch was one of those aircraft which appear from time to time and which, though not accepted into service, contribute materially to the development of other aircraft in their category.

Specification F.9/26 was received by H G Hawker Engineering Co Ltd in April 1926 and laid down requirements of a replacement for the Armstrong Whitworth Siskin and Gloster Gamecock fighters which, between them, equipped thirteen squadrons of the RAF at home. Furthemore, the Fairey Fox, a bomber with a top speed of slightly over 150 miles per hour and equivalent performance to the current Siskins and Gamecocks, was scheduled to enter service later in 1926, an event that was to cause embarrassment among the fighter squadrons.

However, despite use of an in-line engine in the Fox (a feature obviously contributing to its relatively high performance), F.9/26 persisted in the traditional preference for the radial engine in the fighter, with the result that the Bristol Jupiter was almost universally favoured by the companies invited to tender.

No fewer than nine prototypes were ordered, including the Boulton-

Paul Partridge, Gloster S.S.19, Bristol Bulldog, Armstrong Whitworth A.W. XVI and Hawkers' competitor, the Hawfinch J8776.

As specified, the Hawfinch, a two-bay biplane with sharply staggered wings, was armed with two synchronised Vickers guns and used the Hawker system of metal construction. The first of the F.9/26 designs to fly, J8776 was flown in March 1927 with a Bristol Jupiter VI, but before delivery to Martlesham Heath in July that year this had been replaced by the 450 hp Jupiter VII.

Because the other F.9/26 contenders were not yet ready for their Service trials, the opportunity was taken to submit the aircraft for deck landing trials, and J8776 spent ten days in July with HMS *Furious*. The aircraft appears to have behaved well, and there can be no doubt that the trials contributed useful experience, particularly as Camm was beginning to take an interest in a new fleet fighter Specification N.21/26, and was already starting to scheme the design of what would evolve as the Hoopoe — and later the Nimrod. At the end of July J8776 returned to Brooklands for preparation before going to Martlesham for the final competitive evaluation.

Extensive performance and handling trials on the various F.9/26 prototypes continued at Martlesham until early in 1928, by which time the Bulldog and Hawfinch had established a clear lead over their rivals. Moreover, it seems that the A&AEE was unable to decide its preference between the two, with the result that both aircraft were delivered for squadron trials, visiting Kenley, Hornchurch, Northolt, Biggin Hill

The Hawker Hawfinch, J8776, with Fairey Reed metal airscrew.

143

and Upavon for short spells of handling by squadron pilots. Finally the Bulldog was adjudged the superior, apparently simply on account of its fractionally higher top speed of 174 mph.

The decision to adopt the Bulldog was announced in June 1928, but already work at Kingston was in hand on the design that was to materialise as the Fury and which was to join the Bulldog in service. The Hawfinch prototype was returned to the factory, where single-bay wings were temporarily introduced during September 1928, while shortly afterwards the aircraft paid a brief visit to Felixstowe equipped with a twin-float undercarriage.

By early 1929 J8776 had been returned to Company Charge, and although a civil Certificate of Airworthiness was taken out and registration G-AAKH allotted, there is no record that the letters were ever painted on the machine. Nevertheless, from July 1929 on, the Hawfinch was used by Hawkers and the RAE for trials with heavily cambered aerofoil sections. These were incorporated in the outboard sections of the upper mainplanes in the region of the ailerons, and were used to investigate the improvements bestowed on the low speed lateral control of the aircraft.

After a further spell at Farnborough, J8776 returned to Martlesham Heath in November 1933 for a final series of handling trials with No.22 Squadron, and although it never achieved the fame and fortunes of some of its stablemates the design undoubtedly provided a wealth of vital research data. This indicated the potential superiority of the single-bay wing design for fighters over the older and hitherto preferred two-bay type, and the need for powerful in-line engines for fighters.

TECHNICAL DATA FOR HAWFINCH

TYPE: Experimental single-seat interceptor fighter.

STRUCTURE: All-metal construction with fabric covering.

MANUFACTURERS: H G Hawker Engineering Co Ltd, Kingston.

POWERPLANT: 450 hp Bristol Jupiter VII nine-cylinder air-cooled radial engine driving Watts 2-blade wooden propeller. (Also fitted with 455 hp Jupiter VI and 400 hp Armstrong Siddeley Jaguar V.)

DIMENSIONS: Span (2-bay wings), 33 ft 6 in. Span (Single-bay wings), 31 ft 3 in. Length (wheel undercarriage, 23 ft 8 in. Length (float undercarriage), 25 ft 6 in. Height (wheel undercarriage), 9 ft 4 in. Wing area (2-bay wings), 294 sq ft.

WEIGHTS: (Jupiter VII, 2-bay wings, wheel undercarriage.) Empty, 1,925 lb. Loaded, 2,910 lb.

PERFORMANCE: (Jupiter VII, 2-bay wings, wheel undercarriage). Max speed, 171 mph at 9,850 ft. Climb, 7 min 40 sec to 10,000 ft. Service ceiling (rate of climb, 100 ft/min), 24,000 ft.

OTHER DATA: Fuel capacity, 55 gallons. Armament, two fixed forward-firing Vickers guns with 600 rounds per gun. Provision also made to carry four 20 lb bombs on light series racks under the wings. Wheel track, 5 ft 0 in.

The Hawfinch with Watts wooden propeller.

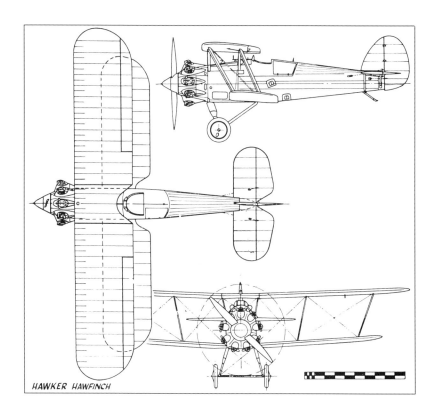

HAWKER HAWFINCH

145

The Hawker Harrier, J8325.

The Hawker Harrier

The Harrier was a large biplane designed during 1926 to Specification 23/25 and which was flown by Bulman early in 1927.

Specification 23/25 had set down standard day bomber load requirements for the RAF following the inadequacies recognised in a previous bomber Specification, 26/23. The Horsley had been conceived under the 1923 requirements, but, such was the design adaptability achieved, it also conformed satisfactorily to the revised 1925 load capacity. It was however recognised that for optimum performance with the latter, at the altitudes required for operation, another design with an engine differently rated would be required, and it was before the Horsley had completed its final evaluation that design work on the Harrier commenced. As with current production Horsleys, a metal structure was adopted and, with an eye on a possible torpedo-carrying requirement, the Harrier featured a split-axle undercarriage. The engine chosen was the geared Bristol Jupiter VIII, though, because of relatively high power absorption of the reduction gear, the aircraft was somewhat underpowered.

Registered initially under the Company number T.60, but later as J8325, the Harrier was retained at Brooklands from March to November 1927 for flight trials. Thereafter it was evaluated at Martlesham during the winter of 1927–28 and again in the following summer, but on each occasion the aircraft was criticised for the lack of power at take-off.

These initial trials were carried out with various bomb-loads ranging from eight 112-pound to four 250-pound bombs but, as had been anticipiated, a requirement was issued to adapt the design to meet the

146

The Harrier during assessment at Martlesham Heath.

torpedo-carrying Specification 24/25 and J8325 was returned to Martlesham in January 1929 with the tubular bomb gear removed and Admiralty Type VIII torpedo crutches substituted. Although by now the Jupiter's power output had been increased to 583 hp, the aircraft, with nearly 3,000 pounds of torpedo and associated equipment, was still underpowered at take-off and trials were conducted with the rear gun and mounting removed, and with only half fuel load at take-off.

In November 1929 J8325 was assigned to the Bristol Engine Company at Filton for use as an engine flight test bed, being fitted in turn with a 495 hp Bristol Orion radial and the 870 hp Bristol Hydra 'double-octagon' engine. It remained at Filton until struck off charge in February 1933.

The Harrier, after relegation to engine test bed duties, fitted with the Bristol Hydra at Filton.

147

TECHNICAL DATA FOR HARRIER*

TYPE: Experimental two-seat bomber/torpedo-bomber biplane.

STRUCTURE: Steel (T5) and duralumin construction with fabric covering.

MANUFACTURERS: H G Hawker Engineering Co Ltd, Kingston.

POWERPLANT: 583 hp Bristol Jupiter VIII geared radial engine driving 12 ft 3 in diameter 2-blade Watts wooden propeller.

DIMENSIONS: Span, 46 ft 3 in. Length 29 ft 7in. Height 13 ft 4 in. Wing area, 496.8 sq ft.

WEIGHTS: Empty, 3,278 lb. Loaded (bombs), 5,656 lb. Loaded (with 2,844 lb torpedo), 7,179 lb.

PERFORMANCE: With bombs. Max speed, 135.5 mph at 5,000 ft. Climb, 18 min 30 sec to 10,000 ft. Service ceiling (rate of climb, 100 ft/min), 13,800 ft. *With torpedo.* Max speed, 127 mph at 5,000 ft. Climb, 29 min 15 sec to 10,000 ft. Service ceiling (rate of climb, 100 ft/min), 10,500 ft.

OTHER DATA: Fuel capacity, 191 gallons. Fuel, Petrol Benzol (60/40 Sp G 0.77). Armament, provision for single Lewis gun on Scarff ring on observer's cockpit and one forward-firing Vickers gun on nose. Bomb-load, either four 250 lb GP or eight 112 lb bombs; alternatively, one Admiralty Type VIII 2,844 lb torpedo. Undercarriage, split-axle type, 9 ft 6 in track, with 1,000 × 180 mm wheels.

---

* Ref. A & AEE Reports M522/Inst 1 & 2/29.

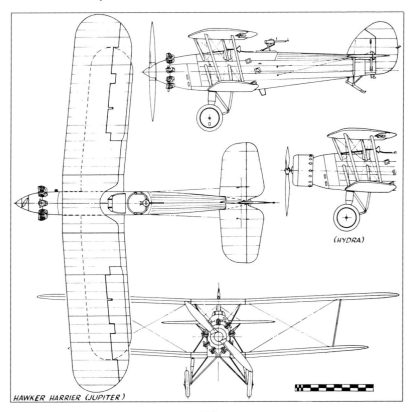

(HYDRA)

HAWKER HARRIER (JUPITER)

148

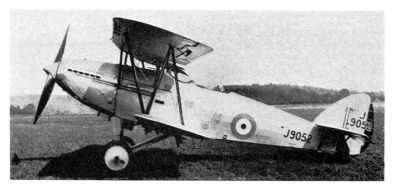

The Hawker Hart bomber prototype, J9052, in its original form.

The Hawker Hart

More aircraft of the Hawker Hart origin were built between the First and Second World Wars than of any other basic design in Great Britain, and among all the pilots of Britain's Regular Air Force in 1939 there can have been very few who had not trained or served at least one tour on one or other of the many Hart variants.

The Hart was the outcome of Specification 12/26, issued in May 1926, a Specification which by all current standards demanded performance qualities regarded by most as quite impossible to attain; there can be no doubt that in surpassing these requirements, as indeed the Hart did, as much credit is due to Rolls-Royce Ltd, for superlative engine design, as may be claimed for the evolution of the highly efficient airframe.

Specification 12/26 required a day bomber to enter service some five or six years hence, possessing a top speed in the region of 160 miles per hour, investigations being made into the possibility of using the 450 hp Rolls-Royce Falcon F.1 water-cooled supercharged in-line engine. The Hawker design staff commenced work on the project in collaboration with Rolls-Royce, and by December 1926 the tender was complete. The design offered employed the now-familiar Hawker steel tube primary structure, single-bay wings and split-axle undercarriage with pneumatic shock absorbers. The tender was accepted and a mock-up commenced early in 1927.

In this design Camm introduced a new form of wing spar consisting of top and bottom rolled steel strip booms connected by a light-gauge plate web. This spar gave maximum strength for minimum weight, since the materials were functioning near their permissible stress at full factored load. During 1927, however, the design of the aircraft was modified appreciably. First the heavy 'I' interplane struts were replaced by much

149

lighter and stronger 'N' struts, then a cross-axle undercarriage with Vickers oleo-pneumatic shock absorbers was incorporated, a pump-operated fuel system replaced gravity feed, and, most important of all, the Rolls-Royce F.XIB engine was adopted. This engine differed fundamentally from the original Falcon in having cylinder blocks cast in one instead of individual cylinder castings. This improvement reduced the installed engine weight by something like 60 pounds and undoubtedly permitted an accelerated development to higher power output.

The first flight by the Hart prototype, J9052, was undertaken by Bulman in June 1928, immediately confirming the high performance expected from it. Flight trials continued at Brooklands for about six

J9052 converted to Spec. O.22/26 naval requirement, with wings folded.

Naval Spec. O.22/26 Stage II modifications of the Hart prototype, J9052; shown here on floats at Felixstowe in 1931, the aircraft also incorporates the enlarged Osprey fin and rudder.

150

The first production Hart bomber, J9933.

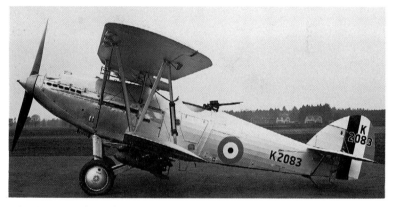

The first Hart (India), K2083, during Service trials at Martlesham in 1931.

months before its existence was announced, and the Olympia Aero Show of July 1929 was the scene of its first public appearance.

Detailed Service evaluation of the Hart commenced before the end of 1928, J9052 visiting Martlesham Heath for no fewer than eight separate trials between November that year and the following May, these trials being held in direct competition with the Avro Antelope and Fairey Fox Mark II. On their completion the Hart was deemed to be superior in performance, handling and maintenance aspects, with the result that Specification 9/29, already drafted early in 1929, was finalised and issued in June. A production contract for fifteen aircraft was also raised, though, in modern parlance, these machines would be termed pre-production development aircraft, such were the complications anticipated by the introduction to the Service of a bomber possessing so high a performance.

Successful, however, the Hart's introduction into the Royal Air Force

A Hart of No.6 Squadron at Ramleh, Palestine, in the late 1930s. Note the small bombs on the wing racks, and the perforated 'breather cowling' over the engine.

Hart K2424 was evaluated at Martlesham Heath with a Kestrel V engine.

proved to be, twelve of the first batch being delivered to No.33 (Bomber) Squadron at Eastchurch during January 1930. This squadron, commanded by Sqn Ldr J J Breen, and previously equipped with Hawker Horsleys, quickly became accustomed to its new machines and within three months had achieved second place in the annual Bomber Command inter-unit operating contest.

While No.33 Squadron were thus working-up with the Hart, further contracts were placed with the Hawker Company. It became immediately evident that the type might be suitable for service in India, replacing the aged Bristol Fighters on the North-West Frontier. Accordingly one of the remaining aircraft of the initial batch was shipped during 1930 to Risalpur for tropical trials with No.39 Squadron. After being severely

Hart G-ABMR with Osprey tail unit.

damaged in a collision with a kite hawk during 1931, the aircraft, J9947, was destroyed in a hangar fire on 31 March 1933.

Produced simultaneously or immediately following the first batch were four other Harts, G-ABMR, G-ABTN, K1102 and an unregistered P.V. aircraft powered by an Armstrong Siddeley Panther. Of these, G-ABMR is undoubtedly the most interesting, for after what must rank as one of the most remarkable careers of any aeroplane it survives in a magnificent condition to this day. Hardly a single version of the Kestrel engine was not installed in 'BMR between 1930 and 1946, while the years 1930–36 witnessed visits to no fewer than fifteen European countries, the aircraft being flown by Bulman, Sayer, Lucas and Hindmarsh. It was flown with wheel spats, Audax hook, Osprey tail, Hardy low pressure tyres, Hind tailwheel and many other features of the Hart

All three Hawker test pilots (Bulman, Sayer and Lucas) airborne in G-ABMR. Note the wheel spats, fitted for the 1932 Hendon Air Display.

153

G-ABMR during the Second World War.

G-ABMR in post-war racing colours.

G-ABMR, having been beautifully restored in 1959, displays the bogus colours of the first production aircraft.

The Bristol Jupiter Hart test bed, G-ABTN.

The Jupiter Hart, G-ABTN, underwent bombing trials at Martlesham Heath either late in 1931 or early 1932.

variants. For years it was used for carrying press photographers on their visits to Brooklands, and during the Second World War it served, in full camouflage paint, as a ferry pilot taxi. After the war it was raced in the Company colours and appeared at numerous displays and garden parties. In 1956 it suffered damage in a forced landing, but by dint of painstaking research sufficient spares were located for the machine to be restored to its pristine glory. Later in its flying life it carried the serials J9933 and then J9941, and in the latter guise it was transferred to the RAF Museum at Hendon in 1972 as a static exhibit.

G-ABTN fitted with a Bristol Pegasus radial engine. This picture was taken shortly before the aircraft was forced down into the English Channel.

The evaporative-cooled Kestrel Hart test bed, K1102. Note the steam condensers on upper and lower wing leading edges.

G-ABTN was less lucky. From 1931 until mid-1932 this aircraft was used as a test bed for Bristol Jupiter and Pegasus radial engines (both cowled and uncowled), but on the return flight from the Paris Aero Show in 1932 it suffered engine failure over the Channel and was lost, its pilot, Gerry Sayer, being rescued.

The manufacture of K1102 was covered by a contract raised by Rolls-Royce Ltd, under Air Ministry sponsorship, to test early evaporative cooling systems on a Kestrel engine. First flown in mid-1930 at Brooklands, this machine featured steam condensers along the full length of upper and lower wings with a large streamlined coolant feed pylon forward of the pilot's windscreen. After having been displayed in the New and Experimental Aircraft Park at the 11th RAF Display at Hendon in the summer of 1930 the aircraft was delivered to Rolls-Royce. During the winter of 1930–31 the coolant system displayed an uncomfortable tendency to shower the crew with supercooled water droplets and K1102 was returned to Brooklands to be fitted with a rudimentary cockpit enclosure.

The last of the quartet was the Panther Hart. Little is known about this machine and the fact that it was not registered either as a civil or military aeroplane suggests that it was short-lived. First flown by Sayer on 21 May 1931, it is known however to have visited Martlesham Heath shortly afterwards.

Meanwhile the Hart in service was at one and the same time, by reason of its superior performance, causing problems for the operational as well as the planning departments at the Air Ministry. Evaluation of a Hart on No. 32 (Fighter) Squadron in the army co-operation rôle during 1930 led the Air Ministry to request the Hawker design staff to investigate adaptation of the Hart to perform all manner of field duties. This, combined with the absolute immunity from interception achieved by No. 33 Squadron's Harts during 1930, gave cause for much concern in the Fighting Area. It undoubtedly accelerated introduction of the Hawker Fury fighter, the first RAF machine capable of more than 200 mph, and as an interim measure, led to the equipping of one experimental flight of Hart Fighters (afterwards named Demons) with No. 23 (Fighter) Squadron at Kenley in 1931.

By February 1931 a second squadron had received Harts. This was No. 12 (Bomber) Squadron at Kenley commanded by Sqn Ldr D F Stevenson, DSO, MC. In the annual Air Exercises of 1931 the two Hart bomber squadrons, No. 12 and 33, ranged invulnerable to interception

The private venture test bed Hart with Armstrong Siddeley Panther.

As part of the Hart Fighter development programme, J9933 was experimentally equipped with inter-cockpit flaps to protect the gunner from the slipstream blast.

A further attempt to protect the crew from the slipstream was this trial installation of a canopy over the front cockpit of J9933.

The Frazer-Nash 'lobster-back' hydraulically-operated gun turret fitted on Hart J9933. This was adopted on late-series Boulton Paul-built Hawker Demons. (see also picture on page 221.)

One of the first batch of Harts (India), K2089.

by all but the Hart fighters of No. 23 Squadron. Records of the day relate how on one occasion No. 33 Squadron crossed the South coast at Bognor Regis flying at 8,000 ft and managed to attack Northolt (dropping tennis balls marked 'bomb') before being attacked by the defending fighters.

The experience gained during trials with the Hart in India led to the production in 1931 of a number of machines especially prepared for duty in the tropics. Known as the Hart (India), the first such machine, K2083, was flown by Sayer at Brooklands on 7 September 1931. During that and the following two months thirty machines were shipped out to Risalpur, where they replaced the Westland Wapitis of Nos. 11 and 39 Squadrons, and within six months were in action in the tribal warfare of the North-West Frontier. No. 60 Squadron, also in India, later received Harts, and these machines continued to serve until 1939, when replaced by Bristol Blenheims.

Another tropical version was the Hart (Special), which was in fact an Audax airframe modified to incorporate desert equipment, a derated Kestrel X engine with tropical radiator, and a braked undercarriage with heavy-duty tyres.

June 1932 saw Harts in service with No.18 (Bomber) Squadron at Upper Heyford and in the 1932 Headquarters Race, a feature of the annual Hendon RAF Display, Harts took first and third places. By the end of the year six home-based Hart bomber squadrons had been equipped; these were No.12 (shortly to move from Andover to Bicester), No.15 (at Abingdon), No.18 (at Upper Heyford), No.21 (at Bircham Newton), No.33 (then at Bicester) and No.57 (at Netheravon). In addition to the three squadrons, Nos.11, 39 and 60 in India, Hart (Special) aircraft were scheduled to equip No.6 Squadron, then based in Egypt. By 1 January 1933, 126 Harts had been built, including a small number of unarmed machines issued to No.24 (Communications) Squadron. These aircraft, K2443, K2450, K2456 (later joined by K3001 and K3002) were used to convey Air Ministry

159

A Hart (Special), K4469, serving with the Royal Air Force in Trans-Jordan during 1940. Note the low-pressure tyres.

staff officers, exercise umpires and official despatches round home stations during 1932–34.

The performance of the Hart had, however, presented training problems, and in February 1932 Hawkers received Specification 8/32, written around the known performance of the Hart bomber but requiring provision of full dual control and deletion of all armament. Within six weeks the prototype, K1996 (the second production Audax, modified), was ready and, flown by Sayer, made its first flight on 20 April. Such were the loading characteristics of the Audax that the modifications to this prototype resulted in little perceptible alteration to the handling qualities, but a pair of interim Hart Trainers, K2474 and K2475, produced later in the year, demonstrated that the tailplane incidence range was insuffi-

The prototype Hart Trainer, K1996.

160

cient to cater for the movement of the centre of gravity caused by the removal of bomb gear and gun ring. The result was that the top wings of the subsequent production Hart Trainers, built from mid-1933 onwards, incorporated only 2½ degrees sweepback, compared with 5 degrees on the bombers.

In August 1933 Hart Trainers were issued simultaneously to the Royal Air Force College, Cranwell, where they replaced the dual-control Armstrong Whitworth Atlas, and to Nos.25 and 43 (Fighter) Squadrons at Hawkinge and Tangmere respectively, replacing Armstrong Whitworth Siskins as the squadron training aircraft.

One further squadron of the Royal Air Force received Hart bombers, No.142 Squadron taking delivery of its machines at Netheravon before moving to Andover. In 1934, with the decision to modernise the Auxili-

First full-standard production Hart Trainer, K3146.

ary Air Force, it was announced that Wapitis were to be replaced by Harts, of both bomber and trainer varieties, and by 1937 Harts had been issued to Nos. 600, 601, 602, 603, 605, 609, 610 and 611 Squadrons, Hind bombers also serving with several of these units.

Harts had become regular features of the RAF Display at Hendon since 1931, Wing Air Drill being performed usually by three of the squadrons equipped with Harts. A Wing of Hart Squadrons, Nos.12, 33 and 142, was sent to reinforce the Royal Air Force in the Middle East at the time of Italy's declaration of war on Abyssinia on 3 October 1935.

Production of the Hart had been accelerated towards the end of 1933 and such was the size of orders placed for both Hart bombers and trainers that widespread subcontract production was undertaken in the aircraft industry. Between 1933 and 1937 Vickers (Aviation) Ltd, Sir W G Armstrong Whitworth Aircraft Ltd and Gloster Aircraft Co Ltd

A late-series Hart Trainer, K4751.

between them built 665 Harts of all types. The vast majority of these aircraft went to the Flying Training Schools, namely No. 1 FTS (at Leuchars), No. 2 (Brize Norton), No. 3 (Grantham), No. 5 (Sealand, replacing Atlas and Bulldog trainers), No. 6 (Netheravon), No. 7 (Peterborough), No. 8 (Montrose), No. 9 (Thornaby) No. 10 (Ternhill) and No. 11 (Wittering). Nos. 1, 2, 3, 4, 5, 6, 7, 8, 9, 10, 13, 15, 16, 19, 20, 21, 25, 29 and 46 Elementary and Reserve Flying Training Schools of the RAF

The first Estonian Hart, 146, with wheel undercarriage.

Volunteer Reserve between them held 288 Harts on strength by the beginning of 1937, while other aircraft were issued to every operational station in the United Kingdom during 1936–37 for Station Flight Communications duties. Harts were also used by the Air Squadrons of Oxford, Cambridge and London Universities.

By 1936 Harts were being replaced on the operational squadrons, those with Nos. 12, 15, 18, 21, 57 and 142 Squadrons being exchanged for Hawker Hinds. The availability of aircraft so caused prompted the Air Ministry to release a large number for service with the South African Air Force, and the deliveries of these commenced towards the end of the year. They mostly featured Kestrel X engines equipped with tropical radiators (fitted at Sealand prior to packing) and subsequently were used as operational trainers in South Africa. Many accompanied the

An Estonian Hart with floats.

The first Hawker-built Swedish Hart, 1301, with Bristol Pegasus IM2 engine.

163

operational squadrons of the SAAF to British West Africa and the Western Desert in the opening months of the Second World War, at least one being used for communications in the Italian campaign as late as 1943.

Little has yet been mentioned of the Harts which were exported abroad during the early 1930s. In fact, compared with the other Hart Variants, relatively few were sold. In 1931 Yugoslavia had ordered four Harts and, although it is known that four such aircraft were based at Novisad towards the end of that year, there is no trace of a manufacturing contract, and it is suspected that these aircraft were temporarily detached for service in the Balkans by the Air Ministry. Eight Harts

A Swedish Hart with float undercarriage at Felixstowe.

At least one Swedish-built Hart was in full airworthy condition as late as 1950.
(*Photo: Gillberg, Linköping.*)

A Swedish-built Hart with licence-built Mercury engine and NACA cowling. Note alsot the 'snow-shoe' tail skid.

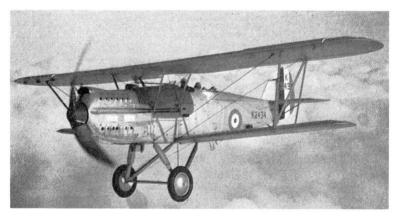

K2434, the Hart test bed powered by a Napier Dagger I 24-cylinder air-cooled engine.

were ordered by the Estonian Government early in 1932, and these were delivered during September and October of that year, equipped with interchangeable wheel and float undercarriages.

Following interest in the type by Sweden in 1932 four Harts, powered by Bristol Pegasus I M2 radial engines, were built, the first, 1301, being flown on 6 January 1934. By July that year all were completed and were delivered to Linköping in Sweden for assessment in company with four Hawker Ospreys. In 1935 licence production commenced and in all forty-two Harts (powered by licence-built engines) were completed. Some aircraft were fitted with ski undercarriages, while at least one machine featured a Pegasus with a long-chord NACA cowling in 1937.

K2434 with Napier Dagger II engine.

THE HART ENGINE TEST BEDS

It is unlikely that during the 1930s any British aircraft appeared with more different engine installations than the Hawker Hart, for, from 1930 onwards, these aircraft were employed both by the Hawker companies and the principal engine manufacturers as engine test beds, either to perform the specified flying hours required for certification or to develop the installations themselves.

As already mentioned, the first of the trial Harts were G-ABMR, G-ABTN and the private venture Panther Hart. All manner of Kestrels were flown in G-ABMR, including the Kestrel IS, IIS, IIB, IIIMS, V,

The Dagger Hart test bed with Hector engine installation — a picture taken at Luton in 1938.

166

VDR, VIS, XFP, XDR, XVIFP, XVIDR, XVI (Special), and it is with a modified Kestrel XVI (Special) that 'BMR exists today.

Hart K2434 appeared in 1933 fitted with the Napier Dagger I 24-cylinder H-type in-line engine, being first flown on 17 November. This powerplant gave continuous trouble, excessive vibration causing periodic fatigue failures of mountings and cowlings. In January 1935 the Dagger II was introduced with little improvement, but within nine months the Dagger III had been installed and proved successful. K2434 was assessed at Martlesham with all three engines, and as a result of the

An experimental exhaust manifold was fitted on the Dagger Hart at the RAE in 1937. (*Photo: Imperial War Museum.*)

The Hart test bed, K3036, with Rolls-Royce P.V.12 engine. This installation was similar in many respects to that of the Hurricane.

The Rolls-Royce Merlin 'F' installation in Hart K3036, used for certification.

One of several engines flown in Hart K3020 was the Bristol Pegasus in a long-chord cowling.

success of the last engine the Specification which brought forth the Hawker Hector was prepared.

The Rolls-Royce P.V.12, which was to become the famous Merlin engine, was flown in Hart K3036 on 21 February 1935. Employing a ventral radiator bath similar to that on the Hurriciane (the prototype of which was in its early stages of construction), this Hart was delivered to Rolls-Royce Ltd in the following April and was fitted in turn with Merlin 'C' and 'E' engines, completing over 100 hours' flying with each.

K3012, having been used for installation certification of the Kestrel X during 1933, was delivered to Bristols for installation of the Pegasus radial. After trials with narrow-chord and NACA broad-chord cowlings this machine was returned to Brooklands, fitted with cockpit enclosure

The Bristol Mercury VI S2 installed in K3020, complete with Hamilton Standard propeller.

Flight refuelling trials were conducted with a Vickers-built Hart, K3014, using a Westland Wallace, K4344, as tanker.

and despatched to Canada for cold weather trials, being equipped at one time with a ski undercarriage.

Another Hart, K3020, was also used by Bristols with Pegasus and Mercury engines, in the latter instance performing the certification programme for the Bristol Blenheim Mercury VIII installation during 1936. Later this aircraft served to test many components of the Perseus and Taurus installations for the Beaufort prototype, though it is believed that neither engine was flown on K3020.

Other engines test flown on Harts included the 720 hp Lorraine Petrel H frs and Hispano-Suiza 12 X brs in-line engines, the former in preparation for a proposed Yugoslav Fury installation and the latter for initial certification of the Spanish Osprey powerplant.

TECHNICAL DATA FOR HART

TYPE: Two-seat light day bomber.

STRUCTURE: All-metal construction with fabric covering.

MANUFACTURERS: H G Hawker Engineering Co Ltd, (1928–33), and Hawker Aircraft Ltd, Kingston (1933 onwards). Subcontracted by Sir W G Armstrong Whitworth Aircraft Ltd, Coventry, Vickers (Aviation) Ltd, Weybridge, Surrey, and Gloster Aircraft Co Ltd, Hucclecote, Glos.

POWERPLANT: (Service bombers), 525 hp Rolls-Royce Kestrel I B or 510 hp Kestrel X DR (Service trainers), 525 hp Rolls-Royce Kestrel I B or 510 hp Kestrel V DR or X DR. (Estonian aircraft), 525 hp Rolls-Royce Kestrel II S; (Swedish aircraft), 580 hp Bristol Pegasus I M2. Test aircraft powered by 530 hp Kestrel I S, 510 hp Kestrel II B, 525 hp Kestrel II S, 525 hp Kestrel III S, 510 hp Kestrel II MS, 640 hp Kestrel V, 695 hp Kestrel VI S, 550 hp Kestrel X FP and 695 hp Kestrel XVI; 450 hp Bristol Jupiter X FAM, 580 hp Bristol Pegasus I M2, 690 hp Bristol Pegasus III MS, 600 hp Bristol Mercury VI, 840 hp Mercury VIII, 890 hp Mercury XI; 890 hp Bristol Perseus; 780 hp Halford-Napier Dagger I, 805 hp Napier Dagger II and III; Hispano-Suiza 12 X brs; 720 hp Lorraine Petrel H frs; 980 hp Rolls-Royce P.V.12; 1,025 hp Rolls-Royce Merlin 'C' and 'E'.

DIMENSIONS: Span (Bombers), 37 ft 3 in. Span (Trainers), 37 ft 4 in. Length (RAF aircraft), 29 ft 4 in. Height (RAF aircraft), 10 ft 5 in. Wing area (Bombers), 348 sq ft. Wing area (Trainers), 349.5 sq ft.

WEIGHTS: (Bombers) Empty, 2,530 lb. Loaded, 4,554 lb. (Trainers) Empty, 3,020 lb. Loaded, 4,150 lb.

PERFORMANCE: (RAF Bombers) Max speed, 184 mph at 5,000 ft. Climb, 8 min 20 sec to 10,000 ft. Range, 470 miles. Endurance, approx 2 hrs 45 min. Service ceiling (rate of climb, 100 ft/min), 21,350 ft.
(RAF Trainers) Max speed, 168 mph at 3,000 ft. Climb, 6 min 30 sec to 10,000 ft. Range 430 miles. Endurance, approx 2 hrs 30 min. Service ceiling (rate of climb, 100 ft/min), 22,800 ft.

OTHER DATA: Fuel capacity, 83 gallons. Oil capacity, 7 gallons. Bomb-load, up to 520 lb. Armament, one forward-firing Vickers Mk II or III machine gun and one Lewis gun on rear cockpit mounting with seven 97-round magazines (armament removed on trainers). Undercarriage, 6 ft 4 in track, 800 × 150 mm Dunlop wheels. Late production aircraft fitted with Palmer hydraulic brakes and Dowty tailwheel.

170

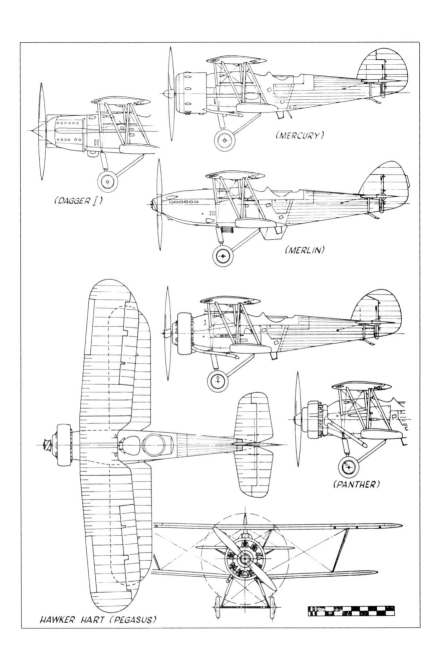

(MERCURY)

(DAGGER I)

(MERLIN)

(PANTHER)

HAWKER HART (PEGASUS)

171

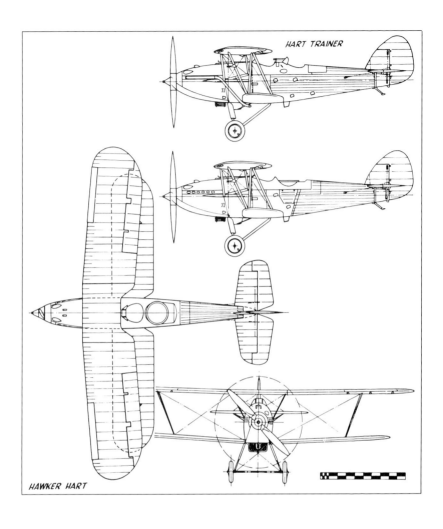

HART TRAINER

HAWKER HART

172

The prototype Hawker Tomtit, as displayed at Olympia in 1929.

The Hawker Tomtit

It might be thought in retrospect that the Hawker Tomtit has never been accorded the place it deserves in the story of British aviation. The fact that so few were built must be attributed principally to its cost, for the advance it represented in the design of elementary service trainers was achieved by the use of such sophisticated features as all-metal construction and the then-unique Reid and Sigrist blind-flying panel. Nevertheless it was, in many pilots' opinion, one of the most delightful light aircraft to fly, and by the time it came to be replaced in service too few had been built to capture the imagination of the sporting flier at large, and because Hawkers had in the meantime received large orders for the Hart variants it was impossible to build more machines for the flying public.

In 1927 the Air Ministry, mindful of the extreme antiquity of the basic Avro 504 design and reluctantly aware of the general neglect of *ab inito* trainer design, sponsored a competition for an elementary training aircraft to supersede the Avro 504N. The engine specified was the Armstrong Siddeley Mongoose five-cylinder radial engine and the aircraft was to be 'as nearly representative of the modern combat machine as to conform to the standards of Service maintenance, having regard to the proposed elimination of the Woodworking Fitters' trades'.

This implied insistence on a metal structure, coming as it did so soon after the initial success of the new Hawker system of metal construction, prompted Camm to enter the field of elementary training aircraft design,

173

and in November 1928 the prototype of Hawkers' contender, the Tomtit — at first unregistered — was flown by Bulman from Brooklands.

Like the Hart bomber, shortly to enter production in large quantities for the Royal Air Force, the Tomtit featured steel and duralumin tubular construction with tubular dumbbell section spars — perhaps rather elaborate for so lowly a task as *ab initio* training but nevertheless apparently likely to find favour in view of the terms of reference. Handley-Page slots were incorporated in the upper leading edges, though these were fixed in the closed position for early flights by the prototype. Moreover, inclusion of the newly-developed Reid and Sigrist blind-flying panel made possible realistic under-the-hood instrument flying training. This innovation was the outcome of financial support for the Reid Panel by Hawkers' joint managing director, Mr Fred Sigrist.

Although the prototype machine featured the specified Mongoose engine (a 150 hp Mongoose IIIC), it was quickly realised that the aircraft might well appeal to the sporting public and an alternative powerplant with commercial prestige was offered in the 115 hp ADC Cirrus Hermes four-cylinder upright in-line engine.

Recognition of the Tomtit's advanced concept came within three months of its first flight, when in March 1929 an order was placed for a production batch of ten aircraft, while the prototype was also brought on to Air Ministry charge and registered J9772. Before, however, being painted in RAF colours this first machine was displayed in its most attractive pale blue glossy finish at the Olympia Aero Show in July that year. Though undoubtedly somewhat overshadowed by the appearance of the new Hart and Hornet, the Tomtit nevertheless attracted much favourable comment, for it must be remembered that for some fourteen

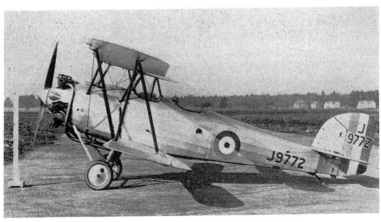

The prototype Tomtit during Service assessment at Martlesham Heath as J9772.

J9772 served with No. 24 (Communications) Squadron from July 1930 until May 1933.

years the elementary training rôle had become synonymous with the rather rudimentary Avro 504.

By the end of 1929 the first production batch had been completed, J9772 had completed its Service evaluation and had been received with unstinted compliment. A follow-up order for further machines had been issued on behalf of the RAF, while an order for two aircraft was placed by the Canadian Department of National Defence in January 1930, and these, together with fourteen Avro Avians, were delivered later that year.

The private venture Cirrus Hermes Tomtit prototype, intended for the flying public, was completed in 1930, being registered G-AASI, while another Mongoose Tomtit, G-AALL, was prepared for HRH The Prince of Wales. 'ASI, however, caught the attention of the Air Ministry

One of the two Canadian Tomtits, 140; note the split-axle undercarriage.

G-AALL, the Tomtit entered by the Prince of Wales in the 1930 King's Cup Race.

and after a preliminary work-out at Brooklands the aircraft was taken on temporary Service Charge for evaluation at Martlesham. Unfortunately, it was found to be somewhat underpowered and in consequence had lost the control precision of the Service version with Mongoose engine. Notwithstanding this 'ASI returned to Brooklands, where it was flown continuously for more than two years by the Hawker pilots and the Brooklands School of Flying, Ltd.

The Cirrus Hermes Tomtit, G-AASI.

176

Two civil Tomtits were entered for the 1930 King's Cup Race. The Prince of Wales entered G-AALL with a Mongoose IIIA and flown by Sqn Ldr D S Don, MVO, CO of No.24 (Communications) Squadron. Similarly powered, G-ABAX was owned, entered and flown by Capt The Hon F E Guest. In a field of no fewer than eighty-eight starters 'BAX achieved twelfth place at 125.5 mph and 'ALL came home eighteenth at 123.42 mph. These speeds and positions were quite creditable, for it should be remembered that the Tomtit was not designed nor prepared for racing, while navigators had to be carried that year. Moreover, handicappers during the 1930s had an unfortunate habit of over-estimating the Tomtit's performance!

The first Tomtit to enter RAF service was delivered to No.24 Squadron; this was the prototype, J9772, and was used on that Squadron by various Air Ministry research and medical departments for further development of the blind-flying equipment. The Tomtits of the first production batches formed the *ab initio* equipment of No.3 FTS at Grantham, pilots completing 60 hours' Tomtit experience before graduating to the School's Armstrong Whitworth Siskins. A batch of four aircraft was shipped out for use by the New Zealand Permanent Air Force.

Another pilot's name that was to become synonymous with the Tomtit was G Lowdell. At the many displays held at Brooklands George Lowdell, a flying instructor at the Brooklands School of Flying, was to be seen performing aerobatics in 'ASI in the lulls between the excitements of Hart and Fury displays by Bulman, Sayer and Lucas.

A new phase in the Tomtit's career started with the introduction of the new Wolseley radial engine in May 1931. That month the first prototype engine, known as the A.R.2, arrived from Castle Bromwich to

The Hon F E Guest's Mongoose Tomtit, G-ABAX, as flown during 1930–32.

177

Entered for the 1933 King's Cup Race, G-ABAX featured a direct-drive Wolseley A.R.9 engine and a faired-over front cockpit.

be installed in G-ABOD, registered and owned by H G Hawker Engineering Co Ltd. First flown by Lucas on 24 July 1931, G-ABOD's engine showed promise from the start and Sir William Morris' plans to put a cheap light engine on the market seemed set for a bright future. A second version, the A.R.7, was fitted in 'BOD and flown on 11 August by Sayer, but troubles with the exhaust system resulted in development of this version being discontinued. A third flight version, the A.R.9, proved completely satisfactory, however, being installed in 'BOD in 1932 and first flown by Sayer on 1 September.

No Tomtits were entered in the major races of 1931, but in the King's Cup Race of July 1932, based on Brooklands, two Tomtits came to the starter's flag. G-AALL was again flown by Guest, but was now fitted with the Mongoose IIIC. The other machine was G-ABII, owned by H Wilcox and flown by Sqn Ldr W Helmore. Both aircraft, however, retired. Guest's machine had fared no better in the *Morning Post*'s Heston–Norwich–Heston race on 21 May 1932. On this occasion Fg Off E C T Edwards had had to fly up from scratch position, but once again the handicap proved impossible.

1932 had also seen the replacement of Tomtits at Grantham by Avro Tutors, the Hawker machines being distributed round the Flying Training Schools and operational squadrons for use as communications aircraft.

By the end of 1932 the Wolseley engine had completed over 50 hours' flying in 'BOD, and with the decision to put the A.R.9 into limited production came Sir William Morris' entry of three A.R.9-powered Tomtits in the King's Cup Race from Hatfield on 9 July 1933. The three machines chosen were 'BOD, to be flown by Gerry Sayer, 'BAX (by now permanently based at Brooklands), to be flown by George Bulman, and 'ASI (now refitted with the A.R.9 in place of the Cirrus Hermes), to be flown by George Lowdell. Racing numbers carried by these aircraft were 8, 9 and 10 respectively, but all aircraft differed in minor respects, mainly concerned with the exhaust system. (Sayer's machine had open exhaust ports, Bulman's a collector manifold and Lowdell's short exhaust stubs.) Yet again the Tomtits fared poorly in the race, Sayer and Bulman retiring early; only old 'ASI remained to be eliminated in the final round.

The Mongoose Tomtit owned by H Wilcox in 1932.

Unfortunately, the formation of Hawker Aircraft Ltd in 1933, together with the urgency to concentrate on production of the growing number of Hart variants, brought an end to the Company's interest in the Tomtit and 'ASI, 'BAX and 'BOD were sold to Brooklands Aviation Ltd towards the end of the year. However, in February 1934 George Lowdell was appointed Chief Test Pilot of Wolseley Motors Ltd, at Castle Bromwich, and with him went the three Tomtits.

July 1934 saw the three Wolseley Tomtits on the starting line for yet another King's Cup Race, entered by Lord Nuffield (Sir William Morris of previous years). 'ASI was now fitted with an A.R.9 Mark IA and, carrying racing number 5, was flown by W H Sutcliffe; 'BAX, similarly powered and numbered 6, was flown by Wg Cdr J W Woodhouse, while Lowdell flew 'BOD as number 7 with an A.R.9 Mk IIA. 'BAX and 'BOD were eliminated in the first and second rounds respectively, but the veteran 'ASI remained in the running until the end, gaining seventh place in a field of forty-one competitors.

179

The Wolseley-powered Tomtit, G-ABOD, flown by Sayer in the 1933 King's Cup Race.

G-ABOD fitted with the certification Wolseley A.R.9 Mk. IIA engine.

The Wolseley Aquarius engine in G-ABOD

In the following month Lowdell flew 'BOD in the Newcastle Trophy Race from London to Newcastle, winning second prize.

By February 1935, five Tomtits held current civil registration: 'ASI, 'ALL, 'BAX and 'BOD being registered for experimental or racing purposes, and 'BII, the sole privately-owned aircraft. In May that year Lowdell demonstrated the Wolseley Aries in the Tomtit, but already private flying in the United Kingdom was being dominated by much later aircraft. The King's Cup Race was almost entirely monopolised by special racing machines, while the handicapping had done little to encourage would-be Tomtit entrants.

'ASI was disposed of by Wolsely Motors Ltd to J G Hopcraft in February 1936 and, flown by Fg Off C F Hughesdon, was entered in the Manx Air Races of June that year. At an average speed of 107 mph 'ASI came in a very good second in the race from London to the Island, but only managed tenth position in the Manx Air Derby.

In September 1936 'BOD and 'BAX were also put up for sale, the S U Carburettor Company taking both on temporary charge. In the 1937 Manx Air Derby a Tomtit gained twelfth place, but, by way of closing this chapter of its life on a happy note, a Tomtit, owned by Mr Brian Field, won the 1938 Manx Air Derby.

So ended the careers of the five original civil Tomtits. However, in 1935 the Tomtit was declared obsolete in the Royal Air Force and the remaining survivors were put up for disposal by the Air Ministry. Of the twelve offered for sale nine were eventually registered on the British Civil Register. These were G-AEES (ex-K1782), G-AEVO (ex-K1451), G-AEXC (ex-J9781), G-AFFL (ex-J9782), G-AFIB (ex-K1781), G-AFKB (ex-K1785), G-AFTA (ex-K1786), G-AFVV (ex-K1784) and G-AGEF (ex-K1783). Five of the machines were bought by Mr Brian Field in 1938 and it was one of these that won the 1938 Manx Air Derby.

One Tomtit remains airworthy today. G-AFTA, the last Tomtit ever built, having been used more or less throughout the War by Alex Henshaw, was put up for sale in 1945 at a price of £250 and was bought by Goodhew Aviation Ltd, of Kidlington, Oxford. Here it remained until 1949, when once more it returned to Hawker Aircraft Ltd, in the capable hands of Sqn Ldr Neville Duke. Painted in Hawker racing colours (royal blue with gold decking lines and letters), the Tomtit was present at many displays and garden parties in company with Hart G-ABMR and Hurricane G-AMAU. As in the days of Lowdell, many are the memories of Duke performing his delightful aerobatics in his aged Tomtit. From June 1950 Hawker Aircraft Ltd at Langley became responsible for its upkeep, but in 1960 it was handed over to the Shuttleworth Collection at Old Warden aerodrome, Bedfordshire. In 1967 its civil markings were replaced by a military scheme and its original serial, K1786.

No record of the Tomtit would be complete without mention of one or two schemes put forward in the early 1930s, but which never came to be built.

The last Tomtit ever built, now registered G-AFTA, here seen being flown by Hawkers' famous test pilot, Neville Duke.

From time to time the Air Ministry required schemes to suit third-line aircraft to front line duties, so that, in times of emergency, training and communications aircraft could be pressed into combat service. The Tomtit was such an aircraft and the proposal included the fitting of light series bomb racks for two 20-pound bombs under the wings, a forward-firing Vickers gun on the port side of the nose and the fitting of a Lewis gun on a light mounting on the rear cockpit. There is, however, no record of any performance calculations for this version!

Another project was the proposal to fit the diminutive four-cylinder Rolls-Royce engine which was planned in the early 1930s.

TECHNICAL DATA FOR TOMTIT (MONGOOSE, CIRRUS HERMES AND WOLSELEY)*

TYPE: Two-seat elementary trainer and light sporting aircraft.
STRUCTURE: All-metal construction with fabric-covering.
MANUFACTURERS: H G Hawker Engineering Co Ltd, Kingston.
POWERPLANT: (Service trainer). 150 hp Armstrong Siddeley Mongoose IIIC five-cylinder radial engine driving 6 ft 8 in diameter Watts 2-blade wooden propeller. Other aircraft fitted with 105–115 hp Cirrus Hermes, 150 hp Wolseley A.R.2, 160 hp Wolseley A.R.7, 185 hp Wolseley A.R.9 Mk I, 190 hp Wolseley A.R.9 Mk II, 170 hp Wolseley Aquarius and Wolseley Aries.
DIMENSIONS: Span, 28 ft 6⅝ in. Length (Mongoose engine), 23 ft 8in. Length (Cirrus engine), 24 ft 1 in. Height (Mongoose engine), 8 ft 4 in. Height (Cirrus engine), 8 ft 1 in. Wing area, 237.8 sq ft.

WEIGHTS: Empty, 1,100 lb (similar for all versions). Loaded (Mongoose engine), 1,750 lb. Loaded (Cirrus engine), 1,695 lb.
PERFORMANCE: Mongoose version. Maximum speed, 124 mph at sea level. Climb, 14.5 min to 10,000 ft. Service ceiling (rate of climb, 100 ft/min), 19,500 ft.
Cirrus version. Maximum speed, 104.5 mph at sea level. Climb, 12.8 min to 5,000 ft. Service ceiling (rate of climb, 100 ft/min), 9,950 ft.
Wolseley A.R.9 Mk II version. Maximum speed, 123 mph at sea level. Climb, 17.5 min to 10,000 ft. Service ceiling (rate of climb, 100 ft/min), 15,600 ft.
OTHER DATA: Fuel capacity, 21.5 gallons. Take-off ground run (Cirrus version), 140 yds with 5 mph headwind. Undercarriage, 5 ft 6in track; Palmer 600 × 100 mm wheels.

---

* Ref. A & AEE Reports M.516a/F.1, Int. 1/30 M.516c/28 and Hawker F.R.123/31 and F.R.124/31.

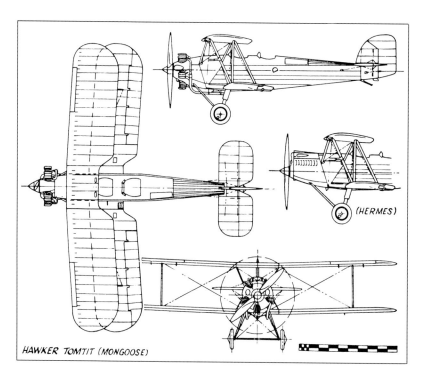

HAWKER TOMTIT (MONGOOSE)

(HERMES)

Two views of the F.20/27 Interceptor, J9123.

The Hawker F.20/27

Undoubtedly the least known of Hawker aircraft, the interceptor fighter designed to Specification F.20/27 nevertheless represented an important stage in the development of the Fury biplane. Moreover it afforded ample evidence of the relative inferiority of radial-engine fighters, for it was the F.20/27 that was used as the basis of the Hornet — the immediate forerunner of the Fury — and since the power/weight ratio, airframe size and contours were almost identical the 10 per cent improvement in performance was directly attributable to the efficient installation and cowling of the new Kestrel in-line engine.

Again employing the recently introduced Hawker system of metal construction which bestowed such strength and lightness, the F.20/27 design was tendered to the Air Ministry in November 1927. A prototype, J9123, was ordered and first flown at Brooklands by Bulman in August 1928. Powered initially by a Bristol Jupiter VII nine-cylinder radial engine, the aircraft followed the current pattern of biplane interceptors, featuring sharply staggered single-bay wings and synchronised twin-Vickers gun armament.

The aircraft was delivered to Martlesham Heath towards the end of 1928 and underwent a number of performance trials during which, using a Fairey Reed metal propeller (in place of the standard Watts), a maximum speed of 190 mph was recorded. In May 1930 J9123 was returned to Kingston for installation of the Bristol Mercury VI prototype engine and, though by now interest was centred upon the Fury, a short performance assessment at Martlesham confirmed a top speed of 202 mph at 10,000 ft. This was a most creditable performance for an aircraft fitted with an uncowled radial, and although designs were prepared for inclusion of a Townend Ring the aircraft met with a minor accident and the engine was returned to Filton for further flight testing in other machines.

TECHNICAL DATA FOR F.20/27

TYPE: Experimental single-seat interceptor fighter.
STRUCTURE: All-metal construction with fabric covering.
MANUFACTURERS: H G Hawker Engineering Co Ltd, Kingston.
POWERPLANT: 450 hp Bristol Jupiter 9-cylinder radial engine driving 2-blade Watts wooden propeller: also fitted with 520 hp Bristol Mercury VI engine.
DIMENSIONS: Span, 30 ft 0 in. Length (Jupiter engine), 22 ft 9 in. Length (Mercury engine), 23 ft 6½ in. Height, 9 ft 5 in. Wing area, 228 sq ft.
WEIGHTS: Empty 2,155 lb. Loaded, 3,150 lb.

J9123 during trials at Martlesham Heath.

185

PERFORMANCE: (Mercury engine) Max speed, 202 mph at 10,000 ft. Climb, 5 min 5 sec to 10,000 ft. Duration, approxiately 3 hrs 10 min. Service ceiling (rate of climb, 100 ft/min), 24,800 ft.

OTHER DATA: Fuel capacity, 55 gallons. Armament, two fixed forward-firing Vickers guns with 600 rounds per gun. Wheel track, 5 ft 9½ in, 750 × 125 mm Palmer wheels (later fitted with Palmer wheel brakes).

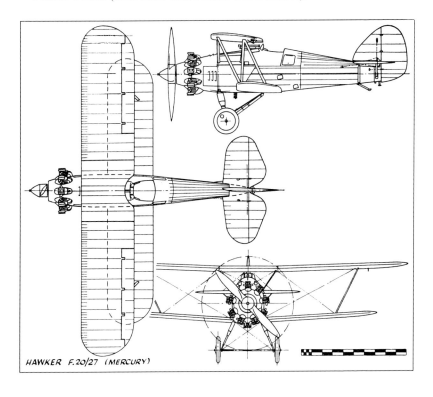

HAWKER F.20/27 (MERCURY)

The Hawker Hoopoe, N237, in its initial form with two-bay wings and Bristol Mercury engine.

The Hawker Hoopoe

There has always been a tendency to regard naval fighters as possessing a markedly inferior performance when compared with their land-based counterparts. This has usually been attributable to a propensity of drag and/or weight-producing accoutrements specified for deck or catapult operations, and prior to 1927 these design features had tended not only to limit the capabilities of the resulting aircraft but to dictate the basic structural design itself. (Examples of this are to be found in the Avro Bison and the Fairey Flycatcher.)

This entrenched belief, together with continued naval preference for radial engines, was further evidenced by the issue of Specification N.21/26, and any design likely to be entirely governed by this requirement was compromised from the outset, despite proposals by the H G Hawker Engineering Company to utilise the new in-line Rolls-Royce F.X engine.

Hawkers' tender, the Hoopoe, while not in fact a design conforming to N.21/26, was submitted and a prototype commenced construction early in 1927 as a private venture. No aircraft succeeded in meeting the requirements but when, in 1928, the Hoopoe was submitted for Service assessment at Martlesham the reports of the trials were such that the company was encouraged to pursue the development further.

At this time the Hoopoe, of which only one (N237) was built, featured two-bay wings and an uncowled Bristol Mercury II engine, but when, in 1929, a twin-float undercarriage was fitted for water handling trials at Felixstowe, the Hoopoe was found to be grossly underpowered and an uprated Mercury VI was fitted. Subsequently, N237 was returned to

187

Kingston, where the engine was again changed, this time to an Armstrong Siddeley Jaguar V with a Townend ring. More significant, however, was the adoption of single-bay wings, and in this guise N237 found more favour with the evaluation pilots at Martlesham. After return to Brooklands early in 1930 a second ring of smaller diameter was added and, though the engine was now more efficiently cooled, no increase in performance resulted.

N237 with Armstrong Siddeley Jaguar engine and single-bay wings.

The Hoopoe with uncowled Armstrong Siddeley Panther two-row radial engine.

The Hawker Hoopoe, N237, in its final form. This picture, taken in 1931, shows Panther engine with concentric Townend rings, spatted wheels and large tailskid.

The final stage in the Hoopoe's career came later in 1930 with the adoption of a 560 hp Armstrong Siddeley Panther III two-row radial, again equipped with concentric Townend rings. The airframe was also at this time generally improved, wheel spats being added and main oleo and tail skid travel being increased. The improved cooling efficiency of the engine installation led to the uprating of the Panther, with the result that a top speed of 196.5 mph was recorded at Martlesham — no mean performance for a heavily-equipped radial engine naval fighter.

The Panther-Hoopoe during its limited deck flying trials.

Nevertheless service interest was, by the autumn of 1930, no more than academic, since the Nimrod prototype (the Norn) had finally demonstrated the superiority of the Kestrel in-line engine and the Hoopoe was shelved. N237 did, however, continue development flying for many months both at Armstrong Siddeleys and at the RAE, before being scrapped in 1932.

The Hoopoe as it appeared at Martlesham for its final Service evaluation, probably in 1931.

TECHNICAL DATA FOR HOOPOE

TYPE: Experimental single-seat naval interceptor fighter.

STRUCTURE: All-metal construction with fabric covering.

MANUFACTURERS: H G Hawker Engineering Co Ltd, Kingston.

POWERPLANT: 450 hp Bristol Mercury II 9-cylinder radial engine.
520 hp Bristol Mercury VI (on seaplane).
400 hp Armstrong Siddeley Jaguar V 14-cylinder radial engine.
560 hp Armstrong Siddeley Panther III 14-cylinder radial engine.

DIMENSIONS: Span (2-bay wings), 34 ft 6 in. Span (single-bay wings, 33 ft 2 in. Length (Mercury engine), 25 ft 4 in. Length (Panther engine), 24 ft 6 in. Wing area (2-bay wings), 306 sq ft. Wing area (single-bay wings), 288.5 sq ft.

WEIGHTS: Mercury II, landplane. Empty, 2,490 lb. Loaded, 3,550 lb. Jaguar V, landplane. Empty, 2,505 lb. Loaded, 3,600lb. Panther II, landplane. Empty, 2,785 lb. Loaded, 3,910lb.

PERFORMANCE: Max speed (Panther III), 196.5 mph at 12,500 ft. Climb (Jaguar V), 8 min 10 sec to 10,000 ft. Climb (Panther III), 6 min 40 sec to 10,000 ft. Service ceiling (rate of climb, 100 ft/min, Panther III), 23,600 ft.

*OTHER DATA:*Fuel capacity, 55 gallons. Armament, two forward-firing Vickers guns with 530 rounds per gun. Provision for four Admiralty 3.5 in flares or 20 lb bombs on light-series racks under the wings. Undercarriage, cross-axle vee-type with Vickers oleo-pneumatic shock absorbers. Wheel track, 6 ft 0 in. 750 × 125 mm Palmer wheels, later fitted with fairings. Twin-float undercarriage (Hawker and A W A manufacture) also fitted, 1929. Float length, 21 ft 9 in.

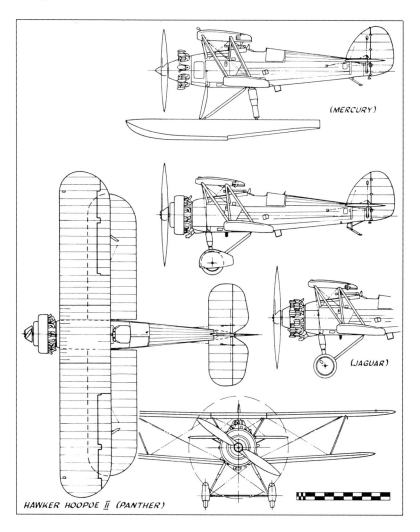

HAWKER HOOPOE II (PANTHER)

191

The Hawker Hornet as it was displayed at Olympia in 1929, before it was given the serial J9682.

The Hawker Hornet

One of the highlights of the 1929 Olympia Aero Show was an attractive single-seat interceptor biplane displayed on the H G Hawker Engineering Company's stand together with the Hart and Tomtit prototypes. This was the first public appearance of the new Hawker Hornet prototype, the forerunner of the famous Fury fighter.

The appearance in the previous year of the Hart bomber with its top speed of over 180 miles per hour had invalidated the provisions of the F.20/27 requirements with the result that they were extensively re-written around the now-confirmed performance potentialities of the Kestrel engine. The Hawker design staff had commenced further studies based on the F.20/27 prototype, and by March 1929 the new Hornet prototype was completed. Powered initially by a Rolls-Royce F.XIA, but almost immediately modified to take an F.XIS delivering 480 hp, this aircraft remained unregistered for several weeks during its period of flight trials at Brooklands, but after the Olympia show, as J9682, was delivered for extensive performance and handling trials at Martlesham Heath.

Reports of the Hornet's trials testify to the RAF's high opinion of the aircraft, for this prototype, still only powered by an early development engine, displayed a top speed of over 200 mph and this performance, combined with beautiful handling qualities and great structural strength, resulted in production orders being placed with Hawkers in 1930.

J9682 paid two further visits to Martlesham late in 1930 before setting out on a tour of the Balkan countries early in 1931; a particularly successful visit to Yugoslavia undoubtedly led to that country's subsequent choice of Fury fighters.

TECHNICAL DATA FOR HORNET (F.XIS)

TYPE: Single-seat experimental interceptor fighter.
STRUCTURE: Steel and duralumin construction with fabric covering.
MANUFACTURERS: H G Hawker Engineering Co Ltd, Kingston.
POWERPLANT: 480 hp Rolls-Royce F.XIS driving 2-blade 10 ft 6 in diameter
  Watts wooden propeller.

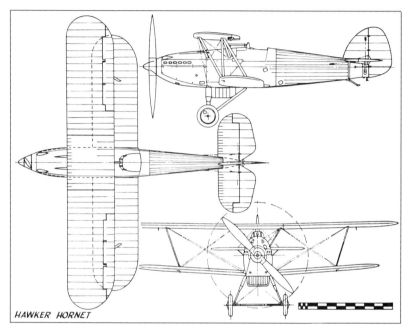

HAWKER HORNET

The Hawker Hornet.

193

DIMENSIONS: Span, 30 ft 0 in. Length, 26 ft 3 in. Height, 9 ft 4 in. Wing area, 250.7 sq ft.
WEIGHTS: Empty, 2,409 lb. Loaded, 3,232 lb.
PERFORMANCE: Max speed, 205 mph at 13,000 ft. Climb, 5 min 9 sec to 10,000 ft. Service ceiling (rate of climb, 100 ft/min), 25,500 ft.
OTHER DATA: Fuel capacity, 50 gallons. Armament, provision for two Vickers Mk III guns with 600 rounds per gun. Take-off ground run, 100 yds (5 kt headwind).

The first production Hawker Fury I, K1926.

The Hawker Fury

The Hawker Fury must surely rank among the most elegant aeroplanes of all time, for in its day it epitomised the compact single-seat interceptor fighter with the clean lines attendant on the finely cowled Rolls-Royce Kestrel in-line engine. It was, moreover, the first front line aircraft to be supplied to the Royal Air Force capable of more than 200 miles per hour in level flight.

Genesis of the Fury lay in the 1927 Specification, F.20/27, which had prematurely brought forth the unnamed Hawker single-seat interceptor fighter powered in turn by Jupiter and Mercury radial engines; for despite relatively efficient fairing of these bulky engines into the nose the performance was already lacking by the time the F.20/27 first flew in 1928, in view of the known performance of the Hart bomber. The result was that another prototype was commenced in 1929 as a private venture, surpassing the requirements of F.20/27, but in place of the radial engine specified in those requirements Camm chose to install the Rolls-Royce F.XIS engine, rated to give maximum power at about 15,000 ft.

This aircraft, the Hornet, as related elsewhere, caused something of a sensation at the Olympia Exhibition of 1929, standing as it did with the equally radical Hart bomber.

F.20/27 had failed in itself to produce the replacement fighter planned (it was, in fact, cancelled soon after issue and a transport requirement substituted in its place), but in the Hornet the Air Ministry was provided with a design which surpassed expectations, and in September 1929 the prototype was purchased, registered J9682, and in accordance with the current nomenclature practice the name Fury was chosen.

By March 1930 the principles underlying the Fury's concept had been amply confirmed by initial evaluation of J9682 at Martlesham Heath, and Specification 13/20 was written around the design.

Fundamentally, the Fury featured Hawker's customary steel and aluminium tubular structure built up on the Warren principle as a rectangular box section faired to an oval section with superimposed stringers. The unequal-span, single-bay wings were mounted with considerable stagger but, unlike the Hart, no sweepback. The wing structure of metal spars and spruce ribs was fabric-covered, only the top planes incorporating ailerons. The undercarriage was of the cross-axle vee type with oleo-rubber shock absorbers. The standard twin-Vickers gun armament was installed in the top decking of the nose.

The engine, now termed the Kestrel IIS, supercharged to develop 525 hp at 14,000 ft, was closely cowled with quickly detachable aluminium panels and drove a wooden Watts two-blade propeller. The radiator bath was mounted between the undercarriage legs.

Another view of the first Fury I.

One of the first Furies for Yugoslavia, photographed early in 1931.

An order for twenty-one Fury Is was placed with H G Hawker Engineering Company in August 1939, and J9682 embarked on an intensive series of trials and demonstration flights, both at home and abroad, while jigging and tooling commenced at Kingston.

Particularly beneficial was a short visit to Yugoslavia paid by Bulman in 1931 with J9682, and following a return call by a Yugoslav delegation to Kingston an order for six Furies was placed by that country before the first true Fury had been flown.

The first flight by Sayer in a production Fury, K1926, took place at Brooklands on 25 March 1931, and such were the production and

The Yugoslav Fury powered by a direct-drive Hispano-Suiza engine in 1931.

assembly techniques adopted in those times that the twenty-one RAF and six Yugoslav machines had all flown within three weeks (the first foreign aircraft, temporarily registered HF1, being flown by Bulman on 4 April).

In April 1931 it was announced that in the coming eighteen months Armstrong Whitworth Siskins were to be replaced in service by Bristol Bulldogs, Hawker Hart Fighters and Furies. The first squadron chosen to receive the Fury was No. 43 (Fighter) Squadron, based at Tangmere, commanded by Sqn Ldr L H Slatter (later Air Marshal Sir Leonard Slatter, KBE, CB, DSO, DFC), and sixteen aircraft were delivered to this unit in May 1931. No.43 Squadron had in recent years earned considerable fame for its aerobatic prowess at the many air displays throughout the country, and in less than three weeks the new machines were being demonstrated in similar fashion by the same pilots. Solo aerobatic displays were also given by that redoubtable test pilot, Gerry Sayer, and

The sole Norwegian Panther Fury during trials at Martlesham.

features of the annual Whit Monday Motor Race Meetings at Brooklands for several years to come were the scintillating performances by Sayer in successive versions of the Hawker Fury.

The new Furies of No. 43 Squadron were to show their true worth in the Annual Exercises, and in 1931 they were easily the fastest participating aircraft; moreover, their remarkable rate of climb resulted in many more interceptions than those by the more numerous Bulldogs.

Meanwhile, deliveries of the first Yugoslav machines had taken place though one aircraft, the third built (HF3), was temporarily retained at Brooklands, fitted with an Hispano-Suiza 12 NB engine (flown first in this form by Sayer on 27 August 1931). The performance in this case was disappointing and the aircraft was later returned to standard.

Further production contracts were placed for the Royal Air Force and

The first Persian Hornet Fury engaged on performance trials with the standard Watts wooden propeller.

A Persian Hornet Fury, (203) with three-blade Hamilton Standard Hydromatic propeller.

during the winter of 1931–32 another famous formation, No.25 (Fighter) Squadron (commanded by Sqn Ldr W E G Bryant, MBE), stationed at Hawkinge, Kent, was re-equipped; No.25's traditional rivals, No.1 (Fighter) Squadron at Tangmere, followed suit in May 1932. Thereafter until 1936, the three Fury squadrons gave displays of aerobatics and air drill at home and abroad that were for years to remain unsurpassed in skill and spectacle. Fury pilots were enthusiastic about the precision with which their aircraft could be flown, the abundance of power available for such a light aircraft being a prime requirement for the formation aerobatics they so spectacularly performed.

On the Continent the Fury was equally outstanding. In July 1932, at the Zürich International Aircraft Meeting, a Fury of the Royal Yugoslav Air Force, flown by Capt Sintic, was the overall winner, leading the field in the single-seater military aircraft class round the Alpine course at an average speed of 201 mph. The Yugoslav machines were interesting, in that they featured wheel spats, for such were not adopted on the RAF Furies until 1936.

Early in 1932 the Norwegian Government had ordered a Fury for evaluation. This aircraft, 401, powered by an Armstrong Siddeley Panther IIIA radial engine, was flown by Sayer on 9 September 1932, and after brief trials at Brooklands and Martlesham was flown by Bulman to Oslo. It had been proposed to build this version in Norway, but the installation was unsatisfactory, as competitive trials in that country proved. It appears that 401 displayed an embarrassing tendency to nose over while taxi-ing, the centre of gravity now being somewhat forward of that of the Kestrel version. At one time 401 was also flown with a ski undercarriage, but despite several visits to Brooklands and Martlesham to rectify the c.g. problems the Panther Fury did not go into production.

Another customer for the Fury was the Persian Government, who announced in January 1933 an order for a squadron of sixteen Furies to be powered by American Pratt & Whitney Hornet radial engines driving metal Hamilton three-blade propellers. The first aircraft was flown on 29 May 1933, and subsequent comparative trials between the standard Watts wooden propeller and the sophisticated Hamilton airscrew showed only a fractional benefit in climb and speed conferred by the

An early picture of the Intermediate Fury, G-ABSE.

199

latter; moreover the weight of the American propeller resulted in a similar nosing-over tendency to that on the Panther version. (A Hornet Fury was on one occasion overturned while taxi-ing at Martlesham.)

The RAF Display at Hendon in June 1933 featured Furies of No.25(F) Squadron performing formation aerobatics, the aircraft being linked together with elastic ropes with streamers attached, the entire performance from take-off to touch-down being accomplished without breaking the ropes. A grim sequel to this fine display came two months later on 7 August, when a Horsley of No. 504 (County of Nottingham) Squadron, in summer camp at Hawkinge, struck a disused shed while landing and fell on a hangar housing No. 25's machines. Both buildings

K3586, the High Speed Fury, seen here powered by an evaporative-cooled Goshawk. The parallel-chord upper wing carried the steam condensers and standard N-type interplane struts were used.

caught fire and, apart from the Horsley, whose crew narrowly escaped by falling from their aircraft to the ground, six Furies were destroyed.

It is necessary here to digress from the record of production Furies to mention two other associated designs which differed from standard to a marked extent.

Soon after the issue of Specification F.7/30 it became evident to Camm that a much developed version of the Fury might meet the requirements, but that two to three years might pass before the new aircraft could be flown. The company therefore decided to construct a Fury, at private expense, on which various trial installations could be

The High Speed Fury with Kestrel VI S, tapered wing and vee interplane struts.

effected, with the result that there would be few unknown factors in the F.7/30 aircraft when eventually flown. Known as the Intermediate Fury, registered G-ABSE, and equipped with ballasted gun and magazine

The High Speed Fury, K3586, fitted with Rolls-Royce P.V.12 engine. (*Photo: "Flight".*)

mountings, the new prototype was first flown by Sayer on 13 April 1932, with a standard Kestrel IIS. Enquiries by the Yugoslavs led to the trial installation of wheel spats and Messier oleo legs on G-ABSE, and by the end of 1932 a special Kestrel IVS had been substituted in order to test the supercharger for the Goshawk, in turn scheduled for inclusion in the F.7/30 design. Many engines were subsequently fitted, among them a Kestrel VI in October 1933, a Goshawk III in May 1935 and a Kestrel Special (uprated Kestrel VI) in August 1935.

The Intermediate Fury did much useful work in preparation for Hawker's F.7/30 design (the P.V.3), but equally important it was to bring about the other design related to the Fury, known as the High-Speed Fury (and sometimes, incorrectly, as the Super Fury). This was yet another private venture aircraft developed by H G Hawker Engineering

The first Portuguese Fury.

Co Ltd, this time to conform to Specification F.14/32, but immediately before its first flight on 3 May 1933 it was placed on Air Ministry Experimental Charge, serialled K3586. Throughout the period 1933–36 K3586 amassed a total of over 800 hours' test flying, being fitted in turn with a 525 hp Kestrel IIS, 600 hp Kestrel S (Special), 525 hp Kestrel IIIS, 600 hp Kestrel VIS (with this engine it underwent handling trials with No.43(F) Squadron in 1934), 695 hp Goshawk III and Goshawk B.41. When fitted with evaporative-cooled engines, K3586 featured a straight wing with built-in leading edge condensers, but for much of its life a swept-back, tapered wing, equipped with vee interplane struts, was fitted. In the latter form the aircraft was flown by Bulman at the SBAC Display in 1933.

But the Fury I was to give several more years service with the Royal

Air Force, for it was still the fastest aircraft in the Fighting Area (as the coastal air defence sector of Southern England was known). In November 1933 Portugal ordered three Furies with Kestrel IIS engines derated to give longer patrol edurance, and the first of these, 50, was flown on 28 May 1934. The following month all three were delivered to the Portuguese Army Air Service, and participated in the Lisbon Aero Shows of 1935 and 1936.

A Flight of five Furies from No.1 (F) Squadron was shipped to Canada under the command of Wg Cdr G C Pirie to participate in the Canadian Centennial Celebrations at Toronto in July 1934, and judging

A late-series Fury I serving with the Royal Air Force College, Cranwell.

A standard Hawker Fury II, K7275.

Two Fury IIs of No. 25 (Fighter) Squadron at the 1937 Hendon Air Display.

by the Press comments at the time the Fury detachment certainly performed in the best flying tradition of this famous squadron.

While Fury I's continued to form the spearhead of Britain's fighter defences in the Air Exercises of 1934 and 1935, the latter year must be regarded as one of the most interesting in the life of the Fury design.

Difficulties with the steam-cooled Goshawk engine had brought the question of an interim replacement for the Fury I into focus. The Hurricane project was under way, but an aircraft, similar in concept to that formulated in Specification F.14/32, was required to equip half a dozen squadrons during the period 1936–38.

Based on the Intermediate and High-Speed Furies, a design using the Kestrel VI was tendered early in 1934 to Specification F.14/32 and was accepted in principle by the following year. An early Fury I, K1935, had been acquired off Air Ministry Charge, returned to Kingston and fitted with a Kestrel VI. Equipped with wheel spats, this aircraft, when evaluated at Martlesham Heath, possessed a maximum speed of 228 mph, but the production Specification, 6/35, issued in March 1935, called for additional fuel tankage to offset the higher consumption of the later engine, with the result that a further fuselage tank was added forward of the cockpit, a modification which caused the top speed to be reduced on production aircraft to 223 mph.

Thus Specification 6/35 brought forth the Fury II, and though only twenty-three aircraft were built by Hawker Aircraft Ltd, a further order for seventy-five was subcontracted to General Aircraft Ltd at Hanworth. The first production aircraft (Kingston-built, K7263) flew on 3 December 1936, and early the following year Mark IIs replaced Fury Is of No. 25 (Fighter) Squadron at Hawkinge. Subsequently No.41 Squadron (Catterick), Nos. 43 and 87 Squadrons (Tangmere) and No.73 Squadron (Mildenhall) were issued with Fury IIs, but by 1939 all had been withdrawn from front line service, being replaced by Gladiators, Hurricanes and Spitfires. A small number of General Aircraft-built Fury IIs was shipped out to the South African Air Force in 1938 and while many others were scheduled to go they remained in store at the Packing Depot at Sealand until scrapped in 1940.

204

Foreign interest, in the meantime, had not slackened. Recurring troubles had beset the Persian Hornet Furies, due in the main to cooling difficulties. The Hornet engine had featured a supposedly ingenious arrangement of sliding shutters disposed radially to regulate the cooling air to the cylinders; in the tropics, however, these shutters were unnecessary and the shield was removed altogether, with the result that the maximum speed was so reduced that cooling troubles again occurred. A further small order for Furies, this time to be powered by Bristol Mercury VISP radial engines, was placed in 1934, while at least one machine was returned from Persia for conversion. This was 203, and was the first aircraft to be fitted with the Mercury VISP, being flown on 25 September 1934, and after another had performed trials at Martlesham in February 1935 deliveries commenced. By all accounts the half-dozen

The Persian Fury, 203, re-engined with a Bristol Mercury.

Persian Mercury Furies found considerable favour with their pilots, at least one being flown as late as 1943.

Following the success of the early Furies in Yugoslavia since 1932 the Government of that country set in train enquiries for a follow-up order towards the end of 1934, and as a result of negotiations it was decided to equip ten aircraft with 720 hp Lorraine Petrel H Frs twelve-cylinder in-line engines. However, having carried out trial installations of this engine first in a Hart, next in a Fury I and, in February 1935, in an old Yugoslav Fury, it was found that a more worthwhile performance improvement would be forthcoming by use of a late-series Kestrel. Moreover, since negotiations by Yugoslavia for purchase of Hinds had already commenced by September 1935, it was thought expedient to choose a powerplant common to both aircraft, and the 745 hp Rolls-Royce Kestrel XVI installation resulted. The order for ten such Furies

The four-gun Kestrel XVI-powered Fury for Yugoslavia.

was signed on 3 October 1935, and the first machine was flown on 14 September 1936, deliveries being completed by the following June. This version, with its low-drag radiator, cantilever undercarriage and internally sprung wheels, was the fastest of all production Furies, possessing a top speed of 242 mph, as well as having provision for the heaviest armament (two additional machine guns could be mounted under the wings to fire outside the propeller arc).

Closely resembling these Yugoslav Furies were the three Spanish Furies, 4–1, 4–2 and 4–3, also ordered in 1935. Powered by Hispano-

The Spanish Fury with Hispano-Suiza engine.

Another view of the Spanish Fury, 4–3.

Suiza 12 XBrs engines these machines (of which the first was flown on 7 April 1936) were delivered to the Spanish Government — in company with the sole Osprey ordered from Hawker Aircraft Ltd — in July, arriving in Spain on the 11th, exactly one week before the outbreak of the Civil War. The result was that two aircraft were initially operated by the Red forces while the third, 4–3, was flown by Nationalist pilots. It is known that at least one of the aircraft changed sides several times, 4–3 being used as a dive bomber before being finally destroyed in 1938.

TECHNICAL DATA FOR FURY (VARIOUS VERSIONS)

TYPE: Single-seat interceptor fighter.
STRUCTURE: All-metal structure with fabric covering.
MANUFACTURERS: Mark I, H G Hawker Engineering Co (and Hawker Aircraft) Ltd, Kingston. Mark II, Hawker Aircraft Ltd, Kingston; also subcontracted to General Aircraft Co Ltd, Hanworth. All foreign versions built by Hawkers.
POWERPLANT: Mark I, 525 hp Rolls-Royce Kestrel IIS driving 2-blade Watts wooden propeller. Mark II, 640 hp Rolls-Royce Kestrel VI driving 2-blade Watts wooden propeller. Norwegian Fury, 530 hp Armstrong Siddeley Panther IIIA. Persian Furies, either Pratt & Whitney Hornet S2B1G or 550 hp Bristol Mercury VI. Portuguese Fury, 525 hp Rolls-Royce Kestrel IIS. Spanish Fury, 700 hp Hispano-Suiza 12 XBrs. Yugoslav Fury, 525 hp Rolls-Royce Kestrel IIS, 500 hp Hispano-Suiza 12 NB, 720 hp Lorraine Petrel HFrs, or 740 hp Rolls-Royce Kestrel XVI.
DIMENSIONS: Span (all versions), 30 ft 0 in. Length (Mk I), 26 ft 8in. (Mk II), 26 ft 9 in. Height (Mk I & II), 10 ft 2 in. Wing area (all versions), 252 sq ft.
WEIGHTS: Empty (Mk I), 2,623 lb (Mk II), 2,734 lb. Loaded (Mk I), 3,490 lb. (Mk II), 3,609 lb. Yugoslav (Kestrel XVI), 3,882 lb. Persian (Mercury VI), 3,490 lb. Persian (Hornet), 3,590 lb. Portuguese, 3,548 lb. Norwegian, 3,575 lb.

PERFORMANCE: Mk I. Max speed, 207 mph at 14,000 ft. Climb, 4 min 25 sec to 10,000 ft. Range, 305 miles. Service ceiling (rate of climb, 100 ft/min), 28,000 ft. Mk II. Max speed, 223 mph at 16,500 ft. Climb, 3 min 50 sec to 10,000 ft. Range, 270 miles. Service ceiling (rate of climb, 100 ft/min), 29,500 ft.

Norwegian Fury. Max speed, 202 mph at 16,500 ft. Climb 5 min 40 sec to 10,000 ft. Range, 310 miles. Service ceiling (rate of climb, 100 ft/min), 27,800 ft.

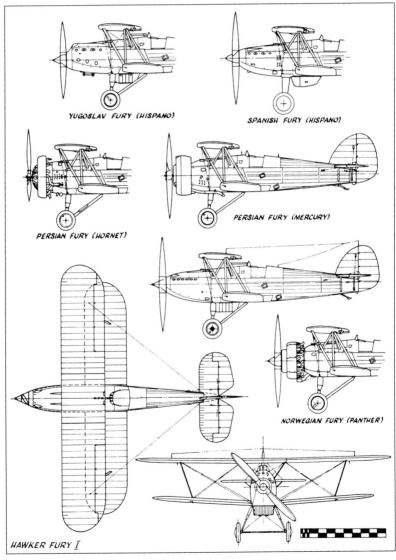

YUGOSLAV FURY (HISPANO)

SPANISH FURY (HISPANO)

PERSIAN FURY (HORNET)

PERSIAN FURY (MERCURY)

NORWEGIAN FURY (PANTHER)

HAWKER FURY I

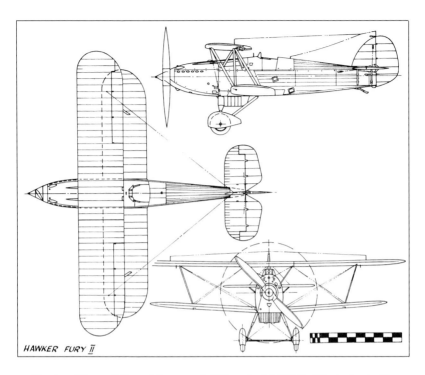

HAWKER FURY II

Persian (Hornet) Fury. Max speed, 178 mph at 6,500 ft. Climb, 4 min 45 sec to 10,000 ft. Range, 300 miles. Service ceiling (rate of climb, 100 ft/min), 26,000 ft.

Persian (Mercury) Fury. Max speed, 212 mph at 16,000 ft. Climb, 3 min 55 sec to 10,000 ft. Range, 310 miles. Service ceiling (rate of climb, 100 ft/min), 28,800 ft.

Portuguese Fury. Max speed, 169 mph at 10,000 ft. Climb, 5 min 42 sec to 10,000 ft. Range, 330 miles. Service ceiling (rate of climb, 100 ft/min), 29,500 ft.

Yugoslav (Kestrel XVI) Fury. Max speed, 242 mph at 15,500 ft. Climb, 3 min 45 sec to 10,000 ft. Range, 395 miles. Service ceiling (rate of climb, 100 ft/min), 29,700 ft.

OTHER DATA: Fuel capacity. Most versions carried approximately 50 gallons. The Yugoslav (Kestrel XVI) Fury incorporated an additional tank amidships and accommodated a total of 65 gallons. Armament. RAF Furies were equipped with two forward-firing Vickers Mk III (on Fury I) or Vickers Mk V (on Fury II) machine guns, with 600 rounds per gun. Foreign Furies were armed with 7.7 mm Mauser, Colt or Spandau machine guns. The Yugoslav (Kestrel XVI) Fury had provision for two additional Colt or Mauser guns under the lower wings. Most versions had provision for light bomb racks under the wings. Wheel track, 5 ft 9½ in; 750 × 125 mm Palmer wheels with Palmer hydraulic brakes. Cantilever undercarriage with internally sprung wheels fitted to Spanish and Yugoslav (Kestrel XVI) Furies.

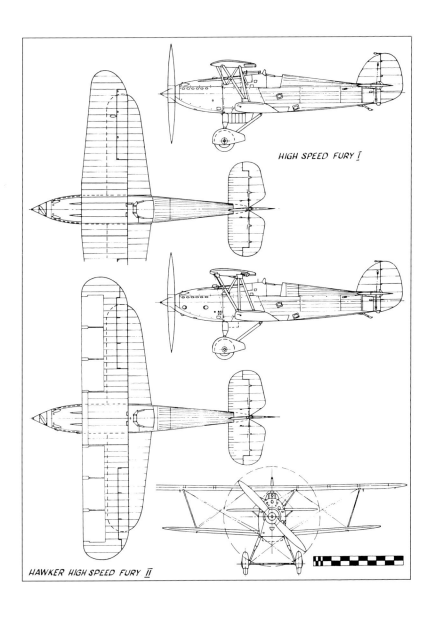

HIGH SPEED FURY I

HAWKER HIGH SPEED FURY II

210

The first aircraft built by Hawkers to Spec. 16/30. Known unofficially as the Norn at first, this machine was renamed the Nimrod later and serialled S1577.

The Hawker Nimrod

Though the Hawker Nimrod fleet fighter bore a distinct resemblance to the Fury fighter of the RAF, the lineal development of each had been entirely separate, being conceived under widely differing operational requirements. The fact that so close a resemblance finally existed was the result of Camm's insistence that, apart from the matter of specialist equipment, the naval requirement need not diverge so radically from that of the metropolitan air force.

Specification N.21/26 had in 1926 formulated requirements for a fleet fighter to replace the Fairey Flycatcher, a rugged little biplane already in its fourth year of service with the Royal Navy. The Hawker Hoopoe, though not specifically designed to this Specification, was eventually evaluated in the light of the 1926 requirements, and the success of these trials led the Hawker Company to persevere not only with the development of the Hoopoe as a private venture, but with a related design using the promising new Kestrel engine in place of the radial.

Thus in 1930 appeared Specification 16/30, drafted round the Hawker Kestrel-engined fleet fighter proposals, while a prototype was already in the process of construction. Known unofficially as the Norn, and bearing the company registration H.N.1, this machine was first flown early in 1930, while a second machine was used for ground tests. A contract was raised and the name Nimrod adopted, both aircraft being taken on Air Ministry Charge. The ground test machine was later used for flotation trials with HMS *Ark Royal* under the registration SCD14.

211

Structurally, the Nimrod was similar to the Fury, employing unswept single-bay wings with pronounced stagger, thereby affording a wide field of view for the pilot. The all-metal structure was fabric-covered, though the aluminium fuselage panels extended further aft on the fuselage of the Nimrod. Flotation boxes were carried in the top wing and rear fuselage, and the prototype was powered by a Rolls-Royce F.XIMS engine, later termed the Kestrel IIMS.

H.N.1 was one of the British aircraft shipped out in HMS *Eagle* to Buenos Aires in March 1931 for the British Empire Trade Exhibition, being flown at the El Palomar display by Fg Off C P Barker. On return to the United Kingdom final evaluation at Martlesham Heath was

Another view of the Norn.

The first prototype Nimrod, S1577, after full modification to Specification 16/30, seen at Martlesham for Service trials.

212

S1577 at Martlesham Heath during comparative airscrew trials, fitted with a
Fairey Reed metal propeller.

completed on the aircraft and a production order for thirty-five aircraft
placed with the Hawker Engineering Company.

The first production machine, S1577, was flown by Sayer on 14 October 1931, being followed by S1578 on 31 October. These two machines completed some ten hours flying at Brooklands before being shipped out to Japan by aircraft carrier, where demonstrations were given by Flt Lt P G Lucas, who had recently joined the company. By the time these aircraft returned in February 1932, the initial batch of production

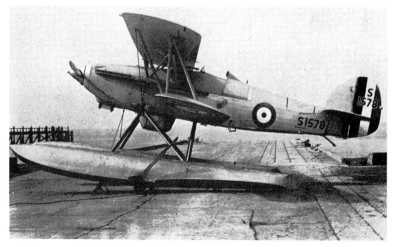

The second Nimrod, S1578, at Felixstowe for handling tests with floats.

213

machines was complete. S1577 was delivered for performance and handling trials at Martlesham Heath and S1578 was fitted with twin floats for water handling trials at Felixstowe (all Nimrods had provision for interchangeable wheel and float undercarriages).

Initial deck landings had been carried out with H.N.1, but in April 1932 further landings were accomplished by S1577 on HMS *Eagle*, with the result that Service clearance was achieved in June that year. Production aircraft were delivered first to No. 408 Flight, commanded by Lt Cdr E M C Abel-Smith, RN, aboard HMS *Glorious*, and soon afterwards to No. 402 Flight aboard HMS Eagle, and to No. 409 Flight, in each case replacing the aged Flycatchers.

With reorganisation of the Fleet Air Arm structure in 1933, and the merging of various shipboard squadrons, No. 800 Squadron (on HMS

K2823, the Nimrod (Intermediate) which became the Mark II prototype.

Courageous), No. 801 (HMS *Furious*) and No. 802 (HMS *Glorious*) took over the Nimrods, each squadron operating two flights of these and one of Ospreys.

Development had continued on S1578 and modifications included the addition of a headrest fairing (found necessary during catapulting and retrospectively incorporated in Nimrod Is). Arrester gear was also developed during 1932 and was included in the Nimrod from K2823 onwards. K2823 was retained by Hawker Engineering Co, and on 28 February 1933 reappeared with swept-back upper and lower wings.

Henceforward referred to as the Nimrod (Intermediate), K2823 paved the way for the Mark II. Specification 11/33, prepared around K2823 as evaluated at Martlesham and Felixstowe, formulated the

This Nimrod, originally a Mark I, was modified to Mark II standard.

requirements for the proposed Nimrod II, but also included was the requirement for a stainless steel primary structure.

Production of the Mark II commenced in September 1933, and the first aircraft, K2909, flew five months later, first deliveries being made in March 1934. Only three stainless steel Nimrods (K2909–K2911) were delivered, the remaining thirty-three Mark IIs being of conventional steel and aluminium construction. The uprated Kestrel IIS engines were replaced early in 1935 by Kestrel Vs, and late series Nimrods featured slightly enlarged tail surfaces (the latter being introduced to improve the inverted spinning characteristics when floats were fitted).

Nimrods remained in service with the Fleet Air Arm until May 1939,

Nimrod II of No. 800 Squadron at Aboukir, Egypt, in December 1935.

Nimrod II of No. 801 Squadron, Fleet Air Arm.

when the survivors still serving with No. 802 Squadron aboard HMS *Glorious* were replaced by Sea Gladiators.

A small number of Nimrods was sold abroad in 1933 and 1934. First of these were two, 170 and 171, delivered to Denmark. Though powered by Kestrel IIIS engines, the Danish Nimrods were essentially Mark Is and were intended as pattern aircraft for proposed licence-production in Denmark. However, although ten sets of proprietary equipment were ordered, it is believed that no further examples were built. 170, fitted with wheel fairings, was first flown at Brooklands on 25 November 1933, and was followed by 171, without fairings, on 8 December.

First of the Hawker-built Danish Nimrods, 170.

One Nimrod was shipped to Japan in 1934 as a result of interest shown during the earlier demonstration. No record of subseqent production in that country can, however, be found.

Finally a single Nimrod was flown out to Portugal and was retained for evaluation purposes, being demonstrated at Lisbon in 1935 and again in 1937.

The Japanese Nimrod.

TECHNICAL DATA FOR NIMROD (KESTREL IIS AND VFP)*

TYPE: Single-seat naval interceptor fighter.

STRUCTURE: Metal construction with fabric covering.

MANUFACTURERS: H G Hawker Engineering Co Ltd (later Hawker Aircraft Ltd), Kingston.

POWERPLANT: Initially 477 hp Rolls-Royce Kestrel IIS, later 608 hp Rolls-Royce Kestrel VFP driving 10 ft 9in dia Watts 2-blade wooden propeller.

DIMENSIONS: Span, 33 ft 6¾ in. Length, 26 ft 6½ in. Height, 9 ft 10 in. Wing area, 301 sq ft.

WEIGHTS: (Landplane) Early aircraft, pre-K2823: Empty, 2,901 lb. Loaded, 3,867 lb. K2823 and after: Empty, 3,115 lb. Loaded, 4,059 lb.
(Floatplane); Empty, 3,294 lb. Loaded, 4,250 lb.

PERFORMANCE: Kestrel IIS Landplanes. Max speed, 196 mph at 12,000 ft. Climb, 6 min 8 sec to 10,000 ft. Service ceiling (rate of climb, 100 ft/min), 26,900 ft.
Kestrel IIS Floatplanes. Max speed, 148.5 mph at 8,800 ft. Climb, 12 min 50 sec to 10,000 ft. Service ceiling (rate of climb, 100 ft/min), 19,800 ft.
Kestrel VFP Landplanes. Max speed, 193 mph at 14,000 ft. Climb, 5.0 min to 10,000 ft. Service ceiling (rate of climb, 100 ft/min), 28,800 ft.
Kestrel VFP Floatplanes. Max speed, 146 mph at 9,000 ft. Climb, 11.5 min to 10,000 ft. Service ceiling (rate of climb, 100 ft/min), 20,100 ft.

OTHER DATA: Fuel capacity, Kestrel IIS versions, 64 gallons (or 80 gallons with auxiliary tank); Kestrel VFP versions, 61 gallons. Armament, all versions, two forward-firing synchronised Vickers Mk III machine guns with 600 rounds per gun. Provision for four 20 lb bombs. Undercarriage, 6 ft 0 in track, 750 × 125 mm Palmer wheels with Palmer hydraulic brakes.

* Ref. A & AEE Reports M.594/32 and 33, M.594a/2/35–16/30. MAEE Report F.97/32.

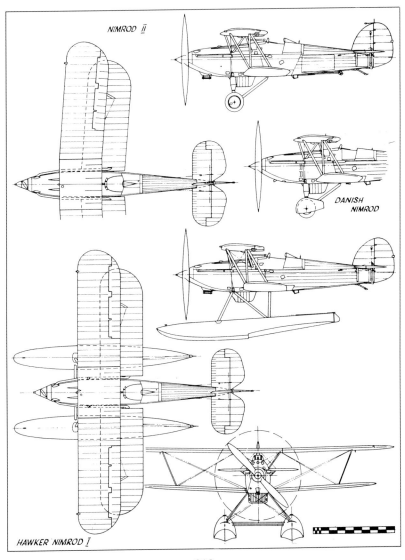

NIMROD II

DANISH NIMROD

HAWKER NIMROD I

The first prototype Demon, K2842, as it was delivered to Martlesham for its Service trials.

The Hawker Demon

When in 1930 the Hart bomber entered service with the Royal Air Force it proved to be faster by a significant margin than any of the current interceptor fighters, and this fact in itself posed a unique training problem during the 1930 Air Exercises. It was therefore logical that a fighter version of the Hart should be developed with the utmost dispatch and Specification 15/30 was drafted with this in mind. Moreover, it was prepared around the measured performance of the first production Hart, J9933, which had been fitted with a fully-supercharged Kestrel IIS and twin forward-firing Vickers machine guns. The rear cockpit coaming level was canted to provide a better field of fire for the observer/gunner and the prone bomb-aiming position was deleted. Similar modifications were also applied to another early Hart, J9937, and together these machines went to Martlesham Heath for evaluation. Performance of the Hart Fighter, as this version was called initially, was approximately the same as that of the bomber variant.

Representing something of an innovation (for this was the first two-seat fighter to be introduced into the RAF since the First World War), only a small initial batch of Hart Fighters was ordered from H G Hawker Engineering Co Ltd, and towards the end of March 1931 the first aircraft were issued to equip one flight of No. 23 (Fighter) Squadron at Kenley. The other machines on the Squadron were Bristol Bulldogs. In the air exercises of July 1931, the Hart bomber formations were successfully intercepted by their fighter counterparts.

The period 1931–32 was spent, not only by Hawkers and the A&AEE but by No. 23 Squadron, developing improvements in the Hart Fighter.

A Demon, K4500, of No. 604 Squadron.

The relatively high performance of the aircraft imposed considerable discomfort on the gunner from the icy slipstream, not to mention the difficulties in sighting the Lewis gun under such circumstances. Various schemes were tried on J9933, including a pair of inter-cockpit flaps to deflect the slipstream, and a rudimentary hood which enclosed the pilot's cockpit and afforded some degree of protection for the gunner. It soon became apparent that these schemes, while perhaps giving more comfort to the gunner, in fact severely restricted his field of fire. (See page 23).

Early in 1932, therefore, benefiting from the operational experience with the Hart Fighter, Specification 9/32 was prepared and a contract raised for the manufacture of seventeen aircraft, and in July that year the type was renamed Demon.

The first production Demon, K2842, was flown on 10 February 1933 (twice — by Lucas and by Bulman), and by April the batch was complete.

No. 74 Squadron re-formed at Malta with Demons during the Abyssinian crisis in 1935. K3757 is seen here with a hurriedly applied camouflage scheme.

A converted Turret Demon, K4496, of No. 604 Squadron.

That month the remaining Bulldogs on No.23 Squadron were replaced and the unit converted wholly to the Demon; in the 1933 Royal Air Force Display this Squadron gave a polished performance of formation air drill.

In the meantime further contracts had been issued for sixty-two Demons, again to be powered by 485 hp Kestrel IIS engines, and it was announced that several squadrons of the Auxiliary Air Force were to be re-equipped. However, early in 1934 a new Specification, 1/34, was prepared on behalf of the Royal Australian Air Force, providing for the installation of derated Kestrel Vs, and almost immediately a similar RAF requirement was issued.

In March 1934 the Australian Government placed an order for

A later series Demon, K5721, of No. 604 Squadron. Note the inclusion of a tail wheel.

221

eighteen Demons, later increasing it to fifty-four and finally to sixty-four, while contracts totalling 108 Demons were placed for the Royal Air Force. Such was the pressure of work now in hand at Kingston that the last fifty-nine aircraft were subcontracted to Boulton-Paul Aircraft Ltd., at Norwich (though production was soon to be transferred to that company's new premises at Wolverhampton).

In 1934 No. 41 (Fighter) Squadron at Catterick exchanged its Bulldogs for Demons and later in the same year No. 64 (Fighter) Squadron at Heliopolis received Kestrel V Demons. In September 1934 Nos. 600, 601 and 604 Squadrons of the Auxiliary Air Force based at Hendon started re-equipping with Demons in place of the Westland Wapitis.

March 1935 saw the delivery of the first eighteen Australian Demons, and these subsequently formed the equipment of No. 1 Squadron of the Royal Australian Air Force (also replacing Wapitis). These aircraft, together with the second batch of thirty-six, delivered during 1936, differed somewhat from the RAF versions in that they were used as army co-operation fighter-bombers and were powered by Kestrel Vs, re-rated to give 600 bhp, whereas the RAF Kestrel VDRs provided only 584 bhp. Later in 1936, the Australian Demon suffered a relatively large number of serious accidents, these being accounted for by the lack of a suitable operational trainer, with the result that ten further Demons were ordered with dual controls and provision for target towing, this version being known in Australia as the Demon II.

Since 1933 Hawker Aircraft had persevered in its efforts to provide protection for the gunner from the slipstream, and by the end of 1934 J9933 had been fitted with the prototype of a Frazer-Nash hydraulically-operated turret with a segmented folding shield. The weight of this turret resulted in the aircraft's centre of gravity being moved to its aft safe limit, but Service clearance was successfully achieved after spinning

The first Australian Demon, A1-1.

222

trials at Brooklands and Martlesham Heath, and from mid-1936 all Demons produced by Boulton-Paul featured the turret and many others were retrospectively modified.

By 1936 two fighter squadrons (Nos. 29 and 65) of the Regular Air Force at home were flying Demons, as were four (Nos. 600, 601, 604 and 607) of the Auxiliary Air Force. In 1935, during the Abyssinian crisis, No. 23 Squadron had been sent to join No. 74 Squadron (also equipped with Demons) at Malta and No. 41 had gone to Aden. Two other squadrons were to take delivery of Demons; No. 608 Squadron at Usworth in 1937 (in place of Wapitis) and No. 25 (Fighter) Squadron at Hawkinge. The latter unit gave up its Hawker Fury IIs in 1938 and continued to operate with mixed flights of Demons and Gloster Gladiators until these were replaced by Blenheim Fighters in 1939.

By September 1939 the Demon had been declared obsolete and had been replaced on all operational squadrons. A small number of aircraft continued to be used as target tugs (at Castle Camps in Cambridgeshire and at Langham in Norfolk) until replaced by the Hawker Henley. The last surviving RAF Demon is believed to have been flying from a Repair Depot at Wooton Turn, North Oxfordshire, early in 1944.

TECHNICAL DATA FOR DEMON (KESTREL IIS AND VDR)

TYPE: Two-seat interceptor fighter (for Royal Air Force) and army co-operation fighter-bomber (for Royal Australian Air Force).

STRUCTURE: All-metal construction with fabric covering.

MANUFACTURERS: Hawker Aircraft Ltd, Kingston. Also subcontracted to Boulton-Paul Aircraft Ltd, Norwich.

POWERPLANT: One 485 hp Rolls-Royce Kestrel IIS (RAF fighters); 584 hp Kestrel VDR (turret aircraft) or 600 hp Kestrel VDR (Australian) engines driving 10 ft 9 in diameter 2-blade Watts wooden propeller.

DIMENSIONS: Span, 37 ft 2 in. Length, 29 ft 7in. Height 10 ft 5 in. Wing area, 347 sq ft.

WEIGHTS: Early RAF Fighters. Empty, 3,067 lb. Loaded, 4,464 lb.
Turret aircraft. Empty, 3,336 lb. Loaded, 4,668 lb.
Australian aircraft. Empty, 3,360 lb. Loaded, (fighters) 4,716 lb, (bombers) 5,176 lb.

PERFORMANCE: Kestrel IIS. Max speed, 182 mph at 13,000 ft. Climb, 7 min 25 sec to 10,000 ft. Service ceiling (rate of climb, 100 ft/min), 24,500 ft.
Kestrel VDR. Max speed, 182 mph at 16,000 ft. Climb, 7 min 55 sec to 10,000 ft. Service ceiling (rate of climb, 100 ft/min), 27,800 ft.

OTHER DATA: Fuel capacity (all versions), 73 gallons. Armament (all versions), two forward-firing synchronised Vickers Mk III (RAF) or Mk V (Australian) machine guns on sides of nose with 600 rounds per gun; one Lewis gun on No 15 Ring (turret aircraft fitted with Frazer-Nash hydraulic turret with 'lobster-back' shield) with six 97-round magazines. Australian version had provision for up to six electro-magnetic Universal or Light Series bomb carriers under wings. Undercarriage, straight-axle type with Vickers Oleo shock absorbers. 6 ft 4¼ in track, 800 × 150 mm Dunlop wheels with Palmer hydraulic brakes.

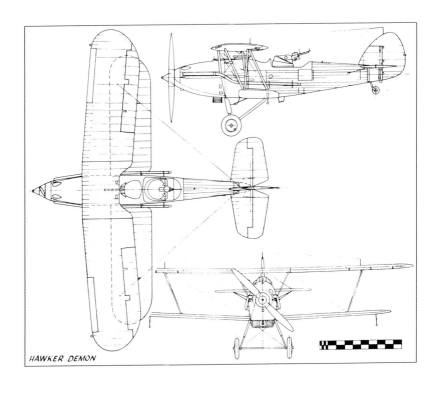

HAWKER DEMON

224

A Hawker Osprey I, S1682.

The Hawker Osprey

Though in no way related to Specification 12/26 to which the Hart bomber had been so successfully tendered, another Specification, O.22/26, was issued soon after in which similar design and performance characteristics were formulated, this time for a Fleet Spotter/ Reconnaissance aircraft. For two and a half years no satisfactory design was tendered to meet the naval requirement until, after the first Hart prototype, J9052, had completed the initial series of trials with the RAF, this aircraft was adapted to naval requirements and the design submitted to O.22/26.

Briefly, the 1926 naval specification was for a high performance fleet spotter and reconnaissance aircraft, also capable of limited interceptor duties. Though principally intended for operation from aircraft carriers, it was also to be sufficiently strong to withstand catapult discharge with either wheel or float undercarriage. Range and endurance requirements were such that the aircraft would be of a size demanding wing folding for lift accommodation and carrier storage considerations.

Modified initially as a private venture but later supported by Air Ministry contract, J9052 amply satisfied the requirements; folding wings were incorporated, as were attachment points for interplane jury struts at the fold line, while local strengthening of the structure to withstand

225

catapult accelerations was included in the wing attachment points and engine mountings. In 1930, J9052 was further modified to feature a twin-float undercarriage, and this was made interchangeable at four principal points with a wheel landing gear.

After initial evaluation in both landplane and seaplane form Air Ministry Specification 19/30 was prepared and a small production contract raised. While production got under way at home, J9052 was taken aboard HMS *Eagle* and in company with a number of other British aircraft was shipped out to Buenos Aires for participation in the British Empire Trade Exhibition early in 1931. having been flown to good effect at the El Palomar display the aircraft was, however, damaged while being hoisted back on board the carrier; thence it was returned to Brooklands for repair, where it continued flying until finally destroyed on 9 May 1931, in a take-off accident resulting from crossed aileron controls.

Production Ospreys began to appear at Brooklands in 1932, and in August of that year it was announced that they were to replace the Fairey Flycatchers aboard HM Carriers *Eagle* and *Courageous*, as well as equiping the 2nd Cruiser Squadron of the Home Fleet.

Early Ospreys supplied to the Fleet Air Arm were of conventional construction, employing aluminium and steel tube structures; towards the end of 1932, however, a change was made to a primary structure of stainless steel tube to counter the corrosive effects of salt water and sea air, and a fuselage of stainless steel construction was displayed at the Paris Aero Show of 1932. The following year six such aircraft were ordered from Hawkers for prolonged trials with the Fleet Air Arm.

1933 saw the widespread adoption of the Osprey by ships and units of

S1699, one of the Stainless Steel Osprey IIIs.

A pair of Osprey Is, S1697 and K2776, of the Fleet Air Arm.

the Royal Navy. Early in the year Nos. 404 and 409 Flights completed re-equipping, while three aircraft formed half the establishment of No. 405 Flight. In February 1933, Ospreys of No. 407 Flight embarked in HM Cruisers *York, Dorsetshire* and *Exeter* serving with the Home Fleet. Two aircraft were also supplied to 'C' Flight at Gosport as instrument trainers, remaining at this Station until 1937.

No. 803 Squadron (such was the new designation given to No. 405 Flight) embarked, under the command of Sqn Ldr H H Graham, in HMS *Eagle* and set sail for the Far East, where it remained for several years, later transferring to HMS *Hermes*. Ospreys of this squadron took part in the operations in January 1935, which led to the recapture of the vessel *Tungchow* threatened by mutiny on its way from Shanghai to Chefoo with many British children on board.

Ospreys issued during 1933 were of the Mark I and II type which had provision for Type I or Type II floats respectively. Although experimental floats designed and built by Armstrong Whitworth were evaluated at Felixstowe on an Osprey during 1932–33, the versions accepted as standard on all Service Ospreys were of Short design. Towards the end of 1933 the Osprey III was announced. This version was equipped with a dinghy (stowed in the starboard upper wing), an engine-driven generator and a Fairey Reed metal airscrew. All these aircraft were powered by Rolls-Royce Kestrel II MS engines.

Also in 1933, an order for four Bristol Pegasus-powered Ospreys was placed by the Swedish Government to equip the new aircraft-carrying cruiser *Gottland*, due to be launched in 1934, the decision to place this order (together with one for Harts) being taken apparently on account of the high accident rate currently being suffered by aircraft of Swedish design. Subsequently a licence to build a further number at Linköping and Gothenburg was acquired and at least one of these machines still survived at Trollhättan in 1950.

227

Over home waters Ospreys of HMS *Leander* and *York* were used to intercept Hawker Harts operating against units of the Home Fleet in the Coastal Exercises of September 1933, and shortly afterwards No. 800 Squadron, now flying Ospreys and Nimrods in place of its aged Flycatchers, embarked in HM Carrier *Courageous*. By the summer of 1934 No. 408 Flight had Ospreys aboard the cruisers *Ajax, Achilles, Galatea, Orion, Leander, Neptune* and *London* in the Home Fleet, while others equipped *Cornwall, Kent* and *Suffolk* in foreign waters. HMS *Emerald* carried an Osprey of No. 406 Flight to Trincomalee, Ceylon, and HMS *Shropshire* of the Mediterranean Fleet embarked the first Osprey of No. 447 Flight in January 1935.

The four Swedish Ospreys were duly delivered to the *Gottland* in April 1935, and in the same month two aircraft, identical to the Fleet Air Arm's Osprey III, were ordered by Portugal.

One final production version of the Osprey was built, the Mark IV. Twenty-six of this type were produced during 1935 and differed from the previous aircraft in having Rolls-Royce Kestrel Vs. These machines were mostly supplied to the 3rd Cruiser Squadron in the Middle East and Mediterranean, though a few were issued as replacements to Nos. 800 Squadron (HMS *Courageous*), 801 (on HMS *Furious*) and 802 (HMS *Glorious*).

By 1938 the Osprey was being withdrawn from units of the Home Fleet and issued to shore establishments, its place in many cases being taken by the Fairey Seafox. It continued to be used, however, as a target tug for naval air-to-air and AA gunnery practice and as an advanced naval trainer, until finally declared obsolete in 1940.

Several interesting trials were conducted on Ospreys at the Marine Aircraft Establishment, Felixstowe, the most notable being the central float installation on S1700. This aircraft, the second stainless steel Osprey III, was delivered to Felixstowe in 1935 with minor modifications to the primary structure to cater for a central Armstrong Whitworth

Float-equipped Osprey I, K2775, of No. 407 Flight embarked in the cruiser HMS *Leander*.

228

Osprey III of No. 802 Squadron, Fleet Air Arm.

float and a pair of outrigger floats mounted under the lower wing tips. A Short central float was also fitted for a period, though in this case the AW design was preferred. Prolonged handling and performance trials continued with these installations until 1937 and, after a minor accident which resulted in the aircraft being hurriedly beached without its landing cradle, S1700 was taken by road to the Royal Air Force College, Cranwell, where it remained as a ground instruction machine until January 1939, when it is believed to have been broken up.

Apart from the Swedish and Portuguese Ospreys previously mentioned, an Osprey was ordered by Spain. This aircraft, privately owned as a demonstration machine, performed a tour of the Iberian Peninsula in 1935, registered as G-AEBD. Apart from prompting the Portuguese order, this sales tour resulted in the aircraft itself being sold, though

Osprey (Special) K3954, in which the Kestrel V was first fitted (leading to the Osprey IV), during Service evaluation at Martlesham. Note the 'kidney' exhaust stubs.

229

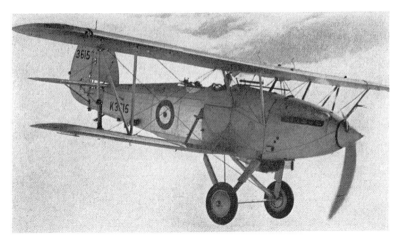

First Hawker Osprey III, K3615, completed to full Spec. 10/33 standard.

A Swedish-built Osprey, 2401, under evaluation at Brooklands.

installation of an Hispano-Suiza 12 X brs engine was specified. Arriving in Spain only a few days before the outbreak of the Spanish Civil War (in company with the Spanish Furies) the Osprey went into action in the hands of the Red forces. It is believed to have ended its days in Portugal as the result of a forced landing in 1937.

TECHNICAL DATA FOR OSPREY III

TYPE: Two-seat naval spotter and general reconnaissance aircraft.
STRUCTURE: Metal construction with fabric covering. Six aircraft delivered with stainless steel primary structure. Interchangeable wheel or twin-float undercarriage.
MANUFACTURERS: H G Hawker Engineering Co Ltd (later Hawker Aircraft Ltd), Kingston.

230

POWERPLANT: 630 hp Rolls-Royce Kestrel II MS driving 2-blade Fairey
  Reed fixed-pitch propeller.
DIMENSIONS: Span, 37 ft 0 in (15 ft 7¼ in folded). Length, 29 ft 4 in (31 ft 10¼
  in as seaplane). Height, 10 ft 5 in. (12 ft 5 in as seaplane). Wing area, 339 sq ft.
WEIGHTS: Empty, 3,405 lb. Loaded, 4,950 lb (as landplane); 5,570 lb (as twin-
  float seaplane).
PERFORMANCE: (Landplane): Maximum speed, 168 mph at 5,000 ft. Climb,
  7 min 40 sec to 10,000 ft. Service ceiling (rate of climb, 100 ft/min), 23,500 ft.
  (Seaplane): Maximum speed, 146 mph at 4,700 ft. Climb, 10 min 30 sec to 10,000
  ft. Service ceiling (rate of climb, 100 ft/min), 20,700 ft.
OTHER DATA: Fuel capacity, 90 gallons. Armament, one fixed forward-firing
  Vickers Mk III machine gun and one Lewis gun on rear cockpit mounting. Six
  97-round drums provided in rear cockpit. Light series racks for either eight 20
  lb or two 112 lb bombs under lower wings.

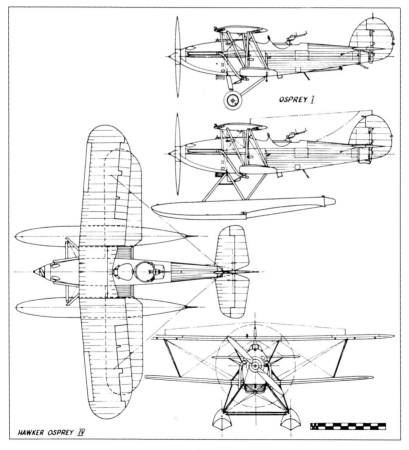

231

Two views of the Osprey S1700 modified with central float undercarriage.

The 'central-float' Osprey after being delivered to Cranwell as Ground Instruction machine M962. The RAF College's coat of arms is painted on the fin.

The Spanish Hispano Osprey. Though seen here registered G-AEBD, traces of the Spanish markings and registration, EA-KAJ, may be discerned.

The Hawker Audax prototype, K1438.

The Hawker Audax

Early in 1931 the Air Ministry issued a Specification, No. 7/31, setting out the requirements of a replacement for the Armstrong Whitworth Atlas army co-operation biplane which was in service with five home-based squadrons and two squadrons in the Middle East, and which had already served four years. Since it had been demonstrated that the Hart was well suited to close-support duties, the additional requirements now issued could be met by simple adaptation of that design.

Accordingly, an early production Hart, K1438, was set aside for evaluation in the army co-operation rôle during the summer of 1931. In the meantime an initial order for forty aircraft was placed and the first production Audax, K1995, was flown by P E G Sayer on 29 December 1931.

With an all-up weight of 4,290 pounds, the early Audaxes were powered by Kestrel IBs and were easily distinguishable from Harts in having lengthened exhaust manifolds to prevent glare from obscuring the pilot's view while flying near the ground. A message pick-up hook

The first production Audax, K1995.

An Audax I, K2012, with extended message pick-up hook.

234

First of the full-standard second production batch of Audaxes, K3055 was
delivered to Gloster Aircraft Co Ltd as a pattern aircraft.

was mounted on the undercarriage spreader bar. The standard Hart
armament of a single forward-firing Vickers gun and one Lewis gun on
the observer's cockpit was retained. Four 20 pound practice bombs or
two 112 pound supply containers could be carried on light racks under
the lower wings.

The first Atlas squadron to be re-equipped with Audaxes was No. 4
(AC) Squadron at Farnborough in 1932, and these machines were flown
at the RAF Display later that year.

More Audax orders were received by Hawker Aircraft and Nos. 2 and
13 Squadrons, at Manston and Netheravon respectively, received their
new machines. Some, fitted with Kestrel IISs, were sent to No. 208
Squadron in Egypt and some to No. 237 in the Sudan. An order placed
in 1933 covered a special version for service in India and the following
year Audaxes started to replace Westland Wapitis with Nos. 20 and 28

Audax trainer of No.9 FTS in 1939; the aircraft was camouflaged on the
upper surfaces and 'training' yellow below. Note that the message pick-up
hook has been discarded.

235

This Audax, K3100, was delivered to Canada and fitted with ski undercarriage. (*Photo: The Royal Aeronautical Society*).

Squadrons on the North-West Frontier. At home, No. 16 Squadron at Old Sarum and No. 26 Squadron at Catterick had also re-equipped.

The Audax was the subject of a number of foreign contracts. As early as March 1933, the Persian Government placed an order for thirty machines to be powered by Pratt & Whitney Hornet S2B radial engines driving three-blade Hamilton metal propellers (several of these aircraft were test flown to compare the relative merits of the American and the Watts two-blade wooden propellers). The first Hornet-Audax flew at

The Audax (India) K4838 was the first to be built by Glosters, and is seen here during Service trials at Martlesham.

236

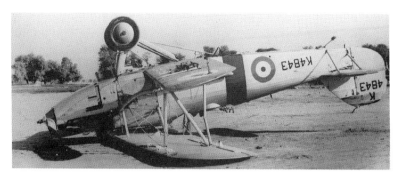

Landing mishap involving the Gloster-built Audax (India), K4843, of No. 28 Squadron while serving in India — possibly Kohat. The aircraft was repaired and ultimately transferred to the Indian Air Force.

Brooklands on 22 August 1933, at a loaded weight of 4,385 pounds, and the order was completed early in the following year. Following up this contract, Persia placed another in 1934, this time for twenty-six Audaxes powered by Bristol Pegasus II or IIM2 engines and these aircraft commenced delivery before the end of the year. The final Persian Audax was shipped from the United Kingdom on 7 April 1935.

The last and largest foreign Audax order was for thirty-four for Iraq. Powered by Pegasus IIM2s (early machines) and Pegasus VIPs the Iraqi Audaxes were delivered throughout 1936, being designated the Nisr by the Iraqi Air Force.

First of the Iraqi Audaxes, 28.

237

Also serving abroad was the Audax (Singapore). The aircraft had been chosen for the Straits Settlements Volunteer Air Force during 1934, and a special aircraft, K3720, fitted with a Kestrel V engine, was used for prototype trials prior to a small batch being shipped to Malaya when the SSVAF was formed in March 1936.

With the gradual expansion of the Royal Air Force during 1935–37 Audaxes continued in production (mainly at A V Roe & Co Ltd) and were issued to the many newly-formed Flying Training Schools throughout Britain. Although production came to an end in 1937, these aircraft continued to serve at home and in the Middle East until well into the war years, although several of the operational units (Nos. 2, 4, 13, 16 and 26 Squadrons) were re-equipped with Hawker Hectors. Many Audaxes were converted into glider tugs, serving at Kidlington, Croughton and Wellesbourne Mountford towing Hotspur gliders.

In the East African campaign against the Italians in Eritrea and Somaliland during 1940, No. 237 (Rhodesia) Squadron, flying Audaxes, operated border patrols in the face of opposition by the *Regia Aeronautica*. Others based at Habbaniyah fought during the Iraqi revolt in May 1941.

In common with all Hart variants considerable subcontracting was arranged for production of the Audax. Apart from Hawkers' production of 265 (including prototypes and foreign aircraft), contracts were arranged with Gloster Aircraft Company Ltd (25 built), Bristol Aeroplane Co Ltd (141 built), A V Roe & Co Ltd (244 built) and Westland Aircraft Ltd (43 built).

TECHNICAL DATA FOR AUDAX I (KESTREL IB)*

TYPE: Two-seat aircraft for Army Co-operation.

A Persian Hornet Audax, 413, in formation with a Persian Hornet Fury.

238

STRUCTURE: All-metal construction with fabric covering.
MANUFACTURERS: Hawker Aircraft Ltd, Gloster Aircraft Co Ltd, Bristol Aeroplane Co Ltd, A V Roe & Co Ltd, Westland Aircraft Ltd.
POWERPLANT: 530 hp Rolls-Royce Kestrel IB.
DIMENSIONS: Span, 37 ft 3 in. Length, 29 ft 7 in. Height 10 ft 5 in. Wing area, 348 sq ft.
WEIGHTS: Empty, 2,938 lb. Loaded, 4,386 lb.
PERFORMANCE: Maximum speed, 170 mph at 2,400 ft. Climb, 8.65 mins to 10,000 ft. Service ceiling (rate of climb, 100 ft/min), 21,500 ft. Endurance, 3 hrs 30 mins. Stalling speed, 55 mph.
ARMAMENT: One fixed forward-firing Vickers gun on port side of nose and one Lewis gun on rear cockpit mounting. Racks for four 20 lb practice bombs or two 112 lb supply containers under the wings.

---

* Ref. A & AEE Report M/599/32.

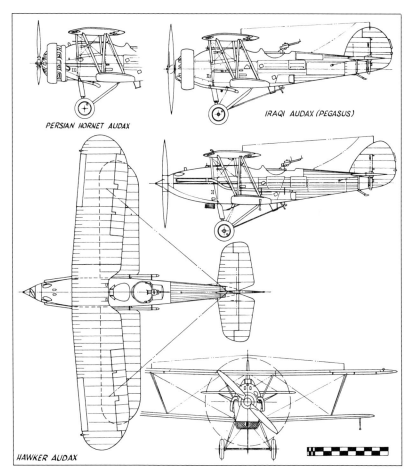

PERSIAN HORNET AUDAX

IRAQI AUDAX (PEGASUS)

HAWKER AUDAX

239

The Hawker-built Hardy prototype, K3013.

The Hawker Hardy

In 1933 Specification G.23/33 was issued to cover a replacement for the Westland Wapitis of No. 30 Squadron engaged in air policing duties in Iraq, and it was decided to adapt the Hart/Audax design to meet the requirement. A production Hart (K3013, built by Vickers and stationed at Kenley) was withdrawn and delivered to Brooklands, where it was progressively modified by the addition of approximately 200 pounds of equipment including tropical survival kit, water containers, message pick-up hook and tropical radiator. As the Hardy prototype, K3013 was first flown by P E G Sayer on 7 September 1934, at an all-up weight of 4,943 pounds. Thereafter this machine underwent trials at Martlesham Heath and was later joined by another Hardy, K5919.

Production of the Hardy amounted to forty-seven aircraft, all of which were built by Gloster Aircraft Co Ltd, at Hucclecote. In October 1934 the first of these aircraft were shipped out to Iraq, where they joined No. 30 Squadron at Mosul. Reserve machines were held at Hinaidi.

Towards the end of 1938, when No. 30 Squadron received Bristol Blenheims, its Hardys were transferred to No. 6 Squadron in Palestine. Most of the survivors had acquired large-section low-pressure tyres (developed at home on K5919) to facilitate operations from desert landing strips.

On the outbreak of war all remaining Hardys in the Middle East were turned over to No. 237 (Rhodesia) Squadron, joining forces with equally veteran Audaxes. Thenceforward their numbers dwindled, for the

The trials Hardy, K5919, undergoing trials at Martlesham Heath with low-pressure tyres.

Squadron was soon in action in Italian Somaliland and Eritrea during 1940. In November that year 'B' Flight lost all its aircraft on the ground during an Italian air attack at Kassala. The rest continued their multifarious duties, which included dive bombing, army co-operation and field reconnaissance. Finally, they were withdrawn from service after the Battle of Keren for breaking up.

K4050, the first Gloster-built Hardy, seen here at Brockworth.

TECHNICAL DATA FOR HARDY I (KESTREL XFP)*

TYPE: Two-seat general purpose aircraft for tropical service.

STRUCTURE: All-metal construction with fabric covering.

MANUFACTURERS: Production aircraft built by Gloster Aircraft Co Ltd.

POWERPLANT: 530 hp Rolls-Royce Kestrel IB (K3013, K4050–K4070): 581 hp Rolls-Royce Kestrel X (K4306–K4321, K5914–K5923).

DIMENSIONS: Span, 37 ft 3 in. Length, 29 ft 7in. Height, 10 ft 7in. Wing Area, 348 sq ft.

WEIGHTS: Empty, 3,195 lb. Loaded, 5,005 lb.

PERFORMANCE: Max speed, 161 mph at sea level. Climb, 10.2 mins to 10,000 ft. Service ceiling (rate of climb, 100 ft/min), 17,000 ft. Stalling speed, 55 mph. Endurance, 3 hrs.

ARMAMENT: One fixed forward-firing Vickers gun on port side of nose and one Lewis gun on rear cockpit mounting. Racks and attachments for water containers, flares or four 20 lb bombs.

---

* Ref. A & AEE Report M/669a/36.

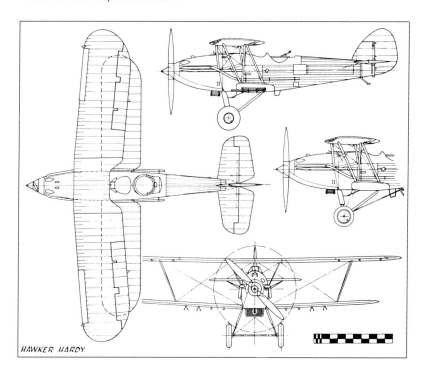

HAWKER HARDY

242

The four-gun Hawker P.V.3 fighter with Rolls-Royce Goshawk III.

The Hawker P.V.3

Specification F.7/30 narrowly missed being one of the most successful and far-sighted fighter requirements ever issued, but the result was an anti-climax, for it failed to produce for the Royal Air Force the high performance heavily-armed aircraft that it presaged. It is also likely that more private money was spent on this requirement than on any other issued between the world wars, such were the production potentialities of the successful tender. True, the four-gun Gladiator, itself a private venture conforming to the terms of the Specification, was ordered in quite large numbers, but it was to become obsolescent within a year of its introduction to service in 1937. The events which in fact totally invalidated the 1930 fighter philosophy were the appearances of the Hurricane and Spitfire proposals in 1933 and 1934. Increases of 40 per cent in speed and 100 per cent in armament made possible in these designs eclipsed even the most optimistic design contender for F.7/30.

Fundamentally, the Specification called for a single-seat fighter capable of mounting four Vickers machine guns and suitable for both day and night fighting. Implicit in the latter stipulation was a wide field of view and ease of landing. Moreover, use of the new Rolls-Royce Goshawk would be 'considered sympathetically'. While other manufacturers placed emphasis on distinct features of the Specification, resulting in a number of somewhat unorthodox configurations, the design favoured by the Hawker Company was strictly conventional, being in fact an enlarged development of the Fury. It having been announced that the official trials and Service evaluation were to commence in 1934, the Hawker F.7/30 aircraft, known as the P.V.3, was not flown until 15 June that year, by which time most of the new features had been flown under test on the Intermediate Fury, G-ABSE, or on the High-Speed Fury, K3586. For instance, an identical engine (a Goshawk III), airscrew and cooling system had been installed in K3586 and flown extensively for three months prior to the P.V.3's first flight.

Structurally, the P.V.3 was similar to the Fury with increased strength factors; four guns were mounted in the nose, two on the top of the cowling as on the Fury, and two on the sides similar to the Demon.

The Goshawk III-powered P.V.3.

Wheel spats, developed on G-ABSE and on the company's Hart, G-ABMR, were fitted; later 'ram's' horn' exhaust manifolds were fitted as a means of reducing glare during night flying. (The development of the latter proved extremely unpopular, due to their tendency to explode during flight.)

After an appearance at the Royal Air Force Display in the New and Experimental Park at Hendon in 1934, it was decided to postpone evaluation of the F.7/30 contenders until 1935 due to delays being experienced by other companies. The Goshawk III-powered P.V.3 continued flying at Brooklands until August 1934, whence it paid a short visit to Rolls-Royce Ltd, and in the following November it was decided, in view of the extra time available before evaluation, to replace the engine with the latest version of the Goshawk.

Two engines were received from Rolls-Royce during May 1935, a Goshawk B.41 and a B.43, the first being flown on 26 June and the other on 9 July. It was with the latter that the P.V.3 was eventually delivered

The Hawker P.V.3 with Goshawk B.41 liquid-cooled engine and fixed radiator.

to Martlesham Heath, and although it found favourable comment on many aspects of design, handling and performance, the outcome was of academic interest only, while the Goshawk, with its weighty and presumed vulnerable evaporative cooling system, had lost support as a fighter powerplant. The Gladiator had already been ordered and all preconceived ideas on fighter performance were undergoing much revision — how much revision was to become evident early in 1936, when the Hurricane prototype was delivered for initial trials at Martlesham Heath.

The Goshawk B.41-powered P.V.3.

TECHNICAL DATA FOR P.V.3

TYPE: Experimental single-seat day and night fighter.

*STRUCTURE:*All-metal construction with fabric covering.

MANUFACTURERS: Hawker Aircraft Ltd, Kingston.

POWERPLANT: 695 hp Rolls Royce Goshawk III steam-cooled engine driving 2-blade Watts propeller. Later fitted with 700 hp Goshawk B.41 and B.43 engines driving 3-blade Fairey or 2-blade Watts propellers.

DIMENSIONS: Span, 34 ft 0in. Length, 28 ft 2 in. Height, 10 ft 5 in. Wing area, 290.5 sq ft.

WEIGHTS: Empty, 3,530 lb. Loaded, 4,670 lb. Overload, 4,850 lb.

PERFORMANCE: Max speed, 224 mph at 14,000 ft. Climb, 4 min 20 sec to 10,000 ft; 12 min 5 sec to 20,000 ft. Service ceiling (rate of climb, 100 ft/min), 29,600 ft.

OTHER DATA: Fuel capacity, 70 gallons. Armament, 4 forward-firing machine guns, mounted one on each side of the nose and two over the engine; total of 1,800 rounds of ammunition. Note, the above weights and performance are for aircraft with Goshawk B.43 engine and Watts propeller.

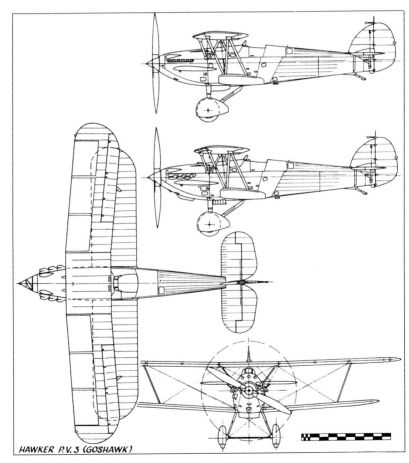

HAWKER P.V. 3 (GOSHAWK)

246

The Hawker P.V.4 as evaluated under Specification G.4/31.

The Hawker P.V.4

Specification G.4/31, issued in July 1931, was an attempt to formulate requirements for a standard general purpose aircraft capable of performing as many duties as possible out of a large number of specified rôles. These included Corps Liaison/army co-operation, light day and night bombing, dive bombing, torpedo-carrying and field reconnaissance. It was thus, in effect, to combine the principal requirements of the three Services in one aircraft. Most of these duties were being or about to be performed by the Hart and its variants separately, and it is therefore hardly surprising that the design favoured by H G Hawker Engineering was to be based on the Hart. The size of aircraft was, however, largely dictated by the necessity to carry a torpedo, though by the time the P.V.4 (as the Hawker design later became known) was tendered the provision to carry a torpedo had been deleted. It was felt, and quite correctly as it transpired, that an aircraft required to launch a torpedo would continue for some years to be of a specialist nature and, so that the design should not be compromised from the start, the P.V.4 featured the familiar spreader bar axle type landing gear.

The inclusion of dive bombing among the requirements was also interesting, for, although by no means new, the dive bomber was to be used with deadly effect within three months of the introduction of the Specification, in the Japanese assault on China of September 1931. At the time no suspicion of its fatal vulnerability in the face of fighter opposition was evident, rather that this was a thoroughly effective means of accurate bomb delivery.

These influences affected the P.V.4 proposal, and account for the fact that the Hawker machine differed fundamentally in concept from that of its competitors. It is undoubtedly true that the Hawker machine was not supported by an official contract because of its apparent shortcomings, despite the fact that its underlying philosophy was amply vindicated. Equally true is the fact that, ambitious though the Specification was, it cannot be said that it was successful, for none of the aircraft tendered and subsequently evaluated were ordered into production, though the Vickers G.4/31 biplane led eventually to the Wellesley (which did not enter service until 1937 and was entirely alien to the original concept).

Nevertheless, the Hawker P.V.4 did not represent the step forward that was evidently anticipated, for it appears in retrospect as little more than a larger and stronger Hart. Its ability to carry 570 pounds of bombs was no better than the Hart, yet it possessed increased strength factors to permit diving attacks with this load. The principal difference lay in the powerplant and when it was first flown at Brooklands on 6 December 1934, the engine fitted was an 800 hp Bristol Pegasus III.

It soon became evident that official confidence in the 1931 Specification was disappearing and already the dive-bombing requirement clause had been dropped, with the result that when competitive trials between the various aircraft commenced in 1935 the result —if one was declared — would be of academic interest only.

By May 1935 the P.V.4 had been re-fitted with an 820 hp Bristol Pegasus X engine, the small increase in power, however, hardly being reflected in an increase in performance. It was with this powerplant that the machine was delivered to Martlesham Heath in June that year for evaluation trials.

Serialled K6926, the P.V.4 was later fitted with a Bristol Perseus engine.

The Martlesham trials lasted until October 1935, after which the P.V.4 was delivered to the Bristol Aeroplane Company at Filton for further trials on the Pegasus engine, and during the course of these the engine was uprated to about 900 hp. At this stage the aircraft was placed on Air Ministry Charge and serialled K6926, though it was to remain an engine test bed for the rest of its life.

On 20 February 1936 it paid a brief visit to Brooklands to carry out spinning tests, but during the following month it returned to Bristol's, where it was later fitted with early Perseus and Taurus radial engines.

TECHNICAL DATA FOR P.V.4 (PEGASUS X)*

TYPE: Two-seat experimental general purpose bomber.
STRUCTURE: Metal construction with fabric covering.
MANUFACTURERS: Hawker Aircraft Ltd, Kingston.
POWERPLANT: 820 hp Bristol Pegasus X radial engine driving 12 ft 0½ in diameter Watts 2-blade wooden propeller.
DIMENSIONS: Span, 40 ft 0in. Length, 29 ft 10in. Height, 11 ft 10 in.
WEIGHTS: Empty, 3,728 lb. Loaded, 6,650 lb.
PERFORMANCE: Max speed, 183 mph at 6,600 ft. Climb, 6 min 45 sec to 10,000 ft. Service ceiling (rate of climb, 100 ft/min), 23,700 ft.

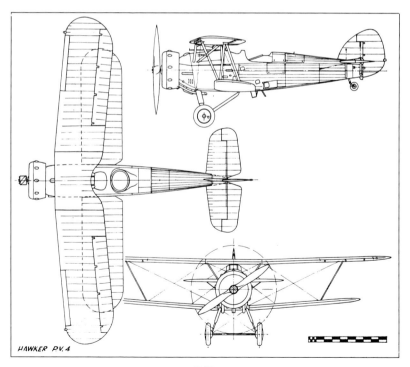

HAWKER P.V.4

OTHER DATA: Fuel capacity, 140 gallons. Armament, one fixed forward-firing Vickers Mark III gun on port side of nose with 600 rounds, and one Lewis gun on Somers mounting on rear cockpit. Bomb-load, up to 570 lb, made up of 112 lb, 230 lb, and 20 lb bombs and 3.45 in flares.

* Ref. A & AEE Report M.675/35–4/31.

One of the Hawker-built Hartbees, 804, before its despatch to South Africa.

The Hawker Hartbees*

The Hawker Hartbees was the outcome of negotiations between Mr Oswald Pirow, South African Defence Minister, and the British Government in 1934. The stated intention to expand the South African Air Force to include some 250 aircraft by 1937 was to be effected by purchase of a small number of foreign prototypes and negotiation for acquisition of licences.

The Hartbees was a development of the Audax, adapted for general close support duties in tropical climates. Four aircraft were built by Hawker Aircraft, Nos. 801 and 802 being standard 'light' machines, and Nos. 803 and 804 incorporating additional armour protection for the crew. A Rolls-Royce Kestrel V (Full-power) engine was installed in the standard fashion, but three years later in service in South Africa

* Some confusion exists as to the correct designation of this aircraft. The names Hartbees, Hartbee and Hartebeeste have all been applied authoritatively by manufacturers, Government departments, the South African Air Force, the Press, etc. The name Hartbees has been adopted throughout this book as being that which appears on manufacturer's drawings, contracts, production licence and Customs Receipt and Clearance Certificates.

considerable modification was carried out on the cowlings to incorporate breather louvres round the nose.

Nos. 801 and 803, being the first aircraft flown (on 28 June 1935), were shipped out to South Africa in October 1935, were assembled at the Maitland aerodrome, Cape Town, and flown to Pretoria. A production licence agreement had been secured by Mr Pirow through the British Government from Hawker Aircraft Ltd, and production of the Hartbees commenced at the Roberts Heights factory at Pretoria. The first South African machines were completed during the spring of 1937 and by July of that year had successfully passed their acceptance trials.

Sixty-five Hartbees were built at Pretoria and in 1938 entered service with two squadrons of the SAAF, based at Waterkloof aerodrome, also on the outskirts of Pretoria.

At the outbreak of the Second World War fifty-three Hartbees were on SAAF charge, and in company with a large number of ex-RAF Harts moved north for service in Kenya. By mid-1940 they were in action against the Italians in East Africa, their most notable action being a massed attack against Italian Moyale and Banda Hill on the Kenya–Ethiopia border on 11 June, 1940.

Shortly afterwards, however, the Hartbees was withdrawn from operational service and relegated to training duties in Southern Rhodesia and South Africa, the last machines surviving until 1946.

TECHNICAL DATA FOR HARTBEES

TYPE: Two-seat ground support aircraft.

STRUCTURE: All-metal construction with fabric covering.

MANUFACTURERS: Hawker Aircraft Ltd, Kingston (4 aircraft); South African Air Force Depot, Roberts Heights factory, Pretoria (65 aircraft).

POWERPLANT: 608 hp Rolls-Royce Kestrel VFP driving 10 ft 9 in dia Watts 2-blade wooden propeller.

DIMENSIONS: Span, 37 ft 3 in. Length, 29 ft 7 in. Height, 10 ft 5 in. Wing area, 348 sq ft.

WEIGHTS: Empty, 3,150 lb. Loaded, 4,787 lb.

PERFORMANCE: Max speed, 176 mph at 6,000 ft. Climb, 8.40 min to 10,000 ft. Service ceiling, 22,000 ft. Endurance, 3 hr 10 min. Stalling speed, 57 mph.

ARMAMENT: One fixed forward-firing Vickers gun on port side of nose and one Lewis gun on rear cockpit mounting. General purpose carriers under wings for light bombs, supply canisters, water containers or smoke laying equipment.

Another view of the Hartbees.

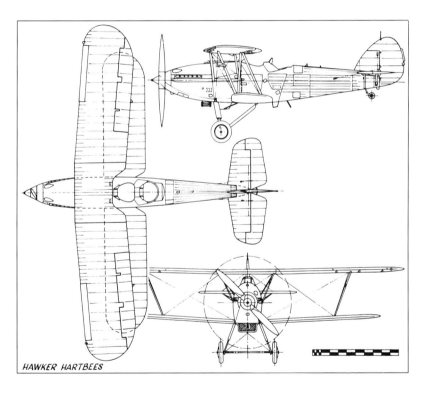

HAWKER HARTBEES

252

The first production Hawker Hind, K4636.

The Hawker Hind

With the expansion of the Royal Air Force already planned and starting to get under way the provision of increased Air Estimates in 1934 coincided with the issue of Specification G.7/34. This called for an interim replacement for the Hart bomber so that the extra squadrons could be brought into being as early as possible without waiting for the more radical Blenheims and Battles which were likely to take several years to introduce into service.

To meet G.7/34 Hawker Aircraft designed the Hind bomber; this differed in many respects from the Hart, principally in the provision of the considerably more powerful Rolls-Royce Kestrel V. Accommodation for the observer/gunner was also improved both in the prone bomb-aiming position and in the design of the rear cockpit, which was cut down in a way similar to that on the Demon so as to afford greater protection from the slipstream and to give a better field of fire for the Lewis gun. Other refinements included 'ram's-horn' exhaust manifolds and a tailwheel in place of the old skid.

The prototype Hind, K2915, was flown for the first time on 12 September 1934, the speed with which this was accomplished being due to the private venture work carried out on Specification 25/31. The result was that K2915 was built and flown to production standard of preparation in a very short time. During the year that followed, however, this machine underwent considerable development. By the end of September 1934 it was flying at almost the design overload weight. During October, trials with a Fairey Reed metal propeller were conducted and despite the increased weight over the standard Watts wooden airscrew a small

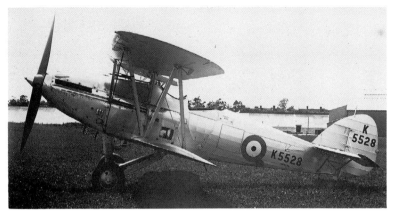

A standard second-batch Hind bomber awaiting delivery at Brooklands; it was later to be destroyed in an accident with No. 83 (Bomber) Squadron.

increase in performance resulted. The same month the 'ram's-horn' manifolds were introduced, while in November a Kestrel VI was installed, only to be changed back to a Kestrel V early in 1935 in time for the service evaluation programme at Martlesham Heath.

The first production Hind, K4636, was flown by P G Lucas on 4 September 1935, and within two months the production rate had reached six machines a week. While K4636 remained at Brooklands for performance trials the other machines of the first production batch were being delivered to Bircham Newton in Norfolk to equip one flight in each of Nos. 18, 21 and 34 Squadrons. In the meantime a further order

A late series Hind bomber.

254

A Hind Trainer, L7226, one of the many converted by General Aircraft Ltd.

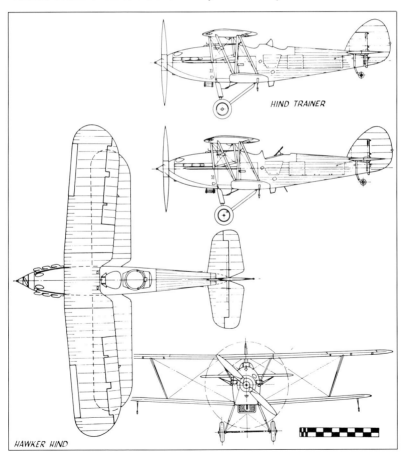

HIND TRAINER

HAWKER HIND

for 193 aircraft was placed with Hawkers and these three squadrons completed their re-equipment, and Nos. 12 and 142 Squadrons at Andover gave up their Harts in exchange for Hinds. Thereafter no fewer than twenty bomber squadrons of the Royal Air Force (many of them newly-formed) received the new machines. Another order for 244 aircraft followed, and by April 1937 338 Hinds were on the strength of RAF Bomber Command and a further 114 were in service with seven squadrons of the Auxiliary Air Force.

Several Hinds were at this time being used on trials programmes at Brooklands. K5555 had been returned from No. 18 Squadron for evaluation of a new Rolls-Royce oil vent system (later adopted for production aircraft). K6770 was being used both by Hawkers and the Aeroplane and Armament Experimental Establishment at Martlesham Heath for spinning tests and for steep dive bombing trials.

By the autumn of 1937 several squadrons in RAF Bomber Command had received Fairey Battles and Bristol Blenheims and a new requirement was realised, that for a trainer to equip the proposed Volunteer Reserve Flying Training Schools. In November 1937 General Aircraft Co Ltd, at Hanworth, received a contract to convert 124 Hind bombers to dual control trainers. Other aircraft were modified to training standard by Hawker Aircraft Ltd, as well as by units of the Royal Air Force.

Countless bomber pilots who were later to fly the famous heavy bombers over the Continent underwent their flying training on the Hind during 1938 and 1939. The trainer differed externally from the bomber in having the gun ring on the observer's cockpit removed and the rear cockpit reshaped to accommodate the instructor with duplicated controls and instruments. The prone bomb-aiming position was deleted on some aircraft, as was the forward-firing Vickers gun. Furthermore, those aircraft whose engines required replacing were usually fitted with de-rated Kestrel Vs (the first such installation being completed by Rolls-Royce Ltd on the Hind engine test bed, K5412).

Blind-flying hoods were introduced on Hind trainers during 1938 and a small number of aircraft returned to Brooklands for installation of special night flying equipment. These machines were later used in various parts of the country to observe the effects of trial 'black-outs' in large towns.

By the outbreak of the Second World War Hinds had disappeared from operational use both with the Regular and Auxiliary Air Forces and were used mainly for training, although their number was fast diminishing. A few were still in use as squadron communications aircraft and at least one was used to carry despatches to France during September 1939. Some were also used for glider towing as late as 1942, serving as tugs for the Hotspur training glider. One Hind was still flying at Stoke Orchard, Gloucestershire, in 1943.

Before turning to the variants of the Hind which were built under foreign contracts, mention should also be made of a small number of aircraft which were prepared for Dominion governments. During 1937 a few early Hind bombers were delivered to the Royal New Zealand Air Force for evaluation, and a development order was received by Hawker Aircraft Ltd, from the Australian Government. Preliminary design work and limited trial installations were carried out, but the project was abandoned and the Hind did not enter squadron service with the Royal Australian Air Force.

FOREIGN HINDS

At about the time that the first production Hinds were beginning to appear in the autumn of 1935 the Swiss Government ordered a single Hind for performance evaluation, and with the exception that no military load was carried the machine, appropriately registered HB-HAL, was similar to the production Hinds of the Royal Air Force. No quantity order followed and HB-HAL was used subsequently for general communications duties.

In 1936 the Portuguese Government signed an order with Hawkers for four Hinds to be powered by Kestrel Vs. The first aircraft was flown on 5 June 1937, this and the second machine both being delivered as standard light bombers. The other machines were equipped as dual control trainers. At least one Portuguese Hind was airworthy in 1944.

At about the same time as the Portuguese contract was received the Yugoslav Government also ordered Hinds. This was a direct result of close liaison between Hawker pilots and the Yugoslav Air Force during the past seven years, and though the order was small (only three aircraft) the machines were undoubtedly among the most interesting of the Hind variants. Yugoslav Hind No. 1 was first flown by John Hindmarsh from Brooklands two days before the first Portuguese aircraft on 3 June 1937, and differed from the standard version in having a 690 hp Rolls-Royce Kestrel XVI (this was the engine for which Yugoslavia had negotiated a licence to manufacture, and it was also fitted in a version of the Yugoslav Fury). The second Yugoslav Hind was completed as a floatplane and underwent a short programme of evaluation at the Marine Aircraft Experimental Establishment during September 1937. It is believed that this aircraft was delivered with wheel undercarriage, though the Armstrong Whitworth floats were also undoubtedly despatched. The third of the Yugoslav trio was powered by a Gnome-Rhône Mistral K-9 nine-cylinder air-cooled radial engine, for this French powerplant was also scheduled for licence production in Yugoslavia. Licence negotiations were initiated for production of the Hind itself in Yugoslavia, but it is believed that the idea was subsequently abandoned.

The next foreign customer for the Hind was Persia (Iran). No fewer than thirty-five machines were ordered, to be powered by Bristol Mercury VIII engines. Despite considerable experience with radial engine

The Swiss Hind, HB-HAL.

installations on various Hart versions, it was some time before the first Persian Hind (No. 601) flew. First flown by Lucas on 28 April 1938, this aircraft experienced persistent engine overheating troubles, overcome largely by minor improvements to the engine cowling and finally by limiting the engine speed. Deliveries commenced in July 1938, and were completed by the end of the year. These Hinds continued to fly until the late 1940s; in 1948 Hawker Aircraft Ltd was approached by the Persian Government on the subject of spare parts for the old machines, but unfortunately the order could not be fulfilled!

Eight aircraft were delivered to Afghanistan during 1938. The first

One of the Portuguese Hinds.

The first Kestrel XVI-powered Yugoslav Hind.

The third Yugoslav Hind with Gnome-Rhône K-9 Mistral radial engine.

four machines were similar to the second batch of RAF Hinds with Kestrel V (Full power) engines and increased capacity oil coolers, but the engines of the remainder were derated. In addition twelve other Hinds were turned over to the Afghan Air Force direct from the Royal Air Force. Like the Persian machines, several Afghan Hinds survived ten years in service. One of these veteran aeroplanes was acquired in 1968 by the Royal Air Force Museum for renovating and permanent display.

Three aircraft were ordered by Latvia in January 1938 and the first machine, 176, was flown on 4 May that year. These aircraft, intended as trainers, differed from the Persian Hinds in having Bristol Mercury IX engines, full dual control and skids in place of tailwheels. Broad chord Watts two-blade propellers were also fitted. The final machine, 178, was for·a short time fitted with a Bristol Pegasus engine.

One of the three Latvian Hinds with Bristol Mercury IX.

A Persian Hind, 601.

Six Royal Air Force Hinds were supplied to Eire during 1939–40, being used by the Irish Air Corps for operational training as late as 1944.

TECHNICAL DATA FOR HIND (KESTREL V AND VDR)

TYPE: Two-seat general purpose light bomber and trainer.

STRUCTURE: All-metal construction with fabric covering.

MANUFACTURERS: Hawker Aircraft Ltd, Kingston. Trainer conversions (124 aircraft) by General Aircraft Ltd.

POWERPLANT: RAF, Swiss, Portuguese and Afghan bombers: 640 hp Rolls-Royce Kestrel V driving Watts 2-blade wooden propeller. *Trainers:* 599 hp Rolls-Royce Kestrel VDR. *Yugoslav aircraft:* Kestrel XVI and Gnome-Rhône K-9 Mistral. *Persian aircraft:* Bristol Mercury VIII. *Latvian aircraft:* Bristol Mercury IX.

DIMENSIONS: Span, 37 ft 3 in. Length, 29 ft 3 in. Height, 10 ft 7 in. Wing area, 348 sq ft.

WEIGHTS: Bomber (Kestrel V): Empty, 3,251 lb. Loaded, 5,298 lb.
  Trainer (Kestrel VDR): Empty 3,195 lb. Loaded, 4,657 lb.

PERFORMANCE: Kestrel V. Max speed, 186 mph at 16,400 ft. Climb, 8.1 min to 10,000 ft. Service ceiling (rate of climb, 100 ft/min), 26,400 ft.
  Kestrel VDR: Max speed, 185.5 mph at 15,500 ft. Climb, 8.4 min to 10,000 ft. Service ceiling (rate of climb, 100 ft/min), 24,450 ft.

OTHER DATA: Fuel capacity, 103 gallons. Armament, one forward-firing synchronised Vickers Mk III or V machine gun on port side of nose, with 600 rounds. Bomber versions had Lewis gun on No. 15 ring on observer's cockpit, with five 97-round magazines. Bomb-load, up to 510 lb of 230 lb, 112 lb, 25 lb or 20 lb bombs, or 3.45 in flares. Undercarriage, straight-axle type with Vickers oleo shock absorbers, 6 ft 3½ in track, 760 × 185 mm Dunlop wheels with Palmer hydraulic brakes.

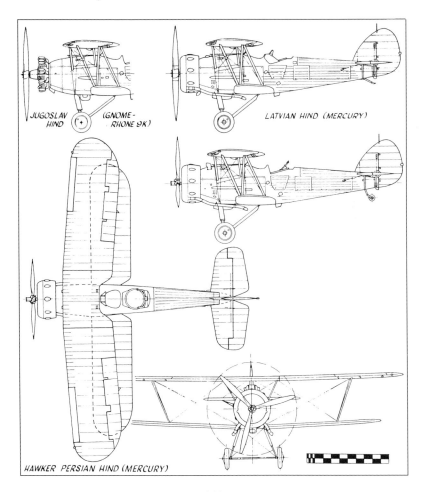

JUGOSLAV HIND (GNOME-RHONE 9K)

LATVIAN HIND (MERCURY)

HAWKER PERSIAN HIND (MERCURY)

The Hawker-built Hector prototype, K3719.

The Hawker Hector

The heavy demands made on supplies of the Rolls-Royce Kestrels by large orders for Hinds prompted the issue of a Specification, 14/35, outlining a requirement for an Audax replacement in the army co-operation rôle, to be powered by an alternative engine. Following flying trials which had been progressing since 1933 on a Hart, K2434, fitted with the Napier Dagger engine, Hawkers decided to tender a similar design to meet this requirement. Experience with K2434 had shown that although the Dagger I and II versions were unreliable and had been dogged by frequent failures, the Mark III showed better promise, with the result that this engine was chosen. The high engine weight, however, had so displaced the centre of gravity on the Hart test bed that, when equipped with bombs, longitudinal control was little more than marginal, and a straight upper wing was therefore adopted on the new aircraft. Moreover, all structural refinements developed in the Hind bomber, including improved rear cockpit profile and provision of a tailwheel, were incorporated in the design.

This Hawker proposal was accepted and, such was the urgency claimed by the rearmament programme of 1935, production plans were laid before even the prototype had flown. The name Hector was adopted in August 1935, and after construction of a prototype by Hawker Aircraft it was intended to place the production order in the hands of A V Roe & Co Ltd, a company which was shortly to become merged into the new Hawker Siddeley Group.

262

The prototype, K3719, was flown by Bulman on 14 February 1936, from Brooklands, and was shortly delivered to Martlesham Heath for acceptance and evaluation trials. In the meantime, however, Avros had been awarded large contracts for the Anson towards the end of 1935, and it therefore became necessary to transfer the Hector to Westland Aircraft Ltd at Yeovil. Among the reasons for the choice of this company was the fact that a later requirement for an army co-operation aircraft to supersede the Hector in turn had been met by the Westland Lysander, and it was felt that the experience gained by the Hector in the field would be beneficial to the manufacturers of the later design.

Production details for the Hector were ratified in April 1936, and by the following month 178 aircraft were on order. Tooling up got under way and the first Westland-built machine, K8090, was flown by H J Penrose during February 1937; thereafter the production rate reached a peak of twenty aircraft a month with the result that the order was completed by December that year.

Service clearance had been achieved in 1936 and in the same month as the first Hectors were flown at Yeovil deliveries were made direct to the new Army Co-operation Wing, No. 50, at Odiham, Hampshire, where they replaced the Audaxes of No. 4 (AC) Squadron, commanded by Sqn Ldr G H Loughnan. The following month No. 13 (AC) Squadron, under Sqn Ldr S C H Gray, also at Odiham, received Hectors; later both squadrons camped at Debden for their annual summer field exercises. No. 13 Squadron appeared at the Hendon RAF Display demonstrating Corps Liaison tactics, picking up messages from the ground on hooks suspended from the undercarriage spreader bars and attacking a target tableau.

By the end of the year five home-based army co-operation squadrons had received Hectors, while two more followed in 1938. These were No.2 (at Hawkinge), Nos. 4 and 13 (at Odiham), Nos. 16 and 59 (at Old

The Hector prototype.

K8090, the first Westland-built Hector, during Service trials at Martlesham.

K8100, the eleventh Westland-built Hector. These machines differed from the Hawker prototype principally in being equipped with tailwheels. (*Photo: Westland Aircraft Ltd.*)

Sarum), No. 26 (at Catterick) and No. 53 (at Farnborough South). However, the Lysander began to appear in numbers in December 1938, and No. 16 (AC) Squadron was the first to exchange its Hectors for the new aircraft. In 1939 the Hawker machines were withdrawn from the operational strength of the regular Air Force and were issued to No. 602 Squadron (at Abbotsinch), No. 612 (at Dyce), No. 613 (at Ringway), No. 614 (at Llandow) and No. 615 (at Kenley).

Although scheduled to accompany the Air Component to France with No. 22 Army Co-operation Group in September 1939, no Hector squadron was sent. From time to time, however, during the winter of 1939–40 detachments from the Auxiliary Squadrons moved south to Lympne in Kent, and when, in May 1940, the German armies were moving through North France six Hectors of No. 613 Squadron were sent into action on 26 May, dive bombing enemy troops investing Calais; the following day

Hector K8122 serving at the Royal Air Force College, Cranwell.

these aircraft returned and joined Lysanders of No. 4 Squadron, dropping supplies to the beleaguered Allied forces in the Calais garrison. Two Hectors were lost during the course of these operations and No.613 Squadron was withdrawn to be re-equipped with Lysanders.

By the middle of 1940 seventy-two Hectors survived on Air Ministry Charge and it was decided to relegate these to target and glider towing duties, although a small number was used during the Battle of Britain for inter-airfield communication purposes. During 1941 Hectors were distributed to Wellesbourne Mountford (sixteen aircraft), Croughton (sixteen aircraft) and Kidlington (ten aircraft) to tow General Aircraft Hotspur troop training light gliders. A few were also used at Stoke Orchard, Gloucestershire, in 1942 before the survivors (some of them having exceeded 1,500 flying hours) were eventually struck off Air Ministry Charge later that year.

Other ex-RAF machines were supplied to Ireland as general purpose aircraft and several of these were still in existence in 1945.

TECHNICAL DATA FOR HECTOR

TYPE: Two-seat Army Co-operation biplane (later Glider Tug).
STRUCTURE: All-metal construction with fabric covering.
MANUFACTURERS: Prototype built by Hawker Aircraft Ltd, Kingston; Production by Westland Aircraft Ltd, Yeovil.
POWERPLANT: 805 hp Napier Dagger III MS 24-cylinder H-type air-cooled engine driving 2-blade Watts wooden propeller.
DIMENSIONS: Span, 36 ft 11½ in. Length, 29 ft 9¾ in. Height, 10 ft 5 in. Wing area, 346 sq ft.
WEIGHTS: Empty, 3,389 lb. Loaded, 4,910 lb.
PERFORMANCE: Max speed, 187 mph at 6,560 ft. Climb, 5 min 40 sec to 10,000 ft. Endurance, 2 hr 25 min. Service ceiling (rate of climb, 100 ft/min), 24,000 ft.

OTHER DATA: Fuel capacity, 84 gallons. Armament, one fixed forward-firing 0.303 in Vickers Mark V machine gun on port side of nose with 600 rounds; one Lewis gun on Hawker mounting on rear cockpit with six 97-round drums of ammunition. Equipment included mounting for one F.24 camera, racks for 3.45 in flares, two 112 lb bombs or supply containers under the lower wings. Undercarriage track, 6 in 4¼ in, Pattern 'E' wheels, 19 in × 3½ in fitted to take standard 6 in tyres. Palmer wheel brakes.

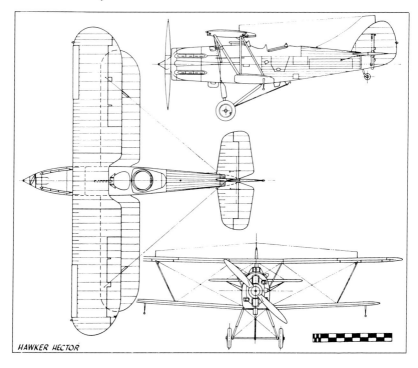

HAWKER HECTOR

266

The Hawker Hurricane prototype, K5083.

The Hawker Hurricane

It is unlikely that any aeroplane has been written about more than the Hawker Hurricane, as the part played by and the responsibilities vested in its pilots in those critical years of world history have placed it in the ranks of the greatest aircraft of all time. No other aircraft fought on more fronts or proved itself more adaptable to tactical requirements, nor, if the need arose, was any aircraft able to withstand battle damage better than the Hurricane.

The first steps in the development of the Hurricane were taken six years before the outbreak of the Second World War. In case it might be thought that these steps were entirely logical it should be remembered that, despite the proven ascendancy of the monoplane in such events as the Schneider Trophy contest, and the fact that monoplane fighters were known to be under active development elsewhere on the Continent, there was still an entrenched belief, some twenty years old, in certain Air Ministry quarters that monoplane interceptors were likely to be fundamentally unsound. In August 1933, discussions were held between Sydney Camm and Major Buchanan of the Directorate of Technical Development, Air Ministry, and proposals were put forward for the design of a monoplane fighter based on the Fury. The Rolls-Royce Goshawk engine (at that time favoured as a fighter powerplant), a fixed spatted undercarriage and four guns were included in the design, but early the following year this was altered to take the new Rolls-Royce P.V.12 engine that was to achieve world fame as the Merlin. The fixed undercarriage was replaced by an inwards retracting type and an enclosed pilot's cockpit was introduced.

After partial conformity with an interim Specification, F.5/34, a new Specification, F.36/34, was drafted around the design as it stood in August 1934, and it was to these requirements that the new monoplane fighter was tendered on 4 September.

The F.36/34 design was accepted and in February 1935 a contract was raised for the manufacture of a prototype to have provision for an armament of four guns — a Vickers gun on each side of the nose and either a Browning or Vickers gun in each wing. Arguments in favour of a heavier armament were, however, accepted and the contract was amended to provide for the inclusion of a wing-mounted battery of eight Browning machine guns.

First flown by Bulman on 6 November 1935, the prototype F.36/34, K5083, was powered by a Rolls-Royce Merlin 'C' driving a Watts two-

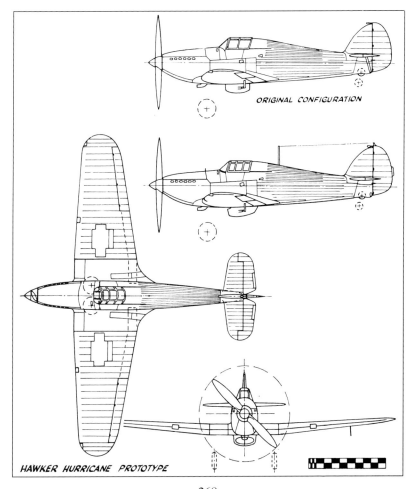

ORIGINAL CONFIGURATION

HAWKER HURRICANE PROTOTYPE

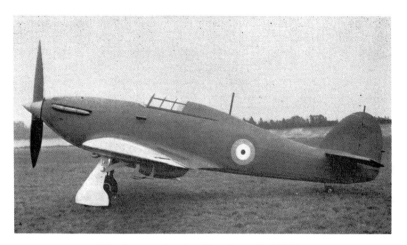

The first production Hurricane I, L1547.

blade fixed-pitch wooden propeller, and weighed 5,416 pounds. Structurally the aircraft combined the well-proven tubular metal cross-braced fabric-covered Warren fuselage with a new fabric-covered cantilever twin-spar wing with Warren girder interspar structure. Many small features, subsequently modified, distinguished K5083 at this time from its later and more familiar outline. Initially the undercarriage fairings included wheel doors hinged to the top wheel segment covers, but following damage caused during taxiing over rough ground at Martlesham Heath these flaps were removed. Also removed were the tailplane struts, fitted at first. The side panels of the sliding hood canopy were unstiffened during K5083's early flights and first one and later two

An early Hurricane I, L1562, the first to be fitted with a D.H. two-position three-blade propeller.

vertical frames were added. The tailwheel was fully retractable and there was no underfin. The radiator bath was increased in size and exhaust ejector stubs were soon added.

THE HURRICANE MARK I

Brief preliminary handling trials were conducted at the Aeroplane and Armament Experimental Establishment, Martlesham Heath, early in 1936, and in June of that year (soon after the name Hurricane had been officially adopted) a production order for 600 aircraft — large by any peacetime standards — was received by Hawker Aircraft Ltd. Due principally to a decision to discontinue development of the Merlin I and to concentrate on the Merlin II, the first production Hurricane I did not fly until 12 October 1937, the change in powerplant necessitating redesign of engine controls, mountings and header tank, as well as the nose cowlings.

From the outset the production rate of the Hurricane was high, some forty aircraft being completed in the first three months. Moreover, inside two months the first aircraft was delivered to the Royal Air Force and by Christmas 1937 one Flight of the first Squadron, No. 111 at Northolt, had received its machines, supplanting Gloster Gauntlets.

These early machines were delivered to the Service with rear fuselage contours similar to the prototype, but as a result of spinning trials it was decided to enlarge the rudder and incorporate an underfin, and all aircraft delivered from February 1938 onwards carried this modification.

Build-up of RAF Squadrons continued throughout 1938, No. 3 and 56 following No. 111 Squadron with Hurricanes. By the end of the year about two hundred machines had been delivered to Fighter Command and despite the urgency to accelerate production and expansion, resulting from the Munich Crisis, Hawker Aircraft Ltd was able to accept contracts with foreign Governments, including Belgium, Yugoslavia and Romania. Hurricane production by the parent company was enhanced by the completion of its new factory at Langley, and when a further contract for 1,000 aircraft was raised by the Air Ministry in 1938, subcontracts were arranged with Gloster Aircraft Company. Furthermore, on 4 January 1939 an Air Ministry Specification was issued to cover manufacture of Hurricanes in Canada by the Canadian Car and Foundry Company.

By 1939 several improvements had been made in the standard Hurricane I design. The Merlin II had been superseded by the Merlin III and the first Hurricane to be fitted with a two-pitch de Havilland three-blade propeller, L1562, had been flown on 29 August 1938. Triple ejector exhaust manifolds were standardised, while most of the early aircraft had been retrospectively modified with the underfin.

Metal stressed-skin wings started to appear in the assembly shops at the beginning of 1939 and the first set, fitted to L1877, was flown on 28

A Yugoslav Hurricane I.

April. On 23 March the first Yugoslav Hurricane was flown, to be followed by the first Hurricane for Belgium on 13 May. The Belgian machines differed from the RAF aircraft in having provision for two 0.5 in and two 7.7 mm machine guns alternative to the eight Browning gun armament. In the sphere of armament, a trial installation of two 20 mm Oerlikon guns was fitted under the wings of L1750 and flown on 24 May 1939. (It is perhaps significant here to remark that, in 1935, Specification F.37/35 had called for a single-seat fighter to be armed with four 20 mm cannon and that in January 1936 Hawker Aircraft had tendered a

271

Hurricane design with this armament (see Appendix). The Hurricane was evidently not considered suitable for such an armament at that time, with the result that the twin-engine Westland Whirlwind was ordered in small numbers. As will be told later the Hurricane IIC with the four-cannon armament was to be ordered in large numbers, but only after the Battle of Britain was over, four years after the original Hurricane proposal had been rejected.)

Events in 1939 indicated the likelihood of Hurricanes being required to operate in the Middle East, and experience with Audaxes and Hardys in that theatre enabled successful trial installations to be carried out with sand guards and tropical filters on a Hurriciane I, L1669, flown on 17 May 1939, and a small number of similar machines was supplied to Turkey shortly afterwards. Another trial installation was that of a

The Company's Trial Installation Hurricane, G-AFKX, previously L1606.

Merlin XII in L2026, for at that time it was proposed that this engine would become the standard production Merlin. As it transpired, further modifications were incorporated to facilitate manufacture and the Merlin XX was adopted as standard.

One further pre-war aircraft deserves mention. This was G-AFKX, a Company-owned machine incorporating the principal structure components from an early Mark I, L1606, returned from the Service. First flown by Lucas in its new colours on 27 February 1939, the aircraft was initially fitted with fabric-covered wings and powered by a Merlin III driving a Watts two-blade propeller. These were replaced in turn by the Merlin R.M.4.S., Merlin 45 and Rotol R.X.5/2 three-blade constant speed propeller. (Propellers of this type started to appear on production Hurricanes from October 1939 onwards and contributed in no small measure to the enhanced climb performance enjoyed by Hurricanes during the Battle of Britain.)

At the outbreak of war on 3 September 1939, the Royal Air Force possessed nineteen fully-equipped Hurricane squadrons and two of these, Nos. 1 and 73, flew out to France with the Advanced Air Striking Force, to be joined shortly afterwards by Nos. 85 and 87 Squadrons of the Air Component. It was a Hurricane flown by Pt Off Mould of No. 1 Squadron, then based at Vassincourt, that claimed the first RAF victory over a German aircraft in France when it shot down a Dornier Do 17 on 30 October 1939. Activity on the Western Front, however, was limited during those first months of the war to patrols, due mainly to the static nature of the opposing armies.

The Hurricanes, for the most part, were early machines with fixed-

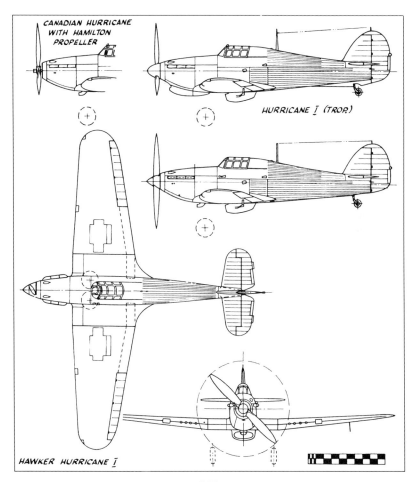

CANADIAN HURRICANE WITH HAMILTON PROPELLER

HURRICANE I (TROP)

HAWKER HURRICANE I

pitch propellers, but soon aircraft with variable-pitch airscrews arrived at the front and it was in one of these that Fg Off 'Cobber' Kain of No.73 Squadron shot down another Dornier Do 17 from 27,000 feet, an almost unprecedented altitude for combat.

The German invasion of Norway in the spring of 1940 and the legendary actions fought by Nos. 46 and 263 Squadrons with Hurricanes and Gladiators respectively, operating from improvised landing grounds and frozen lakes, brought realisation of the RAF's inadequacy as a long-range fighter force. A scheme, already under consideration at Kingston, to adapt the Hurricane to carry auxiliary fuel tanks under the wings, was therefore awarded the highest priority, and Hurricane P3462 was flown by Reynell with two fixed 44 gallon long range fuel tanks on 7 May 1940.

Other schemes to suit the Hurricane for the Norwegian campaign included the proposals to fit float and ski undercarriages. In the former

One of the last Hurricane Is built by Hawker Aircraft Ltd., V7826, seen here equipped with tropical filter and fixed 44-gallon long-range fuel tanks.

case a pair of Blackburn Roc floats was received at Kingston on 26 April and mounted on a Hurricane centresection, but, although flight trials were scheduled for June 1940, the Norwegian campaign came to an end and the project was cancelled. Plans to fit the ski undercarriage were also abandoned in this country, though a trial installation was later carried out on a Hurricane in Canada.

Production and development of the Hurricane had nevertheless progressed smoothly; the first Gloster-built Mark I had flown on 20 October 1939, and the first deliveries from Hucclecote were made in December of that year. The first Canadian-built Hurricane (a Mark I with Rolls-Royce-built Merlin III) flew early in 1940 and aircraft from Canada started to arrive in the United Kingdom during June.

On the eve of the Battle of Britain Fighter Command possessed twenty-six Hurricane squadrons of which three were only partly operational and four were hurriedly re-equipping after their severe losses incurred in the withdrawal to Dunkirk. Production rates continued to increase, no fewer than seven out of every ten fighters built under the Harrogate Plan up to that time being Hurricanes, and by the first week in August thirty-two fully operational Hurricane squadrons were available. Between 10 July and 31 October 1940, the average strength of Hurricanes in the RAF was 1,326 (compared with 957 Spitfires); moreover, there was seldom a period during the Battle in which there were fewer than 200 Hurricanes in reserve.

The Hurricane's part in the Battle of Britain is too familiar to warrant a lengthy discourse; the Hawker fighter was, quite simply, the cornerstone of Britain's figher defences. Because Hawker Aircraft Ltd (including the Hurricane production line at Brockworth) had been alone among the fighter manufacturers in exceeding its production targets in every month since before the war, the Hawker fighter far outnumbered all of Fighter Command's other interceptors combined. Though possessing a lower maximum speed than the most elegant Spitfire, it proved to be more manoeuvrable, was a steadier gun platform — allowing more accurate aiming and firing — was capable of withstanding much greater battle damage and was simpler to fly. On account of the latter attribute, all the squadrons newly created during the Battle of Britain were equipped with Hurricanes. Of equal importance was the simplicity of its structure, which, unlike that of the Spitfire, could be maintained and repaired at almost any of Fighter Command's aerodromes operating during the Battle. Because of the relative impotence of RAF night fighters, the day fighters were often given the additional rôle of flying night patrols, their pilots seeking to spot enemy bombers being illuminated by searchlights. Once again the Hurricane proved superior to the Spitfire — not least on account of its ease of landing, with its sturdy, wide-track undercarriage.

Nevertheless, it was on account of the Spitfire's superior speed and altitude performance that, whenever possible, Hurricane pilots were ordered to attack the German bombers, while the Spitfire pilots attempted to hold off the enemy escort fighters. That is not to suggest that an average Hurricane pilot could not hold his own against the excellent Messerschmitt Bf 109E, provided the combat opened on fairly equal terms, and many of the German single-seaters fell to Hurricanes' guns. It was also quickly discovered that much-vaunted enemy aircraft, such as the Junkers Ju 88 and Messerschmitt Bf 110, could be — and frequently were — outflown and outfought by the Hurricane. So it was that, time and again, the Hurricane squadrons bore the brunt of the desperate fighting over Southern England during that memorable summer of 1940.

The only Victoria Cross ever to be awarded to a member of Fighter Command was won by a Hurricane pilot. Flight Lieutenant John Brindley Nicolson was a flight commander on No. 249 Squadron, and was leading a three-Hurricane patrol near Southampton on 16 August, and was preparing to attack some Bf 110s when his Section was suddenly attacked from above and astern by some Bf 109s. Nicolson's aircraft was badly hit and was soon ablaze. However, braving the flames that engulfed the cockpit, he remained at his controls long enough to continue his attack on a Bf 110 before baling out; he survived his wounds and burns to receive Britain's highest award for valour.

One other pilot deserves special mention. Dick Reynell, who had been on the RAF's pre-war Reserve of Officers, had been seconded to Hawker Aircraft Ltd as a test pilot at the outbreak of war. At the height

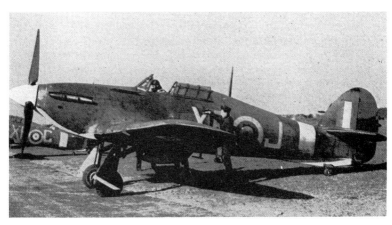

Early Hurricane IIA Series 1s serving with No. 71 (Fighter) Squadron, the famous 'Eagle' Squadron, towards the end of the Battle of Britain.

of the Battle of Britain he volunteered to spend his leave flying with No. 43 Squadron to obtain operational experience on the Hurricane. In the vital air battle on 7 September — the critical moment when the tide of fortune turned in Fighter Command's favour — Reynell and his popular squadron commander, the South African Sqn Ldr Caesar Hull, were shot down and killed over North Kent.

When the Battle drew to an end and stock was taken, it was realised that Hurricane pilots had destroyed far more enemy aircraft than all the other British defences — both fighters and ground defences — combined. Therein lay the reward for the foresight displayed by the Hawker company in ordering the Hurricane into production in advance of a Government contract, and the Company's continuing determination that nothing should stand in the way of achieving maximum production in the shortest possible time.

As a footnote to the Hurricane's part in the Battle of Britain one encounter deserves special mention. After the *Luftwaffe* had switched its attacks to London by small numbers of high-flying fighter-bombers, the *Corpo Aereo Italiano* attempted a single raid against the South of England on 11 November 1940. Hurricanes of Nos. 46, 249 and 257 Squadrons were sent up to intercept, and apart from breaking up the raid they destroyed eleven Italian aircraft without loss to themselves.

Despite the urgent need for Hurricanes at home, entry by Italy into the war had brought about the demand to strengthen British forces in the Mediterranean and Middle East theatres, and on 2 August 1940 twelve Hurricane Is equipped with tropical air filters were flown off HM Carrier *Argus* and landed on Malta to join the hard-pressed Gloster Gladiators in the vital defence of that gallant island. A month later, on 5 September, six Hurricanes and six Blenheims arrived by sea at Takoradi

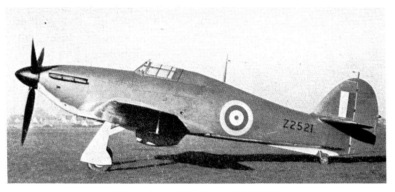

A Hurricane IIA Series 2, Z2521.

in the Gold Coast, and on the 19th of that month these aircraft set off for Egypt, so inaugurating the aerial supply line that was to prove so important in the following months for the Allied forces in the Western Desert. By October 1940, two Hurricane squadrons, Nos. 73 and 274, had become operational and were ready for action in North Africa.

At home, after the *Luftwaffe*'s onslaughts had failed to destroy the Royal Air Force, the fighter squadrons, although still actively engaged in the country's defence, set about re-equipping. Several Hurricane I squadrons were withdrawn temporarily to train in night fighting, and before 1940 was out these formations joined the Blenheims and Defiants in the night defence of London.

THE HURRICANE MARK II

As part of the normal development programme the Hawker Design Staff had studied alternative powerplants for the Hurricane in 1939. Apart from various projects to fit the Rolls-Royce Griffon and Bristol Hercules engines, installations which were abandoned because the airframe modifications required would severely disrupt the essential flow

277

An early Hurricane IIB with twelve guns.

The Hurricane IIB fighter-bomber. This aircraft is carrying two 250 lb bombs and two of the twelve guns, normally fitted, have been removed.

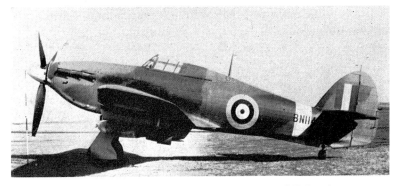

The trials Hurricane IIB, BN114, with two 500 lb bombs.

of production aircraft, the two-stage supercharged Merlin XX engine was proposed in February 1940. This engine — initially giving 1,185 bhp, but later 1,280 bhp — demanded only limited alteration to the airframe and, having been designed with ease of production of prime importance, was scheduled to become available in massive quantities. The first aircraft so fitted, P3269, was flown by Lucas on 11 June 1940.

Known as the Hurricane II, the Merlin XX version did not achieve full production status until August and the first aircraft, designated Mark IIA Series 1s, were of similar appearance to the Mark I. Retaining the Mark Is wings with eight guns, and similar nose profile, these early Mark IIs were pure interceptor fighters possessing a top speed of 342 mph, and it was aircraft of this type that squadrons received as replacements from 4 September onwards.

During October further modifications were included, resulting in the Hurricane IIA Series 2, with slightly lengthened nose accommodating an extra fuselage bay and frame, and with allowance made to substitute the eight-gun wing for later versions with heavier armament.

These early Hurricane IIAs were used with limited success in the night defence of London during the Blitz of the winter of 1940–41, but more spectacular was their participation in the early offensive sweeps over North France and the Channel ports, despite their paucity of offensive armament. Among the Hurricane IIA squadrons participating in these sorties was No. 71 Squadron, the celebrated 'Eagle' squadron of American pilots, formed at the end of the Battle of Britain.

The question of increasing the Hurricane's gun armament, as has already been mentioned, was under investigation as early as 1939 with the trial installation of two Oerlikon 20 mm guns on Hurriciane I L1750. During 1940, however, Camm put forward two further proposals; in

An early Hurricane IIC of No. 3 (Fighter) Squadron, BD867. Though not strictly a night fighter, this machine displays an exhaust shield just forward of the windscreen.

279

January he submitted a scheme to install four additional Browning guns in the eight-gun wing and in April this was accepted by the Air Ministry, who stated that the new gun battery should be introduced in the Merlin XX Hurricane II. A shortage of guns towards the end of the Battle of Britain, however, resulted in the interim Hurricane IIA retaining the eight-gun wing, and it was the Hurricane IIB which carried the heavier armament.

Returning to the early pre-war trials of Oerlikon 20 mm cannon in the Hurricane I L1750, it had emerged that the necessity to grease the ammunition for these guns was not acceptable in the RAF (use of this gun being confined to the Royal Navy), and a change-over was made to the Hispano weapon, already being incorporated in the Bristol Beaufighter and Westland Whirlwind twin-engine fighters. Camm resurrected his 1936 proposals for a four-cannon Hurricane, and Hawker was given permission in June 1940 to carry out a trial installation (T.I.) of four

A late production Hurricane IIC, KZ466. Unlike earlier machines which possessed bead sights, this machine has a reflector sight.

Hispanos, using a Hurricane with a set of repaired wings. Immediately afterwards these wings were fitted to an aircraft, V7360, on the Hawker production line and delivered to Boscombe Down. Brief trials demonstrated the feasibility of the installation, and on 3 September V7360 was delivered to North Weald (a fighter station in the thick of the Battle of Britain). Here it was allocated to Flt Lt Alexander Rabagliati of No. 46 Squadron who, in due course, flew the aircraft in action on several occasions, destroying at least one enemy aircraft and damaging several others.

Later in September V7360 was returned to Brooklands and given a new set of four-cannon wings, now incorporating semi-tooled production techniques, and was flown in this form by Lucas on 5 December.

A Hurricane IIB (Gloster-built), Z5252, of the Red Air Force. Only eight guns have been fitted on this aircraft, which also features a tropical filter.

However, the cannon installation differed from the production version — to be designated the Hurricane Mark IIC — in having spring drum-fed gear, whereas the Mark IIC (whose first true prototype, V2461, was first flown by Seth-Smith on 6 February 1941) featured the Chatellerault feed mechanism. On 20 January 1941 came official authority for Hawker to proceed with 100 sets of four-Hispano-cannon wings.

Among the trials and projects concerning the Hurricane at this time was the testing of P3899 with 'blister' hood (first flown by Broad on 26 October 1940), Hurricane II P3269 with Rotol four-blade propeller (first

One of the relatively small number of genuine presentation Hurricanes; this Mark IIC fighter-bomber, HW603, was presented in memory of Sqn Ldr John Gillan by his mother.

A long-range Hurricane IIC fighter, here fitted with jettisonable 44-gallon tanks.

A Hurricane IIC with a pair of 90-gallon ferry tanks.

flown by Lucas on 8 December 1940) and the first flight by a tropical Hurricane II, V7480, by Lucas on 8 February 1941.

In January 1941 discussions were held between Short Bros Ltd, the Ministry of Aircraft Production and the Hawker Design Staff on the mounting of a Hurricane atop a Liberator long range bomber as a means of providing fighter protection for these aircraft on Atlantic patrols. An equally unorthodox proposal resulted in the towing of a Hurricane behind a Wellington for the same purpose, this experiment being conducted by Flight Refuelling Ltd. However, severe icing inevitably prevented the Hurricane's engine from being started up when the moment to cast off arrived, and this led to the abandonment of the scheme. Anticipation of similar trouble caused cancellation of the composite Liberator scheme.

By March 1941 production of the Hurricane from the Kingston, Brooklands, Langley and Hucclecote factories had reached an average of twelve aircraft per day, while a further ten aircraft per week were arriving from Canada. No fewer than thirty-six squadrons of the RAF at home and overseas were equipped with Hurricane Is and IIs. Furthermore, resulting from a contract raised in 1940, production of the Hurricane II had got under way at the Austin Motor Company, an early aircraft, AP517, being flown to Langley early in May 1941, and test flown by Seth-Smith.

On 22 June 1941 Germany attacked Russia and following assurances that the new ally would receive all possible aid from the United Kingdom it was decided to send No. 151 Hurricane Wing (Nos. 81 and 134

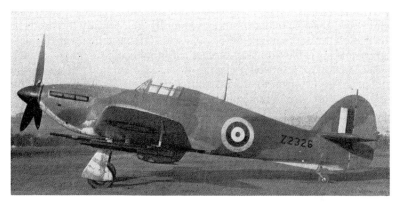

The Hurricane IID prototype with trial installation of the 40 mm Rolls-Royce anti-tank guns. (*Photo: Imperial War Museum.*)

A production Hurricane IID, KZ320, with 40 mm Vickers "S" guns.

283

Squadrons), under the command of Wg Cdr H N G Ramsbottom-Isherwood, with the first convoy in August that year. Thirty-nine aircraft, Mark IIA Series 2s and Mark IIBs, were sent, twenty-four in a flyable condition and the remainder in crates. The Wing was to provide cover for the ports during the unloading of the convoy and to remain until the winter, when the aircraft were to be handed over to the Red Air Force and the RAF personnel to return home. Hurricanes represented by far the major part of British aid to Russia during the war, each subsequent convoy delivering many aircraft. Others, principally Mark IIBs and IICs, were delivered from the Middle East, while quantities of Canadian-built Mark XIs and XIIs (of which more anon) were shipped direct from Canada to Iceland, thence to join the famous PQ convoys to Petsamo, Murmansk and Arkhangel'sk. No fewer than 2,952 Hurricanes were despatched to the Red Air Force though, in view of the heavy losses suffered by the North Cape convoys, the actual number received is likely to have been a good deal less.

At least one Russian Hurricane was converted for use by a Free French Wing as a two-seat trainer, while others were equipped with American 0.5 in machine guns. Many aircraft featured tropical air intakes even when flown in sub-Arctic conditions, this equipment being a relic of their Middle or Far Eastern intentions.

Effective as the 20 mm Hispanos proved against ground targets, they were surpassed in 1942 with the appearance of the Hurricane IID with two 40 mm guns carried in fairings under the wings. The prototype installation was made on Z2326 (a T.I. aircraft for external stores) and was first flown by Seth-Smith on 18 September 1941, while production aircraft commenced deliveries the following year. The Hurricane IID served only with No. 184 Squadron in North Europe against targets in France and the Low Countries, the bulk of deliveries being shipped either to the Middle East or Burma. The home-based machines (early production aircraft) were equipped with Rolls-Royce B.F. guns with twelve rounds per gun, but the remainder carried Vickers Type S guns with fifteen rounds per gun. A pair of Browning machine guns was retained, firing tracer ammunition for sighting purposes.

Hurricane IIDs were in action for the first time in the defence of the famous Free French Brigade at Bir Hakim on 6 June 1942, with No. 6 Squadron, RAF, and by 23 October 1942, at the Battle of El Alamein, the number of Mark IID squadrons had increased to four out of a total of twenty-two Hurricane squadrons serving in the Western Desert.

The 'tank-busting' Hurricanes continued to operate with conspicuous success throughout the remainder of the North African campaign, but their feats against Rommel's armour were at least matched by the action of Hurricanes in Burma, though the comparatively light armour protection of the Japanese tanks was offset to a certain extent by the protection afforded by the dense jungle cover. Notwithstanding, the three Hurricane IID squadrons achieved many successes during the first

Arakan campaign of December 1942, as well as in the scattered operations of 1943 which culminated in the second Arakan campaign. By 1944 six squadrons of the Indian Air Force had been equipped with Hurricanes (each unit retaining a composite strength of tropical Mark IIBs, IICs and IIDs), and these formations participated in the defence of Kohima and Imphal during March and April that year.

Still the principal home-based variant in 1942 was the Hurricane IIC, either equipped with bombs or long-range drop tanks. A total of 4,711 Mark IICs was built by Hawker Aircraft Ltd alone and, although many of these were issued to training units during 1943 and 1944, others were still performing combat missions, albeit under heavy escort by other fighters, immediately prior to the Normandy landing in June 1944. Carrying two 500 pound bombs they were used on many occasions as dive bombers to attack the heavily defended flying bomb sites in the Pas de Calais.

Many of the superseded Hurricane Is and early IIAs were re-introduced in 1942 for service with the reorganised Air/Sea Rescue organisation. These aircraft usually retained their armament, being used to search for 'ditched' aircrew and mount guard in relays over them until the arrival of a rescue launch. On the other hand Hurricane IIBs and IICs, based in Northern Ireland, Wales and Cornwall with Meteorological Reconnaissance Squadrons, invariably flew unarmed on their laborious but essential 'Met Flights'.

THE HURRICANE MARK IV

With this multitude of duties being proposed for the Hurricane it became obvious that some form of universal wing would be more readily adaptable in the front line. It was thus in 1942 that design commenced on such a universal wing, it not being considered necessary to include the four-cannon armament as this would still remain in production on the Hurricane IIC.

The universal wing incorporated a fixed-gun armament of two Browning machine guns for sighting purposes but was capable of mounting alternative loads comprising the 40 mm anti-tank Vickers guns, ferry or drop tanks, rocket projectiles (eight with 60-pound warheads), Small Bomb Carriers, Smoke Curtain Installations (SBC and SCI), 500 pound or 250 pound GP, HE, AP or Incendiary bombs.

The new Hurricane, termed the Mark IV — the Hurricane III was a proposed version powered by a Packard-built Merlin but did not materialise — and powered by a 1,620 hp Merlin 24 or 27, entered production in 1943, the first aircraft, KX405, being flown by Lucas on 14 March. This aircraft was retained for test purposes by Hawker Aircraft Ltd, and although its first flights were performed with a Merlin 32 and a Spitfire-type Rotol four-blade propeller subsequent production aircraft featured the Merlin 24 or 27 with three-blade airscrew.

285

A Hurricane IV, KX877.

A tropical Hurricane IV, KZ198, with two 40 mm Vickers guns.

A tropical Hurricane IV armed with eight 3 in rocket projectiles.

Five hundred and twenty-four IVs were issued to the Royal Air Force during 1943 and 1944, being used both at home and abroad. Essentially ground attack machines, they featured 350 pounds of additional armoured protection, being readily identifiable from the Mark II by the angular radiator armour. Mark IVs arrived in the Mediterranean theatre in time to replace No. 6 Squadron's Mk. IIDs for the Sicilian campaign, thereafter using their 40 mm guns to good effect throughout the battles in Italy. (After the war No. 6 Squadron was moved to Palestine, retaining its Hurricane IVs until 1946, being thus the last Hurricane squadron in the Royal Air Force.)

The mention of rocket projectiles as being part of the Hurricane's ground attack load merits amplification, for the Hurricane was the first Allied fighter to use such weapons in the Second World War. Proposed as early as October 1941, the first trials had been conducted on a Hurricane II, Z2415, at Boscombe Down in February 1942, using three launching rails attached to the underside of each outer wing panel. From the outset the rockets were rudimentary, employing 3 in tube on the front of which was screwed the warhead. The tube contained the solid fuel rocket, and cruciform plain plate tail fins were attached at the rear. Apart from the launching fittings these rockets remained fundamentally unchanged in the RAF over the next eighteen years, and cannot be said to have advanced aerodynamically in the same way as their launching aircraft!

Nevertheless, during the war the 3 in RP was a most effective weapon, being used to a limited extent on Hurricane IIBs and IICs, but more extensively on the Hurricane Mk. IV. They were first used operationally by Hurricane IIs and IVs of No. 137 Squadron on 2 September 1943; flying with a Typhoon escort, this squadron successfully attacked lock gates on the Hansweert Canal in Holland. Fitted by now with four rockets under each wing, Hurricanes continued their attacks into 1944, being joined by the Typhoon, whose rocket firing exploits after D-Day are now legendary.

As with previous Hurricanes the Mark IV was flown in many theatres, perhaps nowhere more spectacularly than in India and Burma. Ground attack Hurricane IVs were introduced into No. 221 Group at the end of the first Arakan campaign, replacing Spitfires, Mohawks and Blenheims and equipping Nos. 11, 20, 34, 42, 60 and 113 Squadrons. On one occasion, in support of the victorious Fourteenth Army's advance on Rangoon early in 1944, No. 20 Squadron destroyed thirteen Japanese tanks in a single attack with their 40 mm guns and RPs. No. 222 Group, charged with coastal patrol and protection, was also equipped with Hurricanes, Nos. 5 and 17 Squadrons receiving Hurricane IVs in March 1944.

THE HURRICANE MARK V

A short-lived proposal for a specialised 'low-attack' Hurricane, to be employed exclusively in South-East Asia, had been designated the Mark IIE, but came to nothing. Instead, Rolls-Royce was able to show that it was possible to ground-boost the Merlin 32 to develop almost 1,700 hp, and it was therefore decided to combine this engine, driving a four-blade Rotol propeller, with the universal wing of the Mark IV and alter the designation to Mark V. Two conversions from Mark IVs were undertaken, the first, KZ193, being flown by Lucas and Fox on 3 April 1943; a second conversion, KX405, with 40mm anti-tank guns, followed soon afterwards. A production order, believed to be for 200 aircraft, was raised, and a single prototype, NL255, was completed and flown.

By the autumn of 1943, however, with very large stocks of Hurricanes now being assembled in India, it was decided that the relatively modest advance in performance did not justify perseverance with a new version of the Hurricane and, although the three Mark V examples underwent prolonged trials, the project was abandoned.

One of three Hurricane Vs, NL255.

THE CANADIAN HURRICANES

As previously mentioned, production of the Hurricane was undertaken by the Canadian Car and Foundry company early in 1939. The first Canadian-built Hurricane, P5170, was flown in January 1940, and was shipped to the United Kingdom the following month. After evaluation by the Royal Air Force this aircraft was delivered to Brooklands and, flown by Russell-Stacey, assessed with various propellers. Powered by Rolls-Royce-built Merlin IIIs these early Canadian Hurricanes were Mark Is, and as such remained in production until the end of 1945, when, with the completion of the first Packard-built engines, new designations were adopted, commencing with the Hurricane X.

288

Production Mark Xs, powered by Packard-Merlin 28s driving Hamilton Standard Hydromatic airscrews (without spinners), appeared in 1941 and corresponded to the Hurricane IIB with twelve machine guns. Although scheduled for delivery to the RAF, few arrived in Britain, many being lost in transit and others being retained by the RCAF in Canada. The Mark XI was similar to the Hurricane X but was developed to RCAF requirements, some being used as trainers for American fighters with the unconventional 'pull-to-open' throttle system (a similar system had been tried on Hurricane I L2026 in 1939, together with an interconnected throttle and pitch lever.)

The Hurricane XII was the principal Canadian production version, being first flown in November 1941. Powered by a Packard-Merlin 29 with Hamilton propeller, the Mark XII retained the twelve-gun wing initially but later four-cannon and universal wings became available.

A Canadian Hurricane XII, 5624, with twelve-gun wings, equipped with ski undercarriage.

A Canadian Hurricane X, AG111, of No. 1 Squadron, Royal Canadian Air Force.

289

Many were delivered to Russia, commencing in October 1942, and to the Indian Air Force squadrons of No. 221 Group in South East Asia Command.

The Hurricane XIIA was an eight-gun version of the Mk. XII, and a navalised Sea Hurricane XIIA was built in small quantities, being used on escort carriers plying between St John's, Newfoundland, and Iceland during 1943–44.

An interesting action, in which Canadian Sea Hurricane XIIs flew with the Royal Navy in American markings and fought against French aircraft in North Africa, was that in support of Operation Torch, the Allied landings in Algeria of November 1942. To provide air cover for the American landings at Oran, the carriers HMS *Biter* and *Dasher* embarked a dozen Sea Hurricanes of No. 800 Squadron, Fleet Air Arm. These were called into action when Vichy French Dewoitines shot down an entire formation of Albacore bombers; the Sea Hurricanes then shot down five of the French fighters. (The twelve-gun Sea Hurricanes displayed US markings to enable the American gunners to distinguish friend from foe, as they were unfamiliar with European aircraft.)

THE SEA HURRICANES

No accurate figures exist as to the exact number of Sea Hurricanes delivered, for, apart from a very few newly-built aircraft, large numbers of Hurricanes were returned from the RAF for conversion. Moreover other modification work was undertaken at Fleet Air Arm shore establishments at home and abroad.

Following the experience of No. 46 Squadron during the Norwegian campaign of May 1940, in which Hurricanes were successfully taken-off and landed aboard the aircraft carrier *Glorious*, the steadily-increasing Allied shipping losses in the Battle of the Atlantic prompted the order for modification of the Hurricane to suit it for shipboard operation, an order characteristically endorsed by Mr Winston Churchill himself early in 1941.

A Sea Hurricane IC, V6741. (*Photo: Crown Copyright.*)

290

The first Sea Hurricane, a modified Mark I with catapult spools and arrester hook, was delivered to Farnborough in March 1941, though the following fifty machines, known as Sea Hurricane Mk. IAs, did not feature hooks. It was proposed that merchant ships were to be equipped with catapults on their bows and, on appearance of enemy aircraft, the Hurricane was to be launched to intercept. Thirty-five such ships (known as CAM-Ships — Catapult Aircraft Merchantmen) were so modified and the first, the s.s. *Michael E*, set sail on 27 May 1941. Unfortunately, however, the *Michael E* was torpedoed and sunk before its Hurricane could be launched.

The pilots at first responsible for these arduous duties were initially volunteers drawn from the Fleet Air Arm, but when, during the summer of 1941, modifications commenced to equip naval vessels as catapult ships, the naval pilots returned to their own surroundings, and their place was taken by RAF pilots, many of whom had fought in Hurricanes in the Battle of Britain.

No other duty performed by pilots during the war can have been fraught with more hazard and difficulty, for the fact that they were usually sent up to intercept the Focke-Wulf Fw 200C Condor long-range maritime patrol aircraft implied that their own aircraft would possess insufficient fuel to reach land. Forty-five-gallon drop tanks were carried from August 1941 onwards (after introduction of increased-power catapults), but more often than not the pilots were obliged to bale out or ditch their machines in the path of their convoy, hoping that some passing vessel would pick them up.

The first success by a Sea Hurricane IA came when a machine, piloted by Lt R W H Everett, RNVR, launched on 3 August 1941 from HMS *Maplin*, one of the recently-converted naval catapult escort ships, intercepted and destroyed a Focke-Wulf Condor, a feat for which Everett was awarded the DSO. By the end of the year five further German aircraft had fallen to the guns of the 'Hurricats'.

Meanwhile, trials had proceeded with the prototype Sea Hurricane embodying catapult spools and a V-frame arrester hook, resulting in further conversion orders being placed. Some 300 Hurricane Is were scheduled for conversion and the bulk of this work was carried out by General Aircraft Ltd. These aircraft, Sea Hurricane Mk. IBs, retained the Merlin IIIs and eight-gun armament but shortly afterwards, in November 1941, twenty-five Hurricane IIA Series 2s were modified to the same standard, being henceforward variously but equally officially referred to as Sea Hurricane IBs or Hooked Hurricane IIs.

Sea Hurricane IBs were embarked from October 1941 onwards in converted merchantmen, called MAC-ships. These vessels were provided with a small flight deck on which were parked their limited complement of fighters and anti-submarine aircraft (there being no hangar accommodation) and perfomed magnificent service on the PQ convoys to Russia. The aircraft served with No. 801 Squadron (On HMS *Argus*),

A late-series Sea Hurricane IIC conversion, NF717. (*Photo: Crown Copyright.*)

No. 802 (HMS *Avenger*), No. 804 (HMS *Pegasus, Eagle, Argus, Furious* and *Dasher*), No. 806 (HMS *Formidable*), No. 824 (HMS *Striker*), No. 825 (HMS *Vindex*), No. 835 (HMS *Chaser* and *Nairana*), No. 880 (HMS *Furious* and *Indomitable*), No. 883 (HMS *Avenger*), No. 885 (HMS *Victorious*) and No. 891 (HMS *Dasher*). Moreover, the crises of early 1942 brought a shortage of fighters in North and West Africa, with the result that Sea Hurricanes of Nos. 803 and 877 Squadrons, Fleet Air Arm, were added to the land-based air forces to offset the deficiencies.

The Sea Hurricane Mk. IC followed the Mk. IB into service in February and March 1942; this employed new Hurricane IIC (four-cannon) wings on late-series converted Hurricane Is and again featured catapult spools and arrester hook. Mark ICs re-equipped Nos. 802 and 883 Squadrons in the American-built Escort Carrier HMS *Avenger*, this vessel sailing as escort for the Russian-bound convoy, PQ18, from Loch Ewe on 2 September 1942. As was customary, the convoy was subjected to incessant air attacks, but the fighter escort now provided destroyed five enemy raiders and damaged seventeen others. Though four Sea Hurricanes were lost, three of their pilots were saved.

Shortly after the introduction of the Mk. IC, one other version was delivered, the Sea Hurricane IIC. Originally intended to be newly-built Sea Hurricanes equipped with arrester hooks and naval radio, but without catapult spools, Sea Hurricane IICs were first delivered to units of the Mediterranean Fleet in December 1942, and were also based on Malta during the following year. By the end of 1943 Sea Hurricanes had been superseded on most naval squadrons, although they remained in service until mid-1945 in the Far East. As previously mentioned, a small number of Canadian-built Sea Hurricane XIIAs served in the North Atlantic.

No account of the Sea Hurricane would be complete without mention of what was undoubtedly its greatest action. 1942 saw Sea Hurricanes (mostly IBs and ICs) serving aboard the large Fleet Carriers

Indomitable, Eagle and *Victorious*, equipping Nos. 800, 801 and 885 Squadrons respectively, and these aircraft, in company with Fairey Fulmars and Grumman Martlets, formed the air defences of the vital convoy which sailed for Malta in August that year. During the voyage that followed, the seventy carrier-borne fighters endured three days of continuous attack by as many as 500 German and Italian bombers, torpedo-bombers and their escort. Thirty-nine of the enemy were destroyed for the loss of only eight naval aircraft (apart from the loss of the *Eagle*, torpedoed and sunk by U-boats), one pilot, Lt R J Cork, DSC, alone claiming six enemy aircraft.

FOREIGN HURRICANE VARIANTS

Hurricane Is were supplied abroad in small quantities in 1939, being delivered by arrangement with the Air Ministry to South Africa and

A Hurricane IIC, HV608, supplied to Turkey from the Middle East Air Force during 1942.

HU460, one of a batch of 12 Hurricane Is supplied to the Finnish Air Force in 1940 (*Photo: William Green.*)

293

One of the Hurricane IIC single-seat fighter trainers, 2-13, supplied to Persia after the Second World War.

The Persian Hurricane IIC two-seat trainer, 2-31.

2-31, the Persian two-seat Hurricane with enclosed rear cockpit.

Canada, and by Company Contract to Poland, Yugoslavia, Belgium, Romania and Turkey. Only one machine reached Poland before the Nazi invasion of September 1939, and the invasion of Belgium in 1940 interfered with plans to build the Hurricane under licence in that country. It is known, however, that at least one such machine was completed (probably using spare components supplied by the RAF) and captured intact by the enemy.

Of the contract for Hurricanes placed by Persia in 1939, only one aircraft, 252 (an ex-RAF Mark I, P3270), was flown by Reynell at Brooklands in Persian colours on 16 May 1940, and later shipped out to Persia. The contract was then held in abeyance until after the war.

As already recounted, large numbers of Hurricanes were supplied to the Russians, commencing in 1941. A further fourteen Hurricanes were delivered to Turkey during 1942 (mostly tropical Mark IICs), and although these aircraft could scarcely be afforded from the stocks available they were considered necessary in view of suspected German territorial ambitions in Turkey.

Another country that was to receive Hurricanes at a time when perhaps Britain could ill afford to supply them was Finland. Twelve Hurricane Is were supplied in 1940 shortly after that country was attacked by Russia.

Towards the end of the war the Air Ministry released a dozen Hurricane IIBs and IICs for service with the Irish Air Corps, these aircraft serving at Baldonnel between 1945 and 1947.

The Egyptian Air Force, manned principally by Egyptian pilots flying beside the Desert Air Force in defence of home bases, received about twenty tropical Hurricane IIBs and IICs.

The only other air force to receive Hurricanes during the war was that of India. Commencing in 1941, something like 300 Hurricane IIBs, IICs, IIDs, IVs and XIIs, all tropically-equipped, were delivered.

In 1946 the Persian contract was reopened, again ex-RAF machines being delivered. Sixteen Hurricane IICs were converted as single-seat trainers, the guns being removed, cannon fairing stubs substituted and Merlin 22 engines installed in place of the Merlin XXs. More interesting, however, was the Persian two-seat Hurricane, 2-31 (previously KZ232), which was first flown by Humble on 27 September 1946; although flown with open and closed rear cockpit in turn, it is believed to have been delivered with a sliding hood on the rear cockpit and an open front cockpit.

Something like forty Hurricane IICs were sold to Portugal during 1946 and 1947 (having been returned from the RAF in 1945), many being equipped with tropical filters and delivered carrying 45-gallon drop tanks. These machines were chosen from the large stocks of surplus late-series Hurricane IICs.

A Portuguese Hurricane N.F.IIC at Lisbon in 1948. (*Photo: Comando Geral da Aeronautica Militar.*)

The Hillson F.H.40 Slip-wing Hurricane.

OTHER HURRICANES

Many Hurricanes could be included under this heading, but in the space available mention of only a few is possible. Perhaps the most unconventional of all was the Hillson Slip-Wing Hurricane of 1942. Using an old Hawker-built Hurricane I, L1884 (shipped in 1939 to Canada as a 'pattern' aircraft, numbered 321 and afterwards returned to the United Kingdom), Hill and Sons Ltd conducted experiments employing a jettisonable top wing to provide extra lift for take-off. Known as the Hillson F.H.40, this aircraft was flown several times under Air Ministry contract before the scheme was finally abandoned.

A Hurricane IV, KZ706, was used late in the war for trials of the large rocket projectile known as Long Tom. With a 500 pound warhead on each missile and equipped to carry one under each wing, this Hurricane underwent trials over the Pendine Sands in 1945. Another extraordinary experiment, employing the Hurricane, involved fitting an enormous degaussing ring, reminiscent of those attached to Wellington bombers and other aircraft to explode magnetic sea mines. This forty-feet-diameter hoop was fitted to a Hurricane at Hullavington in April 1943, and the aircraft was flown to Hatfield on the 18th for inspection by Winston Churchill. The aircraft subsequently underwent trials at Boscombe Down and Farnborough, although the true nature of these trials has not been discovered.

The last Hurricane ever built, PZ865, labelled *The Last of the Many!*, was purchased by Hawker Aircraft Ltd, and is maintained to this day in

KZ706, the Hurricane IV used for experiments with the large rocket, "Long Tom".

LF363, the last Hurricane (a Mark IIC) held on RAF Charge. This aircraft led the annual Battle of Britain Fly-Past for many years.

full flying condition, though somewhat modified. All armament was removed, a Merlin 22 engine installed and a whip aerial substituted for the original mast. Registered G-AMAU and painted blue and gold, it was raced on several occasions between 1948 and 1953. In 1950 it was temporarily returned to semi-authentic markings and used in the shooting of *Angels One-Five*, a film about Hurricanes in the Battle of Britain. Due to the lack of surviving RAF Hurricanes, several Portuguese machines joined G-AMAU for the occasion. More recently it was restored to its original wartime camouflage and markings as a more realistic member of the Hawker museum. At the time of writing PZ865 flies with the RAF's Battle of Britain Memorial Flight in company with LF363, another wartime Hurricane.

G-AMAU, *The Last of the Many!*, seen here in Hawker racing livery, royal blue with gold trimmings.

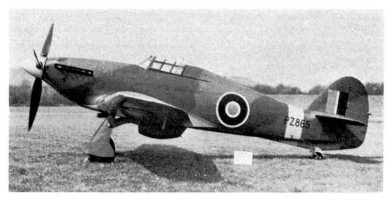

The last Hurricane (G-AMAU and PZ865) at Dunsfold in 1960.

TECHNICAL DATA FOR HURRICANE

TYPE: Single-seat interceptor fighter and fighter-bomber.

STRUCTURE: All-metal construction with fabric-covered rear fuselage and tail. From 1939 Mark Is and subsequent aircraft had metal stressed-skin-covered wings (early aircraft had fabric-covered wings). Fabric covered control surfaces.

MANUFACTURERS: Hawker Aircraft Ltd, Kingston, Brooklands and Langley. Subcontracted by Gloster Aircraft Co Ltd, Hucclecote; The Austin Motor Co Ltd, Longbridge, Birmingham; The Canadian Car & Foundry Company, Canada.

POWERPLANT: (Mark I), 1,030 hp Rolls-Royce Merlin II or III. Watts 2-blade, D.H. or Rotol 3-blade propellers.

(Mark II), 1,280 hp Rolls-Royce Merlin XX or 1,460 hp Merlin 22. 3-blade D.H. or Rotol constant speed propeller.

(Mark IV), 1,620 hp Rolls-Royce Merlin 24 or 27. 3-blade D.H. or Rotol constant speed propeller.

(Mark V), 1,635 hp Rolls-Royce Merlin 27. 4-blade Rotol constant speed propeller.

(Mark X and XI), 1,300 hp Packard-Rolls-Royce Merlin 28. 3-blade Hamilton-Standard propeller.

(Mark XII and XIIA), 1,300 hp Packard-Rolls-Royce Merlin 29. 3-blade Hamilton-Standard propeller.

Note. Tests showed that inclusion of tropical air intake and cleaner resulted in approximately 4 per cent loss of power from the figures quoted above.

DIMENSIONS: Span, 40 ft 0in. Length (Mk. I), 31 ft 5 in. Length (all other versions), 32 ft 0 in. Height (when fitted with Rotol constant speed propeller), 13 ft 1 in. Wing area, 257½ sq ft.

WEIGHTS: (Mark I) Empty, 4,670 lb. Loaded, 6,600 lb.

(Mark IIA) Empty, 5,150 lb. Loaded, 8,050 lb.

(Mark IIB) Empty, 5,640 lb. Loaded, 8,250 lb.

(Mark IIC) Empty, 5,800 lb. Loaded, 8,100 lb.

(Mark IID) Empty, 5,550 lb. Loaded, 7,850lb.

(Mark IV–'C' armament) Empty, 6,150 lb. Loaded, 8,450 lb.

(Mark V) Empty, 6,405 lb. Loaded, 8,510 lb.

(Sea Hurricane Mk IIC) Empty, 5,880 lb. Loaded, 8,100 lb.

Note. The above loaded weights are quoted as overload with (where applicable) two 90-gallon ferry tanks. Inclusion of tropical equipment added approximately 230 lb to the above weights, though aircraft serving in the tropics seldom operated at anything like the overload condition. With the exception of the Mark I, the above weights are quoted for aircraft fitted with Rotol propellers. The Mark I weight is with D.H. 2-pitch propeller.

PERFORMANCE:*

	Max. Speed, m.p.h. (See note)	Climb to 20,000 ft. Minutes.	Range Statute Miles (See note)		Service Ceiling, feet. (rate of climb, 100 ft./min.)
			(a)	(b)	
Mk. I (Watts 2-blade propeller)	318	11.7	440	—	33,400
Mk. I (Rotol 3-blade propeller)	324	9.8	425	900	34,200
Mk. I (Trop.)	312	12.2	380	860	32,100
Mk. IIA	342	8.6	470	950	36,300
Mk. IIB	340	8.9	470	940	36,000
Mk. IIB (Trop.)	324	11.6	440	880	33,600
Mk. IIC	336	9.1	460	920	35,600
Mk. IIC (Trop.)	320	11.9	430	910	33,200
Mk. IID	322	12.4	420	900	32,100
Mk. IV	330	9.3	430	910	32,600

FIXED ARMAMENT: (Mk. I, IIA, X, XI and XII, Sea Hurricane IA, IB and IC), eight 0.303 in Browning machine guns in wings; (Mk. IIB and XII), twelve 0.303 in Browning machine guns in wings, but one pair of guns was usually removed when carrying bombs; (Mk. IIC, XII and Sea Hurricane IIC), four 20 mm Hispano guns in wings; (Mk. IID), two 40 mm Rolls-Royce or Vickers anti-tank guns and two fixed 0.303 in Browning guns; the Mk. IV and V were fitted with Universal wings containing a pair of fixed 0.303 in Browning guns; in addition, two 40 mm guns, two 250 lb or 500 lb bombs, eight rocket projectiles, two 44-gallon or 90-gallon drop tanks might be carried.

EXTERNAL STORES: The following alternative stores could be carried by Hurricane Mks. IIA, IIB, IIC, XII or Sea Hurricane IIC: Two 250 lb or two 500 lb bombs; two Smoke Curtain Installations; two Small Bomb Carriers or two Universal AP Bomb Carriers; two 44-gallon or two 90-gallon drop tanks; eight 3 in rocket projectiles with 60 lb warheads; miscellaneous light bombs, flares and other naval equipment carried by Sea Hurricane.

* Note. Maximum speed is quoted at Rated Altitude of engine; it is also quoted for the clean aircraft (i.e. no external stores). Range is quoted for clean aircraft (a), and for aircraft carrying two combat-stressed 44-gallon drop tanks (b). The performance of production Hurricanes varied greatly; wherever possible the figures quoted represent the average of a number of aircraft 'production checked' from time to time at Langley and Brooklands.

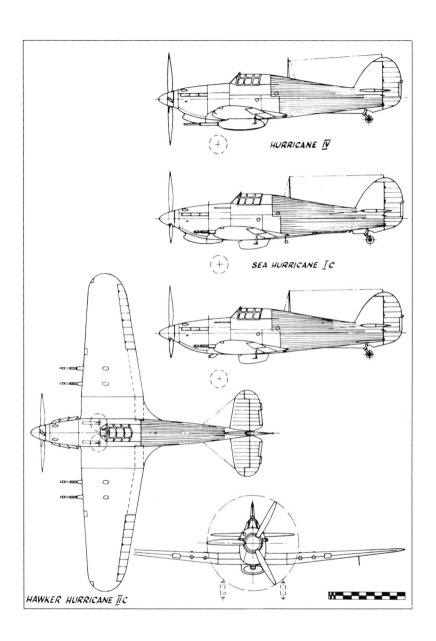

HURRICANE IV

SEA HURRICANE IC

HAWKER HURRICANE IIC

301

The first Henley prototype, K5115.

The Hawker Henley

The Hawker Henley's career as a target tug did less than justice to what was undoubtedly an extremely sound design, and came about as a result of the Air Ministry's wavering attitude towards the light bomber in 1936. Whether the new attitude, albeit difficult to define, was justified will for ever be in doubt, for in the critical days of 1940, when the British and French armies were in retreat, it is certain that the one type of aircraft lacking was the close support high performance light bomber. Instead, the Fairey Battle, with a maximum speed almost 50 mph inferior to that of the Hawker Henley, was used in this rôle at enormous cost and with relatively little effect.

In February 1934, Air Ministry Specification P.4/34 was issued, setting out a requirement for a light bomber capable of tactical support. It was to be fully stressed for dive recovery with full bomb-load and a speed requirement of approximately 300 mph was mentioned. Among the companies that tendered designs were Fairey (whose prototypes were later used in the development of the Fulmar fleet fighter), Gloster and Hawker Aircraft Ltd.

In order to fulfil the performance requirements it at once appeared obvious to the Hawker Design Staff that the aircraft should be of a similar size to that of the aircraft being currently designed as an interceptor (i.e. the Hurricane) and that it should be similarly powered, since no other engine approached the power-to-weight ratio of the projected Rolls-Royce Merlin.

Structurally, therefore, the Hurricane and Henley (as Hawkers' P.4/34 design came to be known) were closely related and the designs

302

proceeded on parallel lines. In fact the outer wing sections and tailplane were built on identical jigs, though of course the eight-gun battery was absent from the Henley. Fundamentally, however, the Henley differed in being a two-seater, a pilot and observer/gunner being accommodated in tandem under a somewhat complex canopy superstructure. Internal stowage for up to 550 pounds of bombs was proposed, while light series racks for up to eight 25-pound bombs could be added under the outer wings. The central stowage for bombs prompted the adoption of a low-mid wing position which in itself demanded a new wing centresection, for the undercarriage was thus of wider track than on the Hurricane. Defensive armament was to consist of a wing-mounted Vickers Mark V machine gun and a Lewis gun in the rear cockpit. The Vickers gun's mounting could alternatively accommodate a Bren light machine gun, though the significance of this provision has never been suitably explained.

Construction of the first Henley prototype, K5115, was commenced at Kingston in mid-1935, but due to the change of attitude towards the design implied by extensive amendment of the 1934 Specification and the eventual issue of a replacement, work on the aircraft was subordinated to that on the Hurricane. The first flight by K5115 took place at Brooklands on 10 March 1937, power being provided by a Merlin 'F' (No. 13) driving a Hamilton Hydromatic three-blade propeller. During the first three months some forty hours flying were carried out with this engine, but on 5 June K5115 was flown with a Merlin I (No. 235), again driving the Hamilton propeller.

Fabric-covered wings had been fitted on K5115 at first, but on 20 August 1937 the aircraft, at an all-up weight of 8,393 pounds, was flown with metal stressed skin wings. The aircraft then embarked on a programme of general handling, spinning and diving with various centre of gravity positions, a programme which confirmed a viceless design allied with pleasant handling characteristics. Bearing this in mind it is difficult to find justification for subsequent events, for the Henley not only

Although painted in target towing colours, Henley L3276 underwent trials at Boscombe Down in March 1942 as a light bomber trainer, seen here carrying two 112 lb and eight 20 lb practice bombs.

303

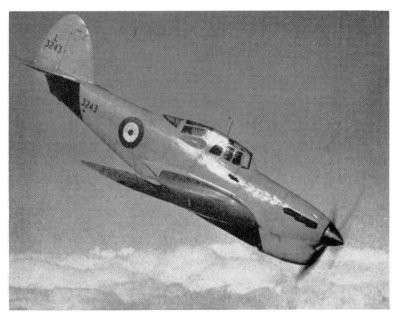
A Henley target tug, L3243.

suffered relegation in the attitude of the Air Ministry, but an unhappy spate of accidents in service.

A second prototype Henley, K7554, was completed at Brooklands in 1938, this aircraft being flown by Lucas on 26 May with a Merlin II (No. 25) driving a two-position de Havilland three-blade propeller.

In the intervening months, however, the Air Ministry's policy had made clear that the aircraft was to be relegated to target towing, and a production order — initially for 350 aircraft but now reduced to 200 — was subcontracted to the Gloster Aircraft Company at Hucclecote. K7554 remained at Brooklands only long enough for preliminary flight trials before being delivered to Glosters to be modified to the Target Towing Standard of Preparation.

Production got under way at Hucclecote during 1939, the service version being officially termed the Henley Mark III (the Mk. I being the first bomber prototype, K5115, and the Mk. II, though seldom used as an official designation, being the prototype conversion K7554). The 200 Gloster-built Henleys were completed in mid-1940, their production space being filled immediately by a further vital Hurricane assembly line.

Though production of the Henley had been transferred to Glosters, development of the type was retained by the Hawker Design Department, and early in 1939 came a request that the original prototype K5115 be modified to take the Rolls-Royce Vulture for engine

304

development flying by Rolls-Royce Ltd, and this was delivered to Hucknall in 1939. Such was the trouble experienced with the Vulture (due principally to fatigue failure of connecting-rod components) that a second aircraft, L3302, was similarly modified in 1940. Yet a third Henley test bed, L3414, was adapted (also in 1940), this time for the Rolls-Royce Griffon II, and much of the Fairey Firefly's engine installation was flown in this aircraft.

Production Henleys entered service with the Royal Air Force towards the end of 1939, serving as target tugs with Nos, 1, 5 and 10 Bombing and Gunnery Schools, and with the Air Gunnery Schools at Barrow, Squires Gate and Millom. Towing the relatively small Mark III Air Towing Sleeve, the Henley's speed was in the region of 265 mph, though for

The prototype Henley with Rolls-Royce Vulture trial installation.

L3414, the Rolls-Royce Griffon Henley engine test bed.

305

short periods at full throttle the aircraft could be coaxed another 10 mph faster. The high rate of engine attrition, however, resulted in a towing speed limit of 220 mph being imposed, a speed likely to afford little benefit to aspiring fighter pilots and quite unrepresentative of modern enemy aircraft.

Thus the Henley came gradually to be withdrawn as an air-to-air target tug and the survivors (130 remained on Charge in October 1940) were distributed amongst the Anti-Aircraft Co-operation Units and Nos. 639 and 695 (AA Co-operation) Squadrons.

The Henley's troubles now started in earnest, for, with the larger drogue target on tow, it was as much as the aircraft could do to achieve 200 mph at near full throttle, with the result that the Merlin (always an

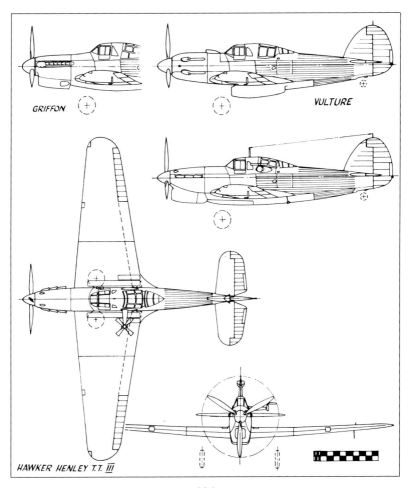

GRIFFON

VULTURE

HAWKER HENLEY T.T. III

306

engine requiring a reasonable airspeed for cooling in the best of circumstances), now suffered perpetual overheating, excessive wear and engine failures by the score. How serious the resulting accidents proved, therefore, depended on how quickly crews could release their targets. Reference to the Notes on Individual Aircraft will indicate the extent to which No. 1 AACU, based at Langham, Norfolk, suffered in this context.

Relegation of the Defiant to target-towing duties and introduction of the Miles Martinet brought the service career of the Henley to an end in 1942, though by June that year fewer than forty aircraft remained on Charge.

TECHNICAL DATA FOR HENLEY MARK III

TYPE: Two-seat target tug.

STRUCTURE: All-metal construction with fabric-covered rear fuselage and tail. Metal stressed skin-covered wings. Fabric-covered control surfaces.

MANUFACTURERS: Prototypes built by Hawker Aircraft Ltd, Kingston. Production by Gloster Aircraft Co Ltd, Hucclecote, Gloucester.

POWERPLANT: 1,030 hp Rolls-Royce Merlin II or III driving de Havilland 3-blade two-pitch propeller.

DIMENSIONS: Span, 47 ft 10½ in. Length, 36 ft 5 in. Height, 14 ft 7½ in. Wing area, 342 sq ft.

WEIGHTS: Empty, 6,010 lb. Loaded, 8,480 lb.

PERFORMANCE: Maximum speed (towing Mk. III Sleeve), approximately 270 mph. Maximum speed (with Ground/Air Gunnery Drogue), approximately 200 mph. Climb (Gunnery Drogue), 22.5 min to 20,000 ft. Range (clean), 940 miles. Service ceiling (rate of climb, 100 ft/min), 27,200 ft.

OTHER DATA: Fuel capacity, 94 gallons. Armament provision removed. Wind-driven winch for cable drum operation. Undercarriage, inwards retracting with retractable tailwheel; track, 12 ft 3 in.

The Hawker Hotspur, K8309.

The Hawker Hotspur

Early in 1935 the Air Ministry issued Specification F.9/35 for an interceptor fighter to replace the turret-equipped Demon, by now regarded as falling short both in armament and performance when compared with aircraft known to be under development abroad. The new requirements called for increased midship turret armament and speed capability comparable with the forthcoming generation of single-seat interceptors.

Despite heavy preoccupation with the Hurricane, project work commenced on a redesign of the Henley in which the whole cockpit enclosure was changed to incorporate a semi-power-operated Boulton-Paul turret mounting four 0.303 inch Browning guns. Standard Hurricane outer wing panels were used but all wing armament was omitted, provision being made for a single synchronised forward-firing Vickers gun on the port side of the nose. Moreover, slight modification of the fin shape was necessitated by the increased side area of the turret and cockpit superstructure.

Construction of the prototype, K8309, commenced in the Experimental Shops at Canbury Park Road, Kingston, in 1937, and production was scheduled to be undertaken by A V Roe & Co Ltd, under Specification 17/36.

Completion of K8309 was delayed until 1938, by which time the prototype Boulton Paul Defiant (also tendered to F.9/35) had already flown. Furthermore, it soon became evident that all factories in the newly-formed Hawker Siddeley Group were fully committed to production of designs already accepted, and the Hotspur project was abandoned.

Powered by a Rolls-Royce Merlin II engine, K8309 was first flown by

Another view of the Hotspur.

K8309, as used by the RAE for flap trials. Note the rear cockpit fairing.

P G Lucas on 14 June, 1938, but no effort was made to bring the aircraft up to a representative Service standard of preparation. It carried only armament ballast and a wooden mock-up of the turret. A brief programme of performance trials which followed showed that the Hotspur was some twenty miles per hour faster than the prototype Defiant (also fitted with a Merlin II), due mainly to its lighter loaded weight.

When it became obvious that there was little that the Hotspur could contribute as a turret fighter, the cockpit superstructure was drastically modified, the turret being removed and the gunner's position faired over. The machine then embarked on a series of trials with various flap and dive brake designs as part of the Henley light bomber development programme and was delivered to the RAE late in 1939, in whose hands it remained until 1942.

TECHNICAL DATA FOR HOTSPUR (MERLIN II)

TYPE: Two-seat interceptor turret fighter.

STRUCTURE: All-metal construction. Stressed skin wings; fabric-covered rear
fuselage and control surfaces.

MANUFACTURERS: Hawker Aircraft Ltd, Kingston.

POWERPLANT: 1,025 hp Rolls-Royce Merlin II engine driving 3-blade de
Havilland 2-position propeller.

DIMENSIONS: Span, 40 ft 6 in. Length, 32 ft 10½ in. Height, 13 ft 10 in. Wing
Area: 261.6 sq ft.

WEIGHTS: Empty, 5,800 lb. Loaded, 7,650 lb.

PERFORMANCE: Max speed, 316 mph at 15,800 ft. Climb, about 10.5 min to
15,000 ft. Service ceiling (rate of climb, 100 ft/min), about 28,000 ft.

Since the 1960s, the dimensions quoted for the Hotspur have become confused with those for the Henley. The figures
given here appear on Hawker Aircraft general arrangement drawing No. E.75821, dated 30 June, 1938, and agree with
the dimensions given in the RAE handling report and on the official recognition silhouette of the period.

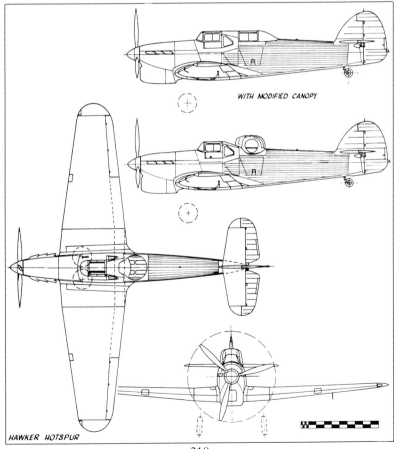

WITH MODIFIED CANOPY

HAWKER HOTSPUR

The first Hawker Tornado prototype, P5119, with 'midships radiator.

The Hawker Tornado

In 1937 a single-seat interceptor design was prepared by Hawkers using either a Napier Sabre or Rolls-Royce Vulture twenty-four-cylinder liquid-cooled engine. Specification F.18/37 was prepared and both versions were tendered, the former known initially as the 'N-type' and afterwards the Typhoon, and the latter the 'R-type', later to become the Tornado.

Both designs were made the subjects of contracts and due to delays with the Sabre, the Tornado's future appeared the more promising, and construction of a prototype commenced during 1938. The Vulture engine (No. 12) to be used in the first machine, P5219, was received at Kingston in December 1938, and on 31 July the following year the aircraft was moved to Langley. The first flight, undertaken by Lucas, was made on 6 October 1939, and on the strength of promise shown by the new design an Instruction to Proceed was received for the construction of 500 Tornados, 250 Typhoons and a further 250 aircraft whose engines were to be decided later.

Production of the Tornado was to be undertaken by A V Roe & Co Ltd at Manchester, after an initial batch had been completed at Langley.

For the first few flights of P5219 the radiator bath was positioned under the fuselage amidships in a similar fashion to that on the Hurricane, but the onset of compressibility at high speeds caused adverse airflow conditions round the fairing, resulting in the decision to move the radiator forward under the engine. With the now-familiar 'chin' radiator, P5219 first flew on 6 December 1939. This aircraft, with an all-up weight of 9,250 pounds, was powered by a Vulture II and provision was made for an armament of twelve Browning machine guns. The Tornado was most readily distinguishable from the Typhoon in having

311

two rows of exhaust manifolds on each side of the engine cowling, whereas the Typhoon had a single set each side.

The second prototype, P5224, flew on 5 December 1940, also with a Vulture II and Rotol constant-speed propeller, but at an increased weight of 9,600 pounds, provision for four 20 mm Hispano cannon being made. Within two months, flying with full fuel and gun ballast, the weight had been increased to 10,580 pounds. During March 1941, the Vulture IIs in both prototypes were replaced by Vulture Vs, the type planned for the production line.

Meanwhile, as experience had shown on the Vulture-Henley test beds and in service with the Avro Manchester, the Vulture was in serious trouble as a result of frequent connecting-rod bolt fractures (though evidence does not necessarily show this to have been any worse than on the equally temperamental Sabre) and due to the absolute priorities afforded to Rolls-Royce Merlin production the Vulture was abandoned.

An alternative proposal to install the Wright Duplex Cyclone Type C engine in Tornados had been put forward in January 1941, and although much design work was carried out on this project at Kingston the Ministry of Aircraft Production suspended all work on the engine in July that year.

Production at Avros had nevertheless got under way and one Vulture-engined production machine, R7936, was completed and flown at Woodford on 29 August 1941. After a further flight at Langley two days later R7936 was delivered in turn to Rotol Ltd, at Staverton, and de Havilland Propellers Ltd, Hatfield, for use as an airscrew flying test bed. During the following eighteen months this machine was fitted with various Rotol and D.H. six-blade contra-rotating propellers.

As far back as January 1940, Sydney Camm had suggested the installation of the new Bristol Centaurus eighteen-cylinder air-cooled

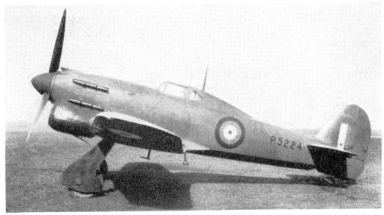

The second Tornado, P5224, with the familiar "chin" radiator.

312

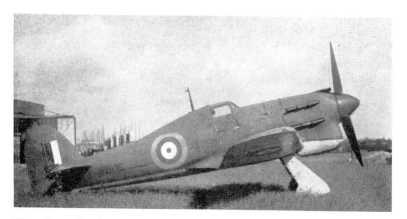

The sole production Tornado, R7936, before relegation to contra-propeller testing.

radial in the Tornado, but work in other directions had caused this project to be delayed. In April the same year it was proposed to order an additional prototype, but in the event only a new centre fuselage was built, the rear fuselage being taken from the Langley production line and the wings from stock. The new prototype, HG641, was completed at Langley and with a Centaurus C.E.4S engine was flown by Lucas on 23 October 1941. Early cooling problems with the installation led to considerable redesign of the engine cowling, the oil cooler fairing being made integral with the bottom of the cowling itself. Furthermore, a large spinner now fully enclosed the Rotol propeller hub.

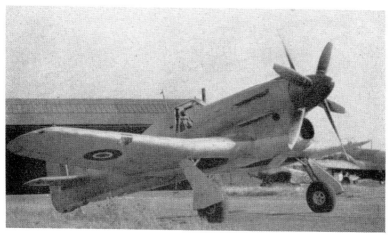

R7936 at Rotol's test aerodrome, Staverton, with six-blade contra-propeller.
(*Photo: Rotol Ltd.*)

313

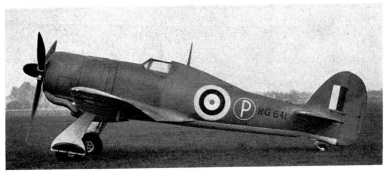

The much-modified Tornado airframe, HG641, with an early Bristol Centaurus installation.

Flight trials with HG641 were encouraging to the extent that high priority was given to the Centaurus development of the Tornado. However, with the abandoning of Tornado production, development of the installation became henceforward associated with the Typhoon, and six Centaurus prototypes were ordered. As is related on page 337 this project developed into the Typhoon II and subsequently the Tempest.

Thus, despite an early demise as a design in its own right, the Tornado was to foster development of Hawker radial engine fighters which were to fly for another twenty years.

HG641 with modified Centaurus installation and four-blade Rotol propeller.

TECHNICAL DATA FOR TORNADO (VULTURE II AND V)

TYPE: Experimental single-seat interceptor fighter.

STRUCTURE: All-metal tubular and stressed-skin construction, except fabric-covered rudder.

MANUFACTURERS: Hawker Aircraft Ltd, Kingston (three aircraft completed). A V Roe & Co, Manchester (one completed).

POWERPLANT: P5219. 1,760 hp Rolls-Royce Vulture II driving 14 ft 0 in diameter D.H. Hydromatic 3-blade propeller. Later fitted with 1,980 hp Rolls-Royce Vulture V driving Rotol constant-speed 13 ft 3 in diameter 3-blade propeller. R7936: Fitted with Vulture V used to test various Rotol and D.H. 6-blade contra-rotating propellers. HG641: 2,210 hp Bristol

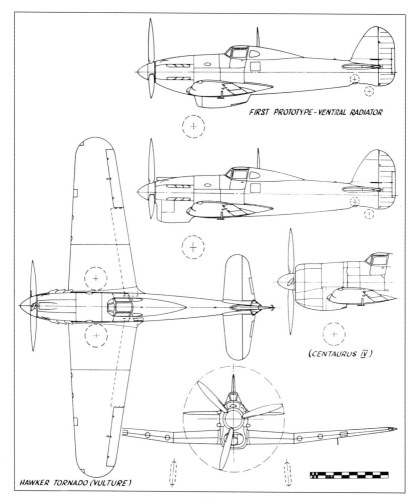

FIRST PROTOTYPE - VENTRAL RADIATOR

(CENTAURUS IV)

HAWKER TORNADO (VULTURE)

315

Centaurus C.E.4S radial engine driving various 3- and 4-blade Rotol and D.H. propellers.

DIMENSIONS: Span, 41 ft 11 in. Length (Vulture versions), 32 ft 10 in. Height (Rotol propeller), 14 ft 8 in. Wing area, 283 sq ft.

WEIGHTS: (Vulture versions); Empty, 8,377 lb. Loaded, 10,668 lb.

PERFORMANCE: Vulture V. Max speed, 398 mph at 23,000 ft. Climb, 7.2 min to 2,000 ft. Service ceiling (rate of climb, 100 ft/min), 34,900 ft.

Centaurus C.E.4S. Max speed, 402 mph at 18,000 ft. Climb, 8.4 min to 20,000 ft. Service ceiling (rate of climb, 100 ft/min), 32,800 ft.

OTHER DATA: Fuel capacity, 140 gallons. Armament, none carried, but machines had provison for either 12 Browning machine guns or 4 Hispano 20 mm cannon in the outer wing panels. Undercarriage, inwards retracting; track, 13 ft 8 in. Wheels, Dunlop, 11 in × 12 in.

P5212, the first Hawker Typhoon prototype in its original form. Note the small fin, triple exhaust stubs, absence of armament and large-diameter, low-pressure tyres.

The Hawker Typhoon

At about the time that the first production Hurricanes were nearing completion at Kingston in 1937, the Hawker design team was anticipating the requirement for a successor, and by the time Specification F.18/37 was issued much work had already been done. The new aircraft was to be a twelve-gun interceptor powered by either the Rolls-Royce Vulture or Napier Sabre twenty-four-cylinder engines and from the start design work on both installations continued in parallel. Owing, however, to development delays with the Sabre it was the Vulture prototype,

316

This photograph, taken during manufacture of the second Typhoon prototype, gives an excellent impression of the size and complexity of the
Napier Sabre engine.

The second Typhoon, P5216, with twelve-machine-gun armament. Note
hinged wheel flaps.

known as the Hawker Tornado, which was completed first, being flown
on 6 October 1939.

The Sabre-engined Typhoon prototype, P5212, was however completed soon after and was flown by Lucas on 24 February 1940.
Simultaneously arrangements were made to place both the Tornado and

Typhoon in production, the initial batches of each to be built by Hawkers and the main production subcontracted, the Tornado to Avros and the Typhoon to Glosters.

The Typhoon combined what was becoming regarded as orthodox stressed skin construction with the traditional Hawker tubular construction. The forward half of the fuselage, extending just aft of the cockpit, was a braced tubular structure similar to that on the Hurricane, but aft of this the fuselage consisted of a monocoque shell attached at four points to the fore structure. Each wing was made in one piece with the exception of the detachable tip, the anhedral section of the spar members bolting directly to the forward fuselage. A

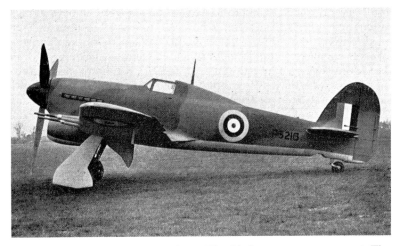

P5216 modified as prototype Typhoon IB with four-cannon armament. The standard central wheel bay doors have also been fitted.

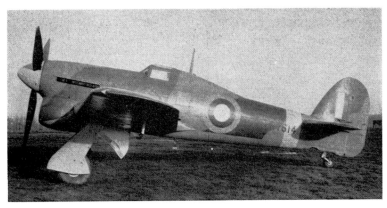

A rare photograph of an early production Typhoon IA, R7614.

318

very wide track undercarriage retracted inwards into the anhedral wing section.

Many setbacks were suffered in the early days of the Typhoon, and after Dunkirk production plans were considerably delayed due to the urgency to increase the flow of Hurricanes for the difficult times ahead. Test flying of P5212 continued uninterrupted until 9 May 1940, when failure of the monocoque structure aft of the cockpit nearly caused the loss of the aircraft. Lucas managed, however, to make a safe landing, thereby permitting modifications to be made to rectify the fault; the feat also brought to Lucas the award of the George Medal, such was the importance now attached to the successful development of the Typhoon, and the aircraft was flying once more within a month.

Provision had been made on P5212 to mount the twelve Browning machine guns originally called for in the Specification, and this version became known as the Typhoon Mk. IA. The second prototype, P5216, which flew on 3 May 1941, was armed with four 20 mm Hispano cannon and was the Mk. IB. The latter armament had by now become regarded as of greater importance, but owing to delays in delivery of the Chatellerault cannon feed mechanism the first production aircraft both at Hawkers and Glosters were of the Mk. IA type. Moreover, plans were

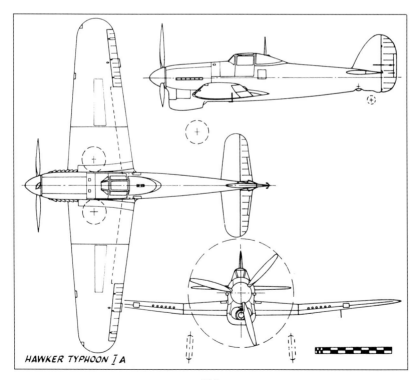

HAWKER TYPHOON I A

319

This Typhoon IB, R7646, displays the second hood design but retains the "car door" access.

under way to equip the Typhoon with six 20 mm guns, and although a set of wings so fitted was completed the installation was not flown. Other investigations called for in 1941 were for the fitting of an exhaust-driven supercharger in the Typhoon, but again this was not flown. A trial installation which did fly, however, was a set of wings with extended tips in an attempt to increase the high-altitude performance. These were flown on P5216 on 9 November 1941.

While the prototype flying was progressing at Langley production was

The first trial installation of a single-piece sliding hood, on Typhoon IB R8808. Note the paint scars left by the "car door".

getting under way at Hucclecote, and the first Gloster-built machine, R7576, was flown by Michael Daunt on 27 May 1941. The first flight by a Langley-built Typhoon, R8198, was on 26 November 1941.

These early Typhoons, both Mks. IA and IB, were powered by Napier Sabre I engines and featured hood fairings which severely restricted the pilots' rearward field of view. During September 1941, four Gloster-built aircraft were delivered to the RAF, two to the AFDU and two to No. 56 (Fighter) Squadron at Duxford, though the latter was moved to the forward aerodrome at Matlask within a week. As more aircraft followed it soon became evident that all was not well with the Typhoon. As an interceptor fighter it had a disappointing rate of climb, while frequent engine failures showed that the Sabre was an engine which, although committed to operational service, was still suffering fundamental teething troubles.

One of three Typhoons, DN323, despatched to the Middle East for Tropical Trials in 1942. The only significant distinguishing feature is the ventral air exit fairing.

Hardly had the Typhoon arrived at Duxford than reports were received that carbon monoxide contamination of the cockpit had been encountered, and all Typhoons were grounded pending investigation. This was eventually discovered to have two causes, the first being the breakdown of a seal round the hot-air trunk from the engine to the wing gun bays (for de-icing) where it passed through the bulkhead forward of the cockpit. No sooner had this been rectified than it was found that exhaust fumes were seeping into the cockpit at the forward edge of the starboard 'car door' — which itself was not popular with Typhoon pilots; this was in time cured by the introduction of longer exhaust ejector stubs, and ultimately by incorporation of a conventional sliding cockpit canopy and elimination of the doors altogether.

These troubles occurred around the end of 1941, by which time about 150 Typhoons had been taken on charge by the RAF, but soon afterwards a much more alarming series of accidents occurred, following the loss of Typhoons' entire tail units, the fuselage failing at the rear transport joint. For several months it was believed that failure of this joint constituted the primary cause of the accidents until, following the death of Hawker test pilot Kenneth Seth-Smith, after the tail of his Typhoon broke off in flight, detailed examination of the wreckage disclosed that a tiny bracket securing the elevator mass-balance weight had failed through fatigue. It was immediately deduced that such a failure would be followed by instantaneous and vigorous elevator flutter, imposing catastrophic loads on the entire tail unit and causing breakage at the structure's weakest point, the transport joint. The joint itself was found to be entirely strong enough to accommodate any normal flight loads — as was demonstrated by Typhoons under test recovering from near vertical dives at 500 mph. The remedy cost no more than a few shillings! (Even so, the Air Ministry insisted that fish plates be riveted round the rear transport joint, an 'expedient' that contributed nothing to the strength of the Typhoon's tail structure.)

Nevertheless, the Typhoon had acquired a bad name early in its Service life, and against a background of rumours — entirely unfounded — that squadrons were to give up their Spitfires in favour of the 400 mph Typhoon, a powerful lobby raised its voice to suggest that it should be the Typhoon that should be abandoned.

Already it was known that the aircraft possessed a very poor performance above 20,000 ft — due in the main to its thick wing — and the idea of meeting the new Focke-Wulf Fw 190 at heights below 20,000 ft

The only Typhoon N.F. IB to be built, R7881, with AI Mk. IV radar; it was not considered a successful experiment due to the difficulty of flying the Typhoon on night operations.

did not appeal to Spitfire pilots at all. Injury was added to insult when, because of a superficial resemblance between the Typhoon and Fw 190, several of the British fighters were shot down by Spitfires, as well as by the ground defences along the east coast.

Notwithstanding these problems, the Typhoon was now issued to an increasing number of fighter squadrons — mostly formerly flying the Hurricane — and the first Typhoon Wing came into being at Duxford during the summer of 1942. This Wing received its baptism of fire during the Allied combined operations at Dieppe on 19 August but, owing to inept planning by No. 11 Group, the Typhoons were committed to patrol at the wrong place and time. The Wing was bounced by Fw 190s which shot down one of the RAF aircraft and damaged another. Immediately afterwards a Canadian Spitfire squadron joined in — and shot down the damaged Typhoon.

A two-gun Typhoon F.R. IB, EK427.

Clearly the Typhoon's days as an interceptor were numbered. Fortunately a series of operational trials had been concluded which, involving No. 609 Squadron under the inspired command of Sqn Ldr R P Beamont, suggested the suitability of the Typhoon for ground-attack operations. This perceptive pilot had strongly condemned the Typhoon in some respects, not least in the matter of poor visibility from the cockpit, but had quickly demonstrated that its low-level performance and hard-hitting potential should be exploited to the full, with the result that from the end of 1942 more and more Typhoon squadrons transferred from home defence duties to offensive operations across the Channel.

In the rôle of close support the Typhoon was to excel. Adopting the tactics of the older Hurricane figher-bombers (by 1943 far too slow in the presence of fighter opposition), the Typhoon proved its worth. Most

323

A rocket-equipped Typhoon IB, EK497.

of the early machines had been withdrawn from operational service and many of them had been used to develop close support tactics carrying a wide variety of external stores. At Boscombe Down 500 pound bombs had been carried by R7646 in 1942 and later American 1,000 pounders were tested on MN551. Forty-five- and ninety-gallon drop tanks were fitted to R8672. MN466 was used to develop 500 pound smoke bomb containers, while M.10 smoke tanks were carried by JR448. Later still A Mk. VIII mines were tested under the wings of SW518.

But no weapon proved so effective as the Typhoon's rocket projec-

A late-series Typhoon IB with Sabre IIB and DH four-blade propeller.

tiles. After the success of the Hurricane RP installation trials were initiated by Hawkers and conducted by the A&AEE in 1943 with a Typhoon (MN861) carrying eight 3 inch RPs with 60 pound heads. By the end of 1943 rocket-firing Typhoons had joined forces with the many fighter-bomber squadrons based all along the south coast. Together they operated to deadly effect against enemy coastal shipping in the prolonged 'Channel Stop' campaign, as well as performing offensive sweeps on the Continental mainland. Bombs, rockets and cannon-fire were all brought to bear on enemy communications in France and the Low Countries, with the result that the supply organisation supporting the 'Northern Wall' fortifications was rendered chaotic.

Typhoon F.B. IB JR128 of No. 183 (Fighter) Squadron.

By D-Day on 6 June 1944 Typhoons had switched their attention to fixed military installations on the French coast. As a prelude to the Allied landings Typhoons of Nos. 198 and 609 Squadrons attacked and destroyed the enemy radar station at Dieppe/Caudecote on 2 June, while three days later Nos. 174, 175 and 245 Squadrons' Typhoons destroyed the Jouourg installation which virtually overlooked the proposed beach-heads in Normandy.

As the Allied armies broke out of the Northern perimeter in France and more Typhoons operated close up with the advancing forces, so the new pattern of close support was demonstrated by the Royal Air Force. Maintaining a standing patrol (or 'Cab Rank') at about 10,000 feet over the battle area, the Typhoons could be called down by an RAF officer accompanying the land forces to strike any convenient target with guns, bombs and rockets as the necessity arose. Perhaps the most dramatic of

325

all Typhoon battles was that at Falaise. With the swiftly moving American armoured forces sweeping up from the south and the British and Canadian forces in the north, a beaten German army was trying to extricate itself from the pocket through a narrowing gap at Falaise. The Typhoons of no fewer than ten tactical squadrons attacked the congested roads, destroying enemy vehicles of all descriptions, with the result that few Germans escaped, the survivors being eager to surrender rather than endure the terrifying salvoes of rockets.

The advance through France and Belgium brought the Typhoons to the Dutch frontier by October 1944. On the 24th of that month, No.146 Wing, consisting of Nos. 193, 197, 257, 263 and 266 Squadrons of No. 84 Group, staged one of the famous 'set pieces' of the North European campaign. Led by Gp Capt D E Gillam, three formations of Typhoons

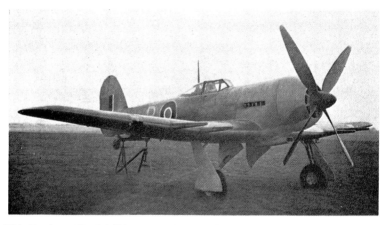

This Typhoon IB, R8694, was used by Napiers for trials with an experimental annular radiator.

were sent to attack the headquarters of the German Fifteenth Army in the old Dutch city of Dordrecht. The raid, planned to the last detail, was entirely successful, resulting in the destruction of the headquarters building and the deaths of two German generals and over seventy other Staff officers.

Typhoon squadrons were, however, to be hardest hit in the *Luftwaffe's* mass attack, Operation *Bodenplatte*, launched against Allied aerodromes in the Low Countries on 1 January 1945. Soon after dawn on that New Year's Day, the low-level strikes by a total of about 800 enemy fighters and fighter-bombers achieved almost total surprise at a dozen aerodromes, among which those at Eindhoven, Volkel and Antwerpe-Deune were occupied by seventeen Typhoon squadrons. Of some 160 Typhoons destroyed or damaged beyond repair, no fewer than 141 were lost at Eindhoven, where the German attackers arrived just as

Final production version of the Typhoon was the Mark IB with Sabre IIC, D.H. four-blade propeller, faired cannon, single-piece hood, whip aerial and exhaust stack plinth.

the Canadian Typhoon Wing was in the act of taking off. At any other time in the war such losses would have been regarded as catastrophic; as it was, such were the reserves of aircraft now held by the Allies that all losses had been made good within two days and all squadrons were fully operational within three. German losses, generally said to have been more than 200 pilots and aircraft, were, however, irreplaceable.

By the end of the war in Europe the Typhoon was being replaced by the Tempest V, while several squadrons were simply disbanded, their aircraft being returned to Maintenance Units in the United Kingdom for breaking up.

Altogether, 3,330 Typhoon IAs and IBs were built, all but a mere handful by Gloster Aircraft Co Ltd. Sub-variants of the Mark IB included versions used for fighter reconnaissance duties, known as the F.R.IB. Two variations were developed, one employing two vertical cameras in the rear fuselage and retaining the four-cannon armament; the other, used to a small extent during the Normandy campaign, featured a forward-facing ciné recorder in place of the port inner cannon.

An interesting project which did not materialise was a naval Typhoon design tendered to Specification N.11/40 early in 1941. With a greatly increased wing centresection for additional fuel, folding wings, and undercarriage with increased travel, and lengthened fuselage, this design bore a striking resemblance to the Blackburn Firebrand, the aircraft finally adopted under this Specification.

TECHNICAL DATA FOR TYPHOON IA AND IB

TYPE: Single-seat interceptor fighter and fighter-bomber.

STRUCTURE: All-metal construction with stressed skin covering. Monocoque rear fuselage. Fabric-covered rudder.

MANUFACTURERS: Prototypes and early production machines built by Hawker Aircraft Ltd, Kingston and Langley; main production undertaken by Gloster Aircraft Co Ltd, Hucclecote, Glos.

POWERPLANT: Early aircraft powered by 2,100 hp Napier Sabre Is driving 3-blade D.H. propellers. Later machines powered by 2,180 hp Sabre IIAs, 2,200 hp Sabre IIBs and 2,260 hp Sabre IICs driving 3- or 4-blade D.H. or Rotol propellers.

DIMENSIONS: Span, 41 ft. 7in. Length (early machines), 31 ft 10 in. Length (late machines), 31 ft 11½ in. Height (early machines), 14 ft 10 in. Height (late machines), 15 ft 4 in. Wing area, 279 sq ft.

WEIGHTS: Empty, 8,840 lb. Loaded (late aircraft with two 1,000 lb bombs and D.H. 4-blade propeller), 13,250 lb.

PERFORMANCE: (with Napier Sabre IIB and 4-blade propeller). Max speed, 412 mph at 19,000 ft. Climb, 5 min 50 sec to 15,000 ft. Range 510 miles with two 500 lb bombs; 980 miles with two auxiliary drop tanks. Service ceiling (rate of climb, 100 ft/min), 35,200 ft.

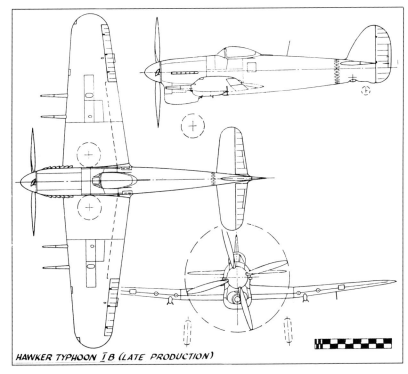

HAWKER TYPHOON IB (LATE PRODUCTION)

OTHER DATA: Armament (Mark IA), twelve 0.303 in Browning machine guns with 500 rounds per gun. Armament (Mark IB), four 20 mm Hispano cannon and provision for up to eight 3 in rocket projectiles with 60 lb warheads or two 1,000 lb bombs under the wings. Undercarriage; inwards-retracting main-wheels and forward-retracting tailwheel. Track, 13 ft 6¾ in.

The Hawker Tempest I prototype, HM599.

The Hawker Tempest

Having regard to the disappointing début of the Typhoon at the end of 1941, it is perhaps surprising that the Tempest ever survived the project stage of its career. Survive it did, however, to become one of the most effective Allied fighters in Europe during the Second World War, for its introduction into RAF service in 1944 resulted to a large extent in the defeat of the flying bomb attack on Southern England.

The Tempest owes its inception to discussions held in 1941 between Camm and the Director of Technical Development, during which it was suggested that the Typhoon might be improved by incorporating a thin elliptical wing, the new Sabre EC.107C (later to become the Sabre IV) and wing leading edge radiators.

The Typhoon had employed a NACA 22-Series wing section possessing a root thickness:chord ratio of about 18 per cent, and while this was found to be quite satisfactory at all level speeds attainable by the Typhoon, the aircraft displayed severe buffeting and aileron reversal tendencies when dived at speeds of about 500 mph, making it quite impossible to aim the guns accurately. Camm's staff had, in 1940, commenced design of a new wing with a root T/C ratio of 14.5 per cent

329

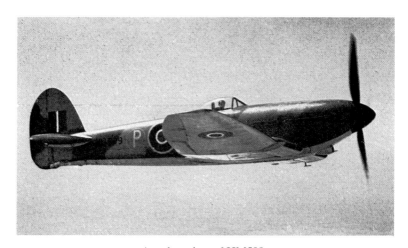

Another view of HM599.

decreasing to 10 per cent at the tip, the maximum thickness occurring at 37.5 per cent of the chord. Applying this section to the new design resulted in a maximum root thickness some five inches thinner than on the Typhoon, necessitating provision of an extra fuselage tank in which

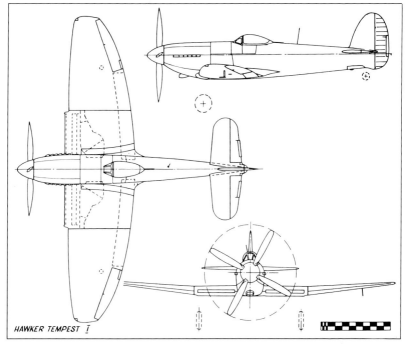

HAWKER TEMPEST I

to carry the fuel previously accommodated in the Typhoon's thick wing.

Known as the Typhoon II, this design was tendered to Air Ministry Specification F.10/41, and on 18 November 1941 a contract was awarded to Hawker Aircraft Ltd for two prototypes, HM595 and HM599.

With the cancellation of the Tornado programme, the various alternative powerplant proposals which had been associated with that aircraft in anticipation of difficulties with the Vulture engine henceforward were applied to the Typhoon II.

After the Typhoon II had been renamed Tempest (for the new design differed radically in many respects) early in 1942, the number of prototypes was increased to six: one with Sabre IV (Tempest I, HM599), two with Centaurus (Tempest II, LA602 and LA607), two with Griffons (Tempest III and IV) and one with Sabre II (Tempest V, HM595). The

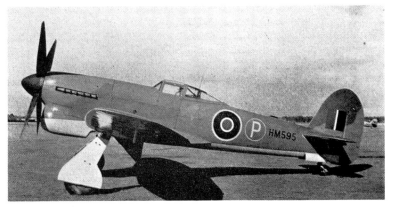

HM595, the prototype Tempest V, here seen with Typhoon tail unit.

two Griffon prototypes, LA610 and LA614, were to be fitted initially with Mark IIB engines and known as the Tempest III, but subsequently replaced by Griffon 61 'power eggs' at a later date, the aircraft thus becoming the Tempest IV. It transpired that neither of these prototypes was completed as a Tempest, although LA610 became a prototype Fury.

In August 1942, before any Tempest prototype had flown, production contracts for 400 Tempest Is were issued to Hawkers though due to subsequent delays and difficulties with the Sabre IV this programme was transferred to the Tempest V. It was in fact the Tempest V prototype, HM595, which flew first, being flown by Philip Lucas on 2 September 1942. This aircraft, in its original form, featured a tail unit and cockpit enclosure similar to that on the current Typhoons, but two months later a dorsal fin fairing was added and the tailplane chord increased; these features, necessary in view of the lengthened fuselage, were incorporated in all subsequent production Tempests.

HM595 with interim dorsal fin. The white bar on the fuselage was a datum line used during evaluation trials.

On 24 February 1943 the Tempest I prototype, HM599, flew and with its finely contoured nose cowling and unobtrusive leading edge radiators, this aeroplane was undoubtedly the most attractive member of the Typhoon/Tempest family. Moreover, by reason of the thin wing and high power output of the Sabre IV, the top speed at 24,500 feet was 466 mph. This high speed capability was only manifest in FS gear at relatively high altitudes, and when the production difficulties arose with the engine, the Tempest I development was abandoned. An alternative proposal was submitted, however, for the installation of a Sabre V using the Napier annular radiator system; this was flown experimentally on a Tempest V, NV768, and later employed a huge ducted spinner.

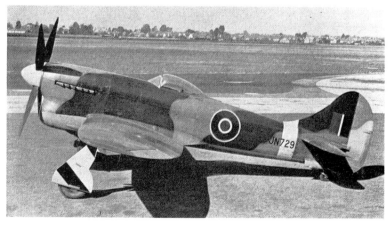

The first production Tempest V Series 1, JN729.

A Tempest V target tug, SN329, with wind-driven target winch under the port wing

SN354, one of the last Tempest Vs built, with two 40 mm "P" guns.

THE TEMPEST V

Tempest V production had meanwhile got under way at the Hawker factory at Langley, Bucks, the first machine from the lines, JN729, being flown by Bill Humble on 21 June 1943. The early aircraft, termed Mark V Series 1, were armed with four British Hispano Mark II 20 mm guns, of which the barrels extended forward of the wing leading edge. On the Mark V Series 2 aircraft the Hispano Mark V guns in this instance were fully contained within the wings, and spring tabs were also fitted. Napier Sabre IIA and IIB engines powered the Tempest V.

During the period August–December 1943, several of the first production Tempest Vs underwent extensive service trials at Boscombe Down, being developed, like the Typhoon, to operate with a wide range of external stores, including 500 and 1,000 pound bombs and 3 inch RPs with 60 pound warheads. The following April the Tempest gained its Service clearance and fifty machines were delivered to Newchurch in Kent. Here, under the command of Wg Cdr R P Beamont, DSO, DFC (who had until recently been engaged in flight testing the Tempest with the Hawker pilots at Langley), the first Tempest Wing was formed consisting of Nos. 3 and 486 Squadrons. They were joined in June by No. 56 Squadron, which had received Tempests in exchange for its Typhoons.

The long range of the Tempest enabled the Newchurch aircraft to operate well into Northern Europe, and in the first three months of operations the Wing flew over 3,000 sorties, attacking with guns and bombs enemy aerodromes, radar installations and transport facilities in France and the Low Countries.

The newly established system of launching sites for the German flying bombs was also attacked constantly, but such was the structure and defence of these sites that many escaped destruction. When the V.1 offensive was eventually launched in June 1944, the Tempests were immediately switched to the defensive, and in company with five other squadrons, similarly equipped, quickly established themselves as the keystone of the fighter defence system against the flying bomb. Faster even than the early Gloster Meteor jet fighters (which were temporarily introduced into service during the V.1. attacks), the Tempests destroyed 638 bombs out of the RAF's total score of 1,771 during the period 13 June to 5 September 1944.

It is worth remarking here that Wg Cdr Beamont led the Newchurch Tempest Wing for eight months from March 1944. His 'personal' aircraft, JN751, was the first Tempest to fly a ground-attack sortie over Northern Europe (on 28 May, over a week before the Normandy landings), the first Tempest to shoot down an enemy aircraft (a Messerschmitt Bf 109G on 8 June) and the first Tempest to shoot down a flying bomb (on 16 June). Beamont also led the first Tempest sortie over Germany — on 11 September — the Tempests of Nos. 3, 56 and 486 Squadrons flying with wing drop tanks for the first time on offensive operations.

On 12 October Beamont was leading No. 3 Squadron over Germany when his aircraft, now NV768, was hit by *flak* and forced down in enemy territory; the pilot was unhurt, but spent the last seven months of the war in Europe as a prisoner of the Germans. (Shortly before this last flight, Beamont had been approached with an offer to become Chief Test Pilot with Hawker Aircraft Ltd, an offer he declined to accept until he had completed his 100th operational sortie over enemy territory. He was to be shot down on his 95th.)

After the launching sites had been overrun by the advancing British and Canadian armies towards the end of 1944, the Tempests were again employed in attacks against ground targets on the Continent. Nine

The experimental annular radiator installation on Tempest V NV768.

NV768 with a ducted spinner forward of the annular radiator.

squadrons were moved forward to landing grounds in France and Belgium, operating with conspicuous success with bombs and rockets against the many objectives specified by the Air Liaison Officers accompanying the Army.

At the time of the *Luftwaffe's* famous mass attack on New Year's Day 1945, against Allied landing grounds, by good fortune the majority of Tempests were already airborne on support missions, for when they returned with light fuel loads and bereft of external stores they did great execution among the German fighter-bombers, including the destruction of a few of the potent Messerschmitt Me 262 jet fighters. It is now known that a total of at least eleven Messerschmitt Me 262s was destroyed by

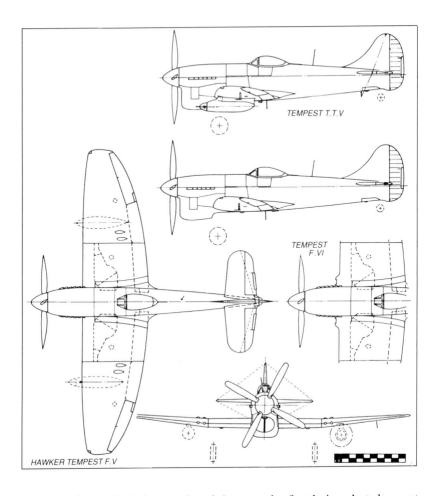

TEMPEST T.T.V

TEMPEST F.VI

HAWKER TEMPEST F.V

Tempests in the final six months of the war, the first being shot down at Grave by Plt Off R W Cole of No. 3 Squadron shortly before the end of November 1944. No other Allied fighter approached this tally of enemy jets.

Tempest Vs continued operating until the end of the European war and remained in BAFO Squadrons until replaced by Tempest IIs, Vampires and Meteors. Thereafter, they were modified for target towing duties, either employing a winch pack under the port wing or snatching a static tow line off the ground at take-off. These (together with a number of similarly modified Tempest VIs) were stationed at the RAF Armament Training Station at Sylt in North Germany, some surviving until 1953 when they were finally replaced by Meteor 7s and 8s.

One Tempest V which deserves individual mention was SN354, a late production machine equipped, in 1945, to mount a long-barrel 40 mm 'P'

The first Tempest II prototype, LA602, with Typhoon tail unit.

gun under each wing. First flown by Bill Humble on 19 October 1945, it was later delivered to Boscombe Down for extensive firing trials. Compared with the fifteen rounds per 40 mm 'S' gun carried by the Hurricane IID, the Tempest V with 'P' guns could accommodate thirty-eight rounds per gun.

Total production of the Tempest V amounted to 800 aircraft, some 1,200 having been cancelled at the end of the war in Europe.

THE TEMPEST II

The Tempest II was a joint outcome of the decision to transfer alternative engine proposals for the Tornado to the Typhoon II, and the independent decision to build a separate Typhoon I with Centaurus. This

An early Hawker-built Tempest II fighter, MW764.

latter prototype, LA594, was never completed, sufficient experience being gained on the Centaurus Tornado, HG641. Two prototype Centaurus Tempests, LA602 and LA607, were however ordered and in view of the promise shown by the Tornado installation a contract for no fewer than 500 production Tempest IIs was placed in September 1942, ten months before the first of the prototypes flew.

Powered by a Centaurus IV with rigid mounting, the first prototype Tempest II, LA602, was flown by Lucas on 28 June 1943, and plans were made for production of this version to be undertaken by Gloster Aircraft Company. The high priority, however, subsequently given to production of the Gloster Meteor, together with continued preoccupation with the Typhoon, rendered these plans impracticable, and in August 1943, the contract (by now increased to 600 aircraft) was transferred to the Bristol Aeroplane Company.

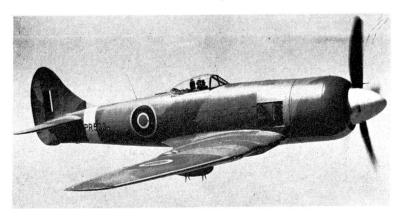

A late-series Tempest II fighter-bomber, PR533.

One of the Indian Tempest IIs HA547 (previously PR874).

338

At this time vibration troubles were being experienced with the rigid engine mounting and it was at first decided to adopt a Rotol five-blade propeller. Subsequent tests, however, showed that a six-unit soft rubber engine mounting in conjunction with an aerodynamically-balanced Rotol four-blade wooden propeller provided a satisfactory remedy.

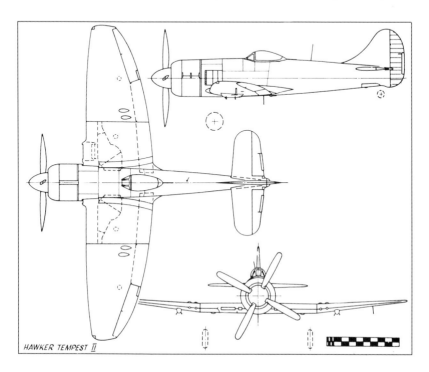

HAWKER TEMPEST II

A Pakistani Tempest II, A128, (previously PR866).

The second prototype Tempest II, LA607, flew for the first time on 18 September 1943, also fitted with a Centaurus IV, though the heavy engine development programme planned for this engine resulted in LA607 being used for handling trials with several powerplants, including the Centaurus IV, V (at Mk. VII rating), XII, XV and XVIII. The aircraft itself, fitted with its original Centaurus IV, was eventually delivered to the College of Aeronautics at Cranfield, where it remains to this day.

Production of the Tempest II started slowly at Bristol's Weston-Super-Mare factory, the first machine, MW374, flying on 4 October 1944; moreover it became obvious that the swift tide of events in Europe would overtake the development of the Tempest II and it was proposed that a Wing of fifty aircraft should be sent to the Far Eastern theatre in May 1945, under the command of Wg Cdr R P Beamont, as part of Tiger Force. The abrupt conclusion of the Pacific War again thwarted the Tempest and when the first Squadron was eventually equipped, it was Beamont who flew the leading aircraft in the Victory Commemoration Fly-past over London on 8 June 1946.

This Squadron, No. 54, based at Chilbolton, was unique in being the only home-based Tempest II squadron to be formed. The other aircraft were sent overseas, serving with Nos. 16, 26 and 33 Squadrons in BAFO in Germany, and Nos. 5, 20, 30 and 152 Squadrons in India. No. 33 Squadron moved in 1949 with their Tempests to Hong Kong and later to Malaya, where they operated against the terrorists until replaced by de Havilland Hornets in 1951.

Production RAF Tempest II fighters and fighter-bombers were powered by Centaurus V engines, though in 1947 many were replaced by Centaurus VIs. In that year the Indian Government negotiated through the Ministry of Supply for the delivery of eighty-nine Tempest IIs, these aircraft being returned from RAF Maintenance Units to Langley for modification to the Indian Specification. Only one significant difference existed, apart from tropical preparation; this was the deletion of the fuel transfer system.

The following year Pakistan placed an order for twenty-four fighter-bombers, all of which featured Centaurus Vs, tropical conversion and the standard fuel transfer.

Tempests of both the Indian and Pakistani Air Forces continued in service until 1953, when they were replaced by more modern types.

THE TEMPEST VI

After abandonment of the partially successful Tempest I with Sabre IV engine, it was decided to fit a Sabre V as a trial installation in the prototype Tempest V, HM595. Flown by Bill Humble on 9 May 1944, the aircraft was henceforward termed the Tempest VI. The new engine, rated at 2,340 hp, required a larger radiator frontal area which now occupied the whole cross-section of the radiator fairing. A second (subsidiary) oil cooler was fitted in the leading edge of the starboard wing root, while carburettor intakes were placed in each wing. The patented Hawker spring tabs, so popular on later Tempest Vs, were again included.

These aircraft, destined for service with the RAF in the Middle East, carried full desert survival kits, tropical clearance trials having been conducted at Khartoum in December 1944.

Like the Tempest II, however, the Mark VI was not in service in time to see action during World War Two, and the end of hostilities brought about drastic abbreviation of production contracts, the number on order being reduced from 250 to 142. Nevertheless, four BAFO Squadrons in Germany received Tempest VIs, and five in the Middle East, where they remained in service until 1949, when de Havilland Vampire fighter-bombers were issued.

A production Tempest VI, NX135.

TECHNICAL DATA FOR TEMPEST (ALL PRODUCTION VERSIONS)

TYPE: Single-seat fighter and fighter-bomber.
STRUCTURE: All-metal stressed-skin construction.
MANUFACTURERS: Hawker Aircraft Ltd, Kingston (Mks. II, V and VI). Bristol Aeroplane Co Ltd, Weston-super-Mare (Mk. II).
POWERPLANT: 2,520 hp Bristol Centaurus V or VI (Mk. II). 2,180 hp Napier Sabre IIA, IIB or IIC (Mk.V). 2,340 hp Napier Sabre V (Mk. VI).
DIMENSIONS: Span (all versions), 41 ft 0 in. Length (Mk. II), 34 ft 5 in. Length (Mk. V), 33 ft 8 in. Length (Mk. VI), 33 ft 10½ in. Height (Mk. II), 15 ft 10 in. Height (Mks. V and VI), 16 ft 1 in. Wing area (all versions), 302 sq ft.
WEIGHTS: Mark II, Empty, 8,900 lb. Loaded (with two 90 gallon drop tanks), 13,250 lb.

341

Mark V. Empty, 9,000 lb. Loaded (with two 1,000 lb bombs), 13,540 lb.
Mark VI. Empty, 9,150 lb. Loaded (with two 1,000 lb bombs), 13,700 lb.
PERFORMANCE: Mark II. Max speed, 442 mph at 15,100 ft. Climb 4½ min to
15,000 ft. Range (normal), 800 miles; (maximum), 1,640 miles. Service ceiling
(rate of climb, 100 ft/min), 37,500 ft.
Mark V. Max speed, 426 mph at 18,500 ft. Climb, 5 min to 15,000 ft. Range
(normal), 740 miles; (maximum), 1,530 miles. Service ceiling (rate of climb,
100 ft/min), 36,500 ft.
Mark VI. Max speed, 438 mph at 17,800 ft. Climb, 4 min 40 sec to 15,000 ft.
Range (normal) 750 miles. Service ceiling (rate of climb, 100 ft/min), 38,000
ft.
OTHER DATA: Armament: Four 20 mm Hispano cannon. Mk. II guns on
Tempest II Series 1 and Tempest V Series 1; Mk. V guns on Tempest II Series
2 and Tempest V Series 2 and Tempest VI. Except for early Mark IIs and Vs,
provision was made to carry either two 500 lb or two 1,000 lb bombs under
the wings or various combinations of RPs on British Mk VIII (zero-length)
launchers. Provision made later to carry Napalm, Smoke or Oil bombs.

The first Hawker F.2/43 Fury prototype, NX798.

The Hawker F.2/43 Fury and Sea Fury

THE F.2/43 PROTOTYPES

Shortly after the first Tempest prototype had flown in September 1942,
discussions were held at Hawkers to consider the possibility of creating a
smaller and lighter version of the Tempest by eliminating the wing
centresection and bringing the outer wing sections together on the aircraft centreline.

In January 1943 it was decided that, in producing the new design,
efforts should be made to conform to the requirements of Specification
F.6/42, and the resulting aircraft became known as the Tempest Light

342

The second Fury prototype, NX802.

Fighter (Centaurus). Shortly afterwards a new Specification, F.2/43, was prepared, written around the proposals submitted with the Hawker design.

In April 1943, on receipt of yet another Specification, N.7/43, for a naval interceptor fighter, Camm suggested to the MAP that the F.2/43 aircraft, using an uprated Centaurus XII engine, would be equally capable of meeting the naval Specification. The result was that both RAF and naval requirements were henceforward pooled under F.2/43, Hawkers preparing the prototype and production drawings for the land-based fighter while the responsibility for the naval conversion would be entrusted to Boulton-Paul Aircraft Ltd, Wolverhampton.

Alternative powerplants to the Centaurus XII were considered, and by December 1943, six F.2/43 prototypes were on order of which two

A post-war picture of NX802 in display colours at Langley. Note the Centaurus 18 with Rotol five-blade propeller.

343

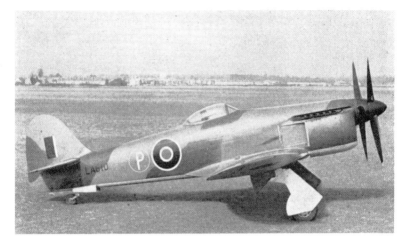

The Rolls-Royce Griffon 85-powered Fury prototype, LA610, with Rotol contra-propeller.

were to be fitted with Griffons, two with Centaurus XXIIs, one with a Centaurus XII and one to be used as a test structure.

Early in 1944 another naval Specification, N.22/43, was received in which the production Standard of Preparation was set out, and in April that year a contract for 200 F.2/43 and 200 N.22/43 aircraft was placed, of which 100 of the latter were to be built by Boulton-Paul.

The first of the new aircraft to fly was NX798. Flown by Lucas on 1 September 1944, this was an F.2/43 with a rigidly-mounted Bristol Centaurus XII with Rotol four-blade propeller. Next was LA610, flown on

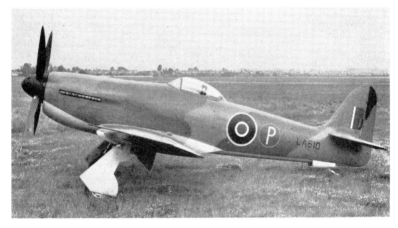

Fastest of all Hawker piston-engine fighters was the Sabre VII-powered Fury, LA610.

Registered G-AKRY, the first F.2/43 Fury prototype (previously NX798) was sold to Egypt.

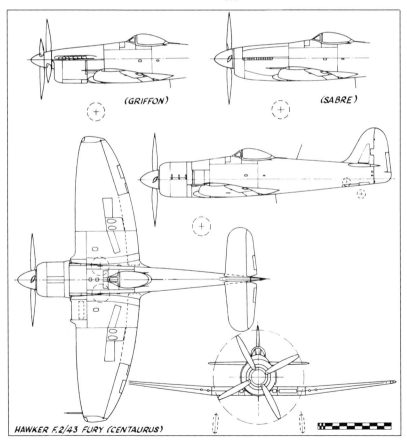

(GRIFFON)

(SABRE)

HAWKER F.2/43 FURY (CENTAURUS)

The first Sea Fury "semi-navalised" prototype, SR661, with short arrester hook.

27 November 1944, also to F.2/43 but powered by a Rolls-Royce Griffon 85 driving a Rotol six-blade contra-rotating propeller. At this point it was decided to name the F.2/43 aircraft the Fury I and the naval version the Sea Fury X.

With the end of the war in Europe in sight the Sea Fury order was reduced to 100 aircraft, and the Boulton-Paul contract was cancelled in January 1945, while the Boulton-Paul Sea Fury prototype, VB857, was delivered for completion at Kingston.

The "fully-navalised" Sea Fury prototype, SR666.

346

The first Sea Fury prototype, SR661, flew on 21 February 1945, also fitted with a Centaurus XII engine and Rotol four-blade airscrew. This aircraft was 'semi-navalised', in that it featured a deck arrester hook under the rudder but retained fixed wings. The second prototype, SR666, which flew on 12 October 1945, differed from the first in being 'fully-navalised' with folding wings. This machine was powered by a Centaurus XV driving a five-blade Rotol propeller (the Centaurus XXII on dynafocal mounting having been delayed).

The remaining Fury prototype, NX802, with Centaurus XV, had flown on 25 July 1945, and the Boulton-Paul machine, VB857, now completed to the same standard as SR666, flew on 31 January 1946.

An early Sea Fury X fighter, TF906, with short hook and four-blade Rotol propeller.

A Sea Fury F.B.11, VR952. Note the lengthened hook and five-blade propeller.

One of the ex-Fleet Air Arm Sea Furies, TG129, repainted in Royal Canadian Navy colours.

With the end of the war in Europe came cancellation of the contract for RAF Furies, and interest now centred on the Sea Fury, although the Centaurus in LA610 was later replaced by the Sabre VII for test purposes (in this form the aircraft was probably the fastest piston engine Hawker aircraft, possessing a top speed in the region of 485 mph).

The first fifty production Sea Furies, termed Mark Xs, were fighters

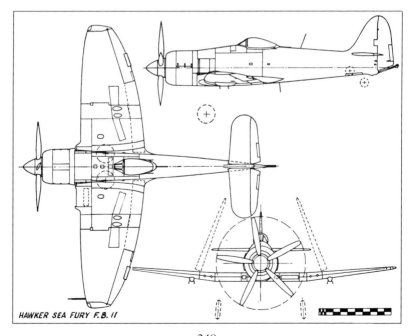

HAWKER SEA FURY F.B. II

based fundamentally on the prototype SR666, and passed through the Kingston shops during 1946, the first machine, TF895, being flown by R V Morrell on 7 September. Early Mark Xs featured four-blade Rotol propellers, but, resulting from tests on SR666 and TF895 (the latter retained by Hawkers for development), Rotol five-blade airscrews became standard on all subsequent Sea Furies.

Deck trials with Sea Fury TF898 commenced aboard HMS *Victorious* during the winter of 1946–47, but Service clearance was delayed until the spring of 1947 due to arrester hooks being damaged on several occasions, resulting in an interim modification. Sea Furies were issued to Nos. 778, 802, 803, 805 and 807 Squadrons of the Fleet Air Arm, but during 1948 their replacement commenced with the introduction of the Sea Fury F.B. Mk. 11.

Trials had been continued during 1947 on SR666 at Langley with various combinations of 1,000 pound incendiary bombs, Type 2 Mk. II Smoke Floats, sixteen 60 pound warhead rocket projectiles, 90 gallon drop tanks and Napalm tanks; similar parallel trials had been conducted on a production Mk. X, TF923, at Boscombe Down. Other alterations had also been introduced, including the lengthening of the arrester hook, and provision made to incorporate rocket-assisted take-off gear (RATOG). The outcome of these improvements was the introduction to service, with immediate clearance, of the Sea Fury Mark 11 fighter-bomber.

In the seven years that followed no fewer than 615 Sea Fury 11s were delivered from Kingston to the Royal Navy, these aircraft constituting the Fleet Air Arm's principal single-seat fighter equipment until their replacement by the Sea Hawk in late 1953. The first unit to receive the F.B. 11 was No. 802 Squadron at Eglinton in May 1948; Nos. 801, 804, 805 and 807 Squadrons followed, embarking in HM Light Fleet Carriers *Ocean, Theseus* and *Glory* during 1949–51.

The outbreak of war in Korea in June 1950 led to the despatch of the carrier *Theseus* with No. 807 Squadron's Sea Furies, these aircraft being used with considerable skill in the ground support rôle, with the result that *Ocean* and *Glory* followed several months later. Another vessel which carried Sea Furies into action in Korean waters was HMAS *Sydney* of the Royal Australian Navy (for a number of ex-Fleet Air Arm Sea Furies had been transferred to that Service during 1949 and 1950. Others were also supplied to the Royal Canadian Navy.)

The Sea Furies of *Theseus* first went into action in North Korea on 7 December 1950, thereafter attacking enemy targets with bombs, rockets and Napalm; on occasion they were used to sow mines outside Communist ports. Inevitably, as enemy fighter strength grew these naval formations came under fire from Russian-built MiG-15 jet fighters and though several Sea Furies were lost, the Hawker machines destroyed a number of the enemy, the first being claimed by Lt P Carmichael of No. 802 Squadron.

In November 1951 Sea Fury F.B. 11s were introduced into service

The ex-Iraqi Sea Fury T. Mark 20 prototype, VX818.

A standard production Sea Fury T. Mk. 20, VX297, of the Fleet Air Arm.

with the Royal Naval Volunteer Reserve, being first issued to No. 1832 Squadron, replacing Supermarine Seafire 17s; Nos. 1831, 1833, 1834, 1835 and 1836 Squadrons, RNVR, also received Sea Fury 11s.

THE SEA FURY T. MARK 20

The Sea Fury two-seat trainer was unusual in that it was developed for the Royal Navy *after* negotiations for such an aircraft had been

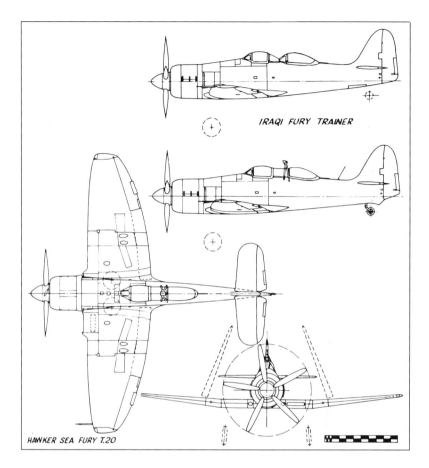

IRAQI FURY TRAINER

HAWKER SEA FURY T.20

completed between the Iraqi Government and Hawker Aircraft Ltd. The result of these was an order for four two-seat Furies for Iraq, but the first machine was completed to an Admiralty Standard of Preparation and serialled VX818. First flown at Langley on 15 January 1948, VX818 was delivered shortly afterwards to Boscombe Down for development trials, and it was during these that, following collapse of the rear canopy, the interconnecting cockpit 'tunnel' was added. Also developed was a Hawker-designed periscopic sight mounted on a tripod just forward of the instructor's cockpit, while the armament was reduced to two 20 mm guns in order to permit installation of equipment displaced by the introduction of the second cockpit.

Sixty production Sea Fury T. Mk. 20s were built and delivered to the Fleet Air Arm, deliveries to RNAS Anthorn commencing in mid-1950 and continuing until March 1952. They entered service with the RNVR, serving alongside Mark 10s and 11s on Nos. 1830, 1831, 1832, 1834, 1835

A Netherlands Sea Fury Mark 50 fighter.

An Iraqi Fury, 231, single-seat fighter.

An Iraqi Fury Trainer, 263.

and 1836, and on No. 1843 Squadrons. They were also based at Donibristle, Culdrose, Syerston, Lossiemouth, Abbotsinch, Stretton, Benson, Culham and Yeovilton. They were not equipped with arrester hooks and did not embark with carrier-borne units of the Royal Navy.

FOREIGN FURIES AND SEA FURIES

The first foreign variant of the Fury was the Netherlands Sea Fury Mark 50, of which ten fighters were ordered from Hawkers on 21 October 1946, for service on the ex-Royal Naval Escort Carrier *Nairana*. Twelve further machines, mostly fighter-bombers, were ordered in 1950, while licence production at Fokkers had got under way in 1948. Other Sea Furies served with the Royal Netherlands Navy aboard the *Karel Doorman*, a Light Fleet Carrier also previously a British vessel, HMS *Venerable*. These aircraft were superseded in 1959 by Sea Hawk Mark 50s.

As already mentioned the Iraqi Government also became interested in the Fury in 1946, and thirty fighters and fighter-bombers were ordered in December of that year. Known unofficially as Baghdad Furies, these were delivered to Iraq during 1948 and were joined a year later by two two-seat Iraqi Fury trainers. Originally four such machines had been ordered, but one had been diverted to become the naval prototype VX818 while another was sold to Pakistan. A further twenty-five single-seat and three two-seat Furies were ordered by and delivered to Iraq in 1953.

The largest foreign orders for the Sea Fury were received by Hawkers from Pakistan, a total of no fewer than ninety-three single-seaters being delivered between 1949 and 1954, including five ex-Fleet Air Arm Sea Fury 11s. Five two-seaters, including the aircraft previously destined for Iraq, were also ordered.

Twelve Sea Fury fighters were ordered by Egypt during 1949, and

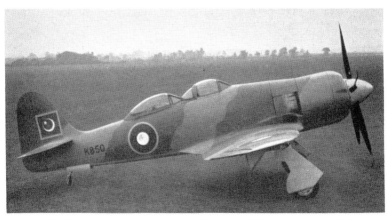

Originally destined for Iraq, this Fury Trainer, K850, was sold to Pakistan.

An Egyptian Sea Fury, 703.

A German Sea Fury T.T. Mk. 20 target tug, D-CABU, ES8507 (*ex.* G-9-56)
as delivered to *Deutsche Luftfahrt Beratungsdienst* in 1960.

delivered during the following two years. One or two of these were still
in service at the time of the Suez operations in November 1956.

Another chapter in the Sea Fury's story was opened in 1957. In that
year a large number of surplus Fleet Air Arm Sea Fury 10s, 11s and
T.20s was purchased by Hawker Aircraft Ltd. Of these, eighteen Mark
11s and three T. Mark 20s were re-sold by the Company to Burma and
delivered in 1958.

Fifteen Mark 11s and two T. Mark 20s were sold to Cuba in 1958,
though these were not assembled until 1959 after the revolution against
the Batista Government from whom the contract had been secured.

Despite considerable interest in the Sea Fury by other foreign air
forces, only one further country had placed orders by 1960. Six Mark 20s
were ordered by *Deutsche Luftfahrt Beratungsdienst* during 1959, being

under contract to the West German *Luftwaffe* for target towing duties.
Two further machines were ordered in 1960.

TECHNICAL DATA FOR SEA FURY (ALL PRODUCTION VERSIONS)

TYPE: Mark 10, naval single-seat interceptor fighter. Mark 11, naval single-seat
fighter-bomber. Mark 20, naval two-seat operational trainer. German Mark
20s used for target towing.

STRUCTURE: All-metal stressed-skin construction.

MANUFACTURERS: Hawker Aircraft Ltd, Kingston-on-Thames.

POWERPLANT: 2,480 hp Bristol Centaurus 18 18-cylinder radial engine. Early
Mark 10s had 4-blade Rotol propellers; other Mark 10s, 11s, 20s and foreign
variants had Rotol 5-blade propellers.

DIMENSIONS: Span (all versions), 38 ft 4¾ in (16 ft 1 in folded). Length (Mark
10), 34 ft 3 in. (Mark 11), 34 ft 8 in. (Mark 20), 34 ft 7 in. Wing Area (all
versions), 280 sq ft.

WEIGHTS: (Mark 11) Empty, 9,240 lb. Loaded, 12,500 lb. (Mark 20) Empty,
8,697 lb. Loaded, 11,930lb.

PERFORMANCE: (Mark 11) Max speed, 460 mph at 18,000 ft. Climb, 10.8 min
to 30,000 ft. Range (without external tanks), 700 miles at 30,000 ft. Range
(with two 90 gallon drop tanks), 1,040 miles. Service ceiling (rate of climb, 100
ft/min), 35,800 ft.
(Mark 20) Max speed, 445 mph at 18,000 ft. Climb, 10.1 min to 30,000 ft.
Range (without external tanks), 940 miles. Service ceiling (rate of climb, 100
ft/min), 35,600 ft.

OTHER DATA: Armament (Mark 10) four 20 mm Hispano Mk. 5 guns. Mark
11, in addition to full gun armament, possessed underwing racks for 1,000 lb
bombs, 90 gallon drop tanks or napalm bombs, and attachment points for up
to twelve 3 in rocket projectiles with 60 lb warheads. Mark 20s armed with
two 20mm guns only, and provision for external stores. The German Mark
20s were unarmed.

The Hawker P.1040, VP401, at Boscombe Down in September 1947. This
picture illustrates the early jet exit fairings, the nose attitude reference mast
and unfaired tailplane/fin intersection.

The Hawker P.1040 and Sea Hawk

The fact that the Sea Hawk entered the project stage in 1944 and was
still in front line service with the Royal Navy seventeen years later lends

ample testimony to an excellent design, despite it being Hawkers' first experience in the field of jet aircraft.

It was during the autumn of 1944 that preliminary details of the Rolls-Royce B.41 jet engine became available, and following discussions with the Ministry of Aircraft Production in November of that year Hawkers forwarded a scheme (the P.1035) incorporating this engine in the centre fuselage of the F.2/43 Fury. The following month a more detailed proposal, this time using bifurcated jet pipes exhausting on either side of the fuselage amidships, was commenced under the designation P.1040.

Early in the new year general approval of the design was received from the Air Staff and Hawkers went ahead with detailed design, securing patents on the split tailpipe scheme and undertaking a programme of testing in collaboration with Rolls-Royce on the powerplant installation. A tender was submitted in February 1945, but such was the conservative reluctance to accept such an apparently unorthodox design out of hand that no Specification was forthcoming for many months.

In the meantime both the Air Staff and the Admiralty maintained an attitude of academic interest while tests of intakes, engine and jet pipe schemes were carried out. By October 1945 sufficient data had been collected to support the proposals and to prompt Hawker Aircraft to issue a Production Order for the manufacture of a prototype.

At this stage Air Staff interest declined, as it was not considered that the P.1040 would represent a sufficient advance in performance over the Gloster Meteor IV which had just established a new World Speed Record at 606 mph; on the other hand the Naval Staff saw in the design a considerable future as a fleet support fighter, with the result that it was again tendered in January 1946, as a naval interceptor. The aircraft was accepted in this form, Specification N.7/46 was prepared and an Instruction to Proceed on three prototypes and one test specimen was issued.

In May 1946, Contract cover for the prototypes was received and it was decided that the first, while being aerodynamically representative of the naval fighter, would not feature armament or other operational equipment.

The P.1040 prototype, VP401, was first flown at Boscombe Down on 2 September 1947, but was transferred to Farnborough three days later for continuance of flight trials. Structurally, the aircraft featured a mid-wing attached to stub wings integral with the centre fuselage and which incorporated wing root engine air intakes. The engine, a 4,500 pound thrust Rolls-Royce Nene I (later replaced by a Nene II giving 5,000 pounds thrust), was situated in the centre fuselage and exhausted through the bifurcated jet pipes leading out of the fuselage side just aft of the wings. A single fin and rudder was employed, together with a conventional tailplane and elevator mounted midway up the fin. Manually-operated controls were incorporated for the pilot, whose cockpit was in the extreme nose. The wings were relatively thin, possessing a thickness:chord ratio of 0.095, while the fuel was accommodated in

The P.1040, VP401, being flown by W Humble in 1948.

fuselage tanks forward and aft of the engine. Their capacity of 395 gallons bestowed a useful duration of well over two hours' flying.

During the two months following VP401's first flight several minor modifications were made, including fitting of an acorn fairing at the intersection of tailplane and fin, and replacement of the rectangular exhaust exit fairings by the more familiar 'pen-nib' fairings adopted on all Sea Hawks. At this stage initial proposals were made to incorporate drop tanks, it being intended either to fit a pair of oval section 100-gallon or circular section 90 gallon tanks on pylons under the wings. The latter

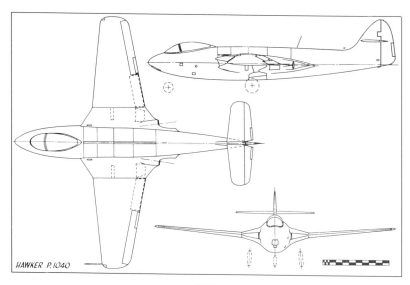

HAWKER P.1040

scheme was adopted, though drop tank provision was not forthcoming until the third prototype appeared some two years later.

The purely research P.1040 prototype was followed by the first truly naval N.7/46 prototype, VP413, which was flown on 3 September 1948. This machine featured folding wings, catapult spools and full gun armament in the nose of four 20 mm Hispano cannon with 200 rounds per gun. After initial dummy deck assessment trials at Boscombe Down during April 1949, VP413 was flown on to HMS *Illustrious* for deck take-off, landing and general handling trials. In July the wing span was increased by 30 inches and thereafter the aircraft commenced the full programme of service testing and evaluation, interrupted only by an appearance at the 1949 SBAC Flying Display in September.

In the meantime, VP401 had been prepared for the National Air Races, and on 1 August 1949, flown by Sqn Ldr Wade, won the SBAC Challenge Cup at Elmdon at a speed of 510 mph. The aircraft was then returned to Kingston for modifications to include the Armstrong Siddeley Snarler rocket motor in the tail (see Hawker P.1072, page 371).

November 1949 saw the return of VP413 to HMS *Illustrious* for further deck trials, in all some twenty-five landings being successfully accomplished.

The last prototype, VP422, had flown on 17 October 1949, this aircraft differing from its precursor in having provision for RATOG. The undercarriage retraction period was also shortened. More carrier trials followed in February 1950, while gunnery and drop tank handling flights were undertaken during the spring.

By now a contract had been received for 151 production aircraft, jigging and tooling was well advanced and the prototypes (VP413 and VP422) commenced a varied programme of service trials, including

The first Hawker N.7/46 Sea Hawk prototype, VP413.

358

catapult take-offs, ventral landings, hood jettisoning and trials with different airbrake schemes.

The first production Sea Hawk F. Mark 1, WF143, differing from the prototypes in having a Nene Mk. 101 engine and modified hood shape, flew on 14 November 1951, and was employed by the manufacturers for stability and control investigations. This programme indicated that, while lateral control was somewhat disappointing (owing to aileron oscillation), only power-assisted aileron control would effect a worthwhile remedy. Such a system was put in hand and, fitted in the fifth production Sea Hawk, WF147 (incidentally thus making it the Mark 2 prototype), resulted in complete cure.

Other early production aircraft engaged in service and other trials included WF144 (first flown on 21 February 1952), used for arrested landing and catapulting trials on HMS *Eagle*, together with WF145 (flown on 18 March), and WF148 delivered to Canada on 4 September 1952 for winterisation trials.

The first operational unit to receive Sea Hawks (in March 1953) was

The second N.7/46 Sea Hawk prototype, VP422, with extra length arrester hook.

No. 806 Squadron at Brawdy, Pembrokeshire, and this squadron subsequently embarked in HMS *Eagle* later that year. Two other squadrons, Nos. 804 and 898, also received Sea Hawk 1s.

With the introduction of the Government's 'super-priority' administrative system, intended to accelerate material acquisition for and production of the Hunter and Sea Hawk, it had become evident in 1952 that the design and production facilities at Kingston and Langley were not sufficient to deal with the very large orders which had been placed for both aircraft. Henceforward, therefore, all further development and production of the Sea Hawk became the responsibility of Sir W G Armstrong Whitworth Aircraft Ltd, at Coventry, another member of the Hawker-Siddeley Group.

Hawker-built production Sea Hawks totalled only thirty-five Mark Is before work was transferred to Coventry, and the first AWA-built machine, also a Mark 1, WF162, was flying before the end of 1953.

Having completed a production batch of sixty Sea Hawk 1s, AWA introduced the Mark 2 fighter incorporating full powered aileron control and spring feel. Forty aircraft of this type were built by early 1954, and replaced Mark 1s in service with No. 806 Squadron. The first flight at Bitteswell by a Mark 2, WF240, took place on 24 February 1954.

Provision had been made to carry 90 gallon drop tanks on the AWA-built Sea Hawk 1s and 2s, but with the introduction of the Mark 3 fighter-bomber, of which 116 were built at Coventry during 1954, the ability to carry either two 500 pound bombs or mines in place of the drop tanks was included. The first Sea Hawk F.B.3, WF280, flew on 13 March 1954.

Sea Hawk F.B.3s entered service with Nos. 800, 801, 806, 897 and 898 Squadrons during the autumn of 1954, and some of these formations embarked in HM Carriers *Eagle* and *Ark Royal*. Other aircraft equipped

One of the thirty-five Hawker-built Sea Hawk F. Mk. 1s, WF159.

An Armstrong Whitworth-built Sea Hawk F. Mk. 1, WF184.

A Sea Hawk F. Mk. 2, WF274.

The first production Sea Hawk F.B. Mk. 3, WF280, used for trial installations, here seen carrying four 500 lb bombs.

WF280 carrying two 500 lb bombs and two Bristol phenolic-asbestos drop tanks.

the Naval Fighter School at Lossiemouth and the Naval Trials and Requirements Unit at Ford.

One trial installation on a Sea Hawk 3 deserves particular mention: WM914 was equipped for naval fighter reconnaissance duties, employing a forward-facing F-94 camera in the nose section of an otherwise standard metal Bristol drop tank. This camera tank was carried under the port wing while a normal drop tank was attached to the starboard pylon. The aircraft underwent trials at Bitteswell and Boscombe Down in 1955, but the scheme was not adopted in operational service.

The Sea Hawk F.B.3 was largely superseded by the F.G.A. Mark 4 ground attack fighter, the first such aircraft, WV792, being flown on 26 August 1954. In this version additional wing strong points were provided to permit carriage of up to twenty three-inch rocket projectiles with 60 pound warheads. Trial installations of these ground support loads had been carried out on a modified Mark 3, WF294, while another, WF280, had been adapted to carry four 500 pound bombs, a load also applicable to the F.G.A. Mark 4.

Ninety-seven Sea Hawk F.G.A. Mk. 4s were built, the first, WV792, being flown on 26 August 1954. Deliveries commenced four months later and by the end of the following year five operational squadrons (Nos. 803, 804, 810, 897 and 898) had been equipped. At Bitteswell

This Sea Hawk F.G.A. Mk. 4, WV825, was used for a trial installation of powered elevators and was distinguishable by the vortex generators on the tailplane.

Among several interesting trial installations performed on this Sea Hawk 4, WV840, was one for flight refuelling. The probes were mounted on the front of standard finned phenolic-asbestos drop tanks.

The fighter reconnaissance installation, originally flown on Sea Hawk 3, WM914, seen here on Sea Hawk F.G.A. Mk. 6 XE369.

The demonstration Sea Hawk 6, XE456, with two drop tanks, two 500 lb bombs and ten rocket projectiles with various warheads.

efforts were being made to increase the performance of the Sea Hawk, for it should be remembered that its maximum speed was only slightly in excess of that of the Meteor, by now being replaced in RAF squadrons by the Hunter. An early Sea Hawk 4, WV825, was modified to incorporate powered elevators (vortex generators being attached above and below the tailplane) in an effort to improve handling at higher Mach numbers. A slightly uprated Nene engine was installed, but this only bestowed an increase of Mach .01, and the experiment was abandoned.

Another trial featured a Sea Hawk 4 equipped for flight refuelling. Probes were fitted in place of the standard nose sections of a pair of Bristol finned plastic drop tanks and carried under the wings of this aircraft, WV840, but because of delays in the preparation of a Canberra tanker, the trials in 1956 were short-lived and were eventually abandoned.

The relatively low performance of the Sea Hawk led to the introduction

The Sea Hawk 6, XE456, adopted as TI aircraft for the German Mk. 100 and 101, seen here carrying a mock-up of the Ekco Type 34 radar pod under the wing.

XE456 with an actual radar pod on the inboard wing pylon. Note the tall fin, standardised on the German aircraft.

A German Sea Hawk Mark 100, VA220.

A German Sea Hawk Mark 101, RB376.

A Netherlands Sea Hawk Mark 50. The principal difference from the Fleet Air Arm Mark 6 lies in the UHF radio, the blade aerial of which may be seen on the rear fuselage.

tion of the Sea Hawk 5 and 6. Both versions were proposed as being Mark 3s and 4s (respectively) modified retrospectively with the uprated Nene Mk. 103, giving 5,200 pounds thrust. About 50 Mark 3s were so fitted during 1955, most of these being issued to Nos. 800, 801 and 806 Squadrons, though no squadron was entirely re-equipped.

Rather fewer Mark 4s were re-engined, these being delivered as replacement aircraft to Nos. 897 and 898 Squadrons towards the end of 1955. Earlier that year, however, a contract was raised for eighty-six newly-built Sea Hawk F.G.A. Mark 6s, and within fourteen months this order had been completed. Embodying all the latest modifications, these Mark 6s were gradually phased into all remaining Sea Hawk squadrons during 1956 and participated in the Suez operations of November 1956. Sea Hawk 6s (accompanied by a few Mk. 4s and 5s) of Nos. 800, 802, 804, 897 and 899 Squadrons, flying from HM Carriers *Albion*, *Eagle* and *Bulwark*, covered the Anglo-French landings in Egypt and performed many ground attack sorties against Egyptian aerodromes.

With the numbers of Sea Hawks slowly diminishing, replacement started in 1958 with the introduction of the first operational Supermarine Scimitars, though other Sea Hawks remained in the front line strength of the Fleet Air Arm until 1960. The aircraft had been very popular in service, pilots speaking highly of its manoeuvrability and ease of control. Evidence of the Sea Hawk's control precision was given at the 1957 SBAC Display at Farnborough, when five scarlet-painted aircraft of No. 738 Naval Training Squadron performed an immaculate formation aerobatic routine, using coloured smoke and taking off and landing in close formation.

FOREIGN SEA HAWKS

Apart from a small number of ex-Fleet Air Arm Sea Hawks passed to the Royal Australian Navy, three principal orders were negotiated abroad.

In 1956, some months after the Sea Hawk production line had been dismantled, the West German Navy placed orders for sixty-four Sea Hawks. The first thirty-two, known as Mark 100s, were to be day interceptor fighters, and the remainder, to be called Mark 101s, were to be equipped with search radar as single-seat all-weather fighters. The Ekco 34 radar specified was carried in an outsize underwing pod, this installation being first flown on a Sea Hawk 6, XE456, in 1956. The German aircraft also featured increased vertical tail surface area.

Simultaneous with the placing of the German order the Netherlands also signed a contract, this time for twenty-two Sea Hawks. Known as the Mark 50, these aircraft differed from the F.G.A. Mk. 6 in being equipped with UHF radio, evidenced by a large blade aerial on the fuselage amidships. Towards the end of 1959 some Dutch Sea Hawks were adapted to mount two Philco Sidewinder IA air-to-air missiles, one under each wing, the work being carried out under NATO funding.

In September 1959, three years after the Sea Hawk production line had been dismantled at Coventry, the Indian government signed an order for twenty-four Sea Hawks, of which twelve were newly built and twelve were rebuilt ex-Royal Navy F.G.A. Mark 6s. Ultimately the Indian order was increased to seventy-four aircraft, these aeroplanes serving aboard the carrier INS *Vikrant*. By the end of the 1970s this number had dwindled to around fifty, of which about half were still in service with No. 300 Squadron of the Indian Navy. During the early 1980s they were progressively replaced in service by British Aerospace Sea Harriers.

TECHNICAL DATA FOR SEA HAWK

TYPE: Single-seat naval interceptor fighter and ground attack fighter/fighter-bomber.

STRUCTURE: All-metal stressed-skin construction.

MANUFACTURERS: Hawker Aircraft Ltd, Kingston (P.1040, N.7/46 prototypes and thirty-five production Mark 1s); Sir W G Armstrong Whitworth Aircraft Ltd, Coventry (all production Sea Hawks from 1953 onwards).

POWERPLANT: P.1040 initially powered by 4,500 lb s.l.s.t. Rolls-Royce Nene I turbojet. Later fitted (together with N.7/46 prototypes) with 5,000 lb. thrust Nene II engines. Sea Hawk Mks. 1, 2, 3, and 4 powered by 5,000 lb thrust Nene R.N.4 (Mk. 101) engines. Sea Hawk Mks, 5, 6 and foreign variants powered by 5,200 lb thrust Nene Mk. 103 engines.

DIMENSIONS: Span, 39 ft 0 in. Length (Mk. 3), 39 ft 10½ in. Length (Mk. 6), 39 ft 8 in. Height (Mk. 3), 8 ft 9 in. Height (Mk. 6), 8 ft 8 in. Width (wings folded), 13 ft 3 in. Height (wings folded), 16 ft 9 in. Wing area, 278 sq ft. Wing thickness:chord ratio, 0.095.

WEIGHTS: (Mk. 3) Empty, 9,190 lb. Normal all-up weight (without drop tanks), 13,220 lb. Max overload weight, 15,225 lb.

PERFORMANCE: (Mk.6) Max speed, 0.84 M at 36,000 ft (clean); 0.80 M at 36,000 ft (with two drop tanks). Time to 35,000 ft, 11 min 50 sec (clean). Service ceiling (rate of climb, 500 ft/min), 44,500 ft (clean).

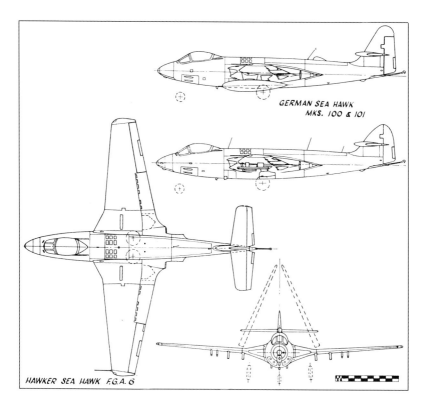

GERMAN SEA HAWK
MKS. 100 & 101

HAWKER SEA HAWK F.G.A. 6

An Indian Sea Hawk, IN151.

OTHER DATA: Fuel capacity (internal), 395 gallons; up to four 90 gallon drop tanks could be carried. Armament, four fixed forward-firing 20mm guns under nose with 200 rounds per gun. Provision made to carry combinations of 500 lb bombs, 90 gallon drop tanks or Napalm bombs, 3 in or 5 in rocket projectiles, mines or sonobuoys. Undercarriage, inwards retracting tricycle type, hydraulically operated; track, 8 ft 6 in.

367

The first Hawker P.1052, VX272.

The Hawker P.1052

In October 1945, when construction of the P.1040 was about to commence, Hawker Aircraft Ltd submitted a design study for an aircraft related to the P.1040 but with a swept-back wing and powered by a rocket engine. Known as the P.1047, this proposal met with interest at the Royal Aircraft Establishment, and following the issue of the Naval Specification N.7/46 it was decided to prepare a research requirement based on this aircraft, but including Hawkers' swept-wing proposal. The rocket engine application was not adopted immediately, though this came to fruition somewhat later in the Hawker P.1072.

Thus, as a result of constant discussions with the Air Ministry and Ministry of Supply throughout 1946 as to the research parameters to be embraced by the new design, a new Specification, E.38/46, was drafted and a Production Order issued in November for the construction of a prototype under the Hawker designation P.1052. The Specification was received by the Company on 16 January 1947, and in March Hawkers submitted tender. This was accepted and in May contract cover was received for the construction of two prototypes, VX272 and VX279.

In layout the P.1052 was similar to the P.1040 except for the swept wing. The fuselage accommodated the engine, a Rolls-Royce Nene R.N.2, amidships with wing root intakes and bifurcated jet pipes. Unswept tail surfaces were to be fitted initially, though as early as January 1947 a swept tailplane was discussed. The principal innovation lay in the swept wing, for this was intended to be the first pressure-plotting high-speed swept wing aircraft to become available for test purposes at the RAE. With a thickness:chord ratio of 0.10 and quarter-chord sweepback of 35 degrees it was anticipated that this wing would furnish flight data up to approximately 0.86 Mach number.

368

Such was the advance in performance over the contemporary Gloster Meteor fighter expected to be achieved by the P.1052 that it was actually proposed in October 1948 to place the type in quantity production, but this was subsequently decided against in view of other designs likely to be forthcoming in the near future.

The first prototype, VX272, was completed at the newly-acquired factory in Richmond Road, Kingston, in November 1948, and was moved to Boscombe Down by road on the 14th. After brief taxiing trials it was flown by Sqn Ldr T S Wade at that aerodrome on 19 November.

The second prototype, VX279, was flown for the first time on 13 April 1949 — again by Wade. The following month the P.1052 was flown by Wade from London to Paris in the record time of eighteen minutes. In June VX272 was delivered to the Royal Aircraft Establishment and XV279 was prepared for assessment by the A&AEE on behalf of the Australian Government as possible future equipment for the RAAF.

A request that Hawker Aircraft Ltd should again investigate the application of a rocket motor (the Armstrong Siddeley Snarler) to the P.1052 was made by the Ministry of Supply in July 1949, and the resulting design study was termed the P.1078. Work, however, was already in hand on the P.1072 (the Snarler-powered P.1040 prototype) and the P.1078 did not proceed.

VX272 suffered a forced landing on 29 September caused by a sheared fuel pump drive, and in carrying out the repairs during the following months it was decided to incorporate a variable incidence tailplane on the aircraft. In the meantime, however, structural tests of a third P.1052 specimen had prompted the decision to increase the strength of the aircraft for a flying weight of 12,500 pounds by reinforcement of the wing spars and main spar fuselage frames. The delay caused in introducing these modifications to VX272 resulted in the variable incidence tailplane and new rear fuselage being fitted on VX279.

Repairs and modification were completed on VX272 by March 1950 and in the following month VX279 was returned to Kingston for conversion to the P.1081. The old rear fuselage from this aircraft was strengthened and fitted with an arrester hook, it being intended to incorporate this on VX272 for deck landing trials later that year; unfortunately the

The second P.1052, VX279, at Farnborough.

369

machine suffered considerable damage in a crash landing and further repairs continued until September 1951; moreover on its first flight after this long absence it again suffered an emergency landing due to partial undercarriage retraction failure, though the resulting damage was only slight. In March 1952, for a period of high speed trials, VX272 was fitted with a large bullet fairing at the intersection of tailplane and fin, this giving considerably improved high Mach number characteristics. The long awaited deck landing trials were carried out using a long stroke Sea Hawk undercarriage during May 1952 aboard HMS *Eagle*, though by then these trials had lost much of their significance. The following month a pressure-plotting variable incidence swept tailplane was at last fitted and VX272 embarked on its final high speed trials programme with the RAE until, in September 1953, the aircraft suffered its last forced landing.

It was superficially repaired and transferred to Air Ministry Charge as a ground instruction machine, still bearing Royal Navy markings, arrester hook, large fin fairing and swept tailplane.

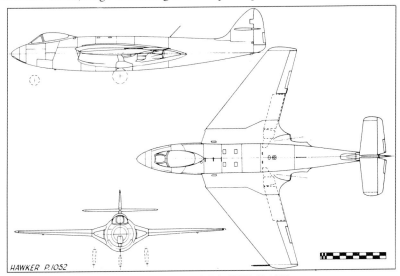

HAWKER P.1052

TECHNICAL DATA FOR P.1052

TYPE: Single-seat swept-wing research aircraft.

STRUCTURE: All-metal stressed-skin construction.

MANUFACTURERS: Hawker Aircraft Ltd, Kingston.

POWERPLANT: 5,000 lb s.l.s.t. Rolls-Royce Nene R.N.2. turbojet.

DIMENSIONS: Span, 31 ft 6 in. Length (straight tailplane), 39 ft 7 in. Length (swept tailplane), 40 ft 3 in. Height, 10 ft 6 in. Wing area, 258 sq ft. Wing thickness/chord ratio, 0.10. Wing quarter-chord sweep-back, 35 degrees.

WEIGHTS: Empty, 9,450 lb. Loaded, 13,488 lb.

PERFORMANCE: Max speed, 0.87 M at 36,000 ft (with swept tailplane). Max speed at sea level, 593 knots. Climb, 9 min 30 sec to 35,000 ft. Service ceiling (rate of climb, 500 ft/min), 45,500 ft.

OTHER DATA: Fuel capacity, 395 gallons. Undercarriage track, 8 ft 8 in.

The Hawker P.1072, VP401.

The Hawker P.1072

The proposal to fit a rocket motor in the P.1040 was originally made in October 1945, before any such rocket existed in this country and before even a contract had been raised to cover the manufacture of the P.1040. Two design studies were put forward; the P.1046, a naval version, and the P.1047 with swept wing, both designs incorporating a rocket in the extreme tail.

At this stage the lack of a suitable rocket powerplant caused both designs to be shelved, though the swept-wing proposal eventually led to the P.1052.

Further interest in the rocket installation was aroused towards the end of 1947 with the commencement of work on a 2,000 pound thrust rocket by Armstrong Siddeley Motors Ltd. It was at first suggested that another P.1040 prototype should be built to accommodate the unit, but it transpired that by the time the prototype rocket would be ready for flight the P.1040, VP401, would have finished its contribution to the development of the N.7/46, and a contract was accordingly drawn up to cover work on the adaptation of this aircraft during 1948.

By September 1949, VP401 had completed the scheduled N.7/46 development programme and was returned to Kingston. Fairly extensive internal modification was carried out, for the fuel used by the rocket was to be methanol-water and liquid oxygen. The Rolls-Royce Nene installation remained almost unaffected, but the entire fuel system was revised, resulting in only 175 gallons of turbojet fuel being carried. In the forward fuselage was housed seventy-five gallons of liquid oxygen in a spherical tank while aft of the rear paraffin tank was a 120-gallon water-methanol tank. The rocket motor itself, the Armstrong Siddeley Snarler, was mounted in the extreme tail under the rudder. A separate pneumatic system operated the rocket fuel supply jacks and valves, the liquid oxygen supply line being situated under the centre fuselage.

The Snarler and its associated equipment was received from Anstey during June 1950 for installation in VP401 at Kingston, and on 16 November the aircraft was flown to Bitteswell under turbojet power only, but on 20 November the Snarler was 'lit' and the total rocket fuel load was successfully expended. However, Air Ministry interest in rocket propelled fighters was by then declining in favour of reheated turbojets and this, the first high performance British rocket aircraft, only performed half a dozen flights under power from the Snarler. A minor explosion in the engine caused slight damage during the last of these flights, but, although the aircraft was repaired by February 1951, the installation in VP401 was never flown again.

TECHNICAL DATA FOR P.1072

TYPE: Single-seat turbojet- and rocket-powered research aircraft.
STRUCTURE: All-metal stressed-skin construction.
MANUFACTURERS: Hawker Aircraft Ltd, Kingston.
POWERPLANT: 5,000 lb s.l.s.t. Rolls-Royce Nene R.N.2 turbojet and 2,000 lb thrust Armstrong Siddeley Snarler ASSn. 1 liquid-fuel rocket.
DIMENSIONS: Span, 36 ft 6 in. Length, 37 ft 7 in. Height, 8 ft 9in. Wing area, 256 sq ft.
WEIGHTS: Empty, 11,050 lb. Loaded, 14,050 lb.
PERFORMANCE: Max speed, 0.82 M at 36,000 ft. Max speed at sea level, 505 knots. Climb, 10.5 min to 35,000 ft. Service ceiling (rate of climb, 500 ft/min), 44,500 ft. Endurance of rocket power, 2.75 min.
OTHER DATA: Fuel capacities. Turbojet fuel, 175 gallons in forward, centre and rear fuselage tanks. Rocket fuel, 75 gallons of liquid oxygen in forward tank and 120 gallons of water-methanol in aft tank. Undercarriage track, 7 ft 11½ in.

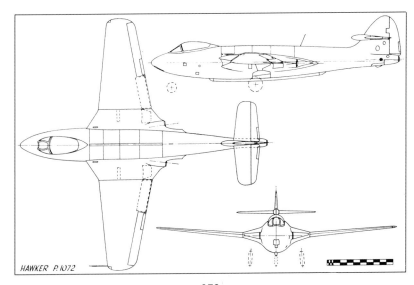

HAWKER P.1072

The Hawker P.1081 at the RAF Display, Farnborough, in 1950.

The Hawker P.1081

In January 1950, following several months of flight testing of the two P.1052s, VX272 and VX279, Hawkers submitted a proposal to fit a Rolls-Royce Tay engine in place of the Nene. This was the outcome of performance investigations to meet an enquiry by the Australian Government which was interested in an operational version of the P.1052.

Due to delays in the development of the Tay it was decided to fit the Nene in the prototype, but using a straight-through jet pipe and a new all-swept tail. This installation was to be carried out on the second P.1052, VX279, though the building of a special Australian prototype with reheat was at one time proposed.

VX279, now termed the P.1081, was first flown with the new tail by Sqn Ldr T S Wade on 19 June 1950. A Supermarine Attacker-type jet pipe was used. Only a few days later, on 23 June, VX279 was flown at a high average speed to Brussels to participate in the 1950 Aero Show.

Flight trials continued throughout 1950 and several modifications were carried out to the airfame, including fitting of an electric tailplane actuator, increased span tailplane, boundary layer fences on the wings, increased chord rudder and an improved rear fuselage fairing.

However, on 14 November 1950, Hawker Aircraft Ltd was notified that work was to stop on the Australian project and two months later VX279 was handed over to the RAE for further handling trials.

On 3 April 1951, the aircraft was totally destroyed in a flying accident the exact cause of which was never discovered. Sqn Ldr Wade, who was flying at the time, lost his life.

TECHNICAL DATA FOR P.1081

TYPE: Single-seat swept-wing research aircraft.
STRUCTURE: All-metal stressed-skin construction.

MANUFACTURERS: Hawker Aircraft Ltd, Kingston.

POWERPLANT: 5,000 lb s.l.s.t. Rolls-Royce Nene R.N.2 turbojet.

DIMENSIONS: Span, 31 ft 6 in. Length, 37 ft 4 in. Height, 13 ft 3 in. Wing area, 258 sq ft. Wing thickness/chord ratio, 0.10. Wing quarter-chord sweep-back, 35 degrees.

WEIGHTS: Empty, 11,200 lb. Loaded, 14,480 lb.

PERFORMANCE: Max speed, 0.89 M at 36,000 ft. Max speed at sea level, 604 knots. Climb, 9 min 12 sec to 35,000 ft. Service ceiling (rate of climb, 500 ft/min), 45,600 ft.

OTHER DATA: Fuel capacity, 400 gallons. Undercarriage track, 8 ft 8in.

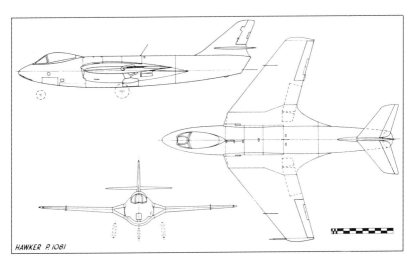

HAWKER P. 1081

VX279, showing the wing fences which were added late in 1950.

374

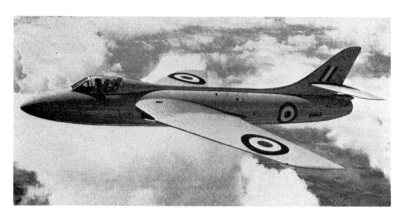

The first Hawker P.1067 Hunter prototype, WB188. Note the anti-spin parachute fairing over the tail cone.

The Hawker Hunter

Following the failure of two Specifications issued in 1946 to produce the required Gloster Meteor fighter replacement, Hawkers set about the preliminary design of an interceptor with the new Rolls-Royce A.J.65 engine (later to become the Avon). Project work continued during 1947 and without waiting for official requirements to be issued the new design, designated P.1067, was tendered in January 1948. Weighing some 12,000 pounds, and armed with two of the new 30 mm Aden guns, the new single-seater featured sweepback on all surfaces, engine intake in the extreme nose, and tailplane set on top of the fin. In March 1948 a new Specification, F.3/48, was issued to replace the old F.43/46 and F.44/46, and Hawkers were invited to tender the P.1067.

Detail design commenced in May of that year and the following month a contract was raised for the manufacture of three prototypes, and it was decided that one should be fitted with an Armstrong Siddeley Sapphire engine, whereas the others would be powered by Avons.

After preliminary wind tunnel tests had been completed the position of the tailplane was moved down the fin, and after installation difficulties with the new radar ranging equipment in the nose the engine intake was moved to the wing roots. After considerable uncertainty as to the future gun requirements it was decided to mount the unprecedented armament of four 30 mm Aden guns in the new fighter and the Hawker design team evolved a detachable gun pack to facilitate rearming. In this all four gun bodies and empty magazines could be removed together in a minute or so and replaced by a fully loaded pack.

The second Hunter prototype, WB195.

Manufacture of the first prototype commenced late in 1949 and the others the following year, but some eight months before the first was ready to fly instructions to proceed with production planning for 200 Avon-powered aircraft were received by Hawker Aircraft Ltd at Kingston, while shortly afterwards similar instructions were received for the same number of Sapphire machines by Sir W G Armstrong Whitworth Aircraft Ltd at Coventry.

The first flight by the Hunter, as the P.1067 was named, took place at Boscombe Down on 20 July 1951. Flown by Sqn Ldr Neville Duke this first aircraft, WB188, was unarmed and featured a spin recovery parachute in a fairing over the tail cone; also, for the first few flights it featured no bullet fairing at the intersection of the fin and tailplane, though this was added soon after and on all subsequent Hunters.

The second prototype, WB195, was fully representative of the production Hunter as then envisaged, fully armed with four Aden guns and

The Sapphire-powered Hunter prototype, WB202, at Dunsfold.

equipped with gun ranging radar. Both these aircraft were powered by Avon engines, but the third prototype, WB202, featured the Sapphire.

Prolonged handling and performance evaluation trials were carried out at Hawkers' newly-acquired aerodrome at Dunsfold and at the various Service and Ministry test establishments.

Benefiting from the temporarily established system of priorities, efforts were made to assist in the speeding-up of Hunter manufacture and on 16 May 1953, the first production Hunter F. Mark 1, WT555, was flown from Dunsfold.

During the period of prototype testing, however, the Ministry of Supply asked for an airbrake to be incorporated in the Hunter which could be operated at all speeds and altitudes without upsetting the aiming characteristics of the aircraft.

By the time the first production Hunters were flying, the optimum airbrake position was only just being decided and deliveries to the Service were somewhat delayed while the new under-fuselage brake was added.

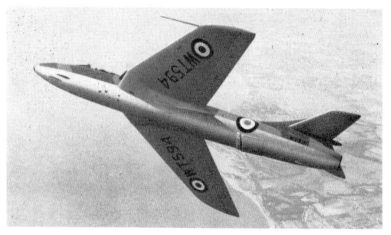

An early production Hunter F. Mark 1, WT594, showing the newly introduced under-fuselage airbrake.

THE HUNTER F. MARK 1

The first twenty or so Hunter F. Mk. 1s from the Kingston production line were set aside for trials with Hawkers, Rolls-Royce and Ministry Experimental Establishments during 1953–54; notable among these were WT568 with extended wing leading edges, WT569 on which the first drop tank trial installation was carried out, WT656 equipped with blown flaps, and WT571. The last had bulged fairings added to the sides of the rear fuselage in pursuance of the Area Rule, but the increase in performance was disappointing.

377

The flap-blowing Hunter 1, WT656.

The Air Fighting Development Squadron at West Raynham was the first Royal Air Force unit to receive Hunters, in July 1954, and these participated in the major air defence exercise that year. By the end of the same month the first fighter squadron proper, No. 43 based at Leuchars, had received its first machines and was followed by No. 54 (F) Squadron at Odiham and No. 222 (F) Squadron, also at Leuchars.

These were the only squadrons to receive the Hunter 1, and in view of the large quantities of Hunters expected to enter service during the

The Hunter 1 WT571 with "area-ruled" rear fuselage.

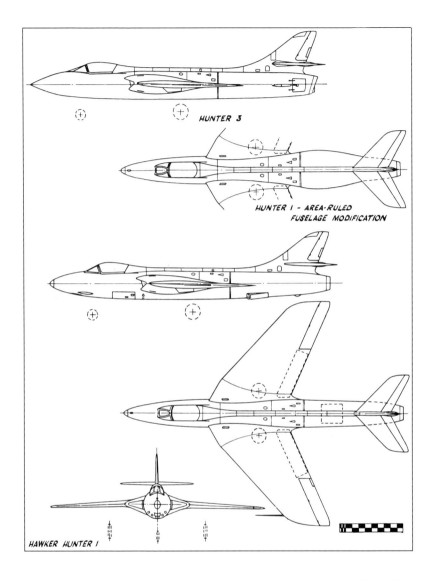

HUNTER 3

HUNTER I - AREA-RULED
FUSELAGE MODIFICATION

HAWKER HUNTER I

coming years, many of the remaining Mark 1 aircraft were issued to Operational Conversion Units.

Trouble, however, was soon encountered with these early Hunters during high altitude gun firing, the Avon Mk. 113 engines being particularly prone to surging when the guns were fired. The Leuchars squadrons embarked on a series of trials, but no satisfactory remedy was found that could be applied to the Hunter 1, and in order to minimise the risk of 'flaming out' an altitude restriction for gun firing was imposed.

The Sapphire Hunter prototype experimentally fitted with four D.H. Firestreak missile mock-ups.

The first AWA-built Hawker Hunter F. Mk. 2, WN888. Note the absence of rear fuselage airbrake.

Despite this serious weakness in the early Hunter, which achieved considerable publicity due in part to Parliamentary concern (although it affected but three fighter squadrons), the aircraft gained immense popularity among those who flew it. In the best tradition of the manufacturers the Hunter proved itself to be extremely strong and its crisp handling qualities at all speeds, made possible by powered controls, earned universal praise. At least one Hunter, having survived a mid-air collision, returned to base minus starboard tailplane and elevator, and without its tail cone.

In all, 139 Hunter 1s were built by Hawkers, of which twenty-six came from their newly-acquired factory at Blackpool.

THE HUNTER F. MARK 2

The Sapphire-powered Hunter F. Mk. 2 suffered none of the gun-firing misfortunes of the Hunter 1, and before the end of 1954 these Coventry-built machines were issued to the two Wattisham-based units, Nos. 257 and 263 (F) Squadrons.

Only forty-five Hunter 2s were built and almost all were issued to the Squadrons. One aircraft, however, WN891, was shipped to Canada during the winter of 1954–55 for winterisation trials, while the Sapphire-powered prototype, WB202, was experimentally fitted with four dummy Firestreak guided missiles under the wings for handling trials at Dunsfold.

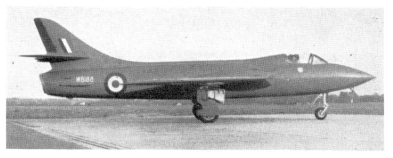

WB188, now termed the Hunter 3, modified for the successful attempt on the world speed record in 1953. Note the side-mounted airbrakes.

THE HUNTER MARK 3

Shortly after the first production Hunter 1s had flown in 1953, the first P.1067 prototype, WB188, underwent trials with a new version of the Rolls-Royce Avon equipped with reheat. This engine, the Avon R.A.7R, delivered 7,130 pounds thrust, or 9,600 pounds thrust with reheat lit, and exhausted through a two-position 'clam-shell' final nozzle. Only this one aircraft was so modified and it became known as the Hunter Mk. 3.

On 7 September 1953, Sqn Ldr Neville Duke flew this machine over a three-kilometre course off Rustington on the south coast to set up a new World's Absolute Speed Record of 727.6 mph. Some days later, on 19 September, the same pilot took WB188 round a 100 kilometre closed circuit to set up a world record for this course at 709.2 mph.

For these record flights WB188 was painted bright red for ease of camera recording and was fitted with a modified nose and a Perspex fairing of increased rake over the windscreen; another feature of the aircraft at this time was the airbrake installation, for WB188 was currently participating in the trials to determine the optimum brake position. During the period of the record flights petal-type brakes were mounted on the sides of the rear fuselage.

WB188 was eventually sold by the Company in 1955 to the Ministry of Supply and was relegated to ground maintenance instruction with the Royal Air Force.

THE HUNTER F. MARK 4

It may be considered in retrospect that the Marks 1 and 2 had been interim versions of the Hunter. They had been introduced into service with only five fighter squadrons and were strictly short endurance interceptors, whereas even before the first prototype had flown, drop tank and external store installations had been proposed to suit the aircraft for long range and ground attack sorties. It will be recalled that drop tanks had been flown on a Mark 1 in 1954 and it was decided to incorporate wing strong points for store pylons in the Hunter production line together with an increased internal fuel capacity. The modifications were

One of the many Hunter aerobatic teams, these are some of No. 54 (Fighter) Squadron's aircraft.

introduced in the 114th machine of the Kingston production line (WT701) and the aircraft thence became known as the Hunter F. Mk. 4. The twenty-seventh and subsequent Blackpool-built Hunters were similarly modified.

No fewer than 365 Hunter 4s were built at the two Hawker factories, the first being flown on 20 October 1954. First Service deliveries were to No. 54 (F) Squadron at Odiham (replacing the unit's Hunter 1s) and No. 111 (F) Squadron at North Weald in March 1955, but simultaneously

The Hunter 4, XF310, modified to carry two Fairey Fireflash beam-riding
air-to-air missiles.

other Hunters were being delivered to the 2nd Tactical Air Force in
Germany, and the following month No. 98 (F) Squadron became the
first overseas unit to receive Hunters. Thereafter squadron after squadron at home and in Germany gave up their Meteor 8s and Venoms in
exchange for Hunter 4s until, by 1956, seven home-based and thirteen
2nd TAF fighter squadrons had been re-equipped.

The first 156 Hunter 4s retained the Avon Mk. 113 but subsequent
machines (WV383 and after) were powered by Avon 115s which incorporated modifications to alleviate engine surge during gun firing. Most of
the early machines were retrospectively modified.

Despite the increased complexity of their new aircraft (the Hunter
was the first widely-used RAF day fighter with radar and fully-powered
controls) Hunter 4 squadrons achieved remarkably high serviceability
rates, and the single point refuelling system and detachable gun pack
contributed to unprecedented turn-round times between sorties, often
as low as seven minutes.

But the Hunter 4 was also the subject of considerable foreign interest
and following the sale of two aircraft to Denmark and Sweden (WW591
and WT770 respectively) for evaluation, these countries placed sizeable
orders for the aircraft (see Hunter Mks. 50 and 51). Licence agreements
were also reached with Fokker in Amsterdam and Avions Fairey in
Brussels for the manufacture of Hunters in their factories, and these
Mark 4s served with Dutch and Belgian squadrons in NATO as a result
of the American system of 'off-shore' payment. Peru also ordered a
number of ex-RAF Mark 4s, these being delivered during 1956 (see
Hunter Mk. 52).

383

The experimental Hunter F.R. Mk. 4, WT780, with five nose cameras.

At Dunsfold in 1955 and 1956 several interesting trial installations were carried out on the Hunter 4. Ammunition link containers had been developed and were now being fitted under the noses of all Hunters. The third production Mark 4, WT703, was retained by the manufacturers for many months undergoing trials with external stores, including 100 gallon drop tanks, bombs and rocket projectiles. WT780 was used to test a Plessey ram-air turbine installed in the starboard side of the rear fuselage as part of a proposed slab tailplane system. Work on the slab tailplane was cancelled in 1956 and the ram-air turbine was removed from WT780. The same aircraft was then converted to accommodate five cameras in the nose in addition to the four guns, and this design, known as the Hunter F.R. Mk. 4, was submitted to Specification FR.164D. The project was, however, temporarily suspended and WT780 was leased to a commercial film company to take many of the exciting sequences in the film *High Flight.*

One other Hunter 4 deserves mention. XF310, a Blackpool-built aircraft, was extensively modified to mount a pair of Fairey Fireflash beam-riding guided missiles under the wings, together with their associated radar in a slightly modified nose. After a number of test firings at British missile ranges, for which the Hunter was commended on its steadiness as a missile 'platform', XF310 returned to Hawkers' charge until 1958, when it was converted into a two-seat Hunter 7 and delivered to the Service.

The Hunter 4 continued in service with operational squadrons of the RAF until 1957, when replaced by the Mark 6. Many aircraft were then delivered to the OCUs and AFSs while others, like XF310, were converted into Mark 7 and 8 trainers. Towards the end of the 1960s some

Hunter 4s were being returned to Hawkers for conversion, refurbishing and resale overseas.

THE HUNTER F. MARK 5

The Hunter 5, like the Mark 2, was powered by an Armstrong Siddeley Sapphire Mk. 101 and was also built by Sir W G Armstrong Whitworth Aircraft Ltd, at Coventry. Just as the Mark 4 possessed wing strong points for stores and had increased fuel capacity over the Mark 1, so the Mark 5 was similarly superior to the Mark 2, and the modifications were incorporated in the forty-sixth Coventry-built aircraft, WN954. This aircraft flew on 19 October 1954, a day earlier than the first Hawker-built Mark 4.

One of the few Hunter F. Mk, 5s, WN958, modified to carry ground attack stores at the outboard station.

Deliveries commenced in 1955 and within a year five squadrons of Fighter Command, Nos. 1, 34, 41, 56 and 263, all home-based, had been equipped with Hunter 5s. The Suez campaign called for RAF reinforcements to be flown to the Middle East and two Hunter 5 squadrons, Nos. 1 and 34, flew from their base at Tangmere to Nicosia, Cyprus, thereafter flying escort for British bombers in the area.

Hunter 5s remained in service until late in 1958, when the last machines serving with No. 56 (F) Squadron were flown to Colerne, and from there a number were repurchased by Hawkers and stored at Langley for possible resale overseas.

One Hunter 5, WN955, was notable in that it was experimentally fitted in 1955 with a Sapphire ASSa.7 (10,000 pounds thrust) engine as an insurance against delays or troubles with the Avon 203, scheduled for the Hunter 6. But lubrication troubles resulted in progressive limitations being imposed, the climb performance being particularly disappointing, and with the successful development of the Avon 203, the Sapphire 7 installation was abandoned.

THE HUNTER F. MARK 6 (HAWKER P.1099)

In November 1951 design work had commenced on a 50 degrees swept-back version of the Hunter using a reheated Avon engine and which was expected to be capable of supersonic speed in level flight. Known as the P.1083, this aircraft was expected to be ready for flight in 1953 and a prototype, WN470, was well advanced in June of that year when the Company was advised that the Air Staff favoured larger un-reheated engines rather than those equipped with reheat; the P.1083 was abandoned and design attention was turned to a more straightforward Hunter with the new 10,500 pound thrust Avon 200-series engine.

Known as the P.1099, and later the Hunter 6, the new prototype was designed and built in a very short time by using the centre fuselage section of the abandoned P.1083. The first flight by the new aircraft, XF833, was made on 22 January 1954, many months before either the Hunter 4 or 5, but after delivery to Boscombe Down in February, engine failure resulted in a forced landing. Flight trials were resumed soon after, only to be delayed again by a further engine failure. The trouble was traced to compressor blade fatigue and modifications resulted in de-rating the engine from 10,500 pounds to 10,000 pounds thrust.

Handling, performance and gun firing trials were conducted on XF833 both at Dunsfold and at MoS establishments, and in 1956 the aircraft was delivered to Miles Aircraft Ltd, for installation of thrust reversal equipment under contract to Rolls-Royce. Thereafter the machine was demonstrated at the 1956 and 1957 SBAC flying displays.

The first production Hunter F. Mark 6, WW592, flew on 25 March 1955, at a time when the first Mark 4s and 5s were just entering service

The prototype Hawker P.1099, Hunter 6, XF833, with the Rolls-Royce thrust reversal installation. The jet deflector louvres may be seen in the sides of the rear fuselage.

A Hunter F. Mk 6, XF389, with late standard modifications: gun blast deflectors, inboard pylons with jettison guns (note the absence of drop tank fins) and leading-edge extensions.

with the RAF. Production acceptance trials commenced on this and the following machines and, by the end of the year, nine aircraft had been completed at Kingston. Production was also undertaken at Blackpool and Coventry and during 1956 and 1957 the three factories produced a further 374 Hunter Mk. 6s.

By the end of 1956 the Hunter 6 was entering squadron service with the RAF, at first in the United Kingdom and later with 2nd TAF in Germany. The improved flying controls and more powerful Avon engine quickly brought forth favourable comment from Service pilots, and it soon became obvious that this aircraft would remain in the RAF as its standard fighter equipment for a long time to come.

Perhaps the context in which the Hunter will be remembered longest by most will be the many superb formation aerobatic displays given by RAF squadrons with their Hunter 4s and 6s, and no account of the aeroplane would be complete without reference to those magnificent spectacles afforded by No. 111 (F) Squadron, which, flying glossy all-black Hunters, gave such inspired demonstrations year after year at the annual SBAC Display at Farnborough. Led by its successive Squadron Commanders, Sqn Ldrs R L Topp and P Lathem, the formation succeeded each year in bettering its previous performance, both by increasing the number of aircraft in the formation and by use of smoke trails.

Development of the Hunter 6 had not been without its setbacks. As far back as 1954 it was found that under conditions of high indicated airspeed, at high altitude and under high *g*-loading, the aircraft had a marked tendency to pitch up. Several remedies were tried and a Hunter 1, WT568, was flown with wing fences and later with wing leading edge extensions. Extensions similar to these were found to cure the trouble and by 1956 all new Hunter 6s were being built with extended leading edges. (Many others, including Mk. 4s, were retrospectively modified.

Partly as a result of the earlier gun firing troubles and partly because ejected cartridge cases were found to be striking the newly-introduced drop tanks, a series of intensive gun firing trials were ordered on the Hunter 6. Apart from a few very minor modifications these trials were completed without hitch, the fact that one aircraft fired no fewer than 40,000 rounds at full throttle and at low altitude without trouble amply demonstrating the Hunter's efficiency.

By 1958 all RAF day fighter squadrons in Europe had been re-equipped with Hunter 6s, while others were on detachment flying from Malta and Cyprus. No. 208 Squadron was re-formed that year in the United Kingdom with late production Mark 6s and flew out to the Middle East under the command of Sqn Ldr J Granville-White, operating as escort for RAF Transport Command Beverleys moving essential supplies into Jordan during the Iraqi revolution.

A year previously, however, the Hunter 6 had been able to demonstrate its superiority in a more peaceable country. Switzerland had for some time been planning replacement of its obsolescent Vampires and Venoms and after a number of demonstration flights by Hunters at Zürich, a series of competitive trials was ordered between the Mystére, Sabre, Gnat, P.16 (a Swiss ground attack design) and the Hunter. The result was a well-earned contract for the latter (see Hunter Mark 58).

About the same time as the Hunter 6 was being chosen by Switzerland, India placed an order for 160 aircraft with Hawkers (see Hunter 56), while further small batches of ex-RAF machines, modified up to the latest standard, were purchased under American funds and supplied to Iraq, Lebanon and Jordan during 1957–58. This period also saw the change-over from Hunter 4 production to the Hunter 6 at Avions Fairey and Fokker, and by the summer of 1959, when production ended, some 460 licence Hunter 4s and 6s had been built.

With an aircraft so widely used as the Hunter 6, it is hardly surprising that much development work was carried out on the design at Kingston. When the aircraft was first delivered to RAF squadrons in 1956, it was used principally as an interceptor possessing an improved rate of climb over the Mark 4 by reason of the more powerful engine. In the NATO defence system, however, the interceptor duties were more adequately performed by the American supersonic fighters such as the F-100 Super Sabre and F-104 Starfighter, and the Hunter gradually became regarded as a ground attack fighter, though well able to defend itself in event of being attacked. For this reason a large proportion of the trials carried out on the Hunter were concerned with external stores.

The Hawker P.1109A, WW594.

The Hawker P.1109B, XF378, showing the de Havilland Firestreak infra-red-seeking air-to-air missiles.

An unusual view of No. 111 (F) Squadron. (*Air Ministry Photograph*).

In addition to the wide range of British and foreign weapons which could be mounted under the wings, Hawkers developed a new drop tank containing 230 gallons of fuel. Two such tanks could be carried on the inboard pylons, while a pair of 100 gallon tanks could be mounted outboard. With this load (a total of 1,050 gallons of fuel), Hugh Merewether, chief experimental test pilot at Hawkers, flew a standard Hunter 6, XF374, from Dunsfold to El Adem in Libya on 2 October 1958, non-stop, a distance of 1,588 nautical miles in 3 hours 19 minutes. (RAF Hunter 6s were not, however, modified until late in 1959 to carry the 230 gallon drop tanks.)

As a result of some buffet trouble when carrying drop tanks on the outboard pylons, a number of specially-shaped tanks were flown on XF374, in attempts to improve the local airflow conditions. XE587 was fitted with a 10 ft 6 in ring-slot landing parachute (later fitted on the Mark 9) in the tail, while XE588 was at one time equipped with an emergency airfield arrester hook (later adopted by the naval Hunter 8). Another aircraft, XG131, was fitted with wing tip fuel tanks during 1956 as part of a projected Hunter night fighter design (known as the P.1114 and P.1115), but severe buffet accompanied use of these tanks and the scheme was abandoned.

Yet another project, which for some time showed considerable promise, was the Firestreak Hunter, designated the P.1109 and based on the Hunter 6. Originally the third production airframe, WW594, had been completed as an aerodynamic test aircraft for the project, featuring a lengthened nose and large radome, and armed with only two guns. This aircraft, the P.1109A, was never fitted with Firestreak missiles, but later a second machine, XF378, the P.1109B, was fully equipped and carried out a number of successful test firings of these infra-red-seeking weapons.

Until 1960 the Hunter 6 continued to represent Fighter Command's principal interceptor fighter equipment, but that year witnessed the gradual process of change-over from absolute reliance upon the manned interceptor, using gun armament, to an integrated defence system based upon medium-range missile-equipped interceptors (such as the English Electric Lightning) and short-range ground-to-air missiles. The age of the manned interceptor in a sophisticated environment was apparently drawing to an end. Hunter 6 fighter squadrons at home and in 2nd TAF were disbanded during the next two years while the rôle of the Hunter was modified to that of a ground-attack fighter. From that time onwards numerous Mark 6s were returned to the manufacturers for modification to suit the aircraft for ground-support duties (*see* Hunter F.G.A. Mark 9 and F.R. Mark 10).

THE HUNTER T. MARK 7 (HAWKER P.1101)

In common with almost every other widely-used single-seat fighter of the 1950s, design work was initiated early to adapt the Hunter to

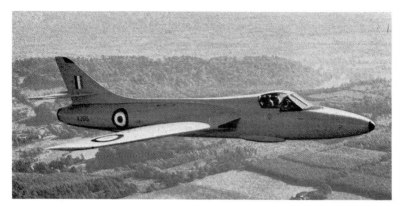

XJ615, the first P.1101 two-seat Hunter prototype displaying an early hood shape.

accommodate a second crew member for training duties. The two-seater design was started as a private venture in 1953 and schemes for both tandem and side-by-side seating were prepared. Specification T.157D was issued in 1954 and the new design, called the Hawker P.1101, was tendered. The side-by-side version was chosen and one prototype was ordered.

Based on the Hunter 4 with R.A.21 Avon engine, the P.1101 prototype, XJ615, first flew on 8 July 1955, but severe local airflow instability around the new hood fairing led to a lengthy programme of trials with various hoods and fairings being carried out. By mid-1956 the P.1101, now termed the Hunter T. Mk. 7, was free of trouble and already production orders had been placed by the Ministry of Supply. Moreover, Hawkers had been authorised to commence a second prototype, this time based on the Hunter 6 with the more powerful Avon Mk. 203, and

XJ615, fitted with metal canopy during development of the hood profile.

391

this machine, XJ627, was flown in 1956 complete with the enlarged hood fairing.

Ministry production contracts concerned only the less powerful version and although XJ615 was flown initially with twin Aden guns semi-buried under the nose, the port gun was removed and the production machines featured the single starboard gun only.

Structurally the Hunter 7 was similar to the Mark 4, and a number of the latter aircraft were returned to the factory, where the single-seat nose was replaced by the two-seat front fuselage section. Apart from the addition of the hood fairing the only other addition was a landing parachute in the tail.

Production of all two-seaters was scheduled to be undertaken at Hawkers' Blackpool factory, but after reduction of Hunter 6 orders in 1957 the Hunter 7 production was switched to Kingston, the first production aircraft, XL563, flying on 11 October 1957. Production orders for the Hunter 7 originally totalled sixty-five aircraft but ten were diverted to Holland and a further ten were selected for completion to a naval standard of preparation and designated the Hunter T. Mk. 8 (*q.v.*). A further order for ten aircraft was placed by the Netherlands

A standard Hunter T. Mk. 7, XL571.

Government direct with Hawker Aircraft, these aircraft being delivered during 1958.

No. 229 Operational Conversion Unit was the first RAF unit to receive Hunter 7s in 1958 and thereafter almost every operational Hunter squadron added a two-seater to its strength for instrument flying training and rating purposes. Some served in Germany and the Middle East, and ultimately in the Far East. Tropical clearance trials had been performed in 1958 using aircraft XL566.

During the *Daily Mail* London–Paris race of July 1959, several Hunter 7s were used by the RAF team flying from Biggin Hill, and both the fastest and third-fastest times were achieved using these aircraft.

392

The first Hunter T. Mk. 7, N-301, for the Netherlands.

Another Hunter 7 was used by No. 111 (Fighter) Squadron on several occasions to lead the aerobatic formation during the period 1959–61.

The introduction of TACAN equipment into the RAF led to limited conversion of two-seaters to include this equipment, this version being termed the T. Mk. 7A.

THE HUNTER T. MARK 8

As mentioned above, ten Hunter two-seaters were selected from the production line for completion to naval standard and designated the T. Mk. 8. These aircraft could only be distinguished from RAF aircraft

The first naval Hunter T. Mk. 8, WW664, converted from a Mark 4 single-seater.

One of the Hunter T. Mark 8s, XL580, allocated for use by Admiral Gick (note his insignia on the nose) and based at Yeovilton; these aircraft featured an attractive colour scheme of glossy dark blue and white.

(apart from colour scheme and markings) by the addition of an airfield arrester hook under the rear fuselage for use with naval airfield emergency arrester gear. The hook was not stressed for deck use.

The prototype Hunter 8, WW664, was completed using a repaired and converted Mark 4 airframe and first flew on 3 March 1958, and the first newly-built aircraft, XL580, flew on 30 May the same year. The production contract was completed and a further seventeen Hunter 4s were converted. Three Fleet Air Arm squadrons were equipped with Hunter 8s, Nos. 738, 759 and 764.

Like the RAF, the Fleet Air Arm commenced introduction of TACAN during the mid-1960s and further Mark 4s were converted, the Mk. 8B (of which four examples were built) featuring a full TACAN installation, and the Mk. 8C (eleven produced) including a partial TACAN installation. In both instances the Aden gun and radar-ranging equipment was removed. The aged Mk. 8 prototype, WW664, was also used as prototype for the Mk. 8B.

A standard Hunter F.G.A. Mk. 9, XE592.

One of the Rhodesian Hunter F.G.A. 9s — ex-RAF Hunter 6s fully modified
to ground-attack standard.

THE HUNTER F.G.A. MARK 9

Despite the fact that no new Hunter 9s were ever built but were all
converted from ex-Fighter Command Mark 6s, the Hunter 9 ground-
attack fighter represented the major equipment bulk of the RAF's close
support force during the 1960s. Originally intended for exclusive service
in the Middle East, the Mark 9 came into being as the result of competitive evaluation trials during the period 1957–59. Owing to the nature of
most aerodromes and runways in the Middle East the main modifications applied were the addition of a tail parachute and increased ventila-
tion for the cockpit. With the gradual contraction of overseas RAF bases
greater emphasis came to be laid upon the reinforcement of distant
theatres from home aerodromes, with the result that the 230 gallon fuel
tank was applied as standard to this Hunter version. Later the requirement was formulated for this tank to be stressed for ground-attack
operation and the inboard pylon was modified to feature a strengthening
strut when carrying the large tank. Associated with the much increased
range possible when using the fuel 'overload' was an increased oxygen
supply for the pilot.

Hunter 9s served with RAF Strike Command for almost nine years,
first joining Nos. 1, 8 and 54 (Fighter) Squadrons in 1960–61. No. 8
Squadron was deployed for operations around Aden in 1961, while Nos.
43 and 208 Squadrons (the latter newly re-formed) started a programme
of reinforcement training detachments from Britain to the Mediterranean and the Middle East. In 1962 Nos. 20 and 28 Squadrons re-
equipped with Mark 9s, the former being sent to Borneo in 1964. During
a detachment to Aden, No. 43 Squadron was ordered to hand over its
aircraft to Jordan as part of the British government's military assistance
to that nation, but No. 8 Squadron retained its Mark 9s until 1968.

There is no doubt that the trouble-free employment of the Hunter by
the RAF in the harsh environment of the Middle and Far East during
these years greatly impressed many of the world's smaller air forces, and
this, as much as any 'sales talk', continued to lend support to the lively
trade in export Hunters.

395

THE HUNTER F.R. MARK 10

Following a trial installation carried out in a Hunter 4 of a forward-facing camera, a Ministry of Supply requirement was issued in 1957 for a version of the Mark 6 to be so modified for service with the RAF in Germany. The result was the Hunter F.R. Mk. 10 whose prototype, XF429 (a converted Mark 6) was first flown by Hugh Merewether on 7 November 1959.

The only RAF squadrons to take delivery of full complements of Hunter F.R. Mark 10s were Nos. 2 and 4 in Germany, the latter at Gütersloh reverting to its traditional fighter reconnaissance rôle after flying Hunter 4s for nearly five years. Several other squadrons were issued with one or two aircraft each, including No. 8 Squadron, at the time based at Khormaksar, Aden, to provide a reconnaissance service for local forces. One such aircraft was passed by Jordan to the Sultan of Oman.

With the appearance in service of such new aircraft as the Phantom and the introduction of its sophisticated reconnaissance packs, the Hunter 10 was phased out of RAF service at the end of the 1960s; many

The prototype Hunter F.R. Mk. 10, XF429.

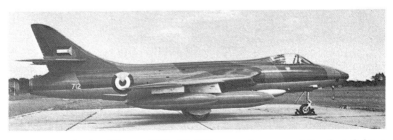

The first Jordanian Hunter F.R. 10, 712, was also one of the first fighter-reconnaissance Hunters to be sold abroad, but different from the RAF version in not being equipped with a landing parachute.

A standard Hunter F.R Mk. 10, XE621.

such aircraft were then repurchased by Hawker Siddeley Aviation for refurbishing and resale overseas.

THE HUNTER MARK 11

The Admiralty order for Hunter two-seaters was followed during 1961–64 by orders for small numbers of single-seaters, designated Mark 11s these aeroplanes being versions of the Mark 4 with Avon R.A.21

A Hunter Mark 11 of the Fleet Air Arm.

engines. In most instances the gun armament was removed, naval radio installed and provision made to mount rocket batteries on inboard and outboard wing pylons for weapon training. A small number of aircraft were fitted with cameras and were designated P.R. Mk. 11s.

The first Hunter G.A. Mark 11, as the standard naval single-seater was designated, underwent brief trials at Dunsfold and Boscombe Down in April and May 1962, and delivery of the remaining aircraft to No. 739 (Training) Squadron at Lossiemouth started in June.

In service with Nos. 738 and 764 Squadrons, the forty Mark 11s flew with a wide assortment of underwing stores, including HE and practice bombs, and rocket batteries of various sorts. At one time aircraft were experimentally modified to carry Martin Bullpup and Philco Sidewinder missiles.

In the 1970s it was announced that the number of single-seat Hunters with the Fleet Air Arm was to be substantially increased to fill the weapons training rôle, but, in line with the then-current policy of limiting expenditure on naval aviation, the Admiralty failed to acquire the funding necessary for further conversion of Hunter 11s. Instead a small number of standard RAF Hunter 4s was temporarily transferred to Admiralty charge.

THE HUNTER MARK 12

One of the more interesting 'one-off' versions of the Hunter two-seater was the Hunter 12. This was a Mark 6 conversion (i.e. with the Avon 203 engine), XE531, ordered by the Ministry of Supply for use by the Royal Aircraft Establishment at Farnborough and Bedford. This Hunter was used for a trial installation of a large vertical survey camera mounted in the nose and a head-up display; it was thought likely at one time that a small conversion order might follow so that the Hunter could be used as an instrument trainer for the BAC TSR-2 but, although nothing came of the project, considerable experience was gained in advanced instrumentation which was obviously of great benefit in the development of the Hawker Siddeley Harrier.

THE SWEDISH HUNTER MARK 50

The first Hunter 4 had still to be completed for the RAF when, on 29 June 1954, a contract was finalised with the Swedish Government for the delivery of 120 Avon R.A. 21-powered Hunter single-seaters. Termed the Hunter 50 (Swedish designation J-34), these aircraft, initially powered by Avon 115s but later progressively modified to Avon 119 and 120 standard, were delivered during 1955 and 1956, the first twenty-four being built at Kingston and the remainder at Blackpool. The first aircraft, 34001, was flown on 24 June 1955, by Frank Murphy.

The Hunter Mark 50 remained in front line service with *Flygvapnet*

The first Swedish Hunter Mk. 50, 34001.

until 1966, flying with four Wings: F8 at Barkarby, F9 at Säve, F10 at Ängelholm, and F18, the latter producing a Hunter aerobatic team, the 'Acro-Hunters', in 1962.

The Swedish Hunters were unusual in not being fitted with wing leading-edge extensions, and it was perhaps surprising that no two-seaters were purchased to accompany such a large order. On the other hand the Swedes undertook conversion of their Hunters to carry Sidewinder air-to-air missiles — a facility that greatly increased their aircraft's combat potential.

Some efforts were made to improve the Hunter 50's performance with the withdrawal from service of several aircraft for installation of the Flygmotor reheat system; however, despite a substantial increase in thrust, the Hunter remained no more than transonic, its wing design being the limiting factor in the quest for speed.

THE DANISH HUNTER MARK 51

Only four days after the Swedish contract was signed, the Danish Government placed an order for thirty Hunters, again similar to the Mark 4, and designated the Hunter 51. All these aircraft were built at Kingston and deliveries were completed in 1956. Like the Swedish machines the engines originally fitted were Avon 115s and were later modified to overcome surge problems during gun firing. The aircraft were flown from Dunsfold to Værløse in Denmark and subsequently served with No. 724 Squadron at Aalborg. This unit participated in many NATO air defence exercises during 1957–58, often operating from 2nd TAF aerodromes in company with RAF, Dutch and Belgian Hunters.

THE PERUVIAN HUNTER MARK 52

The sale of sixteen ex-RAF Hunter 4s to the Peruvian Air Force in 1955 was something of a triumph for the British aircraft industry for, as far as fighters were concerned, the American 'dumping' of surplus F-86 Sabres, F-80 and T-33 Shooting Stars had hitherto monopolised the South American market.

The Hunters for Peru had been returned to Dunsfold during the last months of 1955 for modification up to the latest standard and were repainted with the new insignia. The first to fly in its new colours, 630, was flown by Frank Bullen on 1 December 1955, and, with a few of the subsequent machines, was used for Hunter conversion of Peruvian pilots at Dunsfold. Deliveries to Peru were completed during 1956, the aircraft entering service at Limatambo and Talara.

The second Danish Hunter T. Mk. 53, 35-272.

Early Indian Hunter Mk. 56s await ferrying from Dunsfold.

THE DANISH HUNTER T.MARK 53

Two Hunter two-seaters were delivered to Værløse towards the end of 1958, the first having been flown by Frank Bullen at Dunsfold on 17 October that year. Designated T. Mk. 53, these aircraft were similar to the RAF's T. 7s, having Avon 122 engines, but lacked the wing leading edge extensions as they were intended to reproduce the handling qualities of the Danish Hunter 51s already delivered and which were also without the extensions.

THE INDIAN HUNTER MARK 56

The first overseas order for the Hunter 6 was placed by India in Sepember 1957 when an initial contract for 160 Mark 56s was signed with Hawker Aircraft Ltd. The first thirty-two had already been commenced as part of a Ministry of Supply contract but were completed as standard aircraft for India. The following sixteen aircraft were ex-RAF Hunter 6s returned from Maintenance Units. The forty-ninth and subsequent aircraft were newly-built to an Indian Standard of Preparation which included gun blast deflectors and tail parachutes. Later aircraft were modified to permit carriage of Hawker 230 gallon drop tanks.

The first Indian Hunter 56, BA201, was flown on 11 October 1957, and, after a number of Indian pilots had undergone training at Dunsfold, deliveries commenced the following month and lasted until mid-1960. The aircraft, carrying four 100 gallon drop tanks, were mostly flown out to Karachi by RAF pilots from Benson, and later served at Ambala and Poona with Nos. 7, 17, 20 and 27 Squadrons of the Indian Air Force. They remained at front-line status until the end of the 1960s, having been involved in combat operations over Portuguese Goa and with the Chinese during the northern frontier disputes.

Although outclassed by interceptors current during the 1960s, Indian Hunters quickly proved their adaptability and reliability in the ground-attack rôle with the result that in 1965 a further order for Hunter single-seaters was placed, and was followed by others in 1967 and 1968, these aircraft being modified to a later standard and termed Mark 56As. A total of fifty-three was delivered, having been converted from refurbished ex-RAF and ex-Netherlands Mark 6s.

THE KUWAITI HUNTER (F.G.A.) MARK 57

In a contract signed with Hawkers in 1963, the Kuwaiti Government ordered four Hunters to be prepared to full F.G.A. Mark 9 standard, and these aircraft (previously reconditioned ex-Belgian Mark 6s) were delivered during 1965–66.

THE SWISS HUNTER MARK 58

During June and July 1957 two Hunter 6s, XE587 and XE588, visited Switzerland for demonstrations and participation in a competition with several aircraft (including the F-86), during which performance, handling and weapon delivery characteristics were compared. The Hunter emerged successful and a Standard of Preparation, similar to that of the Indian Mark 56, was included in the contract.

The initial twelve aircraft were ex-RAF Mark 6s, the first, J-4001, being flown by Frank Bullen on 29 March 1958, but all the remainder were newly built.

The first Swiss Hunter Mk. 58, J-4001.

An Iraqi Hunter F.G.A. 59 at Dunsfold before delivery; the aircraft is fitted with tail parachute and stressed 230-gallon tank mountings, but lacks gun blast deflectors.

THE IRAQI HUNTER MARK 59

Following the satisfactory service given by the early group of ex-RAF Mark 6s with the Iraqi Air Force delivered in 1958–59, rather larger orders were placed in 1964 and 1965 for forty-two full-standard F.G.A. Mark 9s (termed Mk. 59 and 59A), and four full-standard F.R. Mk. 10s (termed Mk. 59Bs). The great majority of these were provided from ex-Belgian conversions, though eight ex-Netherlands aircraft were included.

THE PERUVIAN HUNTER T. MARK 62

A single Hunter trainer was ordered by Peru during 1959. It was a converted Mark 4, WT706, was first flown by Don Lucey on 15 September 1959, and differed externally from the standard T. Mk. 7 in featuring a prominent aerial fairing mounted on top of the fuselage amidships.

The Peruvian Hunter T. Mk. 62, 681.

THE INDIAN, JORDANIAN AND LEBANESE HUNTER T. MARK 66

The Indian Hunter T. Mk. 66. The same contract which was placed by India for the single-seat Hunter 56 also covered the manufacture of twelve two-seaters based on the second P.1101 prototype, XJ627, with Avon 203 engine and twin Aden guns. The first machine, BS361, was flown on 6 August 1958, but owing to a lengthy period of trials during which new gun blast deflectors were developed, the first delivery did not take place until February 1959.

One of the Indian aircraft, BS366, had an eventful early career before delivery, being demonstrated at the Paris Air Show in June 1959, and two months later was used by Mr Eric Rylands to achieve the second fastest time in the *Daily Mail* London–Paris air race.

The first Indian Hunter T. Mk. 66, BS361.

403

In Indian service the Mark 66s were issued to the Hunter-equipped fighter squadrons for use as operational trainers. A second contract placed in 1960 brought the total number of Indian Mark 66s delivered to twenty-two.

The Hunter Mark 66A. The Hunter 66A, registered G-APUX, was a company-sponsored demonstration aircraft based on the Indian Hunter T. Mk. 66. It was built during July and August 1959, using the front fuselage section which had been displayed at the Paris Air Show in June together with the wings and rear fuselage of an ex-Belgian Air Force Hunter 6, IF-19. In place of the 10 ft 6 in diameter ring slot parachute of other Hunter trainers, G-APUX was fitted with a parachute of 13 ft 6in diameter, as well as a nosewheel brake. Painted red and white and trailing smoke, this aircraft was flown by Bill Bedford at the 1959 SBAC Display, demonstrating in exciting fashion the full inverted spinning clearance achieved by the Hunter, by executing spins of up to twelve turns on every day of the Show. The following month G-APUX was flown to Switzerland for participation in evaluation trials. In 1960 G-APUX was fitted with nosewheel steering and was flown on several occasions with Hawker 350 gallon ferry tanks. Again demonstrating spins at the 1960 SBAC Display, the aircraft now carried two 100 gallon drop tanks. In 1963, after a demonstration tour of the Middle East, G-APUX was repainted in Iraqi military colours and leased for a year to that country; during 1965 and 1966 it reappeared in Jordanian and Lebanese colours, but in each instance it was returned to Britain when its place in these air forces had been taken by other Hunter trainers delivered on contract. Ultimately G-APUX was standardised to meet a Chilean requirement and was delivered to Chile in 1967 as a Mark 72 (*q.v.*).

The Jordanian Hunter T. Mk. 6B. This designation covered three trainers based on the Indian Mk. 66 delivered between 1960 and 1968. The first was a newly-built aircraft, and the second was delivered as a

G-APUX, the famous demonstration Hunter T. Mk. 66A.

A picture of G-APUX taken shortly before the 1960 SBAC Display, showing the 350 gallon ferry tanks.

replacement for G-APUX. The second and third were converted from ex-Netherlands Mark 6s.

The Lebanese Hunter T. Mk. 66C. Three aircraft were ordered by the Lebanon in 1964, one of which replaced G-APUX. All were ex-Belgian Mark 6s.

The Indian Hunter T. Mk. 66D. To complement the valuable service provided by the original twenty-two Indian Hunter T. 66s, a further contract was placed in 1966 for the supply of a further twelve trainers, modified to the latest standard of equipment and capable of carrying 230 gallon fuel tanks under ground-attack conditions of service. These were all ex-Netherlands Hunter 6s and were delivered during 1968.

THE KUWAITI HUNTER T. MARK 67

To complement the order for four Hunter 57s placed by Kuwait in 1963, two trainers were ordered at the same time. These were ex-Belgian Mark 6s. A further order for three aircraft was placed in 1967, two being ex-Netherlands and one ex-RAF.

THE IRAQI HUNTER T. MARK 69

With the expansion of the Iraqi Air Force during the early 1960s came two contracts for Hunter trainers (apart from the lease of G-APUX). Three ex-Belgian Mark 6s were delivered during 1963–64 and two others during 1965, one of the latter replacing G-APUX.

THE LEBANESE HUNTER F.G.A. MARK 70

Four ex-Belgian Mark 6s ordered during 1964, brought up to full F.G.A. Mark 9 standard and delivered during 1965.

THE CHILEAN HUNTER MARK 71 AND 72

Chile was one of Britain's unfortunate customers to fall victim of doctrinaire embargos applied after the conclusion of legitimate commercial negotiations. After lengthy discussions — in the face of considerable competition from elsewhere — an order for fifteen single-seat Hunters (culled from RAF Dutch and Belgian sources) was finalised with Hawker in 1966, and these deliveries were completed in 1968. These F.G.A. Mark 71s were followed by thirteen more by September 1973, together with six single-seaters (including conversions of the old second prototype P.1101, XJ627, and Hawkers famous G-APUX), T. Mark 72, were also delivered.

In 1974, however, prompted by opinions expressed in some quarters in Britain, an embargo on the supply of spares to Chile was imposed, thereby creating a market vacuum which was quickly filled by the United States, Brazil and Argentina. Chile's effective strength of Hunters thereafter quickly declined as a result of this restriction, so that by 1978 only twenty aircraft remained serviceable, and these were serving with *Grupos* 8 and 9 of *Ala 1* (Support Wing) at Cerro Moreno air force base, Antofagasta.

The final chapter in the long history of G-APUX was reached when it was sold as one of four Chilean Hunter T. Mark 72s, J-718; the famous aeroplane is shown here at Dunsfold before delivery.

THE JORDANIAN HUNTER MARK 73

Late series Standard of Preparation specified of two Mk. 73 and four Mk. 73A single-seat ground-attack fighters ordered in 1968. All were reconditioned ex-RAF Mark 6s.

In June 1972 the Hunters on strength with the Jordanian Air Force amounted to thirty-five single-seaters and three two-seaters, and these aircraft were scheduled for replacement when the Yom Kippur War broke out. Replacement was, however, still awaited early in 1975 when Sultan Qaboos of Abu Dhabi presented to King Hussein his entire strength of twelve Hunters to join the nineteen surviving Jordanian aircraft. Later in 1975 King Hussein in turn presented all his thirty-one Hunters, now accumulated from various sources, to the Sultan of Oman.

THE SINGAPOREAN HUNTER MARK 74 AND 75

In July 1968 the Republic of Singapore contracted to purchase sixteen refurbished ex-RAF Hunter 6s, twelve of them at F.G.A. Mark 9 and four at F.R. Mark 10 standard. Delivered during 1970 and 1971, these aircraft entered service with No. 140 (Osprey) Squadron, RSAF, commanded by Maj Chris Strong, a former RAF Hunter pilot of considerable experience. These F.G.A. Mark 74s and F.R. Mark 75s were based at Tengah, and their pilots were responsible for air defence duties, army support and tactical reconnaissance. They customarily flew with SNEB-Matra rocket batteries on the outboard wing pylons and 230 gallon drop tanks inboard.

Further orders followed for twenty-two Mark 74B single-seaters and nine T.75As and 75Bs (some of these being converted from RAF Mark 4s) during the next two years, and these were delivered by October 1973, although one aircraft ditched in the Bristol Channel and was lost. A second Squadron, No. 141 (Merlin) Squadron, was then formed to fly these late deliveries.

THE ABU DHABIAN HUNTER MARK 76

With the progressive withdrawal of RAF strength from the Middle East and the implied growing threat to the independence of the Trucial Oman States and Sheikdoms during the period 1966–70, a number of these States began to establish small locally-based air forces. The proven adaptability and reliability, allied with the low cost of the Hunter, recommended this aircraft as an obvious choice, and an order for seven F.G.A. Mk. 76s and three F.R. Mk. 76As was placed with Hawkers in 1969. Among the aircraft supplied under this contract were ex-RAF Mk. 4s and 6s, including the first production Mk. 6 ever built, WW592.

The second Hunter 6, 60/602, of a batch of four single-seaters supplied for service with the Royal Saudi Air Force.

THE ABU DHABIAN HUNTER T. MARK 77

Included in the above contract were two two-seaters (ex-Netherlands Mk. 7s) which were delivered during 1970.

THE QATARI HUNTER (F.G.A.) MARK 78

The second of the Middle East independent states to contract for Hunters in 1969 was Qatar, which ordered three ground-attack fighters to be supplied as F.G.A. Mk. 78s.

THE QATARI HUNTER T. MARK 79

One two-seater (an ex-Netherlands Mk. 7) was ordered by Qatar for delivery during 1970.

Representative of the many Hunters supplied to the Middle East and later returned to the manufacturers to be refurbished and updated, this Lebanese Mark 6 was returned to Dunsfold in 1975 to be upgraded to full F.G.A. Mark 9 standard.

408

THE KENYAN HUNTER MARK 80 AND 81

The last customer for refurbished Hunters from Britain was Kenya, whose air force was supplied with four F.G.A. Mark 80s (converted from ex-RAF Hunter 4s and a Mark 6) and two T. Mark 81s (previously Fleet Air Arm Hunter T Mark 8s). These were delivered during 1974 and 1975.

TECHNICAL DATA FOR HUNTER (ALL PRODUCTION VERSIONS)

TYPE: Mks. 1, 2, 4, 5, 50, 51 and 52. Single-seat interceptor fighter. *Mks, 6, 9, Iraqi, Jordanian Lebanese, 56 and 58.* Single-seat interceptor and ground attack fighter. *Mks. 7, 8, Dutch Mk. 7, Mks, 53, 62 and 66.* Two-seat operational trainer. *Mk. 10.* Single-seat reconnaissance fighter.

STRUCTURE: All-metal stressed-skin construction.

MANUFACTURERS: Hawker Aircraft Ltd, Kingson (Mks. 1, 4, 6, 7, 8, 9, 10, 50, 51, 52, 53, 56, 58, 62 and 66). Hawker Aircraft Ltd, Blackpool (Mks. 1, 4, 6 and 50). Sir W G Armstrong Whitworth Aircraft Ltd, Coventry (Mks. 2, 5 and 6).

POWERPLANT: One 5,500–8,000 lb s.l.s.t. Rolls-Royce Avon Mk. 113, 115, 119, 120, 121 or 122 (R.A.7 and 21 rating) in Hunter Mks. 1, 4, 7, 8, 50, 51, 52, 53, 62 and Dutch Mk. 7. One 10,000 lb s.l.s.t. Rolls-Royce Avon Mk. 203 or 207 (R.A.28 rating) in Mk. 6, Iraqi, Jordanian, Lebanese, 9, 10, 56, 58 and 66. One 8,000 lb s.l.s.t. Armstrong Siddeley Sapphire Mk. 101 in Mks. 2 and 5.

DIMENSIONS: Span (all versions), 33 ft 8in. Length (all single-seaters except Mk. 10), 45 ft 10½ in (Mk. 10), 46 ft 1 in (all two-seaters), 48 ft 10½ in. Height (all versions), 13 ft 2 in. Wing area (without leading edge extensions), 340 sq ft (with leading edge extensions), 349 sq ft.

WEIGHTS: Empty. *Mk. 1.* 12,128 lb. *Mk. 2.* 11,973 lb. *Mks. 4, 5, 50, 51 and 52.* 12,543 lb. *Mks. 6, 56, 58, Iraqi, Jordanian and Lebanese.* 12,760 lb. *Mks, 7, 8, Dutch Mk. 7, Mks. 53 and 62.* 13,360 lb. *Mk. 9.* 13,010 lb. *Mk. 10.* 13,100 lb. *Mk. 66.* 13,580 lb.

Loaded, clean aircraft. *Mks. 1 and 2.* 16,200 lb. *Mks. 4, 5, 50, 51 and 52.* 17,100 lb. *Mks, 6, 56, 58, Iraqi, Jordanian and Lebanese.* 17,750 lb. *Mks, 7, 8, Dutch Mk. 7, Mks, 53 and 62.* 17,200 lb. *Mk. 9,* 18,000 lb. *Mk. 10.* 18.090 lb. *Mk. 66.* 17,420 lb. Max overload weight: 24,000 lb with two 230 gallon and two 100 gallon drop tanks.

PERFORMANCE: Clean aircraft only.

Avon (R.A.7 rating) single-seaters. Max speed, 0.93 M at 36,000 ft (608 kts at sea level). Climb, 9.8 min to 45,000 ft. Service ceiling (rate of climb, 500 ft/min), 48,800 ft.

Avon (R.A.21 rating) single-seaters. Max speed, 0.94 M at 36,000 ft (610 kts at sea level). Climb, 9.85 min to 45,000 ft. Service ceiling (rate of climb, 500 ft/min), 50,000 ft.

Avon (R.A.28 rating) single-seaters. Max speed, 0.95 M at 36,000 ft (621 kts at sea level). Climb, 7.5 min to 45,000 ft. Service ceiling (rate of climb, 500 ft/min), 51,500 ft.

Avon (R.A.21 rating) two-seaters. Max speed, 0.92 M at 36,000 ft (603 kts at sea level. Climb, 12.5 min to 45,000 ft. Service ceiling (rate of climb, 500 ft/min), 47,000 ft.

Avon (R.A.28 rating) two-seaters. Max speed, 0.93 M at 36,000ft (608 kts at sea level). Climb, 10.2 min to 45,000 ft. Service ceiling (rate of climb, 500 ft/min), 48,900 ft.

Sapphire Mk. 101 versions. Max speed, 0.94 M at 36,000 ft (612 kts at sea level). Climb, 8.2 min to 45,000 ft. Service ceiling (rate of climb, 500 ft/min), 50,000 ft.

FUEL CAPACITIES: Mk. 1. 334 gallons. *Mk. 2*. 314 gallons. *Mks, 4, 7, 8, 50, 51, 52 and 62*. 414 (+400 in drop tanks). *Mk. 5*. 388 (+400) gallons.* *Mks. 6, 9, 10, Iraqi, Jordanian Lebanese, 56, 58 and 66*. 390 (+660) gallons.

*Few Mk. 5 aircraft were equipped to carry outboard drop tanks.

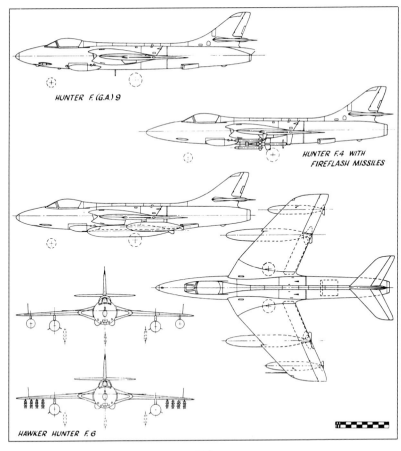

HUNTER F. (G.A.) 9

HUNTER F.4 WITH FIREFLASH MISSILES

HAWKER HUNTER F. 6

410

ARMAMENT: All single-seaters carried four 30 mm Aden guns in detachable pack under nose, with 137–150 rounds per gun. Mk. 66 trainers carried two Aden guns under nose, while all other two-seaters were armed with a single Aden gun under the starboard side of the nose. A wide variety of weapons could be mounted on wing pylons of Mk. 4 and subsequent aircraft. The inboard pylons could carry British and foreign bombs of up to 1,000 lb, two-inch multiple rocket batteries, 100 gallon Napalm bombs and practice bomb carriers. In the outboard position either drop tank pylons or launchers for British 3 in R.P.s (with various warheads), French T.10, Swedish Bofors, American H.V.A.R. or Swiss Hispano and Oerlikon R.P.s could be fitted.

UNDERCARRIAGE: (All versions) Hydraulically-operated inwards retracting main undercarriage with 14 ft 9 in track. Nosewheel retracted forward.

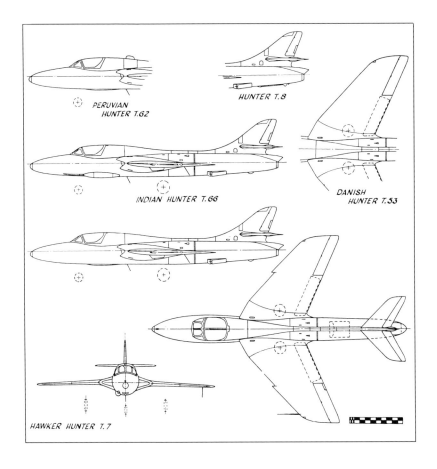

The first Hawker P.1127 prototype, XP831, standing on its special gridded platform at Dunsfold.

The Hawker P.1127

Early in 1957, while deliveries of the Hunter 6 to the RAF were accelerating and others were being cancelled following the ramifications of Duncan Sandy's famous Defence White Paper, the experimental design offices at Hawkers were continuing to work upon the large air superiority fighter, the P.1121, which was expected to fly in 1958. As time went on it became obvious that even this promising project was doomed to be abandoned.

Against this background of growing austerity, following the débâcle of Suez, it seemed likely that Hawkers would have to depend upon the sale abroad of the Hunter to provide the necessary revenue to maintain its 5,000 workforce. It was, however, at this time that Hawkers were approached by Dr S G Hooker, technical director of the Bristol Engine Company, with the design of a radical powerplant which came to be known as the B.E.53. It transpired that a freelance French engineer, Michel Wibault, had evolved an aircraft propulsion system in which a Bristol Orion engine drove four centrifugal compressors enclosed in rotatable involutes to produce either forward or vertical thrust. Wibault had approached the Mutual Weapons Defence Team and this in turn had asked Bristols to examine the possibility of tailoring the system to produce a compact powerplant. The Bristol engine design staff under Hooker adopted an Orpheus engine as a gas generator to drive two stages of an Olympus low-pressure compressor on the sides of which were positioned two rotatable ducts which exhausted and directed the 'cold' air either horizontally or vertically to provide thrust. The 'hot' exhaust from the Orpheus was directed in the conventional method horizontally aft.

It fell to a young project engineer, Ralph Hooper (later Chief Engineer and Executive Director of the company), to scheme up the initial design of an aircraft round this engine project in mid-1957 and his design came to be known as the P.1127. For about a year the project team developed Hooper's basic design, making four fundamental alterations possible in the engine. First, a common intake was used for both compressor and gas generator; a bifurcated tailpipe (similar to that on the Sea Hawk) was substituted, thereby permitting the hot exhaust to be directed in concert with the 'cold' rotatable nozzles, and allowing the aircraft to stand horizontally when on the ground; aerodynamic cascades were used in the rotatable nozzles, permitting much smaller and neater nozzles to be used; and finally the two spools of the engine were made to rotate in opposite directions, thereby cancelling gyroscopic effects during critical hovering manoeuvres.

Despite repeated efforts to enlist official interest in the P.1127 design, work continued at Hawkers on commercial financing, although a substantial proportion of the funds necessary for the engine develoment were forthcoming from the USA. It is also true that a great deal of model testing was undertaken by NASA — such was the interest in the project generated through the MWDP. However, at home it was felt by the Air Staff that it had all the problems it could cope with trying to steer its own major project (GOR 339, later to become the ill-fated TSR-2) through the Treasury in the atmosphere of economy already mentioned.

Notwithstanding this apparent apathy, Hawkers persevered and late in 1959 metal was cut on the first of three prototypes (of which one was to undergo structural testing in Hawkers' huge rig). Their design, to some extent based on a believed NATO requirement for a light tactical close-support fighter to replace the Fiat G. 91, would be subsonic and its emphasis (always one propounded by Camm) was upon simplicity. Meanwhile the first B.E. 53 engine was bench-run on 1 September 1959, when it developed a thrust of around 10,000 pounds.

Shortly before the first flight prototype, XP831, was completed, contract cover was forthcoming from the Ministry of Supply in September 1960. The aircraft was moved to Dunsfold for final assembly and on 21 October that autumn XP831 lifted a few inches from the surface of a special grid under restraint of tethering cables. At an all-up weight slightly under 10,000 pounds (having been stripped of all extraneous equipment) the aircraft, with Bill Bedford at the controls, achieved free hovering fight for the first time on 19 November with a Pegasus (as the B.E. 53 had been named) rated at about 10,400 pounds installed thrust.

Taxiing tests followed during the winter of 1960–61 and XP831 was joined by the second aircraft, XP836. Flown by Bill Bedford, XP836 was first airborne on 7 July 1961, and straightway the two aircraft embarked on a series of trials to 'close the gap' between engine-borne flight and wing-borne flight to achieve the necessary transition from vertical take-off to horizontal flight. By 8 September the 'gap' had been closed and four days later both Bedford and Hugh Merewether made complete accelerating and decelerating transitions.

On 14 December 1961 XP836 was lost in an accident at Yeovilton following the loss of a cold nozzle in flight. The aircraft got out of control on the approach to a precautionary landing and Bill Bedford ejected safely at about 200 feet. Nevertheless, contract cover had been received for the manufacture of four more prototypes, and the next aircraft, XP972 with a 12,500 lb thrust Pegasus 2, joined the test programme with a first flight on 5 April 1962. XP831 was fitted with a 13,500 lb thrust Pegasus 3 engine at about this time. The next aircraft, XP976, flew on 12 July and incorporated streamwise wing-tips; it was on this aircraft that the Hawker production pilots Duncan Simpson and David Lockspeiser commenced familiarisation flying. XP972's life was short, however, the

Three of the P.1127 prototypes (XP831, XP976 and XP980) in formation, flown by Bill Bedford (Chief Test Pilot), Hugh Mereweather (Chief Experimental Test Pilot) and Duncan Simpson (Chief Production Test Pilot). In 1970 Simpson was appointed Chief Test Pilot at Dunsfold.

414

aeroplane being extensively damaged following fire in the air caused by the failure of an engine main bearing in a high-g turn. Merewether managed to put the aircraft down on the disused aerodrome at Tangmere. XP980 flew during the autumn of 1962, introducing the taller fin and anhedral tailplane, and was followed by XP984 which featured the swept wing for the first time.

Already Hawkers had generated considerable interest in the project and it was in 1962 that the company was informed that a special squadron was to be formed with experienced pilots from the American air forces, the *Luftwaffe* and the RAF, for the service evaluation of the P.1127. A Standard of Preparation was drawn up and nine aircraft were ordered (the Hawker Siddeley Kestrel, *q.v.*). In the meantime the prototypes embarked on numerous demonstrations to prove the extraordinary flexibility offered by their radical configuration. Following interest by the Royal Navy, Bill Bedford flew XP831 on to the deck of HMS *Ark Royal*, this despite the fact that he had never previously landed a combat aircraft on a carrier. Night flying provided no difficulty and P.1127s were flown at supersonic speeds in shallow dives.

The first historic prototype, XP831, was lost in unfortunate circumstances to say the least. The aircraft had been flown to the Paris Air

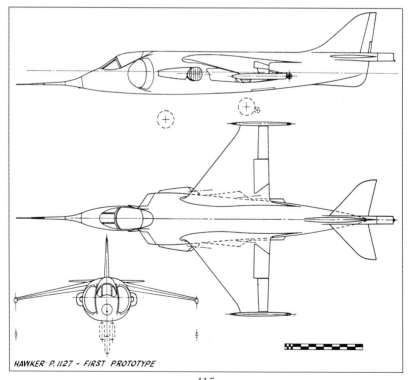

HAWKER P.1127 - FIRST PROTOTYPE

The prototype Hawker P.1127, XP831, during its second conventional flight on 14 March 1961. The pilot was Bill Bedford.

Show of 1963 to show its paces in the presence of the French Marcel Dassault Mirage 'Balzac V' VTO prototype. As Bill Bedford made a turn in front of the crowd in hovering flight and commenced his acceleration into conventional flight he rapidly lost height and crashed. It was found that a fragment of dirt had penetrated the air motors which rotated the nozzles, so that without adequate forward speed and lift the aircraft simply flew on to the ground out of control. Bedford stepped out unhurt.

The ultimate P.1127, XP984, was re-engined with a 15,000 lb thrust Pegasus 5 engine and with this it came to be regarded as the prototype of the Kestrel, which now followed the P.1127 in the experimental shops at Kingston.

TECHNICAL DATA FOR P.1127

TYPE: Experimental vertical/short take-off aircraft.

STRUCTURE: Semi-monocoque structure of aluminium with local areas of steel in the vicinity of hot exhaust nozzles. Various wing planforms.

MANUFACTURERS: Hawker Aircraft Ltd, Kingston-upon-Thames, Surrey.

POWERPLANT: One Bristol Pegasus vectored-thrust turbofan; experimental development engines installed, giving progressively increased thrust, from approximately 10,500 lb to approximately 13,500 lb. Reaction control nozzles situated in nose, tail and at wing-tips, using engine-bleed air from HP compressor.

DIMENSIONS: (First prototype) Wing span, 24 ft 4 in. Overall length, 49 ft 0 in. Height, 10 ft 3 in.

WEIGHTS: (First prototype) Empty, approximately, 8,900 lb. Loaded, approximately 11,800 lb. Later aircraft operated at loaded weights of up to 14,500 lb.

PERFORMANCE: Max speed, approximately 720 mph (M=0.97 at 36,000 ft). Rate of climb, more than 20,000 ft/min. Service ceiling, over 50,000 ft.

Four Hawker Siddeley Kestrels of the tripartite evaluation squadron based at West Raynham; the numeral painted on each aircraft's nose was the same as the last of the related serial number, thus aircraft No. 8 was in fact the first of the batch, XS688.

The Hawker Siddeley Kestrel

As previously mentioned, the constant efforts by Hawkers to demonstrate the extraordinary capabilities of the P.1127 prototypes had in 1962 prompted the announcement of the formation of a 'tripartite' evaluation squadron to assess these potentialities under limited service conditions. This interest had to a great extent been spurred by the widespread design participation in a NATO competition for an exotic V/STOL (vertical and short take-off and landing) tactical strike aircraft. Numerous designs had been tendered and of these the Hawker P.1154 was generally regarded as the best but, following injection of bitter political acrimony, the competition was ultimately abandoned. The P.1154 was pursued to the point of tendering designs for both RAF and naval versions to the British Ministry of Defence, but these designs also fell victim to the political hatchet of 1965.

Nevertheless, as if acknowledging the propriety of the VTO concept as put forward by Hawkers, but not accepting the risks which might attend such a step forward as that presented by the supersonic P.1154,

417

the Ministry of Defence ordered nine developed examples of the P.1127 to be put into production so that they might equip the forthcoming squadron in 1965.

These aircraft, designated the Kestrel, XS688–XS696, were completed during 1964 and 1965, the first being flown on 7 March 1964. The Tripartite Squadron came into being at West Raynham on 15 October 1964, and was composed of ten pilots from the RAF, America and Germany; they were Wg Cdr D McL Scrimgeour, RAF (Commanding Officer), Col Gerhard F Barkhorn, *Luftwaffe* (Deputy Commanding Officer), Cdr J J Tyson Jr, US Navy (Deputy Commanding Officer), Sqn Ldr F A Trowern RAF, Maj K K Campbell, USAF, Maj Paul R Curry, US Army, Maj John A Johnston, DFC, US Army, Flt Lt R J A Munro, AFC, RAF, Flt Lt D J McL Edmonston, RAF, and 1st Lt V Suhr, *Luftwaffe*. Ground support personnel amounted to seven other officers and 112 other ranks drawn from these services. The purposes of the evaluation may be summarised as follows: (a) To determine the suitability of V/STOL aircraft for operations in the field away from sophisticated, permanently sited support facilities, (b) to compare various methods of take-off and landing, (c) to develop flight operating techniques and procedures, (d) to explore jet-borne applications of flight in the operating envelope, apart from landing and taking off, (e) to examine instrument flying techniques on a V/STOL aircraft and (f) to examine night flying techniques on this type of aeroplane.

One of the aircraft was involved in an accident but was not replaced. An extremely concentrated flying programme was undertaken and the total number of take-offs, at 938 in eleven months, gives some indication of the concentration attained, having regard to the radical nature of the aeroplane. There is no doubt that the experience gained by these small nuclei of pilots represented a vital yardstick by which the whole scope of V/STOL operations of the future would be measured.

After completion of the 'syllabus' the squadron was disbanded, and it was intended that each nation would purchase its share of aircraft. Germany, however, declined its option so that six Kestrels were handed over to America; these were XS688, XS689, XS690, XS691, XS692 and XS694, and were allocated BuAer Nos. 64–18262 to 64–18267 respectively. They were initially designated VZ-12 but, in conformity with the designation of other American flat-risers, were ultimately referred to as XV-6A. During the course of the next three years these aeroplanes underwent a comprehensive Tri-Service assessment, being flown by pilots of the US Air Force, US Army and US Navy, and also by the US Marine Corps. Based for much of this time at the Naval Air Station, Patuxent River, they were flown on to USS *Independence* and *Raleigh*. Two aircraft were transferred to NASA for advanced environmental assessment (being registered by NASA as Nos. 520 and 521, the former aircraft being involved in an accident on 27 August 1967). At least one aircraft was preserved in an American national museum.

XV-6A Kestrel 48263/No.3 during trials aboard CVA-62 (USS *Independence*) on 11 May 1966.

Meanwhile at home in Britain the two remaining Kestrels continued to provide valuable fundamental information on V/STOL flight operations. One aircraft was attached to the Blind Landing Experimental Unit while the other (XS693) was transferred to the Blackburn Division of Hawker Siddeley Aviation at Brough, Yorkshire, for extensive modification to accommodate the much uprated Pegasus 6 engine during the second half of 1966. The principal modification associated with this engine (apart from local structural alteration) was the provision of annular suction-relief doors around the engine air intakes. Since the earliest days of the P.1127 it had been clear that at zero or low forward speed the leading edge of the intakes required profile modification to ensure smooth inflow entry, and a system of inflatable intake lips had

One of six Kestrels sent to the United States early in 1966, aboard the USS *Raleigh* for evaluation trials on 17 May.

been adopted. These were inflated during hovering flight to provide the necessary blunt lip profile, but during normal forward flight were deflated so as to lie flat, thus maintaining the sharp, low-drag lip. It was suspected that such an arrangement would be susceptible to considerable wear in service and the more conventional suction relief doors were therefore adopted on introduction of the definitive service engine.

XS693 was completed in its new form at Brough and first flew on 10 February 1967, and came to be regarded in effect as the prototype of the proposed production version soon to be ordered for the RAF, and of which the first pre-production examples had already flown. This aircraft continued flying for seven months until on 21 September 1967 it was destroyed in an accident at Filton; the pilot, Sqn Ldr H Rigg, escaped safely.

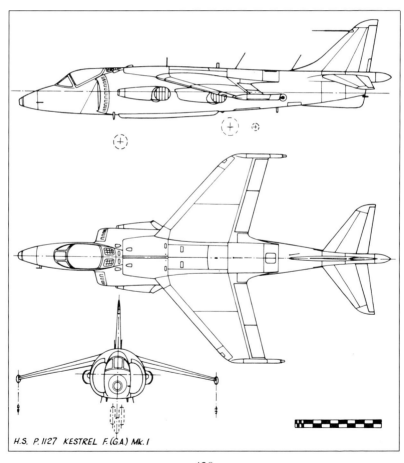

H.S. P.1127 KESTREL F.(G.A.) Mk.1

420

TYPE: Single-seat tactical close support aircraft.

STRUCTURE: All-metal stressed skin construction. Single-piece shoulder wing with fabricated spars, integral fuel cells in wings and fuselage. Zero-track tricycle undercarriage with balancing outrigger wheels at wing-tips. Reaction control nozzles at wing-tips, nose and tail.

MANUFACTURERS: The Hawker Aircraft (Kingston) Division of Hawker Siddeley Aviation Ltd, Kingston-upon-Thames and Dunsfold, Surrey.

POWERPLANT: One 15,000–15,500 lb thrust Bristol Siddeley Pegasus 5 vectored-thrust turbofan engine exhausting through four rotatable nozzles.

DIMENSIONS: Wing span, 22 ft 11 in. Overall length, 42 ft 6 in. Height, 10 ft 9 in. Tailplane span, 12 ft 0in.

WEIGHTS: Empty, approximately, 9,800 lb. Loaded (for VTO), 14,500 lb. Overload (for STO), approximately 17,000 lb.

PERFORMANCE: Max speed, 710 mph at sea level (M=0.92); 635 mph at 36,000 ft (M=0.96). Initial rate of climb, approximately 30,000 ft/min at sea level. Service ceiling, approximately 55,000 ft. Aircraft transonic in shallow dive.

OPERATIONAL EQUIPMENT: No fixed armament. Forward-facing reconnaissance camera. Martin-Baker 6HA rocket-assisted zero-zero pilot ejector seat. Ferranti light fighter sight installed for use with underwing arsenal. Provision for CDC/Bendix homer indicator.

One of the pre-production batch of Harriers, readily identifiable from the production version by the nose probe fitted in place of the nose camera.

The Hawker Siddeley Harrier G.R. Mark 1 and derivatives

Nine years of project development and multi-service evaluation came to fruition on 31 August 1966, when the first pre-production Hawker Siddeley Harrier vertical take-off battlefield-support fighter was flown at

Dunsfold. Benefiting from all the cumulative flying experience achieved with the original P.1127 prototypes and from the Kestrel evaluation aircraft, the Harrier thus became the world's first fixed-wing 'flat-riser' to achieve series production for ultimate squadron service. Those nine years had seen an equally remarkable development of the powerplant, a totally new concept of thrust utilisation, and the proved success of thrust vectoring in a single engine. The thrust of little over 10,000 pounds, available from the old B.E. 53 in 1960, had been increased to around 20,000 pounds available from the Pegasus 10 in 1970.

Such was the measure of experience gained that the practice of ordering prototypes was dispensed with in favour of a batch of six pre-production Harriers (XV276–XV281), all of which flew for the first time during 1966–67. On these aircraft were developed the numerous items of service equipment, ranging from the various cockpit displays to the external stores which could be mounted on the underwing pylons and under-fuselage attachment points.

The Harrier had in effect been conceived early in 1965 when, with the cancellation of the P.1154 in February of that year, the Ministry of Defence's Requirement (O.R. 356) was reissued to cover reduced performance demands, such as to fall more in line with the demonstrated capabilities of the Kestrel. Despite an obvious outward similarity with the Kestrel, the Harrier was however virtually a new design, almost every detailed component of its structure, powerplant and systems having been advanced. For example, the Dowty/Rotol undercarriage,

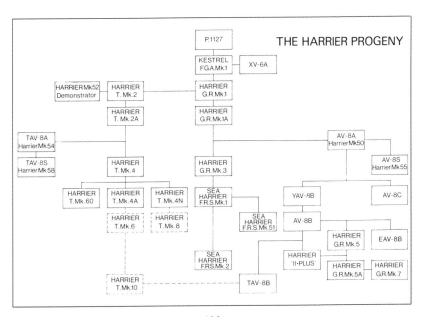

THE HARRIER PROGENY

Cockpit layout of the Harrier G.R. Mark 1; prominent features are the head-up display projected on the windscreen, and the moving map indicator in the central panel.

although retaining the basic tandem layout of the P.1127 (whose under-carriage was designed to absorb 13,000 pounds at 8 ft/sec), had been developed to absorb 16,000 pounds at 12 ft/sec, by increasing the stroke of the oleo legs. The forward-facing nose camera was replaced by an oblique F.95 camera directed to view through an optical flat on the port side of the nose.

Unlike the Hunter, the Harrier carries no fixed gun armament but makes provision for mounting two 30 mm Aden gun pods under the fuselage on either side of the centreline strongpoint, which in turn can carry a 1,000 lb bomb or reconnaissance pod. Four underwing pylons can accommodate combinations of Lepus flares, bombs, bomb clusters, rocket batteries, drop tanks or ferry tanks. The inboard wing strong-points are stressed to mount loads of up to 1,500 pounds apiece, those at the outboard station up to 750 pounds.

The Harrier was the first British military aircraft to enter service with a comprehensive head-up display of primary flight information. The system, designed by the Specto Division of Smiths Industries, incorpor-ates a display showing speed, height and altitude projected on to the windscreen, and collimated to infinity, thereby enabling the pilot to continue viewing through the windscreen without refocusing his eyes.

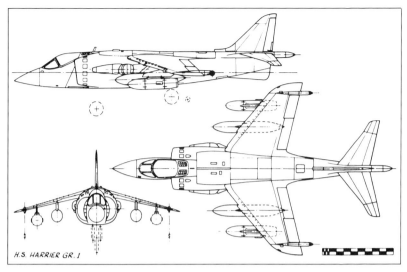

H.S. HARRIER GR.1

The fourth production Harrier G.R.1, XV741, was one of a pair of such aircraft participating in the 1969 Transatlantic Air Race; it is seen here at Victoria Station, London, its British point of departure and arrival. Note the flight refuelling probe near the cockpit — used several times during the crossing to enable the single-seaters to fly to and from the city centres without landing to refuel.

Other cockpit equipment includes a navigation/attack system developed by Ferranti comprising an inertia platform which supplies information on position to a latitude/longitude computer, whose outputs in turn drive a six-inch-diameter moving map display. One notable omission from the Harrier is a conventional autopilot, although at one time it was thought that all VTO aeroplanes would have to incorporate a fairly comprehensive installation. Because of the Harrier's excellent handling characteristics a non-duplicated autostabilising system is included, functioning only in pitch and roll.

Although countless air forces the world over have continued to express more than academic interest in the Harrier (as well as its predecessors), it was not until the Ministry of Defence expressed its own faith in the project by placing a production order that it was possible to identify those nations actively studying the Harrier as possible future

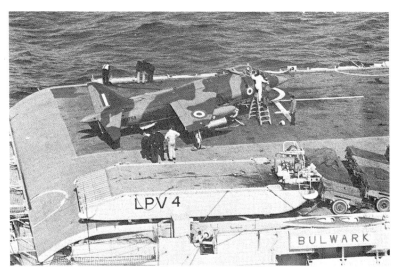

A production Harrier, XV758, undergoing trials aboard the British commando carrier, HMS *Bulwark* (note amphibious craft and road vehicles on the starboard side of the flight deck). These trials were evidence of the continuing interest by the Royal Navy in the Harrier.

A Development Batch Harrier G.R.1, XV277, with a pair of A.S.37/AJ.168 Martel ASMs, under test at Dunsfold in 1977.

equipment. The pre-production aircraft, 'owned' by Mintech, were distributed around the experimental establishments including the RAE, A&AEE and BLEU, as well as Filton and Dunsfold. Tropical trials were carried out in Sicily in August 1967 using the sixth pre-production aircraft, XV281. A Harrier was operated from a helicopter platform on the stern of the Italian warship *Andrea Doria*, and on another occasion from the Argentinian carrier *25 de Mayo*.

The production Harrier G.R. Mark 1 followed the development batch with scarcely any check in the accelerating production flow, the first true production aeroplane, XV738, being flown by Duncan Simpson at Dunsfold on 28 December 1967. Within eighteen months about twenty aircraft had flown out of the initial production order for seventy-seven aircraft destined for the RAF. CA Release had been achieved and the first squadron, No. 1 (Fighter) Squadron based at Wittering, took delivery of its first aircraft on 1 April 1969. The full complement of about twenty aircraft had been reached by the end of the year. An interesting event which occurred that year was the Transatlantic Air Race which featured No.1 Squadron Harriers flying non-stop from downtown New York to the centre of London, the aircraft being air refuelled several times *en route*. For long-distance flying the Harrier incorporated a 'plug-in' point for the temporary attachment of a refuelling probe on the top of the port air intake; extended wing-tips could also be substituted to provide additional lift for take-off at overload weights.

At the outset it was announced by the Ministry of Defence that Harriers would equip two Squadrons of the RAF, one of them based in the United Kingdom (No. 1 (Fighter) Squadron at Wittering) and the other in Germany (No. 4 (Fighter) Squadron at Wildenrath). To provide the necessary pilots a training unit, No. 233 Operational Conversion Unit (OCU), was established at Wittering. However, such was the flexibility of operation successfully demonstrated by these units that two further Squadrons, Nos. 3 and 20, also based at Wildenrath, began re-equipping with Harrier G.R. Mark 1s in 1970.

Meanwhile, No. 1 Squadron had been demonstrating the versatility of

The Harrier single-seat demonstrator G-VSTO.

its aircraft, first by flying to Akrotiri, Cyprus, for its armament practice camp during the spring of 1970. The following year two of its pilots flew Harriers aboard the carrier HMS *Hermes* in order to gain type shipboard clearance and to demonstrate the feasibility of supporting naval operations with RAF aircraft at sea. In due course Harriers undertook dispersed-site operations at Bardufoss in Northern Norway (inside the Arctic Circle) and in Central America at Belize; weapon training was also carried out at Sardinia.

To many observers it seemed that the British Government's support for the Harrier was cautious to say the least, yet it should be remembered that at no time were the manufacturers under any misapprehension as to the relatively modest contribution the aircraft could make to the Royal Air Force's overall operational responsibilities. The first generation of Harriers were, after all, subsonic aircraft of very limited range

A Harrier G.R.1 of No. 20(F) Squadron performs a short take-off among trees in the Borken area of West Germany during Exercise 'Heath Fire' in 1976.

and load-carrying power. Their *raison d'être* was their ability to survive an initial assault by an enemy attack on the RAF's fixed bases; by dispersing to remote sites, after the likely destruction of base runways, they would be able to continue supporting the land forces. Furthermore, in lesser campaigns, their presence would assume considerable importance in the absence of conventional aerodrome facilities. Nevertheless, in view of the Royal Air Force's dependence upon a preponderance of conventional aircraft, the Harrier would represent a small but vital element of its whole arsenal.

On the other hand, an air force whose primary function was that of supporting ground forces, often in conditions of very limited aerodrome facilities, might be attracted to the Harrier concept to a much greater extent. So it proved. The United States Marine Corps, whose air arm was roughly comparable in size with that of Royal Air Force Strike Command, displayed considerable interest in the Harrier since participating in the American Tri-Service Trials (TST) with the Kestrels in 1968. Towards the end of that year two USMC pilots, Col Tom Miller and Lt-Col Bud Baker, were flying Harriers at Dunsfold; they returned to Washington with a glowing report on the aircraft's capabilities. Within three months a US Navy test team had arrived in Britain to carry out a preliminary evaluation of the Harrier, the result of which was funding by the US government for an initial order for twelve aircraft to be delivered during FY 1971–72. Designated AV-8A Harriers, these joined Marine Attack Squadron 513 (VMA-513, commanded by Col Bud Baker) aboard USS *Guam*.

Bearing the manufacturers' designation Harrier Mark 50, this initial batch was followed by four further orders so that, by 1976, no fewer than 110 AV-8As, all built at Kingston, had been delivered to the USMC. Early aircraft were powered by Rolls-Royce (Bristol) Pegasus 102 engines, and retained the Ferranti 541 inertial nav-attack system, but later aircraft introduced the more powerful Pegasus 103 and the American Baseline attack system, as well as Stencel ejection seats.

There is no doubt but that the AV-8A was an exceptionally popular aircraft with the US Marines, and saw service in the Far East as well as in the Atlantic and Mediterranean. Many of them continued to serve for more than a dozen years.

The introduction of the Pegasus 103 (incorporating a re-bladed fan to increase mass-flow, improved combustion and increased cooling of the turbine blades — resulting in a thrust increase to 21,500 lb) was extended to the RAF Harriers, almost all of which were retrospectively re-engined in 1972–73, to become G.R. Mark 1As.

By 1973 the electronics company of Ferranti was starting production of a new laser rangefinder, integrated with the company's established 541 inertia nav-attack system. This laser ranging and marked-target seeking (LRMTS) system was accommodated in a lengthened nose cone, and provided the Harrier pilot with laser-pulse-derived range to a ground target as well as a target-search facility by seeking infra-red (IR) radiation from a coded IR designator laser operated by a Forward Air Controller on the ground. Bombing accuracy was much improved, with target acquisition in single-pass, low-level, lay-down attacks being considerably facilitated.

These systems, together with a radar warning receiver (RWR) which displayed a warning in the cockpit when the aircraft was being illuminated on hostile radar, were incorporated in Harriers as they became due for periodic updating and re-engining. The RWR antennae were located in a fairing at the top of the fin for the forward hemisphere, and in the rear fairing aft of the rudder for the rear hemisphere. With these modifications the Harriers were redesignated G.R. Mark 3s. Normal operating attrition, of which a frequent cause was bird-strikes at low level — to

A Development Batch Harrier modified to G.R.3 standard under test with six 1,197 lb cluster bombs and centreline reconnaissance pod.

Three Harrier G.R.3s of No. 3(F) Squadron during armament training detachment to Cyprus in 1976.

which the Harrier was particularly prone, steadily reduced the number of early aircraft in service, so that two further production orders for Harrier G.R.3s were placed with Hawker in 1975 and 1977 for fifteen and twenty-four aircraft respectively.

A third air force to back its interests in the Harrier with an order was the Spanish Naval Air Arm. However, strained relations between the Spanish and British governments precluded a direct approach to Hawker; instead, a preliminary order for six aircraft was negotiated between Spain and the US government during 1973 and added to the end of the final USMC batch. The aircraft, which of course were all manufactured at Kingston, were thus designated AV-8A (Harrier Mark 50s), and were shipped to the USA in 1976, where Spanish naval pilots underwent their conversion training (one aircraft being lost in the process). Thereafter the aircraft, named *Matadors*, equipped *Escuadrilla 008* of the Spanish Naval Air Arm, based at Rota and frequently embarked in the ex-US Navy carrier PH-01 *Dédalo* of the Spanish Navy.

In 1977 four further aircraft were ordered by Spain, this time the aircraft being delivered direct from Britain. These aircraft were designated AV-8S *Matadors* (Harrier Mark 55s), the final aircraft being purchased as a replacment for the aircraft lost in America.

HARRIER TWO-SEATERS

Such was the radical nature of Harrier operations that, during the first nine months while No. 1 (Fighter) Squadron was taking its first deliveries of Harrier G.R.1s, the pilots on this squadron were all at least second-tour officers with at least one tour behind them on fast jets. With the establishment of No. 233 OCU, first-tour pilots began training on Harriers. Their mentors were a small number of jet Qualified Flying Instructors who had been among the first Harrier pilots to receive their conversion training at Dunsfold early in 1969. (In the normal course of events the senior pilots of No. 1 Squadron were to be posted as squadron and flight commanders to the other newly-equipped Harrier squadrons in Germany). By mid-1970 the first two-seat Harrier T. Mark 2 trainers were being delivered to the OCU at Wittering.

Genesis of the two-seat Harrier dated back to 1960, when, before the first P.1127 had even flown, Sydney Camm directed his project designers to investigate alternative schemes by which a second pilot might be accommodated. Such an exercise was not as straightforward as had been the case, for instance, with the Hunter, for the very nature of vectored jet lift imposed critical design considerations, not least of which were airframe weight, weight distribution, low-speed roll and pitch control and the singular engine configuration with its critical hot-gas recirculation characteristics. Four alternative design layouts were investigated, including conventional tandem and side-by-side seating, twin

The first production Harrier T. Mark 2 two-seater in flight during 1969, shortly before its loss in an accident in which Duncan Simpson was badly hurt.

430

front fuselage (with student pilot and instructor in separate cockpits either side of a central engine intake) and a design which featured the instructor's cockpit immediately forward of the tail fin.

In due course, as engine power from the Pegasus increased beyond 15,000 lb thrust, it was seen that a conventional tandem cockpit *could* be incorporated in a lengthened nose with relatively little alteration to the single-seater's principal structure. Little further design work was carried out for several years (due in part to preoccupation with the Kestrel and the P.1150/P.1154 projects), but in 1964 a feasibility study was carried out by Hawker Siddeley's design facility at Hamble to decide whether one of the surviving P.1127 prototypes might be modified as a two-seater for experimental purposes. On 4 January 1965 a proposal was submitted to the Ministry of Aviation, resulting in the issue of Air Staff Requirement 386 calling for a two-seat version of the Harrier single-seater — then in the process of being ordered. It was not, however, until 1966 that a contract for two prototypes, XW174 and XW175, was signed with Hawker.

The second Harrier T. Mark 2, XW175, at Dunsfold during trials to improve the weathercocking stability. Note the greatly extended fin area.

The first, XW174, was first flown by Duncan Simpson (then Chief Test Pilot at Dunsfold) on 22 April 1969, but this aircraft was soon to be destroyed in a crash at Larkhill, on 4 June, following a fuel system failure; Simpson ejected safely but received injuries. The second prototype, XW175, made its maiden flight on 14 July and, while demonstrating that it retained the single-seater's excellent handling qualities in all normal conditions of flight, suggested that it lacked weathercock stability at very high angles of attack over a narrow Mach number range. This was thought to be due to a breakdown of airflow around and aft of the large cockpit canopy, and led to a series of trials, culminating in the extending of the fin height by some 18 in.

As required by A.S.R. 386, the two-seat Harrier T. Mark 2 possessed all the weapon-carrying and aiming capabilities of the G.R. Mark 1. The initial production order was for twelve aircraft (the first of which, XW264, flew on 3 October 1969), of which most served with No. 233 OCU from the outset, although some of the later aircraft were delivered to the Harrier squadrons, not only representing a backup for their operational strength but also to provide instrument rating facilities and weapon delivery trainers. The last few aircraft were completed as T. Mark 2As (equivalent to the modified G.R. Mark 1As), and most of the others were progressively modified. With the introduction of the uprated Pegasus 103, LRMTS and RWR the designation was changed to T. Mark 4. One of the RAF aircraft (lacking the laser and RWR equipment) was loaned to the Admiralty for use as a trainer by the Fleet Air Arm under the designation T. Mark 4A, but was later returned to RAF charge with the arrival of three T. Mark 4Ns, built from the outset with naval radio; these aircraft were powered by Pegasus 103 engines but also lacked the laser system.

A total of twenty-five two-seaters (excluding the two 'DB' aircraft) was built for the RAF and Fleet Air Arm, of which two were completed as T. Mark 2As, nine as T. Mark 4s and three as T. Mark 4Ns; nine of the original T.2s were progressively modified to T.4 standard.

In addition to the above, Hawker Siddeley produced a special demonstration two-seater, appropriately registered G-VTOL and designated the Mark 52, being granted a Special Category Certificate of Airworthiness in September 1971. G-VTOL performed an enormous amount of work, and was the first Harrier to fly with the Pegasus 102 (and later the 103), as well as undertaking the clearance of a wide range of military stores — it also carried the military serial ZA250. Because it was also required to give demonstrations worldwide, it was equipped with a larger range of radio/navigation systems than the RAF/RN aircraft, such as ILS and ADS.

In July 1972 John Farley, then Deputy Chief Test Pilot at Dunsfold, flew G-VTOL with two 330 gallon ferry tanks to Bombay (via Naples, Akrotiri, Teheran, Kuwait and Masirah) to give a demonstration of carrier operation aboard the Indian Navy's carrier *Vikrant*. In two days Farley flew twenty-one sorties from the carrier, and in the steamy heat of the monsoon season gave a convincing display of the Harrier's versatility. This venture resulted in the Indian government selecting the Sea Harrier (see below) to replace the navy's ageing Sea Hawks, as well as purchasing two two-seaters (Harrier T. Mark 60s).

Later, G-VTOL was used to demonstrate the unique Skyhook recovery system, as well as the ski ramp launching technique.

It was not until 1975 that the US Marine Corps obtained funding to purchase eight two-seaters, these aircraft being designated TAV-8As (Harrier T. Mark 54s) and equipping Marine Attack (Training) Squadron 203 (VMA(T)-203) at USMCS Cherry Point. Two TAV-8S *Matadors* (Harrier T. Mark 58s) were also ordered by the Spanish Naval Air Arm and, like the first batch of single-seat *Matadors*, were shipped to the USA before joining *Escuadrilla 008* at Rota in Spain.

At the time of writing the designations Harrier T. Mark 6, T. Mark 8 and T. Mark 10 had been mentioned as two-seat versions being considered. The first two are likely to be conversions of in-service Harrier T. Mark 4s, probably incorporating equipment and system upgrading to

Spanish AV-8S and TAV-8S Matadors (Harrier Mark 55 and 58 respectively visited RNAS Yeovilton for training on the Royal Navy's ski ramp in 1988.

Harrier G.R. Mark 7 and Sea Harrier F.R.S. Mark 2 standard respectively (see below). The Harrier T. Mark 10 is thought likely to be an RAF version of the American TAV-8B Harrier II two-seat trainer with British equipment. With Harriers apparently set to continue in service with the RAF and Royal Navy into the next century, it seems inconceivable that the relatively small number of two-seaters so far built will suffice for the requirements of the two Services.

The ease with which Harriers achieved entry into service with the RAF, and the outstanding contribution afforded to the Service's rôle in NATO, went far to convince the inevitable sceptics. Despite the aircraft's lack of supersonic performance, it was not long before both the RAF and USMC were investigating new in-flight manoeuvres, made possible by the thrust-vectoring Pegaus. Dubbed 'viffing' — from *vector*ing *in* forward *flight* — the rotation of the engine nozzles during air-to-air combat enabled Harrier pilots to execute extraordinary manoeuvres, not only to tighten turns but to achieve weapon release positions otherwise impossible when engaged by aircraft of superior speed performance.

That is not to suggest that the target of a supersonic Harrier was not coveted at Hawker Siddeley, despite the cancellation of the P.1154 in the mid-1960s. The achievement of such performance centred upon the

A Spanish TAV-8S prepares for take-off at Yeovilton.

433

development of plenum chamber burning (PCB) — in effect the burning of fuel in fully oxygen-rich air at higher pressures than in many reheat systems; this development has been continued by Rolls-Royce so that the system would be ready for application should a supersonic requirement be issued for a Harrier development.

Numerous projects were pursued both by Hawker Siddeley Aviation at Kingston and by McDonnell Douglas at Saint Louis, between whom an agreement on a working partnership was concluded early in the 1970s. This partnership had been conceived to enable an American manufacturer to contribute to the building of the AV-8A Harriers; however, although the basis of collaboration between Britain and America has continued unchecked to the present day, it was decided to complete the AV-8A programme at Kingston.

Four AV-8As of VMA-513 with various external store combinations.

As will be told later (see BAe/McDonnell Douglas AV-8B), the economic climate in Britain and the United States during the 1970s was not conducive to the expenditure on development of a supersonic Harrier derivative. Instead, efforts were made on both sides of the Atlantic to enhance the range and load-carrying abilities of the basic Harrier. These efforts were to bring about the development of the AV-8B/Harrier G.R.5.

In the meantime, both the RAF and the USMC continued to fly the Harrier G.R.3 and AV-8A, and it was the former which (with Sea Harriers of the Royal Navy) fought in the brief Falkland Islands campaign of April–June 1982. As Sea Harriers accompanied the Task Force to the South Atlantic, No. 1 (Fighter) Squadron, commanded by Wg Cdr P T Squire DFC, AFC, flew four Harrier G.R.3s out to the War Zone, with a brief stop at Ascension Island *en route*. Six further Harriers of this squadron were shipped direct to the South Atlantic aboard the *Atlantic Conveyor*, these aircraft being flown off to the carrier HMS *Hermes* nine days before the large merchantman was sunk by enemy air attack.

In the assault on and invasion of the Falkland Islands the RAF Harrier pilots were tasked with ground-support duties, attacking airstrips and targets around Port Stanley and Darwin with laser-guided and

At the time of the Falkland Islands operations of 1982 the Harrier G.R.3s of No. 1(F) Squadron were adapted to mount AIM-9L Sidewinder AAMs.

cluster bombs. Four of the RAF aircraft were to be shot down by ground fire, but all their pilots escaped serious injury. More significantly, not one Harrier was lost in air combat, despite being opposed by enemy land-based supersonic fighters with missile armament.

No finer testimony to the Harrier's operational concept could have been afforded than that of Operation Corporate in the South Atlantic. Had neither the Harrier nor Sea Harrier been available to support the Task Force in hostile waters, there can be no questioning the fact that the operations to repossess the Falkland Islands could not have been mounted.

TECHNICAL DATA FOR HARRIER G.R. MARK 3
(Harrier T. Mark 4 similar except where stated)

TYPE: Single-seat vertical/short-take-off close support and reconnaissance air-craft. (T. Mark 4: Two-seat operational trainer with full combat capability.)

STRUCTURE: Semi-monocoque structure, principally of aluminium but with steel and titanium components in the vicinity of engine bay and exhaust nozzles. Swept wing (quarter-chord sweepback, 34 degrees) built on continu-ous three-spar structure with integrally-machined skins; 'g' limits, +7.8/–4.2.

MANUFACTURERS: Hawker Siddeley Aviation Ltd, (later British Aerospace PLC), Kingston-upon-Thames and Dunsfold, Surrey.

POWERPLANT: One 21,500 lb thrust Rolls-Royce Bristol Pegasus 103 vectored-thrust turbofan. Fuel capacity, 650 Imp. gallons in six integral tanks in fuselage and wing centresection (and provision for in-flight refuelling). Reaction control nozzles located in nose, tail and wing tips employing engine-bleed air from HP compressor.

DIMENSIONS: Wing span, 25 ft 2 in. Overall length, 46 ft 10 in (T. Mark 4, 56 ft 0.2 in). Height, 11 ft 11 in (T. Mark 4, 12 ft 2 in). Wing area, 201 sq ft. Wheel track, 22 ft 0 in.

WEIGHTS: Operating, empty, 13,535 lb (T. Mark 4, 14,010 lb). Max take-off, 25,200 lb. Max warload, 8,000 lb. Internal fuel, 5,060 lb. Max external fuel, 5,300 lb. VTO payload, 5,000 lb.

PERFORMANCE: Max speeds, 740 mph at sea level; Mach 1.3 at altitude (in dive); Mach .98 at altitude (level flight). Service ceiling, 51,200 ft. Max ferry range, 2,340 miles. STO distance at max take-off weight, 350 yards. Initial rate of climb, approx, 22,500 ft/min.

OPERATIONAL EQUIPMENT AND ARMAMENT: Two detachable 30 mm gun pods with 300 rounds of ammunition mounted on either side of fuselage centreline store position. One centreline and four underwing store pylons stressed to carry up to five 1,000 lb iron bombs, retarded bombs, cluster bombs or laser-guided bombs, up to six Matra multiple-rocket launchers, up to ten Lepus flares, two combat drop tanks or two 330 Imp gallon ferry tanks, or combinations of the above up to maximum warload. Operational systems include Ferranti FE541/LRMTS and RWR.

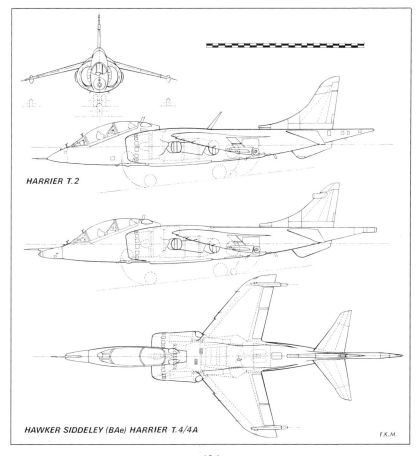

HARRIER T.2

HAWKER SIDDELEY (BAe) HARRIER T.4/4A

F.K.M.

An early production Sea Harrier F.R.S. Mark 1 during deck trials aboard
HMS *Hermes* in 1979.

The Hawker Siddeley (British Aerospace) Sea Harrier

Almost a year before the original Hawker P.1127 prototype first left the
ground in October 1960, the Kingston Project Office prepared a secret
brochure suggesting the suitability of the vectored-thrust principle for
the operation of aircraft, not only from small aircraft carriers, but from
the decks of merchant vessels, and even from assault landing craft.
Whether these ideas fell upon receptive ears at the Admiralty at this
early date is not known, yet it may well have sparked interest which led
to the drafting of a requirement in 1962 for an advanced V/STOL
carrier-borne interceptor to replace the de Havilland Sea Vixen, and it
was the existence of this requirement that prompted the first exploratory
trials by XP831 aboard the fleet carrier HMS *Ark Royal* on 8 February
1963 — the first by a V/STOL aircraft on a ship at sea.

Thus encouraged, the Admiralty entered the 'post-NBMR-3' saga
with support for a naval version of the Hawker P.1154 supersonic
V/STOL aircraft, but did not wait for the entire project to be cancelled
before opting out in favour of a Spey-powered McDonnell Douglas F-4
Phantom for the Royal Navy.

By the end of the 1960s, however, the end of the large fleet carrier
with the Royal Navy was in sight, as was the demise of fixed-wing
combat aircraft (Gannets, Phantoms and Buccaneers) with the Fleet Air
Arm. The Admiralty's attention therefore turned once more to the
vectored-thrust principle as a means of operating high-performance
fixed-wing aircraft from much smaller carriers. Indeed, by the early
1970s the 'aircraft carrier' had become anathema to the Treasury and
other government ministries, so that the new class of small carrier then
starting construction was euphemistically referred to as a 'Through-deck
Cruiser'. As originally conceived, these ships were intended to embark
only anti-submarine helicopters.

It was, however, an open secret — to which Hawker Siddeley was privy — that the Admiralty was looking for a naval version of the Harrier to perform the rôle of shipborne interceptor, capable of operating from the small decks of the Through-deck Cruisers. With this in mind, the Kingston Project Staff started an appraisal of the Harrier in the context of regular shipborne operation, and by 1974 the detail design of a 'navalised' Harrier was all but complete. The following year the Admiralty was ready to embark on the process of obtaining its long-awaited V/STOL fighter, and placed an order for three development Sea Harriers, to be followed by thirty-one production aircraft. Such a small quantity was justified by the fact that it was intended to embark no more than six Sea Harriers in each of the new class of ships, of which three (HMS *Invincible, Illustrious* and *Ark Royal*) were planned, and whose official designation was changed to Command Cruiser.

The Sea Harrier had been designed to perform three maritime rôles: the air interception rôle against long-range maritime patrol and ship-based attack aircraft (for which a 400-nautical-mile radius of action at altitude was demanded); the reconnaissance rôle with sea-search capability over 20,000 square miles in one hour at low altitude; and a strike and ground attack rôle against ships and shore targets (for which a radius of action of at least 250 nautical miles was demanded). These three rôles were to be reflected in the Sea Harrier F.R.S. Mark 1 designation (fighter/reconnaissance/strike).

The principal alterations to the Harrier were divided between those needed to meet the combat demands and those to suit 'ship at sea' compatibility. The former was confined to a revision of the weapons system to include a larger Smiths Industries' head-up display (HUD) driven by a 20,000-word digital computer which functioned as a very flexible weapon-aiming computer; a Ferranti self-aligning attitude-reference platform; and Ferranti Blue Fox radar. The latter was to be the primary sensor, derived from the Seaspray helicopter radar, but

A Sea Harrier F.R.S.1 undergoing trials at the A&AEE Boscombe Down, in 1981, with BAe Sea Eagle computer-programmed sea-skimming anti-ship missiles.

much modified to manage both air-to-air and air-to-surface modes demanded for the Sea Harrier.

Radio navigation aids, apart from the digital nav-attack system, comprised UHF Homing, TACAN with offset facility, and an I-Band radar transponder for ground control guidance. Passive electronic surveillance and warning of external radar illumination was provided by RWR with antennae located as in the Harrier G.R. Mark 3.

The five weapon pylons were of improved design (compared with those of RAF Harriers), including stronger ejector release units, and could mount the entire range of RAF and USMC stores; a new missile control panel also allowed carriage of AIM-9 Sidewinder air-to-air missiles on the outboard pylons, and Martel and Harpoon air-to-surface missiles on the inboard pylons.

The entire nose and cockpit underwent redesign (for the first time since the original P.1127). By raising the pilot by some eleven inches, greatly improved all-round field of vision was afforded, and considerably more space was provided beneath the cabin floor in which the new electronic equipment could be located. A new Martin-Baker Type 10 zero-zero rocket ejector seat was introduced with a 1.5 second total sequencing time (compared with the RAF Harrier's Type 9 seat's 2.25 seconds).

The Pegasus engine was rated at the same thrust (21,500 lb) as the Harrier G.R. Mark 3's Mark 103, although the engine in the Sea Harrier (a Mark 104) differed in that all major casings were changed from magnesium-zirconium to aluminium, and all ferrous components were coated with a sacrificial aluminium paint to retard sea air corrosion.

The unit cost of a Sea Harrier was stated unofficially to be around £6.8m in the late 1970s (or about 18 per cent higher than a G.R. Mark 3), yet the total weight penalty for navalisation of the aircraft was less than 100 lb — an extraordinary achievement unequalled by any other modern aeroplane transposed from land to maritime operation.

While the Sea Harrier was passing through its design stage another innovation was being pursued, that of the 'ski-ramp' — the brainchild of a Royal Navy engineering officer, Lt-Cdr D R Taylor MBE, RN, and also, incidentally, conceived independently by Ralph Hooper at Hawker Siddeley. This ingenious idea involved incorporating an upward curve in the forward end of a carrier's flight deck, so that a V/STOL aeroplane such as the Harrier, with thrust vectoring, would be launched into an upward ballistic trajectory. On clearing the ramp, the aircraft would initially be deficient in wing lift, but accelerating due to the aft component of the engine thrust; by the time the nozzles were moved to the fully aft position the aircraft would be wholly supported by wing lift. The system enabled the Sea Harrier to take off with considerably increased payload compared with that possible using a conventional flat-deck launch.

As a series of ski-launch trials went ahead from a variable-angle ramp at the RAE, Bedford, during 1977-78, in which Harrier 3s and the two-seater G-VTOL participated, the first Sea Harrier, XZ450, was flown at Dunsfold on 20 August 1978, followed by the three Development Batch aircraft. Meanwhile, the first Command Cruiser, HMS *Invincible*, had been approaching completion, incorporating a seven-degree deck launch ramp, and, on 26 March 1979, began her sea trials. On 19 September that year the first Sea Harrier Squadron, No. 700A Squadron of the Fleet Air Arm, was commissioned at Yeovilton, taking delivery of Sea Harrier XZ451. Between 24 October and 8 November five Sea Harriers (and the Harrier Mark 52) completed their type operational trials aboard HMS *Hermes* in the Irish Sea; this former fleet carrier was at that time serving as an anti-submarine carrier and had not yet acquired a deck launch ramp.

Early in 1980 No. 700A Squadron, otherwise known as the Sea Harrier Intensive Flying Trials Unit, was disbanded to become No. 899 Headquarters Squadron of the Fleet Air Arm, and was followed by No. 800 Squadron at Yeovilton, soon to become the first carrier-deployed Sea Harrier squadron aboard HMS *Invincible*. As the remaining aircraft completed manufacture, two more Sea Harrier squadrons, Nos. 800 and 801, were equipped with the new fighters.

Although nationalisation of the British aircraft industry had recently taken place, there was no discontinuity in the flow of ideas emanating from the Kingston design offices. Trials had gone ahead with Harriers operating from smaller ships than the Command Cruisers, and a proposal for a much smaller class of ships — the so-called 'Harrier carrier' — had been put forward by Vosper Thorneycroft. At Kingston the idea was mooted for ships no bigger than frigates to operate Sea Harriers *without recourse to a launching platform of any sort*. The aircraft would be lifted by a universally-mounted crane from its hangar amidships and swung outboard; the engine would be started while the aircraft was still attached to the crane's jib, with the exhaust nozzles directed vertically down. As they were moved progressively aft and the throttle opened, the crane would release the aircraft and the pilot would begin a free-flight accelerating transition to forward wing-borne flight. To recover

The extraordinary Skyhook project. The two-seat Harrier T.52 hovers beneath a crane jib in an overland demonstration.

the aircraft, the pilot would perform a decelerating transition alongside the ship until directly below the crane jib, while moving forward to match the ship's speed; the crane's operator would then engage the jib with special pick-up points in the upper surface of the aircraft. Once the aircraft was secured, the pilot would shut down his engine and the aircraft would be swung inboard to its hangar. Referred to as 'Skyhook', this procedure was demonstrated over land by the Harrier G-VTOL, which hovered beneath a specially modified crane jib. As far as is known the manoeuvre has not been pursued to the stage of trials at sea. As already mentioned, however, Harriers were successfully launched from the restricted deck of a merchantman during operations to recover the Falkland Islands in 1982.

Operation Corporate focused world attention on the Royal Navy's small force of Sea Harriers; however, space does not allow more than a short summary of that remarkable campaign by the British shipborne fighters. At the time that the Task Force sailed from Portsmouth on

Harrier T. Mark 4A XZ445 with the Fleet Air Arm. Although not strictly a Sea Harrier, this aircraft was employed at RNAS Yeovilton to train Royal Navy pilots for the Sea Harrier. The photograph was taken in 1988. Unlike the RAF's T. Mark 4s the aircraft was not fitted with a 'laser nose'.

5 April 1982, twenty-eight of the thirty-four Sea Harriers ordered were available; of these, twenty-four aircraft of Nos. 800, 801 and 899 Squadrons were embarked in HMS *Hermes* and *Invincible*. Shortly afterwards the other four accompanied the Harriers of No. 1 (Fighter) Squadron aboard the *Atlantic Conveyor* (and were to be flown off to join the carriers in the South Atlantic).

The first attack made by the Sea Harriers was a dawn low-level raid on the aerodrome at Port Stanley on 1 May, when nine aircraft, led by Lt Cdr A D Auld, attacked with cannon and cluster bombs in the face of surface-to-air and small-arms fire. Other Sea Harriers attacked a small airstrip at Goose Green, fifty miles to the west. The Argentine Air Force and Naval Air Farm, flying Mirages, Skyhawks and Canberras from the mainland, were engaged by Sea Harriers flying in the intercept rôle, and lost one of each type of aircraft; none of the Sea Harriers was lost.

In the coming weeks, after the arrival of the RAF Harriers, the Sea Harriers engaged increasingly in the air intercept rôle, thereby covering the ground support operations by the RAF Harriers and helicopters.

Not surprisingly, the huge area to be patrolled strained the small Sea Harrier force considerably and, where necessary, the pilots were ordered to provide a defence screen around major ground operations. For instance on 21 May, the day of the major amphibious landings in San Carlos Bay, the Sea Harriers engaged Argentine Mirage IIIEAs, A-4P/Q Skyhawks, IA-58 Pucará and Aermacchi MB-338 ground support aircraft and, according to Argentine accounts, twenty-three of these aircraft were lost; British losses amounted to an RAF Harrier and five helicopters. On another occasion Flt Lt David Morgan, an RAF pilot seconded to fly Sea Harriers, shot down two Mirages out of a section of four, the other two being destroyed by his wingman. The senior Sea Harrier pilot, Cdr N D Ward, AFC, RN, commanding No. 801 Squadron, shot down three enemy aircraft, a Mirage, a Pucará and a Hercules; he was to be awarded the DSO.

By the time of the successful conclusion of the campaign the twenty-eight Sea Harriers and ten Harriers had flown more than 2,000 combat

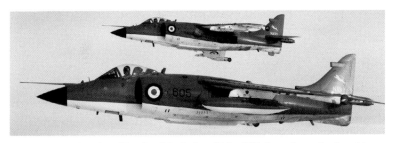

A pair of Indian Sea Harrier Mark 5s of No. 300 Squadron, Indian Navy, ususally based at Goa-Dabolim.

sorties, destroyed at least twenty-eight enemy aircraft and delivered a considerable tonnage of bombs against the Argentine forces on the islands, and achieved an overall serviceability rate of over 90 per cent. Six Sea Harriers had been lost, including two that had evidently collided in cloud during the voyage south to the War Zone. Two other pilots, whose aircraft had suffered battle damage, elected to eject rather than risk fouling the carrier deck on landing; both men were recovered unhurt. As with the RAF Harriers, no Sea Harrier was lost in air-to-air combat.

The outstanding success of the Sea Harriers was recognised shortly after the campaign was over when John Nott, the British Defence Minister, announced an order for fourteen additional Sea Harriers — not simply to make good the losses, but to increase the squadron establishment from eight to ten aircraft.

As already mentioned, India had expressed interest in purchasing a naval version of the Harrier following John Farley's demonstration of the two-seater G-VTOL aboard INS *Vikrant* in 1972. Shortly after the first British Sea Harrier's maiden flight the Indian government confirmed an order for six Sea Harriers, to be designated Mark 51s, and the first of these was flown on 6 August 1982. Unlike the Spanish Naval Air Arm's Matadors, the Indian aircraft were almost identical to the dedicated shipborne Sea Harrier F.R.S. Mark 1s of the Royal Navy (with Blue Fox radar), and began replacing the twenty-year-old Hawker Sea Hawks of the Indian Navy in 1983. Further orders have been placed, and it has been suggested that it is intended ultimately to increase the force to between twenty and thirty Sea Harriers and Harrier two-seaters.

Indian Harrier T.60 of No. 300 Squadron, Indian Navy. Like XZ445, this aircraft was not a Sea Harrier, but often embarked in INS *Hansa*.

THE SEA HARRIER F.R.S. MARK 2

Successful though the Sea Harriers had been in the operation to recover the Falkland Islands in 1982, the nature of the Argentine air attacks highlighted inherent weaknesses in the Blue Fox radar — shortcomings that had been appreciated for some years in the knowledge that the most effective manner by which an attacking force can penetrate any air defence system is to launch numerous attacks by individual or very small groups of aircraft almost simultaneously. This was particularly evident during Operation Corporate, when the number of Sea Harriers available for combat air patrol over the islands at any one time was seldom more than six or eight, while the attacking forces might launch strikes from several directions and at different heights simultaneously. There were thus occasions on which the raiders were able to penetrate the Sea Harrier screen and reach targets of opportunity, and a number of naval ships were sunk or badly damaged.

It was appreciated that the naval interceptor required an advanced look-down/shoot-down radar as well as a track-while-scan facility to indicate the broad radar picture in order to tackle more than one target simultaneously by indicating threat priorities.

Owing to the strictly limited budget available for naval fixed-wing combat aircraft, it was decided in 1983 to undertake a 'mid-life update' (MLU) of the Sea Harrier Mark 1 by replacing its Blue Fox radar with an advanced multi-mode pulse doppler Blue Vixen radar in conjunction with AIM-120 advanced medium range air-to-air missiles (AMRAAM), as well as the new BAe Sea Eagle sea-skimming air-to-surface missile. It

443

Sea Harrier F.R.S.2 ZA195 shows its paces while carrying two combat tanks and four advanced medium-range air-to-air missiles (AMRAAMs).

is intended that this weapons system will meet the demand for a long-range look-down/shoot-down capability and beyond-visual-range (BVR) multiple-engagement capability against the known maritime air threat beyond the end of the century. Owing to the limited available budget, there was no likelihood of the Royal Navy acquiring the second-generation Harrier aircraft (AV-8B/G.R.5/Harrier II-Plus), and it was accordingly decided to update progressively all existing Sea Harriers to the new F.R.S. Mark 2 standard, a process that will extend well into the 1990s.

Two development Sea Harrier conversions were ordered in 1985, together with the conversion of a BAe 125-600B executive jet for use as an avionics test bed with the Blue Vixen radar. The first of the development Sea Harrier F.R.S. Mark 2s, ZA195, was flown on 19 September 1988, and the second, XZ497, on 8 March 1989.

TECHNICAL DATA FOR SEA HARRIER F.R.S. MARK 1

TYPE: Single-seat vertical/short-take-off shipborne interceptor/tactical reconnaissance/strike and ground-attack aircraft.

STRUCTURE: Semi-monocoque structure, principally of aluminium but with steel and titanium components in the vicinity of the engine bay and exhaust nozzles. Swept wing (quarter-chord sweepback, 34 degrees) built on continuous three-spar structure with integrally-machined skins; 'g' limits, +7.8/–4.2.

MANUFACTURERS: British Aerospace PLC, Kingston-upon-Thames and Dunsfold, Surrey.

POWERPLANT: One 21,500 lb thrust Rolls-Royce Bristol Pegasus 104 vectored-thrust turbofan. Fuel capacity, 650 Imp gallons in six integral tanks in fuselage and wing centresection (and provision for in-flight refuelling). Reaction control nozzles located in nose, tail and wing tips employing engine bleed air from HP compressor.

DIMENSIONS: Wing span, 25 ft 3 in. Overall length, 47 ft 7 in. Height, 12 ft 2 in. Wing area, 201 sq ft. Wheel track, 22 ft 0 in.

WEIGHTS: Operating, empty, 13,444 lb. Max take-off, 26,200 lb. Max warload, 8,500 lb. Internal fuel, 5,060 lb. Max external load, 5,300 lb. VTO payload, 5,000 lb.

PERFORMANCE: Max speeds: 740 mph at sea level; Mach 12.3 at altitude in dive; Mach .98 at altitude (level flight). Service ceiling, 51,000 ft. Max ferry range, 2,490 miles. STO distance at max take-off weight, 350 yards. Initial rate of climb, approximately 22,500 ft/min.

OPERATIONAL EQUIPMENT AND ARMAMENT: Twin detachable 30 mm gun pods with 300 rounds of ammunition mounted on either side of fuselage centreline store position. One centreline and four underwing store pylons stressed to carry up to five 1,000 lb iron bombs, retarded bombs, cluster bombs, up to six Matra multiple-rocket launchers, up to ten Lepus flares, up to four AIM-9 Sidewinder AAMs, two combat drop tanks or two 330 Imp Gallon ferry tanks, or combinations of the above up to maximum warload. Blue Fox radar (as primary sensor), Smiths Industries HUD, Ferranti self-aligning attitude-reference platform, UHF Homing, TACAN, I-Band transponder and RWR.

The first YAV-8B, 158394 (originally a Kingston-built AV-8A), launching from the ski-ramp at Patuxent River. Note the double row of blow-in doors on the engine intakes.

The British Aerospace/McDonnell Douglas Harrier II Series

The Memorandum of Understanding signed by Hawker Siddeley Aviation Ltd and McDonnell Aircraft (already mentioned) opened the way both for independent research by each company and collaborative benefit from shared manufacture of production aircraft. The truth was that, so long as the US Navy itself was determined to pursue the worldwide deployment of very large fleet carriers, it saw little advantage in supporting V/STOL subsonic combat aircraft in pursuing what it saw as its primary rôle of maintaining safe mercantile use of the world sea lanes. Thus, with its purse strings firmly controlled by the Navy, the US Marine Corps could see little hope of acquiring the funding necessary to acquire a supersonic version of the AV-8A. It followed that, despite the production sharing agreement between HSA and McDonnell Aircraft (McAir)

445

there was little hope of the RAF and Royal Navy obtaining the Treasury's support 'to go it alone'. Nor would the British Treasury countenance support for British supersonic research and development in the hope of interesting the US Navy in a supersonic naval V/STOL fighter if the production benefits had to be shared with an American manufacturer. The answer seemed to lie in the hands of McAir, which might be able, with the assistance of Rolls-Royce, to develop such an aircraft to interest the US Navy.

To this end McAir began design of an 'Advanced Harrier' based on the AV-8A but powered by a new Pegasus 15-series engine with a 2.75-inch larger fan diameter which, in bench testing, produced 24,500 lb thrust. This aircraft, the AV-16 (in which Hawker Siddeley was invited to participate), would remain subsonic in its basic configuration, but in the AV-16-S6 version, employing PCB, would be supersonic at altitude and would be able to mount up to seven store pylons. However, it was soon appreciated that the increased size of the engine made any retrospective application to existing Harriers and AV-8As economically unattractive, particularly in the mid-1970s with massive worldwide inflation increases. When it transpired in 1975 that a development cost of almost two billion dollars could be expected before either nation received a production aircraft, the AV-16 project was cancelled.

Henceforth Hawker Siddeley at Kingston confined its design activities to investigating improvements in the Harrier's wing, which, by retrofitting to existing Harriers, might claw back some of the load and performance benefits of the subsonic AV-16 while retaining the Pegasus 11 (Marks 103 an 104). Although some progress was made with an improved wing, calculations showed that improvements were only marginal and scarcely worth the costs involved. (It is worth mentioning, however, that calculations being undertaken on the benefits of the ski-launch at this time showed that with a twelve-degree ramp *and no alterations to the Harrier at all*, more than 80 per cent of the USMC's increased load-carrying demands could be met by the standard AV-8A!).

McAir, however, went further and was able to demonstrate that, by use of a supercritical wing of greater span, large slotted flaps with nozzle deflection at STO unstick and a structure largely manufactured in carbonfibre composite, it would be possible to accommodate 2,000lb of additional fuel within the same aircraft weight as the AV-8A, while the use of larger engine intakes with increased pressure-recovery in V/STOL (by means of a double row of intake blow-in doors) would increase the maximum thrust of the Pegasus 103 by 600 lb. A further 1,200 lb in the VTO payload could also be gained by the use of lift improvement devices (LIDs), such as longitudinal fences attached to the gun pods and a retractable cross-dam at the forward end of the pods to capture the ground-reflected jets at take-off. Other airframe refinements included a reduction in wing sweepback to improve longitudinal stability

446

at high angles of attack, while the aspect ratio was increased to achieve better cruise performance. The increased span and aspect ratio allowed the mounting of six underwing store pylons as well as enabling the roll control valves to be moved further outboard, thereby improving lateral control without increased engine bleed. To improve the taxiing radius of turn in narrow spaces, the outrigger wheels were moved closer inboard.

As mentioned above, considerable use was to be made of carbonfibre composites (a manufacturing process in which America led Britain in the 1970s, but one which has become increasingly used in Britain since). The AV-8B's wing, spanning 28 ft, was at concept the largest component manufactured in composite materials. The process was selected for the aircraft simply on account of the overriding demand for major weight reduction in the new aircraft to meet the USMC's payload/range requirement without recourse to a new engine. The process involves cutting and stacking layers of carbonfibre impregnated with epoxy resin, the collated layers being subjected to pressure and heat in an autoclave. Composites are used throughout the airframe, McAir contributing the wing, fuselage nose and forward centre fuselage with engine intakes, and British Aerospace manufacturing relatively small items including the rudders for all aircraft, and the single-piece tailplane for all RAF aircraft.

However, with Britain in the grip of rampant inflation during the late 1970s, the British government was unable to embark on long-term decisions with regard to a second-generation Harrier, and it was clear that any substantial expenditure on such an aircraft would best be undertaken as a joint venture through the collaborative Memorandum of Understanding that existed between British Aerospace and McAir. It was therefore necessary to tailor the future RAF requirement to the direction in which the US Marine Corps AV-8B was moving. Differences in tactical employment, such as navigation and weapon delivery, would be accommodated by means of avionics manufactured in each country to suit the respective air forces. Until the final Air Staff Requirement could be issued, little could be done until the Americans had demonstrated the feasibility of the proposed AV-8B/Harrier II concept.

The programme to develop the AV-8B and prepare it for service with the US Marine Corps was, understandably, fairly lengthy and complex. The first step was to prepare what were in effect two prototypes, YAV-8Bs, which employed the last two Hawker-built AV-8As (158394 and 158395) of the first batch, originally delivered to America in 1972. The first of these made its first flight at Saint Louis on 9 November 1979.

During that year the US Navy purchased a twelve-degree ski-ramp from Britain, and this was erected at Patuxent River for use by the YAV-8Bs to establish the enhanced STO capabilities with large payloads. (Unlike the Royal Navy, the US Marine Corps did not pursue ski-ramp operations at sea.)

447

In the course of four months' flight trials the YAV-8B showed that it could easily exceed the US Marine Corps' performance and load requirements. In the meantime, pending a decision whether to go ahead with the AV-8B, the Marine Corps sought and gained approval to acquire an interim Harrier, the AV-8C, by the expedient of applying limited modifications to AV-8As as they became due for major inspection and overhaul. These alterations included the addition of LIDs, radar warning receiver (ALR-67), flare/chaff dispenser (ALE-39) and an on-board oxygen generating system (OBOGS). Within three years forty-seven such aircraft had been modified, most of them being delivered to Marine attack squadron VMA-542 during 1982–83.

With continuing prevarication in the late 1970s by the British Ministry of Defence as to whether Britain should pursue an advanced Harrier — with or without American collaboration — the US Navy Department authorised McDonnell Douglas to go ahead with full-scale development of the AV-8B, as the Marine Corps indicated its need for 336 production

The first AV-8B, 162068/VL-01, to reach a US Marine Corps line squadron, VMA-331 at Cherry Point — a former A-4M unit. The photograph was taken in June 1985.

aircraft (to re-equip three AV-8A and five A-4M Skyhawk squadrons). By delaying its formal decision to join the AV-8B programme, the RAF was faced with matching the Marine Corps' aircraft to its own operational requirements — always a costly exercise, but now clearly fraught with problems owing to the very different operational tasks demanded of the two air forces. However, the substantial financial savings that would accrue from joining the aircraft production programme, whose cost would be amortised by the size of the American order, appeared attractive, even though it was originally stated that the RAF requirement would be for no more than sixty aircraft.

In 1981, therefore, with development of the AV-8B well advanced, a second memorandum of understanding (MOU) was signed and a commercial work-sharing agreement was negotiated between McDonnell Douglas and British Aerospace. Under this, McAir would contribute about 60 per cent of the airframe manufacture (by man hours) of all Marine Corps and RAF aircraft, and BAe 40 per cent, reflecting the

American company's greater manufacturing experience in composite materials and the much larger proportion of US Marine Corps aircraft. The same proportions applied to the manufacture of aircraft exported to other nations, all assembly being undertaken by McAir. For the powerplant a similar agreement was signed between Rolls-Royce and Pratt & Whitney, under which the British company would be responsible for 75 per cent of the Pegasus engine's construction, and the American company for the balance. This programme accounted for about two-thirds of the entire procurement bill, the remaining one-third covering the development and manufacture of equipment and systems, much of which would be peculiar to the respective air forces; in practice, this equipment increased the unit cost of the British aircraft substantially beyond that of the AV-8B, such were the demands for sophisticated equipment being made by the RAF.

At the time of the signing of the MOU in August 1981, six complete rear-fuselage assemblies had been delivered to America from Kingston, and the first of four Full-Scale Development (FSD) AV-8Bs, 161396–161399, was nearing completion at Saint Louis. This aircraft was flown on 5 November that year by Charles A Plummer, being followed by 'FSD2' and 'FSD3' on 7 and 9 April 1983 respectively. The first two aircraft were characterised by their retention of nose pitot booms, while the second and subsequent aircraft featured wing leading edge root extensions (LERX), these being added to meet RAF turn performance requirements. Joining the programme at the same time at Saint Louis was John Farley, chief test pilot at BAe's Dunsfold facility, to keep abreast of flight developments.

All three aircraft paid visits to the Naval Air Test Center, Patuxent River, Maryland, for preliminary Service evaluation in 1982 by VX-5, but it was not until the following year that the Initial Operational Test and Evaluation Report by XV-5 indicated that limited redesign of the engine intake ducts might result in worthwhile performance benefit. Flight trials confirmed this improvement, and at the same time the trailing-edge flaps were rescheduled for manoeuvring at low altitude and high speed.

In the meantime McDonnell Douglas had received funding for and authority to go ahead with a production batch of twelve AV-8Bs. The final FSD aircraft first flew on 4 June 1983, this aircraft being used to formulate the acceptance criteria for the production aircraft. Later, in 1984, it embarked on development trials of the GAU-12 25 mm five-barrel Gatling gun scheduled for the Marine Corps' AV-8Bs. Mounted in the port LID pod/strake, this gun fired linear linkless ammunition, of which 300 rounds were to be carried in the starboard pod-strake.

In-flight refuelling trials had been carried out by FSD2 in conjunction with USMC Lockheed KC-130F Hercules tankers to confirm compatibility with the aircraft. However, without resorting to air refuelling, or even to external fuel tanks, Charles Plummer demonstrated the capabilities of the A V-8B by flying an FSD aircraft on two simulated operational sorties from Patuxent River in March 1983. Carrying full internal fuel and seven 570 lb bombs, he took off, using only 270 yards of the runway, climbed, and flew 422 miles to his target, which he approached low and fast. After dropping his bombs he climbed to 42,000 ft and returned to base, making a vertical landing and shutting down after a flight of two and a half hours. Eight hundred pounds of fuel remained in his tanks.

On the other sortie Plummer carried full fuel and twelve 530 lb bombs. Using 400 yards of the runway, he flew 160 miles to the target area, loitered at 5,000 ft before descending to 2,000 ft and dropping his bombs. Returning to base at 39,000 ft, he finally landed vertically. On this occasion 600 lb of fuel remained. (The aircraft also carried 800 lb of test equipment which would have been absent in operational service.)

The first pilot production AV-8B, 161573, flew on 29 August 1983, followed by 161574 and 161575 before the end of the year. The production aircraft were identifiable by the removal of the aft row of blow-in

First 'night-capable' AV-8B to be prepared for the Marine Corps, 162968, distinguishable by the FLIR fairing on the nose. Just visible is the special night helmet worn by the pilot.

doors around the air intake cowl. By the end of 1983 production plans for the Harrier II amounted to 336 AV-8Bs (including the twelve pilot production aircraft, but excluding the FSD aircraft) for the USMC, two development batch Harrier G.R. Mark 5s, and sixty production G.R.5s for the RAF. In addition Spain had, in 1983, also ordered twelve AV-8Bs at a cost of $375 million (approximately £250 million). Early in 1984, however, the Marine Corps' proposal to acquire AV-8Bs was reduced by eight aircraft, their cost being diverted to cover the development of a two-seat training version, the TAV-8B, for which procurement funding for twenty-eight examples was sought. (At that time the RAF had no plans to acquire any Harrier II two-seaters, believing that the nineteen surviving Harrier T. Mark 4s would suffice for the training commitment.)

Original plans covered the completion of these 420 aircraft by the middle of 1989. However, in common with so many other major combat aircraft programmes of the 1980s, it was decided to spread costs (although thereby significantly increasing the total bill) over an extended period. A total of 21 aircraft — the balance of the pilot production — was scheduled for 1984, 27 in 1985, 31 in 1986, 51 in 1987, 70 in 1988, 72 in 1989, and the remaining 145 over the next three years. At the time of writing, this production schedule has been achieved, and by the beginning of 1989 a total of 276 aircraft (including TAV-8Bs) had been funded.

The AV-8B 161573 was officially handed over to the US Marine Corps at Cherry Point MCAS on 12 January 1984, this and the remaining pilot production aircraft joining the training squadron VMA(T)-203 during the following fifteen months. All of these aircraft were powered by Rolls-Royce Pegasus F402-RR-404A turbofans, but in December 1984 an FSD aircraft was flown with a new version, the -406, with a modified turbine section which permitted the engine to run 20-30 degrees cooler at a given speed, thereby increasing the time between overhauls and extending engine life. The engine behaved well in flight trials, and the new version was introduced into production aircraft during 1985. In aircraft being produced from 1990 onwards a new version of the engine, the -408, with thrust greatly increased to 24,500 lb, is being introduced.

At the time of writing, seven of the eight Marine Corps AV-8B squadrons scheduled for re-equipment had received their full complement of twenty aircraft each. The first, VMA-331 (a former Skyhawk squadron), became fully operational in September 1986. To provide the AV-8B

A Marine Corps TAV-8B two-seater, 162747, seen in 1988; note the enlarged fin.

with a night-attack capability a forward-looking infra-red (FLIR) system was introduced in the 167th and subsequent aircraft.

The two-seat TAV-8B, whose multi-year purchase of twenty-eight examples was spread over the period 1985–89, was first flown on 21 October 1986, and the first deliveries to the Marine Corps were made in August the following year. This version features an entirely new twin tandem-seat nose and enlarged vertical tail. Employing only two twin-store underwing store positions, the TAV-8B can still lift four LAU-68 rocket launchers or six Mark 76 practice bombs for training purposes.

The twelve Spanish EAV-8Bs were delivered to Rota during 1987–88, the first three aircraft making the flight from Saint Louis to Spain on 6 October 1987. In 1989 the EAV-8Bs were deployed aboard Spain's new ski-deck carrier *Principe de Asturias*.

A British Aerospace/McDonnell Douglas EAV-8B Matador for Spain, shown flying in 1987.

TECHNICAL DATA FOR BAe/MCDONNELL DOUGLAS AV-8B HARRIER II

TYPE: Single-seat day-and-night close-support aircraft (TAV-8B, two-seat conversion/weapons trainer).

STRUCTURE: Cantilever shoulder-wing monoplane. Low-aspect-ratio, swept wing of supercritical aerofoil section with thickness:chord ratio of 11.5 per cent at root and 7.5 per cent at tip. Wing constructed as single-piece carbon-fibre component with marked anhedral. Composite materials also employed in tail unit, ailerons, flaps, LERX and outrigger fairings; wing leading edge reinforced against bird-strike. Drooping ailerons and wide-chord single-slotted flaps. Semi-monocoque fuselage with composite materials for nose section. Large airbrake under rear fuselage. Cockpit raised by 12 in compared with that of AV-8A.

MANUFACTURERS: British Aerospace Ltd, Kingston-upon-Thames, Surrey, England. McDonnell Douglas Corporation, Saint Louis, Missouri, USA.

POWERPLANT: Rolls-Royce Pegasus F402-RR-406A and 408 turbofans (-406 delivering 21,750 lb thrust; -408 delivering 24,500 lb thrust.)

DIMENSIONS: Wing span, 30 ft 4 in. Overall length 46 ft 4 in. (TAV-8B, 50 ft 3 in). Height, 11 ft 7½ in (TAV-8B, 13 ft 4¾ in). Wing area, including LERX, 237.7 sq ft.

WEIGHTS: Empty,13,086 lb (TAV-8B, 14,221 lb). Max take-off, 31,000 lb (TAV-8B, 29,750 lb).

PERFORMANCE: (All figures assuming -406 engine) Max speed at sea level, 647 mph (TAV-8B, 587 mph); at altitude, Mach 0.91. (TAV-8B, Mach 0.90); operational radius, with 4,000 lb of weapons, 553 miles. Unrefuelled ferry range with four 300 US gallon external tanks, 2,440 miles; with two tanks, 1,650 miles.

OPERATIONAL EQUIPMENT AND ARMAMENT: Single 25 mm GAU-12/U cannon with 300 rounds; centreline and six underwing store positions capable of mounting the following typical loads: up to sixteen 500 lb bombs, twelve cluster bombs, ten Paveway laser-guided bombs, eight fire bombs or two underwing gun pods. Provision is made to carry AGM-65E Maverick missiles or ALQ-64 ECM pod (on centreline mounting). Avionics include Litton AN/ASN-130A inertial navigator, AiResearch CP-1471/A digital air data computer, Smiths Industries SU-128/A dual combining glass HUD, Lear Siegler stores management system, Bendix RT-1157/APX-100 IFF, etc.

First development batch Harrier G.R.5, ZD318, which flew on 30 April 1985.

The British Aerospace Harrier G.R. Marks 5, 5A and 7

As previously mentioned, the British decision to join McDonnell Douglas in the Harrier II manufacturing programme was at last reached with the signing of the MOU in 1981, after about four years of indecision, the proposed British aircraft being expected to cost about £9 million each. (In the event, owing largely to inflation and some rearrangement of equipment inventories, the figure was to be slightly over £11 million by the time the first aircraft flew.)

The work-sharing agreement allowed for the interspersing of two 'Development Batch' Harrier G.R. Mark 5s, so designated as to follow on from the T. Mark 4 (and, incidentally, appearing to perpetuate Hawker's practice of designating single-seaters with odd Mark numbers and two-seaters with even numbers), followed by sixty production examples. Division of work on the RAF aircraft was to be fifty/fifty, with some components (such as the tailplane in composite materials) sourced in Britain, which, for Marine Corps aircraft, are otherwise manufactured in the USA. The Pegasus Mark 105 in the G.R.5 is similar to the AV-8B's dash-406 version, but is rated slightly higher at 21,750 lb thrust;

the Mark 105 incorporates a computerised Digital Engine Control system (DCES), produced by Dowty Smiths Industries Controls; the system relieves the pilot of the need to adjust engine ratings for speed, temperature and pressure, and also permits rapid thrust-dumping, thereby improving vertical landings by eliminating 'bounce'. It is, incidentally, interesting to note that, whereas, when landing vertically in the G.R.3, the pilot had to increase power when close to the ground owing to hot-gas recirculation, the G.R.5 pilot has positively to cut the throttle to dump lift, so effective are the LIDs.

The first 'Development Batch' G.R.5, ZD318 (employing the twentieth set of Harrier II components) made its maiden flight at Dunsfold on 30 April 1985, flown by chief test pilot Mike Snelling. The second aircraft followed it into the air on 31 July, and the first two production aircraft, ZD320 and ZD321, underwent manufacturers' tests as ZD322 was delivered to Boscombe Down for Service trials. Formal hand-over of the RAF's first production squadron aircraft, ZD324, was conducted at Wittering on 1 July 1987.

In the meantime it had been announced that a Harrier Conversion Team (HCT) was to be set up within No. 233 OCU at Wittering to convert Harrier G.R.3 pilots to the G.R.5, and several instructors were detached to the US Marine Corps' VMA(T)-203 training squadron at Cherry Point to gain experience in AV-8Bs. A delay was then caused as the result of a tragic flying accident on 1 November 1987; on that day BAe test pilot Taylor Scott was making the final company flight in ZD325 when, without warning, the drogue parachute of the Martin-Baker Mark 12 ejector seat operated accidentally, fragmented the canopy, and dragged

Three Harrier G.R.5s of No. 233 OCU's Harrier Conversion Team in February 1989; note the in-flight refuelling probes on the port engine intake cowlings.

him from the cockpit, leaving the seat itself *in situ*. Scott was killed, and the aircraft was lost at sea when it eventually ran out of fuel.

Harrier G.R.5s were grounded pending the introduction of modifications to the seat, and this was followed by a temporary restriction on the aircraft's operating altitude. It was not until 30 March 1988 that the HCT was able to start training in earnest; however, in slightly over a year a total of thirty-one pilots had been fully converted to the Harrier G.R.5. By August 1989, when No. 233 OCU began *ab initio* training of G.R.5 pilots, the OCU possessed three G.R.5s, in addition to seven G.R.3s, five T.4s and three T.4As.

The original allocation of aircraft under the MOU allowed for up to 100 RAF aircraft but, as already mentioned, only sixty full production examples had been taken up by British orders placed by the end of 1983. However, on 19 March 1988 a follow-on order was placed for a further thirty-four aircraft, and it now seems likely that, after early delays, production will run out in about 1992; moreover a great deal of equipment updating will result in some complication of the delivery process.

The first Harrier G.R.5, ZD378, destined for No. 1 (Fighter) Squadron' at Wittering in 1989, shown here carrying gun pod/strakes, 190 gallon drop tanks, Sidewinder AAMs and bombs. The aircraft displays the pilot's name, Wg Cdr I R Harvey, below the cockpit sill.

No. 1 Squadron, based at Wittering with Harrier G.R.1s and 3s for twenty years, began receiving G.R.5s on 28 November 1988, disposing of its last G.R.3 on 31 March 1989. Among No. 1 Squadron's routine commitments are short-term deployments to one of the Royal Navy's Invincible-class carriers.

As with the previous Harriers, the G.R.5s' main squadron deployment will be in Germany, and No. 3 Squadron at Gütersloh received its first new aircraft, ZD401, on 17 March 1989, completing its conversion early in 1990.

The arrival in service of the Harrier G.R.5, with its greatly increased range and load-carrying potential, has imposed a subtle change in the basic rôle of the aircraft, and it is perhaps necessary to mention some of the new aircraft systems now standardised in the new version to cater for this change.

To explain how the change has come about, one can see that, quite apart from the ability to carry considerably more fuel externally, the G.R.5 carries 915 gallons of fuel internally, compared with 630 in the G.R.3. Moreover, in a typically hi-lo-hi attack sortie, carrying 4,000 lb of external weapons, the radius of action of the G.R.5 is about 550 miles; that of the G.R.3 is no more than 410 miles. More dramatically, in any patrol involving loiter at, say, 100 miles from base, the endurance of the G.R.5 is, at three hours, double that of the G.R.3. Thus, in terms of performance, the G.R.5's rôle is less confined to close battlefield support and more concerned with air interdiction immediately beyond the battlefield. In line with this rôle, the G.R.5's primary weapon is the Hunting Improved BL755 cluster bomb; this weighs 582 lb, and the normal load would be six, carried on the wing pylons (although it is possible to load a seventh on the centreline mounting).

Harrier G.R.5 ZD346 carrying seven cluster bombs and two Sidewinder AAMs in 1988.

In the cockpit are three prominent 'up front' displays. In the centre is the Smith's Industries SU-128/A head-up display; on the left is the Hughes AN/ASB-19 Angle Rate Bombing Set, and to the right is the Harrier's unique Ferranti moving map display, which indicates the aircraft's ground position to an accuracy of less than one mile for each hour flown. Passive defence is provided by a Marconi ZEUS RWR/ECM system capable of providing 360 degree sensing and retaliation by identifying threats from a store of about a thousand emitters, and responding correctly with countermeasures. In the extreme tail is located the antenna for a Plessey Missile Approach Warning (MAW) system, which senses the approach of heat-seeking missiles and initiates immediate response by automatically discharging decoy flares.

Some delay has been encountered in introducing the Ferranti FIN 1075 inertial navigational system; early sets proved so unreliable that the Ministry of Defence was obliged to acquire forty-two Litton AN/ASN-130s, otherwise used in the AV-8B, costing about £4 million. It seems that the troubles (related to water penetration) have been overcome, and deliveries of the FIN 1075 are under way.

The gun armament of the G.R.5 comprises a pair of ADEN 25 gas-operated 25 mm cannon, each one mounted in 'shoulder' pods under the fuselage. Compared with the old 30 mm Aden guns, the ADEN 25 delivers three times higher kinetic energy by reason of greater muzzle velocity and higher rate of fire. Each gun is provided with 100 rounds, sufficient for about four seconds' firing.

The total cost of ninety-six Harrier G.R.5s was early in 1989 estimated at about £1.6 billion, and although, when the programme was initiated in 1980–81, the G.R.5 was expected to represent the definitive version of the Harrier — at least in this century — it is now clear that, hardly had the aircraft entered RAF service than plans were afoot to upgrade the Mark 5 to give it fine-night operating capability, in effect producing a 'force multiplier'. To achieve this a GEC Avionics FLIR is mounted in a fairing above the nose, as well as a new Smiths Industries raster HUD on which the FLIR image can be projected and viewed by the pilot wearing night-vision goggles. The cockpit displays are modified for use with these goggles, and computer capacity will be increased by use of a Computing Devices ACCS 2500 in place of the 2000 in the standard G.R.5. These modifications will be incorporated in the sixty-third and subsequent aircraft, and the designation changed to Harrier G.R.7. Also included in this version is a new GEC Digital Colour Map Unit (DCMU). This unit stores information provided on ordinary paper maps of particular importance to the pilot, over which can be overlaid specific flying hazards, waypoints, targets, etc. Because this version of the DCMU is as

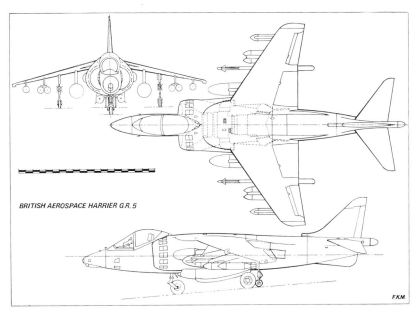

BRITISH AEROSPACE HARRIER G.R.5

F.K.M.

457

yet only employed to a fraction of its memory capacity, it seems possible that any development of terrain-following capability in the Harrier could conceivably result in further versions some time in the future. As it is, aircraft numbers 42 to 62 inclusive are being fitted with the FLIR blister, together with night-goggle-compatible instrument lighting, and this interim version, the G.R. Mark 5A, has already flown. As soon as production of all ninety-four aircraft has been completed, British Aerospace will receive back aircraft numbers 1–41, and later 42–62, to bring them all up to Mark 7 standard. No. 3 Squadron is due to receive the Harrier G.R.7 in 1991, when it will pass its G.R.5s on to No. 4 Squadron, which in turn will update to G.R.7s in 1992. Finally No. 1 Squadron and No. 233 OCU will also receive the Mark 7.

It is relevant here to explain that it was never anticipated that there would be a requirement to obtain a 'G.R. Mark 5 trainer', it being considered that the surviving T.4s and T.4As would be adequate to train the new Harrier force. Such, however, is the nature of the G.R.5/7's changed rôle, to which fine-night operations are about to be added, that the Ministry of Defence decided in March 1990 to acquire fourteen Harrier II two-seat trainers, these aircraft being designated the T. Mark 10; they will, in effect, be similar in appearance to the American TAV-8B.

Finally it may be questioned whether the Royal Air Force will seek to obtain Harriers powered by the 23,500 lb-thrust Pegasus 11–61 engine, and although there are no such indications at the time of writing, it is said that some of the later G.R. Mark 7s may include provision for this engine. The engine was first flown on 9 June 1989 in the Rolls-Royce trials aircraft, ZD402, which had been painted in a distinctive black-and-white colour scheme.

Thus it appears, in the year of the 30th anniversary of the Hawker P.1127's first hovering flight on 21 October 1960 in the hands of Bill Bedford, that the story of the truly remarkable Harrier will continue at least to the turn of the century. Who could have foretold in those days, when to achieve lift-off over a specially prepared grid it was necessary to

The Rolls-Royce engine test Harrier Mark 5, ZD402, powered by the 23,800 lb thrust Pegasus 11-61 turbofan. In this guise the aircraft was first flown on 9 June 1989.

provide sufficient fuel for only a few minutes' engine running time, that thirty years later the natural descendant of the P.1127 would be capable of lifting bomb loads almost as great as the weight of the old prototype itself? Or that the Rolls-Royce Pegasus, that has been at the heart of the Harrier's success, would be producing almost two and a half times the power being demonstrated in 1960?

Stepping stone to the Harrier G.R.7 (pp. 489/490) the first Harrier G.R. Mark 5A,ZD430, at Dunsfold late in 1989, displays the distinctive new nose profile.

TECHNICAL DATA FOR BRITISH AEROSPACE HARRIER G.R. MARK 5

TYPE: Single-seat V/STOL tactical support and battlefield interdiction aircraft.

STRUCTURE: Cantilever shoulder-wing monoplane. Low-aspect-ratio, swept wing of supercritical aerofoil section with thickness:chord ratio of 11.5 per cent at root and 7.5 per cent at tip. Wing constructed as single-piece carbon-fibre component with marked anhedral. Composite materials also employed in flaps, ailerons, LERX, and outrigger pods. Wing leading edge reinforced against bird strike. Drooping ailerons and wide-chord single-slotted flaps. Semi-monocoque fuselage with composite materials for nose section. Large airbrake under rear fuselage. Cockpit raised by 12 in compared with that of the Harrier G.R.3. Retractable in-flight refuelling probe mounted on port air intake cowl.

MANUFACTURERS: British Aerospace Ltd, Kingston-upon-Thames, Surrey. England. McDonnell Douglas Corporation, Saint Louis, Missouri, USA.

POWERPLANT: Rolls-Royce Pegasus Mark 105 vectored-thrust turbofan delivering 21,750 lb thrust.

DIMENSIONS: Wing span, 30 ft 4 in. Overall length, 46 ft 4 in. Height, 11 ft 7¾ in. Wing area, including LERX, 238.7 sq ft.

WEIGHTS: Empty, 13,984 lb; maximum take-off, 31,000 lb.

PERFORMANCE: Max speed at sea level, 661 mph; at altitude, 600 mph at 36,000 ft (Mach 0.91); tactical radius (typical hi-lo-hi sortie profile with two 250 gallon external tanks and seven Mk. 82 bombs), 553 miles; ferry range (with four 250 gallon external tanks retained), 2,015 miles.

OPERATIONAL EQUIPMENT AND ARMAMENT: Twin 25 mm ADEN 25 cannon, each with 100 rounds, mounted in shoulder pods under fuselage; one centreline and six underwing store points capable of loading ordnance up to maximum of 9,200 lb (such as sixteen Mark 82 bombs, six Mark 83 bombs, seven BL-755 cluster bombs, four Maverick ASMs, or ten rocket-launcher pods). Primary weapon delivery sensor is the Hughes Angle Rate Bombing Set; other equipment includes Smiths Industries SU-128/A HUD, Ferranti Moving Map Display, Plessey Missile Approach Warning System, Mark XII IFF system, Ferranti FIN 1075 inertial navigation system, etc.

The first RAF unit to receive Hawker Siddeley Hawk T.1 trainers was No. 4 FTS at Valley, Anglesea, in November 1976, one of whose aircraft, XX235, is shown here in the original red and white colour scheme.

The Hawker Siddeley P.1182 (BAe) Hawk

By the late 1960s the pattern of operational and conversion training in Royal Air Force Strike Command had to a great extent become centred upon use of the Hunter and Lightning two-seaters, while future fast-jet pilots received their first jet experience in Folland Gnats and Jet Provosts. The Gnat imposed its own limitations both by its lack of weapon-carrying potential (in itself not important in a 'pure flying' trainer) and by an inherent attrition among young student pilots of above average stature: its cockpit was extremely cramped, so that there was an in-built selection process that excluded such pilots from progressing to fast jets. This had not been a feature of the Hunter T. Mark 7 trainer, and, although Hawker had offered various operational trainer adaptations of existing airframes (a demonstrably straightforward process), there simply were not enough Hunter airframes available to justify such a scheme. Moreover, the Hunter now represented twenty-year-old technology.

It should be emphasised that, up to that time, it had been for many years a fairly universal practice in Europe, America and elsewhere, to adapt modern operational aircraft to fill the operational training rôle by the simple expedient of enlarging the cockpit, adding a seat for an instructor and providing dual controls. Such had been the process in arriving at the Meteor, Vampire, Hunter and Lightning trainers, and it would continue for years to come. This convention, it has been argued, was relatively inexpensive, demanded no great development gestation,

This No. 4 FTS Hawk T.1, XX292, displays the later red, white and blue colour scheme as well as the traditional 'palm and pyramid' badge on the fin, recalling the unit's long pre-Second World War association with Egypt.

and allowed for straightforward logistics owing to commonality of components, engines and so on. It had, however, one important drawback: it presupposed that the customer could afford to buy the sophisticated operational aircraft in the first place.

Hawker Siddeley had, perhaps with greater success than any other European manufacturer, pursued an exceptionally lucrative trade in second hand, and even third-hand Hunters to a dozen of the world's smaller air forces at costs well below that of new purpose-built trainers of similar capabilities, but, as already mentioned, the availability of aircraft suitable for refurbishing and conversion was diminishing rapidly, such was the demand. It must be remembered that the last newly-built Hunter had left the Hawker factory early in the 1960s!

A new design philosophy had therefore evolved towards the end of the 1960s — with one eye fixed firmly on the fast-growing market among those smaller air forces — in which the fundamental aircraft design would be for a small, high-performance turbojet-powered two-seat trainer, with a *secondary* operational capability. The secondary rôle would be principally in ground support, rather than in air-to-air interception. Protagonists of the new trainer concept saw an enormous potential market opening up as aged American T-33s, British Vampires and Jet Provosts and French Fouga Magisters came to be phased out of service in the 1970s.

First among the West European contenders for a slice of this market was the Franco-German Dassault-Breguet/Dornier Alpha Jet, while Hawker Siddeley Aviation's answer was to be the P.1182, design of which had started in the Hawker Project Office in the late 1960s on the strength of reports that the Ministry of Defence was about to issue a Requirement for a Hunter/Gnat replacement. This was issued at the end

461

of 1970 as Air Staff Requirement 397, and designs were tendered by HSA and BAC (the latter being the P.59). of these the P.1182, originally schemed by Dr John Fozard, was selected. As if to emphasise the fundamental *volte face*, the P.1182, unlike the Alpha Jet, was designed from the outset to incorporate gunsights in both cockpits, a feature that was fundamentally to dictate the fuselage design.

The P.1182 was to have a low wing of very low thickness-chord with moderate sweep, and incorporating double-slotted flaps. Despite a modest engine thrust of some 5,200lb, the aerofoil section of very advanced design bestowed true transonic dive performance — not achieved by the Alpha Jet. The tandem cockpits, each equipped with Martin-Baker Mark 10 rocket-assisted ejection seats, were to be markedly stepped, the rear seat being located some sixteen inches higher than the front, both pilots therefore possessing superb fields of vision. A single-piece, side-hinged canopy featured miniature detonating cords to shatter the transparency an instant before seat ejection. The P.1182 for the RAF was required to embody three external storepoints, two underwing and a centreline attachment; the latter could accommodate a single 30 mm Aden gun pack with integral magazine.

Unlike the twin-engine Alpha Jet, the P.1182 favoured the single-engine layout, both Hawker and the Ministry of Defence pointing to reliable service provided by successive single-engine trainers in the recent past, such as the Vampire, Jet Provost and the Hunter, and this faith has been amply justified by the P.1182's astonishing safety record, only one aircraft being lost from engine malfunction in the first five years' service. Another lesson, learned from long experience with the Hunter (in particular in the punishing ground-attack rôle in the tropics), was that of long fatigue life under frequent flight-load and sortie cycling. Ease of maintenance, of the utmost importance among low-budget air forces, as well as system simplicity and reliability, were constant design priorities, and the aircraft was fully serviceable from ground level.

Almost without precedent, the P.1182 was not ordered in prototype form as such, a straight production order for 176 aircraft being placed by the Ministry of Defence for the RAF with HSA in March 1972. The name Hawk was selected in August 1973. The first such aircraft, XX154 (referred to as a pre-production airframe) made its maiden flight in the hands of Duncan Simpson, chief test pilot at Dunsfold, on 21 August 1974, the flight lasting 53 minutes.

As XX154 embarked on development trials at Dunsfold, an increasing proportion of which were undertaken by 'Andy' Jones, the Hawk project pilot, a number of minor criticisms inevitably surfaced. These were fairly simply rectified, involving some local changes in the rear fuselage contours to improve directional stability, removal of a section of the flap vane to correct excessive downwash on the tailplane, and the addition of vortex generators, a wing leading edge fence and breaker strips to improve handling at the stall.

462

The student pilot's front cockpit of the Hawk T. Mk 1 (upper) and the instructor's rear cockpit (lower).

463

Hawk XX159 of No. 1 TWU, sporting a pale grey scheme with yellow stripe, indulges in some inverted flying. As superbly demonstrated by the famous Red Arrows, the Hawk is unquestionably a 'pilot's aeroplane'.

The delivery of Hawk T Mark 1s to the RAF began when XX162 and XX163 arrived at No. 4 Flying Training School at Valley, Anglesey, on 4 November 1976. Other early production examples had been allocated to Boscombe Down, Farnborough and Rolls-Royce for systems development and clearance, compilation of Pilots' Notes, and so on.

At Valley the Hawk replaced the Gnat in the advanced training rôle, No. 4 FTS being an element of RAF Support Command. At this school, student pilots selected to progress to fast jet squadrons (Harriers, Jaguars, Buccaneers, Lightnings and, more recently, Tornados) each received a total of fifty-six hours' dual instruction and twenty-nine hours' solo flying in a twenty-four-week course.

The next units to receive the Hawk were the Tactical Weapons Units, No. 1 TWU at Brawdy in South Wales, and No. 2 at Chivenor, Cornwall. Whereas the Hawks delivered to Valley possessed no gunsights, those flown at the TWUs were so equipped for weapon training with the Aden gun and underwing Matra rocket launchers. The TWU course provided each pilot with fifty-four hours of weapon training over a period of sixteen weeks. Being components of the RAF Strike Command, each of the TWUs was divided into two 'shadow squadrons', these squadrons and their instructors assuming first-line status in a war emergency by providing aerodrome defence. These 'shadow' affiliations comprised Nos. 79 and 234 Squadrons to No. 1 TWU, and Nos. 63 and 151 Squadrons to No. 2 TWU, their aircraft carrying the appropriate squadron insignia.

After five years' service with the TWUs it had become clear that the Hawk was an extraordinarily agile, robust and efficient aeroplane, and the Ministry of Defence determined to exploit the fundamental dual-rôle philosophy underlying the aircraft's concept. Accordingly, on 31 January 1983, the MoD issued a conversion contract to adapt eighty-eight Hawk Mark 1s to carry a pair of AIM-9P Sidewinder AAMs, to enhance the wartime emergency air defence capability. This programme, involving a change of aircraft designation to T. Mark 1A, was completed during the next four years.

The Hawk is unquestionably best known for the superb displays provided by the famous Red Arrows aerobatic team. This is a detached squadron of the Central Flying School. Considered by many experienced observers to be the world's most proficient formation aerobatic team, the Red Arrows converted from Gnats to Hawks in 1980 and, ever since, have provided the climax of every flying display they have attended. Flying Hawks fitted with converted ventral gun packs containing the oil and dye required to produce their characteristic red, white and blue smoke trails, the pilots have treated literally millions of watchers the world over to unforgettable spectacles of precision flying, coordinated manoeuvres, ingenuity of programme and sheer grace.

There has been another spin-off from the Red Arrows' superb airmanship. Such has been the team's international prestige, that it has been

A Sidewinder-equipped Hawk T. Mark 1A, XX221. Note the centreline cannon fairing.

invited to make a number of foreign tours, attending anniversary displays on the American continent, as well as in the Middle and Far East; and there is no doubt but that the team's performances have drawn considerable attention from potential overseas customers to the Hawk, interest that has reaped rich rewards in substantial orders for the aircraft (see below).

Another Royal Air Force establishment that has flown Hawks for more than a dozen years is the Central Flying School itself, receiving its first aircraft in 1977. The Empire Test Pilots' School took delivery of its first two Hawk T.1s, XX341 and XX342, in 1983, and another, XX343, the following year; the latter aircraft underwent systems changes in the College of Aeronautics shortly afterwards to become an advanced systems training aircraft (ASTRA).

On 22 December 1988 a No. 4 FTS Hawk T.1, XX290, established its own endurance record when Flt Lt John Hurrell flew the aircraft from Valley for 3 hours 49 minutes and 20 seconds. Without the use of drop tanks, Hurrell flew at 39,000 ft where the outside air temperature was minus 61 degrees C, and maintained a speed of between Mach 0.5 and 0.6 — just below the drag curve.

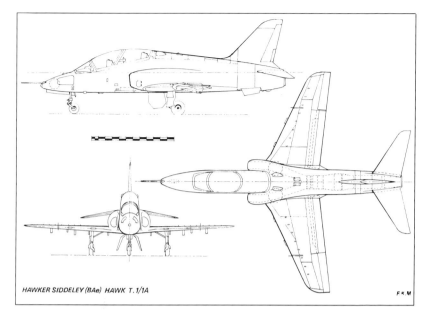

HAWKER SIDDELEY (BAe) HAWK T.1/1A   F.K.M

TECHNICAL DATA FOR HAWK T. MARK 1

TYPE: Tandem-seat advanced flying trainer.

STRUCTURE: Cantilever all-metal low-wing monoplane with one-piece wing (root thickness:-chord, 10.9 per cent; tip 9 per cent; quarter-chord sweepback, 21° 30') with machined spars-and-skin torsion box incorporating integral fuel tanks. Twin side-mounted air intakes to engine in rear fuselage. Bag-type fuselage fuel tank. Hydraulic tricycle landing gear, main units retracting inwards. Airbrake under rear fuselage. Double-slotted wing flaps. Honeycomb structure employed in rudder and ailerons.

MANUFACTURERS: Hawker Siddeley Aviation Ltd, later British Aerospace (Military Aircraft) Ltd, Kingston-upon-Thames and Dunsfold, Surrey.

POWERPLANT: One Rolls-Royce/Turboméca Adour Mk. 151 turbofan of 5,200 lb static thrust. No afterburning.

DIMENSIONS: Span, 30 ft 9½ in. Overall length, 38 ft 10½ in. Height, 13 ft 1 in. Wing area, 179.64 sq ft.

WEIGHTS: Empty, 8,015 lb. Normal loaded, 11,350 lb. Max take-off weight, 12,566 lb.

PERFORMANCE: Max speed, 615 mph at sea level; Mach 0.88 at 36,000 ft. Initial rate of climb, 11,510 ft/min. Service ceiling, 50,000 ft. Normal range, 1,510 miles. Max ferry range with two 190 gallon drop tanks, 2,530 miles. Max diving speed, Mach 1.2.

ARMAMENT: No in-built armament. T.Mark 1 has provision for three storepoints; the centreline point can mount a single 30 mm Aden gun pack with magazine, and the underwing points can mount Matra rocket launchers, BL755 cluster bombs, 1,000 lb iron bombs, practice bomb carriers, drop tanks, etc. (The Hawk T.Mk.1A has provision to mount two AIM-9P Sidewinder AAMs.)

466

The Hawk Mark 50 demonstration aircraft, ZA101.

The British Aerospace Hawk (Exported Aircraft)

Recalling that behind the Hawk's original design concept lay Hawker Siddeley Aviation's determination to attract a large share of what had, in the late 1960s, been seen to be a very large potential market for a relatively lightweight dual-rôle training aircraft with secondary operational ground support capability, it was to be expected that the company should go all out to bring the Hawk to the market's attention as soon as flying examples had been completed.

The pre-production RAF Hawk T. Mark 1, XX154, was therefore followed by a company-owned demonstrator, ZA101/G-HAWK, which first flew on 17 May 1976. In the meantime considerable work had been done to arrive at a standard of preparation that would attract the smaller air forces, bearing in mind that, unlike the RAF, they would be looking for greater operational potential — even though the primary rôle would still be in advanced training. The demonstrator therefore incorporated a wide range of optional equipment, not all of which was to be found in the T. Mark 1.

At the outset the export Hawker version was referred to as the 50-Series, the demonstrator being designated the Mark 50. Its equipment included a twin-gyro attitude and heading reference system, angle-of-attack indicator, Martin-Baker Mark 10B ejection seats, UHF, VHF,

467

TACAN, ADF, VOR, ILS and IFF. The engine was the uprated Adour Mk. 851 turbofan of 5,340 lb thrust, and the wing possessed provision for four store pylons in addition to the centreline attachment point.

FINNISH HAWK MARK 51

Permitted by treaty to possess no more than sixty front-line aircraft (divided equally between Western and Russian origins), Finland's Air Force, the *Ilmavoimat*, had for many years also flown eighty aged Fouga Magisters for advanced flying and weapons training. It was to replace these that, on 30 December 1977, an order was placed for fifty BAe Hawk Mark 51s. However, owing to the fact that insufficient Swedish Drakens existed to make up the permitted balance of first-line fighters of Western origin, Hawks initially equipped Fighter Squadrons 11, 21 and 31, operating alongside MiG-21s at Rovaniemi, Pori and Kuopio. They are also flown by the Finnish Air Academy (*Ilmasotakuolo*), where they replaced Magisters, and with the Special Reconnaissance Unit at Tikkakoski.

The Finnish order for Hawks was unique in being an element of a 'trade package' which involved BAe providing export channels for the Finnish export industry in the West as well as entering into a part-manufacturing agreement with the state-owned Valmet Corporation at the Kuorevesi works at Halli. The first four Hawks (HW302, HW303, HW305 and HW306) were entirely manufactured and assembled in Britain and delivered by air to Finland, but thereafter the remaining forty-six Hawks were delivered in kit form from Dunsfold to Kuorevesi for assembly in Finland, while all fins, tailplanes, airbrakes and flaps were to be manufactured by the Finns. The first Mark 51 made its maiden flight in the UK on 16 October 1960, and the first pair of aircraft was delivered to Finland exactly two months later.

KENYAN HAWK MARK 52

The next export order signed for the Hawk, by Kenya on 9 February 1978, was subject of all the political sensitivity associated with Western arms trading with African states, and British Aerospace is *still* under contractual obligation not to divulge the nation for which the twelve

A Finnish Hawk Mark 51, HW-338, flying over Finland in 1985.

Hawk Mark 52s were destined, nor was the company permitted to release for publication any photographs of the aircraft in Kenyan colours and markings. When, however, the Maltese press photographed the aircraft as they staged through the island during their delivery flight, the 'secret' was out. Furthermore the Hawks soon afterwards took part in the Kenyan presidential flypast over Nairobi, at which the Western Press was invited to be present.

The Kenyan Hawk Mark 52 was the first version to feature braking parachutes, deemed necessary for operation from 'hot-and-high' aerodromes in that country. Registered as Nos. 1001–1012 in the Kenyan Air Force, the first of the twelve Hawk 52s made its maiden flight in Britain on 3 December 1979, and the first deliveries by air were made on 11 April 1980. In service in Kenya the Hawks replaced BAC Strikemasters.

INDONESIAN HAWK MARK 53

The third, and to date the latest, overseas Hawk 50-Series customer was Indonesia, whose twenty Mark 53s were destined for service in the advanced operational flying/weapon training rôle, all aircraft (LL-5301 to LL-5320) being painted in the colours and markings of the *Tentara Nasional Indonesia—Angkatan Udara* (TNI-AU) Flying Training School based at Halim.

The order was won by British Aerospace during comparative evaluation with the Italian Aermacchi MB.326 and MB.329 to replace the elderly Lockheed T-33 trainers with the TNI-AU, but completion and delivery of the twenty Hawks was staged in four parts, signed on 4 April 1978, 18 May 1981, 30 October 1981 and 30 November 1982 (for eight, four, five and three aircraft respectively). Powered by the Adour 851 turbofan, the Hawk 53 made its first flight on 6 June 1980, and the two initial delivery flights (with 130 gallon drop tanks carried) were made to Jogjakarta on 1 September 1980.

Indonesian Hawk 53 LL-5318 in the markings of the TNI-AU's Flying Training School, pictured in 1984. Note the drop tanks and centreline pod.

The Hawk 60-Series

Detecting a growing emphasis among potential customers on the operational capability of the Hawk, BAe (Kingston) fitted an uprated Adour 851 turbofan in the Hawk demonstrator as a means of enhancing its load-carrying ability — with some dramatic results. With 5,700 lb thrust available, the aircraft, operating at up to 17 per cent greater take-off weight, was able to carry 33 per cent greater disposable load. With drop tanks of 190 gallon capacity the range was increased by 30 per cent. Minor changes in the wing design, the inclusion of four-position flaps to improve lift, modified landing gear with strengthened wheels and tyres, a low-friction nosewheel leg and adaptive anti-skid provision all contributed to improved field performance, acceleration, climb and turn rates.

ZIMBABWE HAWK MARK 60

The newly-constituted African state of Zimbabwe, still wracked by dissenting factions inside and outside its borders, was perhaps understandably a logical customer for the new Hawk to complement the diminished number of aged Hunters, such was the residual operational rôle demanded from the air force. On 9 April 1981 an order for eight Hawk Mark 60s was signed and the first four were delivered the following year.

As if to highlight the strife that still pervaded the country, a terrorist attack was made on a ZAF base and the new Hawks became casualties, three aircraft being damaged. Two of these were, however, fully repaired by BAe and returned to service, the third being written off.

DUBAI HAWK MARK 61

An important break-through in Hawk exports to the Arab states in the

First of the Zimbabwean Hawk Mark 60s, 600, with eight underwing bombs on twin carriers, and a centreline cannon pod, at Dunsfold in 1982.

Middle East came with the signing, on 30 June 1981, of an order for eight Hawk 61s for the Dubai Air Wing by the United Arab Emirates. These relatively tiny air forces, dependent on collective security and surrounded by powerful, oil-rich nations such as Iraq and Iran, possessed neither the personnel nor extensive logistic reserves to support aircraft of advanced capabilities, and, within the lightweight dual-rôle aircraft inventory available from the West, the enhanced Hawk 60-series appeared the ideal solution. The first aircraft, 501, was flown on 11 November 1982 and delivered to Dubai on 29 March 1983.

Dubai Hawk Mark 61, 501, in 1983.

[VENEZUELAN HAWK MARK 62]

Towards the end of 1981 the *Fuerza Aérea Venezolana* completed a lengthy evaluation of the various contenders in the dual-rôle advanced trainer category, and arrived at the conclusion that the 60-series Hawk represented the best buy. According to the Venezuelan newspaper *El Diario de Caracas*, the Caracas government had reached agreement to purchase twenty-four Hawk Mark 62s at a cost of £38 million.

Unfortunately, shortly after a contract had been signed, Britain's relations with some South American countries deteriorated with the onset of the Falkland Islands crisis, and as a result of affirmed solidarity with Argentina, Venezuela decided to cancel its order for Hawks, and no Mark 62 was built.

(Shortly afterwards there were reports that Algeria also wished to purchase up to twenty-seven Hawk 60-series aircraft, but competition — political rather than operational — proved too strong, and the order did not materialise.)

ABU DHABI HAWK MARK 63

The second United Arab Emirates order for Hawks was for sixteen advanced flying/weapons training aircraft, Mark 63s, signed on 2 January 1963, this time destined for Abu Dhabi.

471

An Abu Dhabi Hawk Mark 63, photographed in 1985.

KUWAITI HAWK MARK 64

The Abu Dhabi order was particularly significant in that it came at the time the UAE concluded a contract to acquire French Mirage 2000s, and it might have been thought logical to have opted to purchase the Franco–German Alpha Jet as part of a 'package deal'. However, to have been convinced by the obvious superiority of the enhanced Hawk was to have a considerable knock-on effect, and on 31 October 1983 Kuwait placed an order for twelve Hawk Mark 64s.

Hawk Mark 64 No.145 for Kuwait, in 1986.

SAUDI HAWK MARK 65

Against a background of reports that Bahrain was about to place an initial order for four Hawk Mark 65s (negotiations which in fact fell through), the largest single Middle Eastern order to date was placed by Saudi Arabia, for thirty aircraft. On 26 September 1985 Prince Sultan bin Abdul-Aziz signed a contract which included the purchase of forty-eight Tornado strike aircraft, twenty-four Tornado fighters and thirty Pilatus PC-9 basic trainers, as well as the Hawks — the whole order being worth between £3 billion and £4 billion.

Referred to as the *Al-Yamamah* programme, the order stipulated that delivery of the Hawks must begin before the end of 1987, and the first

472

two aircraft were, indeed, handed over to the Royal Saudi Air Force in a ceremony at Dunsfold on 11 August that year. The first four Hawk Mark 65s made the 3,500 mile ferry flight to Arabia on 13 October.

In service, the Saudi flying training syllabus allowed for fast-jet student pilots to complete 100 hours' flying on the Pilatus PC-9, followed by 120 hours' advanced/weapon training on the Hawk before progressing to the Tornado.

SWISS HAWK MARK 66

The Swiss *Flugwaffe* is unique in that its flying personnel serve for annual periods, rather than for continuous terms of service. The training task is therefore rather more protracted, and one result is that the air force's training aircraft remain in service for many years. Thus the de Havilland Vampire trainer has been flying in Switzerland for more than three decades.

In 1985 the Swiss Federal Military Department conducted a competitive evaluation of the BAe Hawk, Dassault-Breguet/Dornier Alpha Jet,

Low-flying Saudi Hawk 65 No.2118 over typical home terrain. The utmost reliability demanded of the single Adour engine is hardly surprising.

the CASA C-101 and the Aermacchi MB.339, to decide on a replacement for the Vampire. By October that year the two last-named contenders had been eliminated, and during March and April 1986 flight evaluation of the Hawk and Alpha Jet was carried out.

On 14 March 1987 the Military Department announced that it was recommending purchase of the Hawk, and on 20 October an order for twenty Mark 66s, worth £167 million, was signed; it was conditional that only the first aircraft would be built and assembled in Britain, the remaining Hawks being assembled in Switzerland. Some components would also be contributed by Swiss industry.

The first Swiss Hawk was delivered by air to the Federal Aircraft

473

Factory at Emmen on 8 November (having spent several months flying in Britain with an RAF serial number, ZG974, for weapons trials). Deliveries of Swiss-assembled Hawks are scheduled to begin in 1990.

With high-visibility panels added, the Swiss Hawk 66 (ZG974) poses for the camera, complete with cannon pod.

THE HAWK 100-SERIES

In mid-1982 British Aerospace announced the Hawk 100-Series, a fully combat-capable two-seat trainer, but featuring a wide range of operational equipment and systems requiring pilot-only management when flown solo. Exploiting the five-pylon store capability, the Hawk demonstrator (formerly the Mark 50), ZA101/G-HAWK, was selected as the pre-production example, and included such equipment as a Singer Kearfott SKN-2416 inertial navigator, air data sensor pack with optical laser ranging and forward-looking infra-red (FLIR), an advanced Smiths Industries head-up display/weapon aiming computer (HUD/WAC), improved weapons management system, manual or automatic weapon release, passive warning radar, hands-on-throttle-and-stick (HOTAS) controls, full colour multi-purpose CRT in each cockpit, and provision to carry an ECM pod.

Enhanced load-carrying ability would permit carrying of up to seven 1,000 lb bombs, four of the bombs being carried on twin carriers on the inboard wing pylons. In a typical combat air patrol sortie, the Hawk 100-Series, armed with its 30 mm gun pod and two AIM-9P Sidewinder AAMs, would be able to loiter for 3 hours 30 minutes on station 160 miles from base. In another guise, ZA101 demonstrated its ability to mount a single Sea Eagle ASM, two long-range radar-guided Sky Flash AAMs and two external 100 gallon combat drop tanks.

In 1989 the Hawk 100-Series aircraft (accompanied by the single-seat Hawk 200-Series — see below) undertook a marathon tour to the Far East, flying out to attend the Australian Bicentennial Air Show at Richmond. On the 12,000-mile journey out the aircraft flew via Malta, Luxor,

Bahrain, Bombay, Calcutta, Singapore, Bali, Darwin, Townsville and Williamtown. On the return flight, the route also included Manilla, Brunei, Kuala Lumpur, Muscat, Dubai, Athens and Nice. The Hawk 100 alone performed fifty-three flying displays during the tour, which was arranged to demonstrate to a large number of potential customers the manner in which the latest two-seat variant is naturally complementary to the single-seat Hawk, and it follows that the two versions will feature together in future sales efforts.

ZA101, further modified with RWR fairing on the fin, in 1988 with under-wing bombs and centreline cannon pod.

The first fruits were reaped on 17 October 1989, when, in a government-to-government agreement, Brunei signed an order for sixteen Hawk 100-series for the Air Wing of the Royal Brunei Armed Forces, although at the time of writing the contract itself still awaits signature.

The single-seat Hawk 200, ZH200, after receiving its paint finish in June 1987.

The BAe Hawk 200-Series

The wheel turned full circle when, on 20 June 1984, British Aerospace announced that Kingston was to build a single-seat combat version of the Hawk, the Series 200. The first aircraft was to be a demonstration prototype, built at company expense as a private venture. This aircraft, ZG200, powered by an Adour 761 turbofan, was first flown by Mike Snelling on 19 May 1986, but was destroyed in an accident on 2 July in which Jim Hawkins lost his life.

A second aircraft, ZH200, with an Adour 871 turbofan giving 5,845 lb thrust, was flown by Chris Roberts on 24 April 1987, its equipment and systems standard being similar to that of the Hawk 100-series two-seater.

Although of diminutive stature, the Hawk single-seater is being offered fully compatible with a wide range of operational rôles in mind, depending on the customer's prime requirement, that is, day, night or all-weather operation. These duties include battlefield interdiction, close air support, airspace denial, long-range photographic reconnaissance, anti-shipping strike, as well as long-range deployment. For instance, in a lo-lo close air support sortie, the Hawk 200 can deliver four 1,000 lb and two 500 lb bombs with precision against a target up to 155 miles from base; in an intercept sortie with guns and AAMs, the maximum intercept radius of action at 30,000 ft is 885 miles. Maximum ferry range for long-distance deployment is no less than 2,237 miles (retaining the 190 gallon external tanks). In the anti-shipping strike rôle a Hawk 200, armed with a Sea Eagle sea-skimming anti-ship missile, could attack a ship 920 miles from base and return with ten per cent fuel reserve; weapon release could be outside the target's radar envelope. Thus a ship almost anywhere in the North Atlantic would be within range of a land-based Hawk. The Hawk 200 features in-built twin 25-, 27- or 30 mm cannon, thereby leaving the centreline attachment free to load other external ordnance.

As already stated, ZH200 accompanied the Hawk 100 demonstrator on its tour to the Far East in 1989, and it seems certain that the single-seater will also be the subject of considerable sales activity, not only among new customers, but among those already flying the two-seater, for the two aircraft, aft of the cockpit, are almost identical — providing about 80 per cent airframe component commonality, an important consideration among relatively low-budget air forces.

In full demonstration trim, ZH200 displays its ability to carry seven bombs on centreline pylon and twin underwing carriers.

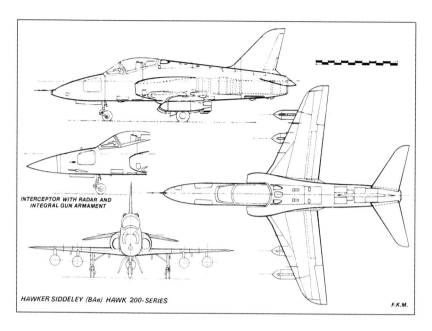

INTERCEPTOR WITH RADAR AND
INTEGRAL GUN ARMAMENT

HAWKER SIDDELEY (BAe) HAWK 200-SERIES

F.K.M.

TECHNICAL DATA FOR HAWK 200-SERIES

TYPE: Single-seat multi-rôle combat aircraft.

STRUCTURE: As for Hawk T. Mark 1 except for minor modifications to wing leading-edge aerofoil sections, single-seat configuration and strengthened landing gear.

MANUFACTURERS: British Aerospace Ltd (Kingston-upon-Thames and Dunsfold, Surrey).

POWERPLANT: One Rolls-Royce/Turboméca Adour Mk. 871 turbofan rated at 5,845 lb thrust.

DIMENSIONS: Span, 30 ft 9½ in. Overall length, 36 ft 1 in. Height, 13 ft 1 in. Wing area, 179.64 sq ft.

WEIGHTS: Empty, 8,818 lb. Max take-off 18,960 lb.

PERFORMANCE: Max speed at sea level, 648 mph; never-exceed speed at altitude, Mach 1.2; max rate of climb at sea level, 11,510 ft/min; service ceiling, 44,600 ft; range on internal fuel, 554 miles; range with max external fuel, 2,240 miles.

ARMAMENT AND SYSTEMS: Twin in-built 25-, 27- or 30 mm Aden or Mauser cannon. Stores on four underwing and centreline pylons, up to maximum of 6,800 lb, including iron bombs, cluster bombs, practice bombs, Sea Eagle ASM, Sky Flash, Sidewinder or Magic AAMs, Stingray torpedoes, ECM pods, rocket launchers, chaff dispensers, reconnaissance pack, combat drop tanks, etc. Systems options (dependent on rôle) include, Singer Kearfott SKN-2416 inertial navigator, Smiths Industries HUD/WAC, laser ranging with optional FLIR, HOTAS, IFF, passive warning radar, etc. Advanced all-weather radar, such as Ferranti Blue Fox, may be fitted as basic equipment.

477

The first development T-45A Goshawk, 162787. Note the rear lateral speed brakes and the strakes immediately above them; also the arrester hook.

British Aerospace/McDonnell Douglas T-45A Goshawk

In 1980–1 the US Navy conducted a preliminary selective evaluation from ten contenders for its VTXTS competition to decide on a replacement for the aircraft element of the then-current Navy Integrated Flight Training System (NIFTS) that had hitherto employed two aircraft, the T-2C Buckeye intermediate trainer and the TA-4J Skyhawk advanced trainer. The VTXTS programme, soon to be renamed the T-45 Training System (T45TS), culminated in a decision, announced in November 1981, to procure about 300 aircraft, evolved closely from the BAe Hawk. However, far from involving the straightforward acquisiton of an aircraft, the basis of the requirement was for a fully-integrated training system for undergraduate jet pilots, including aircraft, academics, simulators, integration system and logistics support. Apart from the overall suitability of the Hawk within the US Navy Requirement, the ready-made Memorandum of Understanding that existed between British Aerospace and McDonnell Douglas, and the fact that joint production of Harriers by the two manufacturers had been 'working' well for several years, was a potent argument in favour of the choice of the British aircraft.

Early in the competitive evaluation the Hawk demonstrator, ZA101/ G-HAWK, had paid a thirty-one-day visit to the United States, during which it flew a total of eighty-five evaluation sorties.

As originally recommended, it was intended to acquire about fifty 'dry' T-45B trainers, of which the first would fly in 1987, followed by about 250 deck-operating T-45As about two years later. This was soon altered, as the result of Senate deliberations, and the 'dry' element of the aircraft programme was abandoned, so that all 300-odd aircraft were to be equipped for deck operation.

Main assembly of the T-45A was to be undertaken at the Douglas factory at Long Beach, California, with British Aerospace working as prime subcontractor to McDonnell Douglas for the aircraft, Rolls-Royce Ltd for the Adour turbofan, and Sperry Systems for the simulators.

Go-ahead and funding for the T-45A was announced in 1984, and an engineering development contract, worth $512 million, was signed with McDonnell Douglas in May 1986. The manufacture of the aircraft is being divided equally between Britain and the United States, with the Adour engine being delivered direct to America. Production of the UK-manufactured components is centred on BAe's facilities at Samlesbury, Brough and Hamble. Brough and Kingston were involved in producing non-flying test aircraft — one for fatigue testing, the other for drop-testing, being dropped from heights of up to twelve feet to simulate a vertical velocity of 25 feet per second, representing carrier deck landings.

The navalised T-45A differs from the standard Hawk T. Mark 1 in the following respects: new main landing gear stressed to withstand sink rates of twenty-five feet per second, twin nosewheels for catapult nose-tow launch and increased-rate-of-descent landings (and improved nosewheel steering), strengthened nosewheel leg, main landing gear doors to sequence closed after wheels are locked down, twin lateral air brakes on the sides of the rear fuselage in place of the Hawk's ventral air brake, addition of arrester hook, reinforced airframe and intermediate engine casing to withstand deck landings, and cockpit instrument alterations to meet US naval requirements. A pair of NACES (Naval Aircrew Common Ejector Seats) is fitted, being based on the Martin-Baker Mark 14 seat.

In assuming the training rôle previously performed by both the Buckeye and Skyhawk, use of the T-45A alone will involve 60 per cent less fuel for the given task, thereby saving some $60 million each year, will require 25 per cent fewer flying hours to train each pilot, and will allow more than 40 per cent reduction in support personnel. The ultimate number of T-45A aircraft (renamed Goshawk in America so as to avoid confusion with the US Army Hawk missile) is, at the time of writing, planned to be 302, with $429.4 million set aside for the first twelve

The T-45A Goshawk 162787.

479

production aircraft, and $517 million announced in 1989 for the next twenty-four. When the full inventory of Goshawks has been delivered to the US Navy, together with thirty-two flight simulators and forty-nine computer-aided instructional systems, it will be possible to train 600 jet pilots each year. The entire T45TS programme is expected to cost about $4.5 billion at 1989 valuation.

The Goshawk was to enter US Navy service at NAS Kingsville, Texas, by the end of 1990, followed by NAS Meridian, Mississippi, and Chase Field, Texas. The aircraft will be based permanently ashore, being flown on to the training carrier, USS *Lexington*, for deck landings. Each aircraft is expected to make 39,000 field landings and more than 1,000 deck landings and carrier catapult take-offs during its lifetime.

The first pre-production T-45A Goshawk (162787) was rolled out at Long Beach on 16 March 1988, and made its maiden flight on 16 April, being airborne for seventeen minutes. In June that year it was joined by

As the T-45A approaches to land, the extended undercarriage shows the levered-suspension mainwheel units and twin nosewheels with towbar, while shadows emphasise the lateral strakes forward of the tailplane.

the second aircraft at Yuma, Arizona, to begin a nineteen-month flight test programme which was continued at the Navy Air Test Center, Patuxent River, Maryland, at the end of 1988.

Production Goshawks were to be powered by 5,450 lb thrust Adour F405-RR-400 turbofans, in effect a derated version of the Adour 861, but during the course of the NATC tests it was decided that the US Navy decision to derate the engine had been ill-advised owing to the greater flying weight of the Goshawk. Furthermore, some criticism of the T-45A's stall characteristics and directional stability was being voiced by Navy test pilots. The result was a decision to change to the Adour 871 engine (5,845 lb thrust) as currently fitted in the Hawk 100 and 200. To correct the stall characteristics, changes were made in the wing leading edge profile, while a six-inch fin extension as well as a pair of small ventral fins were added to improve lateral stability.

Until the effects of these improvements could be assessed in the pre-production aircraft, the US Navy deferred a go-ahead with the FY1989 funding for several months. However, despite these delays, it seems at the time of writing that the T-45A will have achieved full Service clearance before the end of 1990.

As this book went to press in December 1990 it was announced that Malaysia had signed a Contract to purchase 28 British Aerospace Hawks, comprising ten 100-Series and 18 200-Series aircraft in a defence package amounting to slightly over £400m. The aircraft will be manufactured at the British Aerospace factory at Brough, Yorkshire, final assembly and flight clearance being undertaken at Warton, Lancs. The first aircraft is scheduled to be accepted in 1993, and the final deliveries made in 1995.

SERVICE ALLOCATION AND NOTES ON INDIVIDUAL AIRCRAFT

EXPLANATORY NOTE

The following Section sets out the production and service details of each successive Hawker aircraft, type by type, with notes, where available, on each individual machine.

Each aircraft type is dealt with chronologically, but it has not always been possible, of course, to indicate the exact order in which the Contracts were executed, or the date on which each machine was completed, due in many cases to the fact that two or more production lines or factories were working simultaneously on one Contract.

It should be assumed that, unless otherwise stated, the aircraft were built by Hawker Engineering Co Ltd, or Hawker Aircraft Ltd. Where convenient, subcontracted or licence production of a Hawker design follows the Hawker production.

481

NOTES ON INDIVIDUAL AIRCRAFT

The Hawker Duiker. Three aircraft, *J6918-J6920*, designed to Air Ministry Specification D of R 3A (later changed to 10/21 and 7/22, and ordered under Contract No. 195557/21 dated 13-2-22 (superseded by No. 4501/22) to be powered by 380 h.p. Siddeley Jaguar. Only one aircraft, *J6918*, completed; first flown by F.P. Raynham, 7-23. 390 h.p. Bristol Jupiter IV fitted, late 1923. To A. & A.E.E., 12-23. To R.A.E., 15-4-24. *J6919* and *J6920* commenced but not completed. Two further aircraft, *J6995-J6996*, ordered under Contract No. 3693321/22 dated 13-1-23) but cancelled.

The Hawker Woodcock I. Three prototypes, *J6987-J6989*, to be designed to Air Ministry Specification 25/22 and ordered under Contract No. 5222/22 (superseded by Contract No. 356228/22 which reduced cover to one aircraft, *J6987*, the other two being subject to new Contract, see below). *J6987* completed with two-bay wings and 360 h.p. Siddeley Jaguar AS117A engine. To A. & A.E.E., 14-8-23. To H.G.H.E.L., 9-23. Modified tail surfaces. 390 h.p. Bristol Jupiter IV fitted under Contract No. 485021/24. To R.A.E., 21-11-24. Rebuilt to production standard. No. 3 (F) Sqn., deld 1-3-27. Force landed near Maidenhead, 31-3-27, but repaired. Force landed near Tilstock, Berks, 11-5-27. S.O.C., 1928.

The Hawker Woodcock II. One prototype (wood), *J6988*, ordered under Contract No. 422420/23 to Specification 25/22, and completed with single-bay wings and 380 h.p. Bristol Jupiter IV engine; first flown by F.P. Raynham, 8-23. Shown at R.A.F. Display, Hendon, 28-6-24 (New Type No. 2). To A. & A.E.E., 7-24, for night fighter trials. No. 56 (F) Sqn., for Service trials, 9-24. To A. & A.E.E., for armament trials, 11-24. Bristol Jupiter V engine fitted. To. A. & A.E.E., 7-25, for trials with slotted wings and cylinder helmets. Halton Stn. Flt., 1928-1929.

The Hawker Metal Woodcock. One prototype (composite wood and metal), *J6989*, struck from Contract No. 422420/23 and completed as private venture. Renamed **Heron** (see below).

The Hawker Woodcock II. First production batch of six aircraft, *J7512-J7517*, ordered under Contract No. 495946/24 to Specification 25/22. 380 h.p. Bristol Jupiter IV engines.

No. 3 (F) Sqn.: *J7512* (deld, 1-26); *J7513* (deld, 12-5-25); *J7514* (deld, 3-6-25); *J7515* (deld, 28-7-25); *J7516* (deld, 1-7-25); *J7517* (deld, 10-8-25)

No. 17 (F) Sqn.: *J7512* (deld, 27-1-28); *J7514*; *J7515*; *J7516*, *J7517*

Other duties, etc: *J7512* (trials at A. & A.E.E. with Jupiter III exhaust, 1925); *J7513* (investigation of mainspar failure at R.A.E., 1925-1928); *J7515* (King's Cup Race as *G-EBMA*, 1-7-25; force landed in bad weather near Luton and damaged; repaired); *J7516* (to C.F.S., 13-8-25); *J7517* (to A.& A.E.E., for trials with slotted wings, 1925)

The Hawker Woodcock II. Second production batch of 13 aircraft, *J7725-J7737*, ordered under Contract No. 554469/24 (Part 1) to Specification 25/22, as amended for night flying. 14th aircraft, *J7783*, added under Part 2 of this Contract. Aircraft built during 1925. 380 h.p. Bristol Jupiter IV.

No. 3 (F) Sqn.: *J7725* (deld, 8-25); *J7726* (deld, 21-8-25); *J7728* (deld, 8-25; collided with Horsley during practice for R.A.F. Display, 6-28); *J7729* (deld, 8-9-25); *J7730* (deld, 8-9-25); *J7731* (deld, 10-25); *J7732* (deld, 20-10-25); *J7733* (deld, 17-7-26); *J7734* (deld, 10-25; crashed, Upavon, 26-8-27); *J7735* (deld, 10-25; crashed during camera gun practice, 2-2-27); *J7737* (deld, 10-25); *J7783* (deld, 8-26)

No. 4 (AC) Sqn.: *J7727* (deld, 10-3-26)

No. 17 (F) Sqn.: *J7729* (deld, 1928); *J7732* (deld, 1927); *J7735* (deld, 1928)

Other duties, etc.: *J7726* (A. & G.S., 4-28); *J7733* (A. & A.E.E., 6-10-25, for exhaust trials; HCF, 24-5-28); *J7735* (HCF, 5-28).

The Hawker Woodcock II. Third production batch of 18 aircraft, *J7960-J7977*, ordered under Contract No. 626819/25 (as amended by No. 100041/26) to Specification 25/22 as amended in 1924-25. Aircraft built during 1926. 380 h.p. Bristol Jupiter IV.

No. 3 (F) Sqn.: *J7962* (deld, 1926); *J7963* (deld, 1926); *J7964* (deld, 1927); *J7973* (struck by DH.9A while taxying at Eastchurch, 25-10-26, SOC); *J7974* (deld, 1926)

No. 17 (F) Sqn.: *J7960* (deld, 12-26); *J7961* (deld, 7-26); *J7964* (deld, 12-26); *J7967* (deld, 12-26; struck by *J7976* while landing at Northolt, 25-7-27; SOC); *J7968*; *J7969* (deld, 12-26; burnt, 7-27); *J7971* (deld, 7-26); *J7972*; *J7975* (crashed and overturned, 1927); *J7976* (struck *J7967* while landing at Northolt, 25-7-27; SOC); *J7977* (deld, 1927)

Other duties, etc.: *J7964* (Andover Communications Flt., from 2-28); *J7966* (R.A.E., 7-28 to 8-28); *J7973* (A. & G.S., 9-26); *J7974* (R.A.E., trials with slotted wings, from 10-26; A. & A.E.E., 4-28 to 10-28).

The Hawker Woodcock II. Fourth production batch of 25 aircraft, *J8292-J8316*, ordered under Contract No. 709619/26 (and later modified under Contract Nos. 40182/27 and 850848/28) to Specification 25/22 as amended in 1926/27 for night flying. Aircraft built during 1926-28. 380 h.p. Bristol Jupiter IV engines.

No. 3 (F) Sqn.: *J8292* (deld, 3-27); *J8293* (deld, 12-26); *J8293* (deld, 12-26); *J8298* (deld, 12-26); *J8302* (deld, 9-27); *J8303* (deld, 10-27); *J8304; J8305* (1928); *J8316* (collided with *J7728* during practice for R.A.F. Display, 5-6-28)

No. 17 (F) Sqn.: *J8292* (collided with Siskin *J8639* while taxying, 17-7-28); *J8295* (deld, 3-28); *J8296*; *J8297* (deld, 6-27); *J8299* (deld, 4-28); *J8300* (deld, 6-27; caught fire on ground, Upavon, 5-7-27; SOC, 17-11-27); *J8305* (12-27 to 4-28); *J8306* (deld, 5-28); *J8307* (deld, 1-28); *J8311* (deld, 8-28)

Other duties, etc.: *J8295* (placed at disposal of Charles Lindbergh, 2-6-27); *J8301* (A. & G.S., 9-27 to 1-28); *J8305* (Halton Stn. Flt., 1928); *J8308* (R.A.E., 3-28; Halton Stn. Flt., 1929); *J8309* (Home Communications Flt., 6-28); *J8311* (R.A.E., 11-27 to 1-28); *J8312* (A. & A.E.E., 7-27 to 9-27; R.A.E., for cooling trials with cylinder helmets; Packing Depot, Ascot; Aircraft Depot, Aboukir, Egypt, for tropical trials, 1928); *J8313, J8314* (Duxford Stn. Flt., 1927-1928).

The Hawker Cygnet. Two private sporting aircraft, *G-EBJH* and *G-EBMB*, built and entered for the 1924 Light Aeroplane Competition at Lympne. At first *G-EBJH* was fitted with an Anzani vee twin-cylinder air-cooled engine, and *G-EBMB* with an A.B.C. Scorpion. Two years later both aircraft were fitted with 34 h.p. Bristol Cherub III twin-cylinder horizontally-opposed air-cooled engines. *G-EBMB* is now displayed in the R.A.F. Museum at Hendon.

The Hawker Hedgehog. One prototype aircraft, *N187* (also sometime registered *G-EBJN*), designed to Specification 37/22 and covered by Air Ministry Contract, retrospectively negotiated in September 1924. Subsequent Contracts covered conversion to floatplane and amphibian, and engine change from Jupiter IV to Jupiter VI.

The Hawker Hornbill. One prototype aircraft, *J7782*, built under Contract No. 532731/24 to Specification 7/24 during 1925. First flown 7-25, probably by F.P. Raynham. To R.A.E., 15-10-25. To H.G.H.E.L., 23-10-25. To A. & A.E.E., 1-12-25 to 1-26. Contract No. 783184/26 covered modifications to flying surfaces and change to 698 h.p. Napier Condor IV. First flown in this configuration, 5-26, by P.W.S. Bulman. To R.A.E., 29-6-26. R.A.F. Display, Hendon (New Type No. 5), 3-7-26. A. & A.E.E., 7-26 , for performance trials, and wing tip research. To H.G.H.E.L., 4-1-27. To R.A.E., various dates (1927-1933). Last flown, 18-5-33.

The Hawker Danecock (L.B. II Dankok). Preliminary production batch of three aircraft, *151-153*, built by H.G. Hawker Enginnering Co., Ltd., Kingston, under Conract No. 14/660/D.25, and delivered to Denmark early in 1926. Armstrong Siddeley Jaguar engines. Twelve further aircraft built during 1927-1930, *154-165*, at Danish Naval Dockyard Factory. No. *158* was later restored and preserved and remains on display in Copenhagen museum.

483

The Hawker Heron. One prototype aircraft, *J6989*, originally **Metal Woodcock**, but design developed as private venture with composite wood and metal structure. First flown in mid-1925 by F.P. Raynham. 455 h.p. Bristol Jupiter VI engine. To A. & A.E.E., 6-25. R.A.F. Display, Hendon (New Type No. *2*), 27-6-25. To A. & A.E.E. (No. 15 Sqn.), 17-12-25 to 5-27. To H.G.H.E.L., 6-27. To A. & A.E.E. (No. 22 Sqn.), 6-27 to 8-27. To H.G.H.E.L., and registered *G-EBYC* (C. of A. No. 1433, dated 21-5-28); entered for King's Cup Race, 20-7-28, but struck car before take-off and damaged. C. of A. lapsed, 20-5-29; struck off register, 1-30.

The Hawker Horsley (known initially as **Kingston**). Two prototype aircraft, *J7511* and *J7721*, designed to Specification 26/23 and ordered under Contract No. 519932/24 (and amended by No. 41042/25). 650 h.p. Rolls-Royce Condor III. *J7511*: First flight, 3-25. To A. & A.E.E. (No. 22 Sqn.), 4-5-25 for performance trials. To H.G.H.E.L., 24-7-25. To No. 11 Sqn., 31-7-25, for Service trials. Became engine test bed at Rolls-Royce Ltd.: 665 h.p. Condor IIA, 690 h.p. Condor IIIB, 380 h.p. Eagle VIII, and 810 h.p. H-10; and D. Napier & Son Ltd.: 580 h.p. Napier Lion V. Contract No. 782869/27 covered conversion to twin-float undercarriage in 1928-29. *J7721* (composite metal and wood construction): First flight, 6-12-25. To R.A.E., 14-6-26. R.A.F. Display, Hendon (New Type No. *13*), 3-7-26. To A. & A.E.E. (No. 22 Sqn.), 27-6-26 to 5-27, for performance trials.

The Hawker Horsley I and II. First production batch of 40 aircraft ordered under Contract No. 634686/25 and built to Specification 26/23 as amended by 22/25 and 23/25. Mark I (all-wood structure): *J7987-J7996*. Mark II (Composite metal and wood structure): *J7997-J8026*. Production during 1926-27. 665 h.p. Rolls-Royce Condor IIIA engines.

No. 11 (B) Sqn.: *J7990* (deld, 12-4-27); *J7996* (7-28 to 11-28); *J8000* (1-27 to 3-27); *J8001* (3-27 to 8-28); *J8002* (9-11-26 to 1-28); *J8005* (8-28 to 9-28); *J8009* (3-27 to 1928); *J8010* (10-1-27 to 6-28); *J8012* (deld, 11-3-27; crashed, 18-3-27); *J8013* (deld, 8-3-27); *J8014* (3-27 to 9-28); *J8022* (deld, 8-28); *J8023* (6-27 to 9-28).

No. 25 (F) Sqn.: J7995 (target-towing conversion; deld, 5-27)

No. 33 (B) Sqn.: *J7993* (deld, 28-8-29); *J7994* (3-12-29 to 3-30); *J7997* (1-30- to 4-30); *J8001* (9-29 to 3-30); *J8008* (8-28 to 2-30; damaged landing at Brooklands, 9-29, but repaired); *J8009* (deld 1929); *J8010* (8-29 to 3-30); *J8018* (deld 1928); *J8021*; *J8022* (8-29 to 1-30); *J8023* (1929).

No. 36 (TB) Sqn.: *J7991* (12-4-30 to 9-30); *J8001* (1930); *J8009* (deld, 1929); *J8013* (12-29 to 8-30); *J8014* (4-4-30 to 8-30); *J8015* (18-3-30 to 4-30); *J8026* (12-29 to 8-30).

No. 100 (B) Sqn.: *J7988* (22-4-27 to 5-28); *J7989* (6-27 to 9-27); *J7990* (1-6-28 to 1930); *J7991* (deld, 23-8-27; ditched in sea, 1-31); *J7992* (3-27; struck haycart during night landing at Weston Zoyland, 8-27); *J7994* (del, 3-27); *J7996* (deld, 23-5-27); *J7997* (deld, 1-27); *J7998* (3-27 to 4-27); *J7999* (deld, 5-27; damaged while landing at Kenley, 18-6-28; damaged while taxying, 24-7-28, but repaired); *J8000* (3-27 to 7-28; target towing conversion); *J8002* (1-28); *J8003* (from 6-27); *J8004* (4-27 to 1929); *J8005* (from 3-27); *J8006* (from 5-29; airman injured in accident, Gosport, 11-11-30; crashed and overturned, Donibristle, 14-3-32); *J8008* (6-30 to 8-30); *J8009* (1928; force landed at night near Buckingham, 8-11-28); *J8010* (8-31); *J8011* (1929); *J8013* (deld, 25-1-29; collided with *J8015* and crashed in Reres Wood, Leuchars, 25-11-30); *J8014* (3-29 to 5-29 and 8-30 to 2-32); *J8015* (from 8-30; collided with *J8013* and crashed in Reres Wood, Leuchars, 25-11-30); *J8016*; *J8017*; *J8020* (from 2-31); *J8023* (from 10-29); *J8024* (from 6-30); *J8025* (7-28 to 8-28); *J8026* (12-27 to 7-29 and 1-31 to 6-31).

No. 504 Sqn., SR: *J7993* (dual controls); *J7997* (1930); *J8002* (from 9-30; target towing conversion); *J8008* (1933); *J8010* (7-7-31 to 3-32); *J8011* (1933); *J8018* (3-9-28 to 1933); *J8019* (3-9-28 to 8-32; fitted with wing slats); *J8023* (from 7-32; collided with stationary Hinaidi *K1915* while taxying at Boscombe Down, 2-8-32; repaired); *J8025* (from 1930; landed on hangar roof while overshooting at Hawkinge, 7-8-33; 6 Fury fighters of No. 25 Sqn. destroyed by fire).

Night Flying Flight, Biggin Hill (renamed Anti-Aircraft Co-operation Flt. (22-10-31): *J7987* (1931-33); *J7988* (5-32 to 12-32); *J7989* (10-30 to 12-32); *J7990* (5-30 to 9-33); *J7999* (9-30 to 4-34); *J8000* (25-4-29 to 7-31); *J8002* (9-30 to 4-33); *J8004* (from 4-29).

R.A.F. College, Cranwell: *J8011* (deld, 14-6-27); *J8024* (deld, 5-33).

Other Units and duties, etc.: *J9787* (A. & A.E.E., No. 15 Sqn., performance trials, 11-26; R.A.E., 28-3-27 to 20-12-27); *J7988* (R.A.E., 22-3-27); *J7991* (R.A.E., 23-6-27); *J7995* (R.A.E., 19-10-26 to 10-3-27); *J7999* (R.A.E., 25-9-30); *J8000* (Gloster Aircraft Ltd., 1-3-29; R.A.E., 16-3-29); *J8001* (Rolls-Royce Ltd., 9-31 to 9-34; Rolls-Royce Buzzard development); *J8003* (H.G.H.E.L., 8-30; 480 h.p. Condor compression-ignition engine development); R.A.F. Display, Hendon, New Type No. *12*, 24-6-33); *J8006* (Torpedo Bomber prototype. A. & A.E.E., 8-26; Torpedo Development Flt., Gosport, 1-27 to 3-27; R.A.F. Display, New Type No. *7*, 2-7-27; R.A.F. Gosport, 9-29 to 5-30); *J8015* (A. & A.E.E., No. 22 Sqn., 7-28).

The Hawker Horsley II. Second production batch of 25 aircraft, *J8597-J8621* (all composite metal and wood construction), designed to Specification 26/23, as amended by 23/25 and 24/25, under Contract No. 737401/26 (later No. 842148/28 for modifications). Production during 1927-28. 665 h.p. Rolls-Royce Condor IIIA engines.

No. 11 (B) Sqn.: *J8597* (from 6-28); *J8598* (deld, 2-6-27; until 2-28); *J8999* (6-28 to 11-28); *J8600* (5-28); *J8603* (12-27); *J8605* (6-28); *J8610* (8-28); *J8616* (1928); *J8621* (deld, 19-1-28, until 8-28).

No. 33 (B) Sqn.: *J8597* (from 6-28); *J8599* (11-29 to 3-30); *J8602* (from 11-29); *J8605* (12-28 to 11-29).

No. 36 (TB) Sqn.: *J8601* (deld, 7-5-30); *J8602* (deld, 6-30); *J8618* (c. 1930); *J8620* (with Leopard I engine for trials, 1930)

No. 100 (B) Sqn.: *J8597* (8-30); *J8599* (17-3-31 to 12-32); *J8600* (7-28 to 1-30; slotted wings); *J8601* (from 5-31; crashed, 1932); *J8602* (2-31 to 8-32); *J8604* (crashed near Donibristle, 12-2-32); *J8605* (6-31 to 5-32); *J8609* (9-30 to 5-31); *J8610* (2-29 to 1-33); *J8614* (12-3-31 to 6-32); *J8615* (2-31 to 21-33); *J8616* (11-28 to 2-33); *J8617* (various periods between 6-28 and 8-30; aircraft taxied away while unmanned and damaged, 1-11-28); *J8618* (1-29); *J8619* (2-7-28 to 12-29); *J8620* (Service trials with Leopard IIIA engine, 1931); *J8621* (1929).

No. 504 Sqn., SR: *J8605* (1932); *J8609* (1932-33); *J8613* (8-29 to 1-33); *J8614* (1929; slotted wings); *J8617* (from 12-30; crashed, 5-31); *J8618* (1929); *J8619* (deld, 27-1-30; struck fishing boat on Lough Neagh, Co. Antrim, 18-5-31, and crashed).

Night Flying Flight, Biggin Hill (renamed Anti-Aircraft Co-operation Flt. (22-10-31): *J8601* (1928; aircraft crashed in forced landing at Watchet, Somerset, following carburettor icing, 28-6-29; aircraft repaired); *J8602* (aircraft overturned in night landing at Biggin Hill, 8-4-29; repaired); *J8603* (from 3-28; struck by Moth K1210 on ground at Biggin Hill, 4-11-30; repaired); *J8604* (from 11-27; struck two Bulldogs, *J9569* and *J9575* of No. 3 Sqn., while landing at Biggin Hill, 23-7-29; aircraft rebuilt).

Long Distance Aircraft: *J8607* (Flt. Lt. C.R. Carr and Flt. Lt. L.E.M. Gillam took off at Cranwell for a non-stop flight to India at 10.38 hr on 20-5-27, but force landed 45 miles south of Bandar Abbas in Persian Gulf at 21.08 hrs on 21-5-27 having covered 3,419 miles). *J8608* (in further attempts to fly non-stop to India, Flt. Lt. Carr and Flt. Lt. P.H. Mackworth left Cranwell on 16-6-27 but force landed at Martlesham with leaking coolant. On 2-8-27 Flt. Lt. Carr and Flt. Lt. E.C. Dearth left Cranwell but force landed in River Danube at Sommeberg). Both aircraft S.O.C.

Other Units and Duties, etc.: *J8597* (No. 1 F.T.S., 8-27); *J8606* (entered by H.G.H.E.L. in King's Cup Race as No. *7*, 30-7-27, finishing 6th; converted to Special Service Horsley; served with Special Duties Flight between 5-6-30 and c.5-33; smoke screen trials, R.A.E., 5-5-33); *J8611* (Second Merlin test bed, Rolls-Royce Ltd., 1935; first flight with Merlin E, 4-36; also flew with Merlin F and G, and Mark II; last flown, 7-3-38); *J8612* (trials with Condor IIIB, 1928; seaplane trials at M.A.E.E., Felixstowe, 8-33); *J8615* (Torpedo

Development Flt., Gosport, 2-31 to 1-33); *J8620* (Armstrong Siddeley Leopard engine test bed to Spec. 17/27; flew with Leopard I, II, III and IIIA, 1927-1933; development of Junkers Jumo IV engine, 3-33 to 13-4-35)

The Hawker Metal Horsley. One prototype, *J8932*, ordered under Contract No. 707158/26 and built during 1926-27 to employ all-metal primary sructure throughout. 665 h.p. Rolls-Royce Condor IIIA engine. First flight, c.4-27, flown by P.W.S. Bulman. To A. & A.E.E., 5-27, for performance and handling trials. No. 100 (B) Sqn., 3-28 to 5-28 for Service trials. To H.G.H.E.L., 3-29, for conversion to 812 h.p. Rolls-Royce H.10 engine under Contract No. 963090/29. To A. & A.E.E. (No. 15 Sqn.) for performance trials with bombs and torpedo, 4-30 to 12-30. To R.A.E., 4-31; crashed at Farnborough, 4-5-31.

The Hawker Horsley II (Torpedo Bomber). Third production batch of 12 aircraft, *S1236-S1247*, ordered under Contract No. 769876/27 and built during 1927-28. Provision for Admiralty Mark VIII 18-inch torpedo. 665 h.p. Rolls-Royce Condor IIIA engines.

No. 36 (TB) Sqn. (Coastal Defence Torpedo Flight until 1-10-28): *S1236* (3-29 to 9-30); *S1237* (8-8-28 to 9-30); *S1238* (from 9-28); *S1239* (8-28 to 8-30); *S1240* (11-28 to 9-30); *S1241* (1-29 to 3-30); *S1242* (5-29 to 5-30); *S1243* (3-29 to 8-30); *S1244* (from 2-29; crashed in Firth of Forth, 18-4-29, during torpedo drop); *S1245* (from 5-29; crashed in Firth of Forth, east of Forth Bridge, 28-10-29); *S1246* (7-29 to 9-30).

No. 100 (TB) Sqn.: *S1236* (10-31 to 6-32); *S1237* (from 1-31); *S1238* (from 1-31); *S1239* (from 1-31); *S1241* (2-31 to 2-33); *S1242* (from 6-31); *S1243* (1-31 to 1-33); *S1246* (1-31 to 5-31); *S1247* (1-31 to 10-32).

Other Units and Duties, etc.: *S1236* (R.A.E., 20-3-28; A. & A.E.E., 7-28, performance and torpedo trials; Torpedo Development Flt., Gosport, 24-8-28 to 11-28; Anti-aircraft Co-operation Flt., Biggin Hill, 7-33 to 2-34); *S1237* (No. 504 Sqn., SR); *S1238* (R.A.E., 6-5-30); *S1242* (R.A.E., 30-12-31); *S1243* (R.A.F. Gosport, 2-33 to 4-33); *S1247* (fitted initially with twin-float undercarriage; seaplane trials, M.A.E.E., Felixstowe, 10-29. Wheel undercarriage fitted, 1930; aircraft collided with Virginia *K2650* of No. 10 Sqn. while taxying at Catfoss, 31-5-33).

The Hawker Horsley II (Torpedo Bomber). Fourth production batch of 18 aircraft, *S1436-S1453*, ordered under Contract No. 968745/29 and built during 1930. 665 h.p. Rolls-Royce Condor IIIB engines. Two aircraft, *S1452* and *S1453*, later converted for target towing.

No. 36 (TB) Sqn.: *S1437* (deld, 11-8-30; shipped in ss. *City of Barcelona* to Far East, 8-9-30; arrived Singapore, 17-12-30; aircraft "*U*"; crashed in Johore Straits, Malaya, 25-4-33); *S1438* (deld, 12-8-30; shipped in ss. *City of Barcelona* to Far East, 8-9-30; arrived Singapore, 9-12-30; aircraft "*B*"; crashed on take-off, 29-5-33); *S1438* (deld, 18-8-30; shipped in ss. *City of Barcelona* to Far East, 8-9-30; arrived Singapore, 9-12-30; aircraft "*C*"; served on squadron until 3-34); *S1440* (shipped to Far East in ss. *City of Barcelona*; No. 36 Sqn., from 17-12-30, aircraft "*D*"; served on squadron until 10-33); *S1441* (shipped to Far East in ss. *City of Barcelona*; No. 36 Sqn., 12-12-30; crashed and overturned during landing at Penang, 8-6-35); *S1442* (shipped to Far East in ss. *City of Barcelona*; No. 36 Sqn., 12-30; aircraft "*O*"; remained on squadron until 5-35); *S1443* (shipped to Far East in ss. *City of Barcelona*; No. 36 Sqn., 12-30; aircraft "*M*"; remained on squadron until 9-33); *S1444* (shipped to Far East in ss. *City of Barcelona*; aircraft crashed in mangrove swamp on Pulau Khatib Bangsu island, Johore Strait, 17-2-31); *S1445* (from 1-31; ditched in sea during torpedo drop, 25-8-33); *S1446* (2-31 to 5-34; aircraft "*W*"); *S1447* (3-31 to 9-34); *S1448* (3-31 to 11-32); *S1449* (from 3-31; crashed into sea during mock attack on ships, 2-12-32); *S1450* (aircraft "*X*"; 12-31 to 2-33); *S1451* (aircraft "*C*"; 1-33 to 11-33); *S1452* (target tug; No. 36 Sqn., C Flight, 24-2-32 to 1-35); *S1453* (target tug; 24-2-32 to 6-35).

No. 100 (TB) Sqn.: *S1439* (12-33); *S1450* (1933);

Other Units and Duties, etc.: *S1436* (Torpedo Development Flt., Gosport, 11-30; A. & A.E.E., performance trials, 9-31 to 7-32; R.A.E., 10-7-35; became first Horsley Merlin test bed. Rolls-Royce Ltd. Merlin C, first flight 21-12-35; Merlin F and G, 1936-37; Merlin X, first flight, 7-9-37. Withdrawn from use, 1938); *S1452* (Condor III test bed, 1930; target towing winch trial installation, A. & A.E.E., 1-31); *S1453* (R.A.E., 6-3-31).

The Hawker Horsley II (Torpedo Bomber). Fifth production batch of 18 aircraft, *S1597-S1614*, ordered under Contract No. 84220/31 and built during 1931-32. 665 h.p. Rolls-Royce Condor IIIB. One aircraft, *S1610*, later converted for target towing.

    No. 36 (TB) Sqn.: *S1597* (12-32; force landed following engine failure, ran into stream and overturned, Paya Legar, Malaya, 15-1-34); *S1598* (12-33 to 9-34); *S1598* (12-33 to 9-34); *S1599* (2-32; crashed, Port Swettenham, 23-1-33); *S1600* (aircraft "*O*", 3-32 to 6-33); *S1601* (8-32 to 11-33 and 6-35; aircraft "*P*"; crashed into sea during bombing practice near Singapore, 13-6-35); *S1602* (1934); *S1603* (aircraft "*R*", 9-34 to 4-35); *S1604* (Aircraft "*P*", 1936); *S1605* (1934; crashed in storm on Pulan Butang island, 28-6-34); *S1606*; *S1607* (aircraft "*V*", 9-34 to 6-35); *S1608* (10-34 to 6-35); *S1610* (9-35, target tug); *S1613* (aircraft "*U*", 4-35 to 6-35); *S1614* (10-33; suffered engine failure and ditched off Pulan Sungongkong, Malaya, 27-11-34; aircraft salvaged but S.O.C.)

    No. 100 (TB) Sqn.: *S1601* (taxied into Vildebeest *K2932* at Singapore, 12-6-35, and slightly damaged; lost the following day with No. 36 Sqn., see above); *S1602* (12-33 to 1-34); *S1606*; *S1608*; *S1610* (target tug; 3-36 to 5-36).

    Other Units and Duties, etc: *S1614* (A. & A.E.E. (No. 15 Sqn.), performance trials, 5-32).

The Hawker Greek Horsley. Six aircraft built for the Royal Hellenic Naval Air Service in 1927 and delivered in 1928. Based at Tatoi (one aircraft being converted for V.I.P. transport duties). Composite wood and metal construction. Provision for British Admiralty Mark VIII 18-inch torpedo.

The Hawker Dantorp. Two aircraft *201* and *202*, ordered by the Danish Goverment in 1930 and delivered in 1932. Powered by Armstrong Siddeley Leopard II engines, later replaced by Leopard IIIs. Interchangeable wheel and float undercarriage (both delivered). In landplane configuration used for torpedo carrying; later both aircraft equipped with floats and embarked in naval vessels for catapult operations.

The Hawker Hawfinch. One prototype aircraft, later serialled *J8776*. Commenced as private venture but taken up by Air Ministry and ordered under Contract No. 755752/27. First flown with 455 h.p. Bristol Jupiter VI, 3-27. 450 h.p. Jupiter VII fitted, 4-27. To A. & A.E.E., 6-27 to 9-27, for performance trials (deck landing trials aboard H.M.S. *Furious*, 15-7-27 to 25-7-27); Service trials with No. 1 Sqn. (from 3-5-28); No. 23 Sqn. (6-28). R.A.F. Display, Hendon, 30-6-28 (New Type No. *3*); Service trials with No. 41 Sqn., 7-28. Fitted with single-bay wings and float undercarriage under Contract No. 887001/28; M.A.E.E., type assessment, 1928. Wheel gear and two-bay wings replaced, and Armstrong Siddeley Jaguar V engine fitted. (Registration *G-AAKH* allocated but not taken up, 24-7-29). Tests at R.A.E. with cambered aerofoil section on upper wing, 7-29. A. & A.E.E., 2-30. R.A.E., 20-5-31. A. & A.E.E. (No. 22 Sqn.), 11-33 to 1-34.

The Hawker Harrier. One prototype, *J8325*, to Air Ministry Specification 23/25, ordered under Contract No. 716898/26 and built between 9-26 and 1/27. First flight, with geared 583 h.p. Bristol Jupiter VIII, by P.W.S. Bulman, 2-27. To A. & A.E.E., 11-27 and 7-28 for performance and load tests. Contract No. 836740/28 covered conversion to torpedo bomber. To A. & A.E.E., 1-29, for further load and handling tests. Contract No. 898311/29 covered modifications as engine test bed. To Bristol Engine Co., Ltd., Filton, 1929. Fitted with 870 h.p. Bristol Hydra double-octagon engine, and 495 h.p. Bristol Orion engine, 1-30 to 2-33.

The Hawker 12/26 Hart. One prototype, *J9052*, designed to Air Ministry Specification 12/26 as a general purpose light day bomber and ordered under Contract No. 762629/27. Construction started in October 1937 and continued to May 1928. First flight by P.W.S. Bulman, 6-28; 490 h.p. Rolls-Royce F. XIB fitted intially. To A. & A.E.E. (No. 22 Sqn.) for preliminary trials,

10-28 to 1-29. Returned to H.G.H.E.L. for installation of Rolls-Royce Kestrel IB engine. To No. 12 (B) Sqn., Andover, for Service trials, 22-2-29; to No. 100 (B) Sqn., Bicester, 5-3-29. Modified to **Naval Hart** to Specification O.22/26 with 525 h.p. Kestrel IV. To A. & A.E.E. (No. 22 Sqn.) for preliminary assessment with fixed wings, 12-29. To No. 405 Flt., H.M.S. *Furious*, for deck-landing trials, 1-30. To H.G.H.E.L. for folding wings and jury struts, c.3-30. To R.A.E., 10-7-30, for catapult tests (first launch, 2-8-30). To H.G.H.E.L. for enlarged fin and rudder, 10-30. Twin-float undercarriage, 12-30. To M.A.E.E., Felixstowe, 12-30. Accompanied No. 407 Flt. to British sales exhibition, Buenos Aires, 1931. Crashed at Brooklands, 9-5-31, due to crossed control cables, and S.O.C.

The Hawker Hart I. First production batch of 15 aircraft, *J9933-J9947*, designed to Specification 9/29, and ordered under Contract No. 922931/29. Referred to as "Service Development Aircraft" and intended to equip a single Squadron (No. 33) for protracted Service trials. All aircraft fitted initially with 525 h.p. Rolls-Royce Kestrel IB engines; some later replaced by Kestrel IS. Batch built between 6-29 and 2-30.

No. 18 (B) Sqn.: *J9933* (trials with experimental cockpit canopy, from 9-12-32); *J9934* (from 9-11-31); *J9937* (dual control; from 1-36; force landed following engine failure and crashed, 12-3-36); *J9942* (from 24-3-32); *J9943* (from 24-3-32); *J9944* (from 24-3-32); *J9945* (from 24-3-32); J9946 (from 29-10-31).

No. 33 (B) Sqn.: *J9933* (trials with experimental cockpit canopy, 20-9-32); *J9934* (from 15-3-30); *J9935* (from 25-2-30); *J9936* (from 27-2-30); *J9937* (25-2-30 to 5-31); *J9938* (from 28-2-30); *J9939* (5-3-30 to 10-31); *J9940* (1-3-30 to 10-31); *J9941* (15-3-30 to 10-31); *J9942* (from 8-4-30); *J9943* (from 22-3-30); *J9944* (29-4-30 to 2-32); *J9945* (4-5-30 to 2-32); *J9946* (dual control aircraft; 8-5-30 tp 9-30).

No. 57 (B) Sqn.: *J9935* (10-31 to 5-33); *J9936* (from 10-31 and from 4-33); *J9939* (10-31 to 11-33); *J9940* (from 10-31); *J9941* (from 10-31).

Ground Instruction Machines: *J9933* (became *1120M*, 27-8-38, No. 2 S. of T.T.); *J9936* (became *606M*, 7-2-34, No. 1 S. of T.T.); *J9942* (became *610M*, 7-2-34, No. 1 S. of T.T.); *J9945* (became *607M*, 7-2-34, No. 1 S. of T.T.); *J9946* (became *616M*, 7-5-34, No. 1 S. of T.T.).

Other Units and Duties: *J9933* (Became **Demon** prototype to Spec. G.15/30. A. &.A.E.E., 17-7-31; H.A.L. fitted twin Darne machine guns under Contract No. 229414/33 for comparative armament trials, A. & A.E.E., 19-9-33. Trial installations of various gun mountings and turrets, 1935-1936); *J9938* (School of Photography Flt., 1-4-30. Service trials with Nos. 2 and 16 Sqns. for suitability in army co-operation rôle, from 18-7-30); *J9946* (flying demonstration by H.G.H.E.L. at Brussels meeting, 19-8-30); *J9947* (prepared for tropical trials in India. To No. 39 Sqn., Risalpur, 1930; destroyed in hangar fire at Johore, 31-3-33).

The Hawker Hart I. Four experimental Hart airframes, covered by private contracts or Works Orders, used principally for engine test and development, and general demonstration. Completed in 1930-31.

G-ABMR: Originally covered by Contract No. 922931 and laid down as the thirteenth airframe in that production batch, but subsequently completed under Works Order No. 214/30 as a Company demonstrator. Displayed at Paris in 1931 and 1932. Powered in turn by Kestrel IB, IS, IIMS, X, XDR, XVI and XVI(Special) engines. Used as photographer's aircraft, 1937-39 and 1944-46; also as pilot's taxi for delivery pilots during the Second World War. Raced in Company's colours, 1948. Suffered engine failure and forced landing, 1956. Repaired and retained civil registration *G-ABMR* (while also displaying various spurious military serial numbers for demonstration purposes, e.g. *J9933* in 1959. Aircraft preserved in R.A.F. Museum, Hendon, with Kestrel XVI (Special).

G-ABTN: Completed under Works Order 217/30 as a Company demonstrator and engine test bed. Fitted with Bristol Jupiter XFAM engine in 1932 and a Bristol Pegasus IIM2 shortly after. In the same year the aircraft suffered engine failure over the English Channel while returning from the Paris Air Show, and was lost.

K1102: Built to meet an order placed by Rolls-Royce Ltd., and subsequently covered by Air Ministry Contract (No. not known), to undertake flight test of various Kestrels with evaporative cooling. Aircraft completed in August 1930 and delivered to R.A.E. in October. Later fitted by H.G.H.E.L. with rudimentary cockpit enclosure.

Unregistered aircraft: Private venture installation of Armstrong Siddeley Panther MS engine. First flown, 21-5-31.

The Hawker Hart I. Second production batch of 32 aircraft, *K1416-K1447*, built by H.G. Hawker Engineering Co. Ltd., Kingston and Brooklands, to Specification 9/29 (as amended) under Contract No. 26275/30. Rolls-Royce Kestrel IB engines. Production between 11-30 and 1-31.

No. 12 (B) Sqn.: *K1419, K1420, K1421* (SOC., 30-11-33); *K1422, K1423, K1424* (SOC., 11-8-31); *K1425* (SOC, 17-7-33); *K1426, K1427, K1428, K1429* (SOC, 3-11-33); *K1430, K1431* (SOC, 2-10-35); *K1432* (SOC, 1-12-33); *K1433, K1434, K1435* (SOC, 6-8-35); *K1439, K1440, K1441, K1442-K1447*.

No. 18 (B) Sqn.: *K1416, K1423, K1433, K1434*

No. 33 (B) Sqn.: *K1430, K1431* (SOC, 2-10-35); *K1432* (SOC, 1-12-33); *K1433, K1434, K1435* (SOC, 6-8-35).

No. 57 (B) Sqn.: *K1422, K1426, K1446, K1447*.

Ground Instruction Machines: *K1416* (became *1369M*, 3-39); *K1419* (became *1031M*, 1-37); *K1422* (became *705M*, 8-35); *K1426* (became *2310M*, 10-40); *K1427* (became *608M*, 12-33); *K1430* (became *609M*, 2-34); *K1433* (became *712M*, 9-35); *K1434* (became *877M*, 7-36); *K1436* (became *1367M*); *K1437* (became *595M*, 10-33); *K1439* (became *917M*, 12-36); *K1443* (became *611M*, 2-34); *K1444* (became *918M*, 12-36); *K1445* (became *1040M*, 2-38); *K1446* (became *2267M*, 8-40).

Other Units and duties, etc.: *K1416* (A. & A.E.E.; R.A.E.); K1417 (No. 39 Sqn., Risalpur, India; crashed 12 miles west of Dira Dun, 16-3-36); *K1418* (No. 11 Sqn., Risalpur, India; crashed during forced landing near Akora, 11-2-38); *K1419* (School of Photography); *K1420* (Nos. 602 and 609 Sqns., A.A.F.; to South African Air Force, 5-3-38); *K1423* (after service with No. 18 Sqn., went on to Nos. 605, 500 and 503 Sqns., No. 5 ERFTS, and No. 2 FTS; SOC, 6-40); *K1426* (after service with No. 57 Sqn., went to R.A.F. College, Cranwell, and No. 609 Sqn.); *K1428* (after service with No. 12 Sqn., went on to R.A.F. Andover, No. 17 (F) Sqn., and No. 500 Sqn.; SOC, 24-9-36); *K1436* (R.A.F. Kenley; R.A.E.); *K1437* (R.A.F. Kenley; HAL); *K1438* (became **Audax prototype**; A. & A.E.E., R.A.E.; used for Kestrel development; SOC, 4-12-39); *K1439* (R.A.F. Kenley); *K1440* (R.A.F. Kenley, R.A.F. Andover, R.A.F. Upper Heyford. SOC, 26-11-35); *K1441* (R.A.F. Kenley); *K1442* (Cambridge University Air Squadron; R.A.F. Northolt. SOC, 28-9-40); *K1445* (R.A.F. Kenley). K1446 (after service with No. 57 Sqn., went on to No. 142 Sqn.; R.A.F. Andover (Group Pool); *K1447* (after service with No. 57 Sqn., went on to No. 503 Sqn., and No. 9 ERFTS. SOC, 6-39).

The Hawker Hart Trainer Prototype. One aircraft, *K1996*, modified from the second production **Audax** initially as a private venture and subsequently covered by Contract No. 1290218/31. Rolls-Royce Kestrel IB. First flight with dual controls, 20 April 1932, flown by P.E.G. Sayer at Brooklands. Subsequently flown at A. & A.E.E., C.F.S., Royal Air Force College, Cranwell, and R.A.E. Ultimately became Ground Instruction Machine, *1141M*, 10-38.

The Hawker Hart Fighter. Preliminary batch of six aircraft, *K1950-K1955*, ordered under Contract No. 56338/30 to Specification 15/30 for Service evaluation as two-seat fighter. Direct development of Hart *J9933* as modified. First flight by *K1950*, 22-6-31, P.E.G. Sayer. Rolls-Royce Kestrel IIS engines.

No. 23 (F) Sqn.: *K1950* (SOC, 19-4-35); *K1951, K1952, K1953* (SOC, 20-3-33); *K1954* (became Ground Instruction Machine, *916M*, 11-36); *K1955*.

No. 65 (F) Sqn.: *K1951* (Crashed and SOC, 4-7-35); *K1952* (SOC, 2-7-36); *K1954*.

Other Units and duties, etc.: *K1950* (A. & A.E.E., performance trials, 7-31); *K1952* (No. 41 (F) Sqn.)

The Hawker Hart (India). First production batch of 50 aircraft, *K2083-K2132*, built by H.G. Hawker Engineering Co. Ltd., under Contract No. 102035/31 to Air Ministry Specification 9/31. Built between September 1931 and April 1932. Rolls-Royce Kestrel IB. First flight by *K2083*, 7 September 1931, P.E.G. Sayer.

No. 11 (B) Sqn.: *K2085, K2088, K2089, K2091, K2092, K2094, K2095, K2100, K2102, K2103, K2104, K2106, K2107, K2108* (crashed on Peshawar bombing range, 27-7-37); *K2109, K2110, K2111, K2112, K2113, K2115* (crashed at Mardan, 23-7-38); *K2116, K2117, K2118* (crashed on landing, Mergui, Burma, 7-2-34); *K2119, K2121, K2122* (destroyed by fire, 11-8-38); *K2126, K2132* (crashed approaching to land at Risalpur, 20-6-38).

No. 39 (B) Sqn.: *K2085, K2086* (crashed and SOC, 23-4-36); *K2087, K2088, K2089, K2090, K2091, K2092, K2093, K2096, K2097, K2098, K2099, K2100, K2101, K2104, K2105, K2106, K2110, K2113, K2114, K2115, K2116, K2118, K2119, K2120, K2122, K2123, K2124, K2126, K2128, K2129* (crashed while landing, Chakala, 22-5-36); *K2131*.

No. 60 (GP) Sqn.: *K2111, K2112, K2113, K2117, K2121, K2128, K2131*.

No. 1 SFTS (India): *K2084* (SOC, 30-11-43); *K2088* (crashed during forced landing, Lalru, 19-3-41); *K2094* (SOC, 30-11-43); *K2096* (SOC, 6-7-44); *K2097* (SOC, 6-7-44); *K2098* (SOC, 30-11-43); *K2099* (SOC, 17-7-42); *K2100* (SOC, 8-11-43); *K2102* (SOC, 15-11-39); *K2104*; *K2105* (crashed on Shahbad bombing range, 22-11-41); *K2106*; *K2109* (crashed near Ambala, 6-8-42); *K2111*; *K2112* (SOC, 6-7-44); *K2113* (SOC, 6-7-44); *K2114* (crashed 8 miles NE of Ambala, 3-8-42); *K2119* (aircraft blown away in dust storm, Ambala, 25-5-42); *K2120* (SOC, 8-11-43); *K2121* (SOC, 6-7-44); *K2123*; *K2124* (crashed during forced landing, Ambala, 23-1-43); *K2125* (SOC, 6-7-44); *K2130* (crashed during forced landing, Toda, 10-7-42); *K2131*.

No. 1 Armament Training Unit, India: *K2083* (crashed while landing at Peshawar, 19-5-42); *K2091* (crashed while landing at Bairagarh, 9-11-42); *K2104* (crashed while landing at Bairagarh, 23-3-43); *K2111* (SOC, 30-11-43); *K2116* (SOC, 6-7-44); *K2117* (wrecked in gale, Bairagarh); *K2126* (crashed while landing at Peshawar, 23-5-42); *K2131* (SOC, 6-7-44).

Other Units and duties, etc.: *K2083* (A. & A.E.E., Handling and performance trials, 1931); *K2084* (A. & A.E.E.); *K2085* (No. 17 (F) Sqn.); *K2087* (Air Depot, Drigh Road; collided with Wapiti while landing at Drigh Road, 11-10-38); *K2093* (No. 2 Flt., IAF.; crashed at sea off Vesova, 25-10-42); *K2095* (Bengal Communications Flt.); *K2100* (No. 151 OTU; No. 319 MU); *K2103* (No. 1 Flt., IAF.; crashed at Tanjore, 8-10-41); *K2106* (ARSC, Bangalore; crashed during forced landing at Nolus, Mysore, 15-6-42); *K2116* (No. 2 Flt., IAF.); *K2123* (No. 101 Flt.; crashed into sea off Chambaranab, 20-5-42); *K2125* (Air Depot, Drigh Road).

The Hawker Hart (India). Seven replacement aircraft built by Hawker Aircraft Ltd., to Spec. 12/33. The first two aircraft, *K3921* and K3922, covered by Contract No. 265676/33, were built early in 1934 and delivered 5-34. Rolls-Royce Kestrel IB engines. The other five, *K8627-K8631*, covered by Contract No. 440876/35, were built in 1937 and delivered 6-37. Rolls-Royce Kestrel V engines.

No. 11 (B) Sqn.: *K3921, K3922*

No. 39 (B) Sqn.: *K3921*, K3922, *K9627, K8628* (crashed, 19-12-40); *K8629, K8630, K8631*.

No. 1 SFTS (India): *K3921* (SOC, 6-7-44), *K3922, K8627* (crashed near Ambala, 8-9-42); *K8629* (SOC, 30-11-43); *K8630*; *K8631* (SOC, 6-7-44).

Other Units: *K3922* (overturned on landing at Bairagarh, 14-7-42); *K8630* (No. 308 MU. SOC, 6-7-44).

The Hawker Hart Bomber and Hart (C). Third production batch of 50 aircraft, *K2424-K2473*, built by H.G. Hawker Engineering Co. Ltd., to Specification 9/29 (as amended), under Contract No. 117876/31. Four aircraft modified by Home Aircraft Depot for Communications duties, by removal of armament and bomb gear, for use by No. 24 (Communications) Sqn. Rolls-Royce Kestrel IB engines (some later replaced by Kestrel Vs, VDRs and Xs). Built between 2-32 and 5-32.

No. 12 (B) Sqn.: *K2425* (suffered collision in cloud near Andover and crashed, 18-7-32); *K2426*; *K2427*; *K2428*; *K2444*; *K2463*; *K2473*.

No. 18 (B) Sqn.: *K2430* (SOC, 17-7-35); *K2431*; *K2432* (SOC, 6-9-34); *K2439*; *K2440*; *K2441*; *K2445*; *K2450*; *K2451* (collided with Hart *K2441* while taking off at Bircham Newton, 5-5-36); *K2452*; *K2453* (crashed while landing, 23-5-35); *K2454*; *K2461*; *K2462*; *K2464*; *K2468*.

No. 24 (C) Sqn.: *K2452*; *K2455* (aircraft stalled and crashed on Scarborough promenade while avoiding cliffs in cloud, 8-8-38); *K2456* (crashed in bad visibility, 25-6-35).

No. 33 (B) Sqn.: *K2429*; *K2431*; *K2436* (SOC, 30-7-35); *K2437*; *K2438*; *K2439*; *K2440*; *K2442*; *K2443*; *K2455*; *K2459*; *K2460*; *K2461*; *K2462*.

No. 57 (B) Sqn.: *K2429*; *K2435*; *K2446*; *K2447*; *K2448*; *K2457*; *K2458*; *K2459*; *K2464*; *K2465*; *K2466*; *K2467*.

No. 503 Sqn., SR: *K2428* (SOC, 27-9-38); *K2447*; *K2448* (crashed during practice force landing near Waddington, 12-10-36); *K2450*; *K2457* (SOC, 8-10-36); *K2459*.

No. 605 Sqn., AAF: *K2435*; *K2439*; *K2452*; *K2458*; *K2459*; *K2461*; *K2465*, *K2467*.

No. 1 F.T.S.: *K2435*; *K2439*; *K2452*; *K2458* (crashed during forced landing, Llangibby, 6-10-38); *K2461*; *K2465*; *K2467*.

Supplied to South African Air Force: *K2439* (15-4-37); *K2446* (9-3-38); *K2462* (2-3-39); *K2463* (3-1-38); *K2465* (4-39); *K2469* (1-4-39); *K2471* (21-4-39); *K2472* (21-4-39); *K2473* (3-1-38).

Ground Instruction Machines: *K2426* (became *993M*, 10-37); *K2427* (became *1032M*, 1-38); *K2429* (became *889M*, 8-36); *K2431* (became *888M*, 9-36); *K2434* (became *1745M*, 11-39); *K2437* (became *599M*, 11-33); *K2438* (became *652M*, 6-35); *K2440* (became *878M*, 7-36); *K2441* (became *887M*, 9-36); *K2442* (became *932M*, 1-37); *K2443* (became *651M*, 6-35); *K2444* (became *2188M*, 8-40); *K2445* (became *879M*, 8-36); *K2450* (became *880M*, 7-36); *K2454* (became *709M*, 9-35); *K2456* (became *775M*); *K2458* (became *2195M*); *K2459* (became *2186M*, 8-40); *K2461* (became *1502M*, 5-39); *K2464* (became *695M*, 9-35); *K2467* (became *1607M*, 7-39); *K2468* (became *653M*, 6-35); *K2470* (became *1497M*, 5-39).

Other Units and duties, etc.: *K2424* (A. & A.E.E., performance trials. No. 610 Sqn.; crashed at Arley, Nuneaton, Warwicks, 6-2-38); *K2428* (after service with No. 12 Sqn., went on to R.A.F. Andover, R.A.F. Upper Heyford); *K2433* (No. 1 Group Pool; No. 11 Group Pool; Northolt Stn. Flt.; crashed during forced landing, 11-8-36); *K2434* (R.A.F. Kenley. Withdrawn from Service to become Napier Dagger test bed; R.A.E.); *K2435* (No. 1 Ground Defence Gunners' School; Service Ferry Pilots' Pool); *K2437* (No. 607 Sqn., A.A.F.); *K2439* (No. 3 F.T.S.; No. 15 (B) Sqn.; No. 501 (B) Sqn., SR); *K2442* (No. 40 (B) Sqn.; R.A.F. Bircham Newton); *K2444* (Andover Stn. Flt. ; R.A.F. Wyton); *K2446* (No. 2 Coastal Defence Flt.; No. 609 Sqn., A.A.F.); *K2452* (No. 2 Air Armament School; R.A.F. Bircham Newton; No. 10 F.T.S.; R.A.F. Ternhill; No. 510 (C) Sqn.); *K2459* (R.A.F. Henlow; No. 500 Sqn., SR; No. 12 ERFTS); *K2460* (No. 142 (B) Sqn.; *K2461* (No. 1 Air Armament School); *K2462* (No. 142 (B) Sqn.); *K2465* (No. 1 Air Armament School); *K2469-K2472* (Air Armament School); *K2473* (CFS; No. 600 Sqn.; No. 12 Sqn.).

The Hawker Hart Trainer (Interim). Two aircraft, *K2474* and *K2475*, equipped with dual controls, added to Contract No. 117876/31. Rolls-Royce Kestrel IB engines. *K2474:* (CFS; R.A.F. College, Cranwell; crashed during forced landing practice at No. 3 Landing Ground, 31-3-36); *K2475:* (CFS; No. 601 Sqn., A.A.F.; SOC, 6-8-35).

The Hawker Hart S.E.D.B. Production batch of 65 aircraft, *K2966-K3030*, built by Vickers (Aviation) Ltd., Weybridge, Surrey, to Specification 9/29, under Contract No. 198868/32. Rolls-Royce Kestrel IB engines (some changed later to Kestrel Vs). Aircraft built between January 1932 and April 1933.

No. 12 (B) Sqn.: *K2978*; *K2979*; *K2986*; *K2987*; *K2989*; *K2997*; *K3004*; *K3005* (crashed into sea while low flying off Aden, 24-6-36); *K3012*; *K3015*; *K3019*; *K3028*.

491

No. 57 (B) Sqn.: *K3007*; *K3011*; *K3017*; *K3018*; *K3022*; *K3023*; *K3024*; *K3025*.

No. 503 Sqn., A.A.F.: *K3006*; *K3007*; *K3023*; *K3025* (stalled and crashed, Waddington, 6-2-37); *K3030*.

No. 600 Sqn., A.A.F.: *K2979*; *K2980*; *K2981*; *K2982*; *K2983*; *K2984*; *K2985* (crashed while landing at Sutton Bridge, 18-7-35); *K2986*; *K2987*; *K2988*; *K2999*; *K3028*.

No. 601 Sqn., A.A.F.: *K2966*; *K2970*; *K2971* (crashed during forced landing, 13-6-36); *K2972*; *K2973* (damaged while taxying at Hendon, 7-3-37); *K2974* (crashed, 3-33); *K2975*; *K2976*; *K2977*; *K2978*; *K2981*; *K2988*; *K2989*; *K2997*.

Flying Training Schools: No. 1 FTS: *K2966*; *K3010*; *K3017*. No. 2 FTS: *K2981*; *K2989*. No. 6 FTS: *K2979*. No. 12 FTS: *K2992*.

Elementary & Reserve Flying Training Schools: No. 6 ERFTS: *K2988*. No. 7 ERFTS: *K3006*; *K3007*. No. 8 ERFTS: *K2981*. No. 12 ERFTS: *K2982*. No. 15 ERFTS: *K2977*; *K2991*. No. 16 ERFTS: *K2980*. No. 20 ERFTS: *K2972*; *K3008*. No. 22 ERFTS: *K3023*. No. 25 ERFTS: *K3030* (crashed and SOC, 18-11-38). No. 29 ERFTS: *K2989*.

Supplied to South African Air Force: *K2966* (3-39); *K2970* (15-2-38); *K2975* (15-2-38); *K2976* (15-2-38); *K2978* (3-1-38); *K2987* (6-7-38); *K2993* (15-2-38); *K2997* (3-1-38); *K3004* (9-11-36); *K3008* (21-4-41); *K3014* (4-39); *K3015* (7-38); *K3016* (5-8-38); *K3019* (5-8-38); *K3021* (5-8-38); *K3026* (5-8-38); *K3029* (4-39).

Ground Instruction Machines: *K2967* (became *1128M*, 8-38); *K2969* (became *1073M*, 6-38); *K2971* (became *924M*, 12-36); *K2973* (became *960M*, 5-37); *K2977* (became *2331M*, 11-40); *K2979* (became *2390M*, 12-40); *K2980*; *K2982* (became *2262M*); *K2985* (became *773M*, 1935); *K2988* (became *2384M*, 12-40); *K2990* (became *621M*, 8-34); *K2991* (became *2300M*, 10-40); *K2992* (5-40); *K2994* (became *2283M*, 10-40); *K2995* (became *1498M*, 5-39); *K2998* (became *1138M*, 9-38); *K2999* (became *1346M*, 3-39); *K3000* (became *1642M*, 9-39); *K3001* (became *1481M*, 5-39); *K3002* (became *1447M*, 4-39); *K3010* (became *1503M*, 5-39); *K3012* (became *2026M*, 6-40); *K3013* (became *1448M*, 4-39); *K3018* (became *1349M*, 3-39); *K3020* (became *1169M*, 2-39).

Other Units and duties, etc.: *K2966* (No. 611 Sqn., A.A.F.); *K2967* (R.A.E.; No. 15 (B) Sqn.); *K2968* (A. & A.E.E.); *K2969* (R.A.E.); *K2972* (No. 1 Ground Defence Gunners's School; No. 24 (C) Sqn.); *K2977* (R.A.F. College, Cranwell); *K2980* (No. 610 Sqn., A.A.F.); *K2981* (R.A.F. College, Cranwell); *K2982* (No. 610 Sqn., A.A.F.); *K2986* (to Southern Rhodesian Air Force, 3-37); *K2989* (No. 605 Sqn., A.A.F.; R.A.F. College, Cranwell; No. 3 Electrical & Wireless School); *K2990-K2993* (R.A.F. College, Cranwell); *K2994-K2997* (School of Photography); *K2998-K3002* (No. 3 Coastal Defence Flt.); *K2999-K3003* (No. 24 (C) Sqn.); *K3003* (R.A.F. College, Cranwell); *K3004* (No. 17 (F) Sqn.); *K3006* (R.A.E.; No. 18 (B) Sqn.; No. 3 Electrical & Wireless School); *K3007* (No. 3 Electrical & Wireless School); *K3008* (No. 142 (B) Sqn.); *K3011* (Bristol Pegasus test bed; No. 3 Coastal Defence Flt.); *K3013* (converted to **Hawker Hardy prototype**; A. & A.E.E.); *K3014* (Flight refuelling trials; R.A.E.); *K3016* (No. 142 (B) Sqn.); *K3018* (Nos. 605, 500 and 501 Sqns., A.A.F.); *K3020* (Bristol Pegasus and Mercury engine test bed, HAL and Bristols); *K3024-K3027* (R.A.F. Henlow); *K3026* (No. 142 (B) Sqn.); *K3027* (R.A.F. Wyton); *K3029* (R.A.F. College, Cranwell).

The Hawker Hart S.E.D.B. Production batch of 24 aircraft, *K3031-K3054*, built by Sir W.G. Armstrong Whitworth Aircraft Ltd. to Specification 9/29 (as amended) under Contract No. 198870/32 between 7-33 and 11-33. Rolls-Royce Kestel IB engines (some replaced by Kestrel Vs later).

No. 15 (B) Sqn.: *K3037-K3040*; *K3046*; *K3049*.

No. 18 (B) Sqn.: *K3033*; *K3035* (aircraft wrecked in gale, 17-9-31); *K3046*; *K3047*.

No. 57 (B) Sqn.: *K3032*; *K3034*.

No. 142 (B) Sqn.: *K3041-K3044*.

No. 500 Sqn., SR: *K3045*; *K3050*; *K3053*.

No. 501 Sqn., SR: *K3050*; *K3051*.

No. 503 Sqn.; A.A.F.: *K3034* (crashed during forced landing, 11-7-36); *K3046*; *K3053*.

No. 600 Sqn., A.A.F.: *K3040*; *K3045*; *K3048*.

No. 601 Sqn., A.A.F.: *K3031*; *K3049*.

No. 602 Sqn., A.A.F.: *K3044*; *K3054*.

No. 603 Sqn., A.A.F.: *K3045*; *K3052*.

No. 605 Sqn., A.A.F.: *K3032*; *K3051*.

No. 610 Sqn., A.A.F.: *K3040*; *K3054*.

No. 611 Sqn., A.A.F.: *K3044* (taxying collision with Mew Gull *G-AEKL* at Speke, 19-9-36).

Flying Training Schools: No. 1 FTS: *K3032*; *K3040*; *K3045*; *K3051*. No. 2 FTS: *K3031*; *K3037*; *K3050*, *K3053*, *K3054*. No. 6 FTS: *K3051*. No. 10 FTS: *K3032*; *K3043*; *K3046*.

Elementary & Reserve Flying Training Schools: No. 1 ERFTS: *K3052*. No. 6 ERFTS: *K3043*. No. 12 ERFTS: *K3046*. No. 15 ERFTS: *K3031*; *K3045*. No. 19 ERFTS: *K3051*. No. 20 ERFTS: *K3039* (SOC, 6-40); *K3042* (crashed while landing at Gravesend, 30-6-38). No. 22 ERFTS: *K3052*. No. 29 ERFTS: *K3054*.

Supplied to South African Air Force: *K3041* (1-9-39); *K3053* (9-3-38).

Ground Instruction Machines: *K3033* (became *2265M*, 8-40); *K3036* (became *1435M*, 4-39); *K3038* (became *2187M*, 8-40); *K3040* (became *2277M*); *K3050* (became *1348M*, 3-39).

Other Units and duties: *K3031* (R.A.F. Mildenhall. Converted to **Hart (Intermediate)**; to A. & A.E.E.); *K3032* (R.A.F. Brize Norton; R.A.F. Ternhill); *K3033* (No. 3 Coastal Defence Flt.; School of Naval Co-operation); *K3036* (Rolls-Royce Ltd; Merlin test bed: P.V.12, Merlin C and E); *K3037* (R.A.F. College, Cranwell; No. 3 Electrical and Wireless School); *K3045* (No. 1 Ground Defence Gunners' School; Air Transport Auxiliary); *K3046* (R.A.F. Abingdon); *K3049* (R.A.F. Mildenhall; R.A.F. Linton-on-Ouse; ATA).

The Hawker Hart Trainer. Production batch of 13 aircraft, *K3146-K3158*, built by H.G. Hawker Engineering Co. Ltd., Kingston and Brooklands, between April and June 1933, under Contract No. 246227/33. Rolls-Royce Kestrel IB engines.

R.A.F. College, Cranwell: *K3148-K3151*, *K3152* (collided with Bulldog *K3928* and crashed, 1-5-34); *K3153* (crashed while landing at Welbourne, 29-11-39).

Central Flying School: *K3153*; *K3155*; *K3156*.

Flying Training Schools: No. 1 FTS: *K3146*, *K3156*, *K3158*. No. 3 FTS: *K3146*; *K3156* (crashed during forced landing, 29-10-36). No. 7 FTS: *K3147*; *K3157*. No. 9 FTS: *K3146* (crashed at Hankerton, near Malmesbury, Wilts, 16-4-41); *K3149*. No. 10 FTS: *K3154*. No. 11 FTS: *K3146*; *K3147*. No. 12 FTS: *K3147*; No. 13 FTS: *K3147*; No. 15 FTS: *K3146*.

Supplied to South African Air Force: *K3147* (5-41); *K3149* (5-12-41).

Supplied to Egyptian Air Force: *K3154* (30-3-40).

Ground Instruction Machines: *K3148* (became *843M*); *K3150* (became *883M*); *K3155* (became *743M*); *K3156* (became *1767M*); *K3158* (became *1766M*).

Other Units and duties, etc.: *K3147* (No. 600 Sqn., A.A.F.); *K3154* (No. 601 Sqn., A.A.F.); *K3155* (R.A.E.; No. 504 Sqn., A.A.F.; crashed in Denaby Wood, 28-10-35); *K3157* (No. 43 (F) Sqn.); *K3158* (No. 25 (F) Sqn.; R.A.F. Leuchars.

The Hawker Hart Trainer. Production batch of 21 aircraft, *K3743-K3763*, built by Hawker Aircraft Ltd., Kingston and Brooklands, in February 1934, under Contract No. 323239/34. Most aircraft with Rolls-Royce Kestrel VDR engines.

Flying Training Schools: No. 1 FTS: *K3744* (crashed in forced landing on railway line, 31-1-38); *K3745*; *K3757*; *K3762*. No. 2 FTS: *K3757-K3761*. No. 3 FTS: *K3756*. No. 6 FTS: *K3745*; No. 7 FTS: *K3752* (SOC, 24-3-40); *K3758*; *K3759*; *K3762* (crashed at Peakirk, 19-11-39). No. 8 FTS: *K3755* (SOC, 1-7-40). No. 9 FTS: *K3745*; *K3754*; *K3756*. No. 10 FTS: *K3752*; *K3753*; *K3755*; No. 12 FTS: *K3758-K3760*; No. 13 FTS: *K3755*. No. 14 FTS: *K3757*.

Elementary & Reserve Flying Training Schools: No. 10 ERFTS: *K3476*. No. 16 ERFTS: *K3745*. No. 21 ERFTS: *K3751*.

R.A.F. College, Cranwell: *K3743*; *K3746* (SOC, 14-2-40). *K3754*; *K3763* (SOC, 1-7-40).

Supplied to South African Air Force: *K3743* (22-10-44); *K3745* (18-12-41); *K3754* (10-40);

K3756 (8-41); *K3758* (8-10-40); *K3759* (3-1-41); *K3760* (7-10-41).

Ground Instruction Machines: *K3748* (became *770M*); *K3749* (became *970M*); *K3751* (became *1581M, 6-39*); *K3753* (became *1258M*, 2-39); *K3761* (became *1765M*).

Other Units and duties, etc.: *K3743* (No. 25 (F) Sqn.; R.A.F. Odiham); *K3744* (R.A.F. Leuchars); *K3745* (School of Army Co-operation; No. 501 Sqn.; No. 605 Sqn.); *K3747* (No. 24 (C) Sqn.; SOC, 6-2-39); *K3748* (No. 24 (C) Sqn.; crashed during forced landing, 14-1-36); *K3749* (No. 602 Sqn., A.A.F.); *K3750* (No. 603 Sqn., A.A.F.); *K3751* (No. 24 (C) Sqn.); *K3752* (No. 25 (F) Sqn.); *K3753* (No. 43 (F) Sqn.; No. 612 Sqn., A.A.F.); *K3755* (No. 604 Sqn., A.A.F.; Oxford University Air Squadron); *K3756* (Oxford University Air Squadron); *K3760* (Cambridge University Air Squadron).

The Hawker Hart S.E.D.B. Second production batch of 47 aircraft, *K3808-K3854*, built by Vickers (Aviation) Ltd., Weybridge, Surrey, between 2-34 and 4-34, under Contract No. 262680/33. Ten aircraft (*K3820-K3829*) cleared for tropical service. Rolls-Royce Kestrel IB engines (many replaced later by Kestrel Xs).

Air Armament School: *K3808* (SOC, 6-8-35); *K3809-K3811*; *K3812* (crashed during forced landing, 21-11-35); *K3813-K3815*.

No. 15 (B) Sqn.: *K3846* (crashed and SOC, 4-12-35).

No. 18 (B) Sqn.: *K3816, K3845, K3848*.

No. 142 (B) Sqn.: *K3840*; *K3842*; *K3843*.

Auxiliary Air Force Sqns.: No. 500 Sqn.: *K3816*; *K3845*; *K3848*. No. 503 Sqn.: *K3816*; *K3837*; *K3845*. No. 600 Sqn.: *K3831*; *K3847*; No. 601 Sqn.: *K3830*. No. 602 Sqn.: *K3848*. No. 603 Sqn.: *K3847*. No. 604 Sqn.: *K3842*. No. 609 Sqn.: *K3839*; *K3845*. No. 610 Sqn.: *K3831*; *K3853*. No. 611 Sqn.: *K3817*; *K3819*; *K3851*; *K3852*.

Flying Training Schools: No. 1 FTS: *K3830*; *K3851*; *K3852*. No. 2 FTS: *K3816*; *K3840*; *K3854* (SOC, 1-7-40). No. 3 FTS: *K3830*; *K3837*; *K3843*. No. 6 FTS: *K3850*. No. 10 FTS: *K3830*.

Elementary & Reserve Flying Traing Schools: No. 3 ERFTS: *K3816*. No. 4 ERFTS: *K3849*; *K3850*. No. 5 ERFTS: *K3840*. No. 8 ERFTS: *K3847*; *K3853*. No. 9 ERFTS: *K3817*. No. 11 ERFTS: *K3844* (SOC, 27-8-40). No. 12 ERFTS: *K3830*. No. 14 ERFTS: *K3843*. No. 15 ERFTS: *K3848* (SOC, 12-9-41). No. 20 ERFTS: *K3831*. No. 21 ERFTS: *K3854*. No. 22 ERFTS: *K3819* (crashed in snowstorm, Milton Road, Cambridge, 17-2-39). No. 27 ERFTS: *K3837*.

Supplied to South African Air Force: *K3809* (1-4-39); *K3813* (1-4-39); *K3815* (1-4-39); *K3820* (from Aden, 9-11-36); *K3821-K3829* (from Middle East, 3-2-39); *K3832* (1-9-39); *K3833* (6-7-38); *K3834-K3836* (1-4-39); *K3839* (9-3-38); *K3842* (21-4-41); *K3845* (1-38); *K3851* (15-4-39).

Supplied to Royal Egyptian Air Force: *K3831* (30-3-40); *K3847* (30-3-40); *K3852* (30-3-40); *K3853* (30-3-40).

Ground Instruction Machines: *K3810* (became *1504M*, 5-39); *K3811* (became *1499M*, 5-39); *K3814* (became *1501M*, 5-39); *K3819* (became *1335M*); *K3838* (became *2284M*); *K3841* (became *1500M*, 5-39); *K3849* (became *1476M*, 5-39).

Other Units and duties, etc.: *K3817* (No. 3 Electrical & Wireless School). *K3818* (R.A.F. Linton-on-Ouse; SOC, 1-7-40). *K3830* (No. 25 (F) Sqn.). *K3837* (R.A.E.). *K3838* (No. 3 Coastal Defence Flt.; School of Naval Co-operation; Communications Flt., Lee-on-Solent; Communications Flt., Chatham). *K3839* (No. 3 Coastal Defence Flt.). *K3842* (No. 33 (B) Sqn.). *K3844* (R.A.F. College, Cranwell). *K3849* (R.A.F. Wittering).

The Hawker Hart S.E.D.B. and (Communications). Second production batch of 50 aircraft, *K3855-K3904*, built by Sir W.G. Armstrong Whitworth Aircraft Ltd., Coventry, under Contract No. 272678/33, between 3-34 and 7-34. *K3855, K3856, K3873* and *K3874* prepared as Hart (Communications), without armament or provision for bombs. Rolls-Royce Kestrel IB, X and XDR.

No. 12 (B) Sqn.: *K3877*; *K3886*; *K3888*; *K3889* (SOC, 29-3-27);

No. 15 (B) Sqn.: *K3899* (crashed during forced landing, 24-2-36); *K3900*; *K3903*; *K3904* (crashed during forced landing, 22-1-35).

No. 24 (C) Sqn.: *K3855*; *K3856*; *K3873*; *K3874* (SOC, 12-5-41).

No. 33 (B) Sqn.: *K3894*.

No. 142 (B) Sqn.: *K3871*; *K3894*; *K3901*; *K3902*.

No. 500 Sqn., A.A.F.: *K3861*.

No. 501 Sqn., A.A.F.: *K3857*; *K3862*; *K3869; K3883*; *K3885*; *K3890*; *K3891*; *K3892*.

No. 503 Sqn., A.A.F.: *K3900*.

No. 601 Sqn., A.A.F.: *K3889*.

No. 602 Sqn., A.A.F.: *K3857*; *K3858*; *K3861*; *K3862*; *K3865*; *K3866*; *K3869*; *K3870*; *K3875*; *K3877*; *K3878*; *K3880*; *K3897*.

No. 603 Sqn., A.A.F.: *K3859* (crashed and SOC, 24-2-35); *K3860* (crashed while landing, 10-3-35); *K3861*; *K3863*; *K3864*; *K3867*; *K3868*; *K3872*; *K3876*; *K3879*; *K3895* (crashed during forced landing, 20-7-36); *K3898*; *K3903*.

No. 604 Sqn., A.A.F.: *K3893* (crashed while landing at Redhill, 16-12-34); *K3894*; *K3895*; *K3896*.

No. 605 Sqn., A.A.F.: *K3883*; *K3885*; *K3886*; *K3887* (collided with Moth *G-ACOH* and crashed near Castle Bromwich, 9-12-34); *K3888*; *K3890*; *K3891*; *K3892*.

No. 607 Sqn., A.A.F.: *K3861*.

No. 609 Sqn., A.A.F.: *K3870*.

No. 610 Sqn., A.A.F.: *K3865*; *K3867*; *K3869*; *K3881*.

No. 611 Sqn., A.A.F.: *K3878*.

Royal Air Force College, Cranwell: *K3858*; *K3866*; *K3879*; *K3882*; *K3897* (crashed while landing at Barkston Heath, 5-12-36).

Flying Training Schools. No. 1 FTS: *K3861*; *K3868*; *K3878*; *K3880*; *K3883*; *K3885*; *K3890*; *K3892*; *K3903*. No. 2 FTS: *K3866*; *K3879*; *K3882*; *K3900*. No. 3 FTS: *K3865* (SOC, 1-7-40); *K3869*; *K3892*. No. 5 FTS: *K3892*. No. 6 FTS: *K3892*. No. 6 FTS: *K3894*; *K3901*. No. 10 FTS: *K3865*; *K3869*.

Elementary & Reserve Flying Training Schools. No. 3 ERFTS: *K3900*. No. 4 ERFTS: *K3870*. No. 5 ERFTS: *K3882*. No. 7 ERFTS: *K3867*. No. 8 ERFTS: *K3866*; *K3879*; *K3881*. No. 9 ERFTS: *K3894*. No. 11 ERFTS: *K3898* (SOC, 12-12-40). No. 12 ERFTS: *K3892*. No. 14 ERFTS: *K3902* (crashed while landing at Castle Bromwich, 24-7-38). No. 15 ERFTS: *K3858* (SOC, 4-11-40). No. 16 ERFTS: *K3871* (SOC, 8-11-40). No. 19 ERFTS: *K3901*. No. 28 ERFTS: *K3864* (crashed in Dene valley, Cheshire, 28-5-39); *K3865*.

Air Armament Schools: *K3876*; *K3878*; *K3884*; *K3896*.

No. 1 Ground Defence Gunners' School: *K3861*; *K3866* (crashed during forced landing on the Isle of Man, 2-1-41); *K3867*; *K3879*; *K3890*; *K3892*.

Supplied to South African Air Force: *K3863* (4-39); *K3867* (30-5-42); *K3868* (3-39); *K3876* (21-4-39); *K3883* (4-39); *K3884* (5-39); *K3885* (4-39); *K3886* (3-37); *K3890* (5-41);

Supplied to Southern Rhodesian Air Force: *K3877* (29-3-37); *K3888* (3-38 as *SR-8*);

Ground Instruction Machines: *K3857* (became *1347M*, 3-39); *K3862* (became *1351M*, 3-39); *K3870* (became *1153M*, 10-38); *K3872* (became *789M*, 3-36); *K3873* (became *1469M*, 3-39); *K3881* (became *2275M*); *K3891* (became *1350M*, 3-39); *K3893* (became *696M*); *K3896* (became *1586M*, 6-39); *K3899* (became *816M*); *K3903* (became *1185M*, 11-38).

Other Units and duties, etc.: *K3869* (No. 3 Electrical and Wireless School; SOC, 1-7-40); *K3878* (R.A.F. Brize Norton; R.A.F. Ternhill); *K3882* (No. 3 E. & W.S., SOC, 1-7-40); *K3892* (No. 3 Air Observers' School; ATA); *K3900* (R.A.E.; CFS).

The Hawker Hart S.E.D.B. Third production batch of 18 aircraft, *K3955-K3972*, built by Sir W.G. Armstrong Whitworth Aircraft Ltd., Coventry, during June and July 1934. Rolls-Royce Kestrel X and XDR engines.

No. 15 (B) Sqn.: *K3957*; *K3960*; *K3961*; *K3964*; *K3965*; *K3968*; *K3969*; *K3971*; *K3972*.

No. 24 (C) Sqn.: *K3969*.

495

No. 142 (B) Sqn.: *K3955* (crashed and SOC, 30-4-35); *K3956*; *K3958*; *K3959*; *K3962*; *K3963*; *K3966*; *K3967*; *K3970*.

Auxiliary Air Force Sqns.: No. 501 Sqn.: *K3957*. No. 600 Sqn.: *K3957*. No. 601 Sqn.: *K3965*. No. 602 Sqn.: *K3965*. No. 603 Sqn.: *K3969*; *K3972*. No. 604 Sqn.: *K3969*; *K3972*.

Flying Training Schools. No. 1 FTS: *K3957*; *K3960*; *K3972*. No. 2 FTS: *K3964* (SOC, 26-4-40). No. 3 FTS: *K3958*; *K3959*; *K3968*. No. 6 FTS: *K3970* (SOC, 1-7-40). No. 10 FTS: *K3959*.

Elementary & Reserve Flying Training Schools: No. 4 ERFTS: *K3970*. No. 12 ERFTS: *K3958*. No. 15 ERFTS: *K3964*. No. 20 ERFTS: *K3959*. No. 22 ERFTS: *K3969*.

To South African Air Force: *K3956* (3-2-39); *K3958* (12-6-42); *K3962* (5-8-38); *K3963* (3-9-38); *K3966* (3-9-38); *K3969* (14-11-42; damaged beyond repair in shipwreck in transit).

To Royal Egyptian Air Force: *K3972* (30-3-40).

Ground Instruction Machines: *K3960* (became *1608M*, 7-39); *K3961* (became *1696M*); *K3965* (became *944M* (3-37); *K3968* (became *737M*, 1-36).

Other Units and duties, etc.: *K3957* (No. 1 Ground Gunners' School; ATA; SOC, 31-10-43); *K3959* (No. 1 Ground Gunners' School; SOC, 21-11-40); *K3960* (Air Observers' School); *K3961* (Andover Stn. Flt.; No. 81 Sqn.); *K3964* (R.A.F. College, Cranwell); *K3967* (R.A.F. Cardington; SOC, 1-1-41).

The Hawker Hart Special. Production batch of 16 aircraft, *K4365-K4380*, originally ordered as Audaxes to Specification 9/34 but completed to Special standard and termed Harts. Production during July and August 1935. Rolls-Royce Kestrel IB engines. (Intended to equip No. 17 (F) Squadron whose Bulldogs had been set aside as reinforcements during crisis in the Middle East.)

No. 17 (F) Sqn.: *K4365*; *K4366*; *K4367*; *K4368*; *K4373*; *K4375*; *K4376*.

No. 40 (B) Sqn.: *K4371* (collided with Gordon *K2720* and crashed, 9-11-35); *K4372*.

Flying Training Schools. No. 1 FTS: *K4366* (crashed during bombing practice over Skipsea range, 21-7-39); *K4367*; *K4368*; *K4375*. No. 2 FTS: *K4376*. No. 3 FTS: *K4367*; *K4375*. No. 7 FTS: *K4367*; *K4368* (crashed at Tilton-on-the-Hill, Leics, 8-10-40); *K4369*; *K4370*; *K4373*; *K4374*; *K4375*; *K4377* (crashed at sea off West Freugh, 15-5-40); *K4378*; *K4379*. No. 8 FTS: *K4366*. No. 9 FTS: *K4365* (crashed during forced landing, 21-3-38). No. 10 FTS: *K4367*; *K4368*; *K4375*. No. 11 FTS: *K4368*.

No. 7 SFTS: *K4369*.

Elementary & Reserve Flying Training Schools: No. 2 ERFTS: *K4372* (collided with Tiger Moth *G-ACBA* while landing at Filton, 3-5-39). No. 13 ERFTS: *K4376*.

Supplied to South African Air Force: *K4369* (4-9-42); *K4373* (3-10-42); *K4374* (4-9-42); *K4375* (23-6-42); *K4378* (8-10-42); *K4379* (18-8-42).

Ground Instruction Machine: K4370 (became 902M, 1-36).

Other Units and duties, etc.: *K4367* (No. 49 (B) Sqn.; SOC, 24-5-40); *K4369* (No. 1 Armament Training Camp); *K4370* (R.A.E.); *K4380* (No. 5 Sqn., India, 1941-42; crashed during aerobatics, Ichapur, 23-2-42).

The Hawker Hart Special. Production batch of 30 aircraft, *K4407-K4436*, built by Gloster Aircraft Co. Ltd., Hucclecote, Glos., to Specification 9/34, and delivered between November 1935 and February 1936. Rolls-Royce Kestrel XDR engines.

No. 40 (B) Sqn.: *K4407-K4420*.

No. 17 (F) Sqn.: *K4421-K4427*.

Air Observers' School: *K4407*; *K4408*; *K4411*; *K4412*; *K4414-K4420*; *K4428-K4435*.

Flying Training Schools. No. 1 FTS: *K4409*; *K4413* (crashed during forced landing, Burton-on-Trent, 30-5-39); *K4423*; *K4436*. No. 2 FTS: *K4419* (SOC, 6-40); *K4422* (SOC, 13-12-39); *K4432*. No. 3 FTS: *K4411*; *K4414*; *K4420*; *K4423*. No. 6 FTS: *K4408* (SOC, 6-40); *K4418* (SOC, 6-40); *K4422*; *K4428*; *K4429* (SOC, 6-40); *K4433* (SOC, 6-40). No. 7 FTS: *K4409*; *K4424* (crashed, 31-8-40); *K4425* (crashed during forced landing at Eastrea, near Whitlesey, 24-10-39); *K4428*; *K4436*. No. 8 FTS: *K4410*; *K4413*; *K4421*; *K4426*; *K4427*;

K4436. No. 9 FTS: *K4423*; *K4424.* No. 10 FTS: *K4411*; *K4414*; *K4420.*

No. 3 Elementary Flying Training School: *K4407*

Elementary & Reserve Flying Training Schools: No. 3 ERFTS: *K4407*; *K4412*; *K4415* (collided on take-off with Cadet *G-ACCN*, Hamble, 16-6-38); *K4419.* No. 4 ERFTS: *K4418.* No. 5 ERFTS: *K4430* (crashed, 18-6-38); *K4432*; *K4434* (burnt after collision with Blackburn B-2 *G-AEBI* on ground at Hanworth, 31-1-38); *K4435* (crashed in forced landing, 18-3-38). No. 7 ERFTS: *K4428*; *K4435.* No. 12 ERFTS: *K4411*; *K4414*; *K4416*; *K4417.* No. 13 ERFTS: *K4422.* No. 16 ERFTS: *K4408*; *K4415*; *K4420*; *K4429*; *K4431* (crashed 7 miles east of Lewes, Sussex, 14-4-39); *K4433.* No. 56 ERFTS: *K4421*; *K4426.*

Supplied to South African Air Force: *K4428* (18-8-42)

Ground Instruction Machines: *K4407* (became *2302M*, 10-40); *K4409* (became *2702M*, 8-41); *K4410* (became *1763M*); *K4412* (became *1387M*, 4-39); *K4414* (became *2102M*, 7-40); *K4416* (became *1445M*, 4-39); *K4420* (became *2102M*, 7-40); *K4421* (became *2263M*, 10-40); *K4436* (became *2703M*, 9-41).

Other Units and duties, etc.: *K4411* (ATA; SOC, 28-12-43); *K4423* (Flying Training Command Communications Flt.; SOC, 26-5-43).

The Hawker Hart S.E.D.B. Fourth production batch of 59 aircraft, *K4437-4495*, built by Sir W.G. Armstrong Whitworth Aircraft Ltd., and delivered January and May 1935. Rolls-Royce Kestrel X and XDR engines.

No. 6 (B) Sqn. (Ramleh, Palestine): *K4458*; *K4460-K4469*; *K4471*; *K4472*; *K4473* (crashed at Bala, Palestine, 3-9-36); *K4478* (SOC, 31-1-39); *K4481*; *K4482* (crashed in forced landing in Palestine, 27-5-36); *K4483.*

No. 33 (B) Sqn. (Ismailia and Heliopolis, Egypt): *K4443*; *K4444*; *K4445* (collided with Hart *K4494* and crashed, 25-2-38); *K4447-K4451*; *K4452* (SOC, 31-3-39); *K4453-K4456*; *K4475*; *K4476*; *K4478-K4480*; *K4484*; *K4491-K4493*; *K4494* (collided with Hart *K4445* and crashed, 25-2-38); *K4495.*

No. 142 (B) Sqn. (Ismailia and Aboukir, Egypt): *K4447-K4456*; *K4484*; *K4491-K4495* (aircraft passed to No. 33 Sqn.; see above).

Flying Training Schools. No. 3 FTS: *K4441* (SOC, 6-40). No. 6 FTS: *K4439.* No. 10 FTS: *K4441.*

Elementary & Reserve Flying Training Schools: No. 3 ERFTS: *K4442.* No. 5 ERFTS: *K4437*; *K4438.* No. 6 ERFTS: *K4459* (crashed and SOC, 6-2-39). No. 19 ERFTS: *K4439.* No. 22 ERFTS: *K4446.* No. 25 ERFTS: *K4441.*

Supplied to South African Air Force. 5-8-38: *K4448*, *K4449*, *K4451*, *K4453*, *K4458*; *K4461*; *K4467*, *K4470-K4472*, *K4480*, *K4484*, *K4491*, *K4492*, *K4495.* 1-9-38: *K4447*, *K4454*, *K4455*, *K4462-K4464*, *K4469*, *K4474*, *K4475*, *K4486*, *K4489*, *K4493.* 3-2-39: *K4477*, *K4485*, *K4488*, *K4490.* 2-3-39: *K4444*, *K4450*, *K4456*, *K4457*, *K4460*, *K4465*, *K4468*, *K4476.* 7-3-39: *K4479.*

Supplied to Royal Egyptian Air Force: *K4440* (30-3-40); *K4442* (30-3-40); *K4443* (30-3-40); *K4481* (31-1-39); *K4483* (16-3-39).

Ground Instruction Aircraft: *K4437* (became *2309M*, 10-40); *K4438* (became *1361M*, 8-39); *K4446* (became *1231M*, 1-39); *K4466*; *K4487* (became *2020M*, 10-40).

Other Units and duties, etc.: *K4439* (No. 1 Ferry Pilots' Pool (crashed in low cloud at Ewelme Park Corner, Oxfordshire, 7-11-39); *K4441* (No. 610 Sqn., A.A.F.); *K4459* (Nos. 500 and 603 Sqns., A.A.F.).

The Hawker Hart Trainer (Series 2). Production batch of 20 aircraft, *K4751-K4770*, built by Hawker Aircraft Ltd., Kingston and Brooklands, during March and April 1935. Rolls-Royce Kestrel XDR engines.

No. 2 Flying Training School: *K4751* (crashed at Ilchester, Somerset, 13-7-38); *K4753*; *K4754* (crashed and SOC, 15-9-38); *K4755-K4764*, *K4769.*

Other Flying Training Schools: No. 1 FTS: *K4756*; *K4761*; *K4764*; *K4768* (SOC, 29-2-40). No. 3 FTS: *K4767.* No. 5 FTS: *K4766*; *K4768.* No. 6 FTS: *K4765.* No. 7 FTS: *K4757* (SOC, 2-4-40); *K4765.* No. 9 FTS: *K4753*; *K4767*; *K4769* (crashed, 14-11-40). No. 10

FTS: *K4763*. No. 11 FTS: *K4755* (crashed at Shawbury, 6-6-39); *K4758* (SOC, 4-40); *K4762* (SOC, 6-40). No. 12 FTS: *K4759* (crashed while landing, Grantham, 26-6-39). No. 14 FTS: *K47671*; *K4764*. No. 15 FTS: *K4757*.

Elementary & Reserve Flying Schools: No. 8 ERFTS: *K4769*. No. 11 ERFTS: *K4766*; *K4768*. No. 21 ERFTS: *K4767*.

Oxford University Air Squadron: *K4766-K4768*.

Cambridge University Air Squadron: *K4769*.

Supplied to South African Air Force: *K4756* (3-10-41); *K4761* (5-11-41); *K4764* (12-6-42); *K4765* (7-1-41); *K4767* (3-3-42).

Ground Instruction Machines: *K4753* (became *2228M*, 9-40); *K4763* (became *2312M*, 4-40).

Other Units and duties, etc: *K4760* (to Iraq: No. 148 Sqn.; S.O.C., 7-9-42); *K4769* (Duxford Stn. Flt.; R.A.F. College, Cranwell); *K4770* (Straits Settlements Volunteer Air Force; to Iraq: Amriya Stn. Flt.; suffered brake failure and S.O.C., 23-6-42).

The Hawker Hart Trainer (Series 2A). Production batch of 167 aircraft, *K4886-K5052*, built to Air Ministry Specification 8-35 by Sir W.G. Armstrong Whitworth Aircraft Ltd., Coventry, between July 1935 and February 1936. Rolls-Royce Kestrel X and XDR engines. Many modified with sand filters for desert service.

No. 1 Flying Training School: *K4891*; *K4893*; *K4929*; *K4934* (crashed 19-11-40); *K4936*; *K4939* (crashed 22-11-40); *K4940*; *K4941*; *K4943*; *K4946*; *K4961*; *K4974*; *K4979* (crashed near Bath, 19-8-41, after hitting HT cables); *K4981*; *K5004*; *K5021* (crashed at Netheravon, 17-10-40); *K5034*; *K5038* (collided with Blenheim over Bulford, Wilts, 30-9-40); *K5039*; *K5042*.

No. 2 Flying Training School: *K4888*; *K4938* (crashed while landing at Brize Norton, 21-11-38); *K4945*; *K4959*; *K4971-K4974*; *K4977*.

No. 3 Flying Training School: *K4886*; *K4890* (SOC, 5-2-40); *K4891*; *K4892* (crashed, 2-4-40); *K4893*; *K4920* (collided with Audax *K4389*, 2-4-36); *K4926*; *K4927* (crashed, 8-12-40); *K4928* (crashed, 31-1-36); *K4968*; *K5001*; *K5029* (SOC, 6-40); *K5039-K5047*.

No. 4 Flying Training School (Egypt and Iraq): *K4896* (crashed at Abu Sueir, 26-2-43); *K4897* (crashed at Abu Sueir, 10-39); *K4898-K4902*; *K4903* (crashed at Abu Sueir, 24-8-37); *K4904* (crashed in Lake Manzalah, 10-4-42); *K4905*; *K4906* (crashed at Habbaniya, 2-11-39); *K4907-K4911*; *K4912* (crashed at Abu Sueir, 11-5-37); *K4913* (crashed near Habbaniya, 13-3-41); *K4914-K4917*; *K5048* (crashed at Habbaniya, 9-12-39); *K5049*; *K5050*; *K5051* (crashed on Abu Sueir range, 18-8-37); *K5052* (crashed, 29-8-42).

No. 5 Flying Training School: *K4887*; *K4894* (crashed, 13-5-37); *K4895* (crashed at Sealand, 13-4-39); *K4918-K4921*; *K4922* (crashed, 19-12-36); *K4923* (crashed at Sealand, 5-5-38); *K4924* (crashed, 19-12-36); *K4925*; *K4930*; *K4931* (crashed near Wrexham, Denbigh, 12-2-37); *K4932* (crashed at Llanfyllin, Montgomery, 27-1-37); *K4933* (crashed, 13-12-35); *K4934-K3937*; *K4938* (crashed while landing at Brize Norton, 21-11-38); *K4939-K4941*; *K4991*; *K4996* (crashed at Wansillan, 19-12-38).

No. 6 Flying Training School: *K4888*; *K4942-K4949*; *K4950* (crashed, 14-11-35); *K4951*; *K4952* (crashed, 1-1-37); *K4953*; *K4956*; *K4975*; *K4976* (crashed during night landing at Little Rissington, 13-6-39); *K4977*; *K4978*; *K5023* (crashed, 4-3-37); *K5024*.

No. 7 Flying Training School: *K4886*; *K4887*; *K4941*; *K4945*; *K4947*; *K4951*; *K4956*; *K4961*; *K4968*; *K4975*; *K4983*; *K4984*; *K4985* (crashed while landing at Waddington, 28-5-37); *K4986* (crashed into hangar at Peterborough, 16-4-36); *K4987* (crashed at night near Peterborough, 7-10-39); *K4988* (crashed, 21-6-37); *K4990*; *K4991* (crashed, 6-6-40); *K4992*; *K4993* (crashed at Peterborough, 28-11-39); *K4994-K4996*; *K4997* (crashed near Wansford, Hunts., 2-3-40); *K4998*, *K4999*; *K5004*; *K5025*; *K5026*; *K5035*; *K5036*.

No. 8 Flying Training School: *K4949*; *K4955*; *K5000* (crashed while landing at Montrose, 28-12-37); *K5001-K5004*; *K5005* (crashed while taking off at Abbotsinch, 4-6-39); *K5006-K5012*; *K5013* (crashed while landing at Montrose, 25-7-38); *K5014* (crashed while landing at Montrose, 6-7-36); *K5027*; *K5028*.

No. 9 Flying Training School: *K4888* (crashed, 24-8-40); *K4889*; *K4891*; *K4942*; *K4962*; *K4981*; *K4995*; *K5001*; *K5019*; *K5021*; *K5022*; *K5024*; *K5033*; *K5034*; *K5039*; *K5040* (crashed, 14-11-40); *K5042*.

No. 10 Flying Training School: *K5016*; *K5017* (crashed in storm, 23-3-36); *K5018-K5020*; *K5029*; *K5030* (crashed at Longford, Warwicks, 9-1-39); *K5031* (crashed at Childs Ercall, 7-2-39).

No. 11 Flying Training School: *K4891*; *K4929*; *K4942*; *K4944* (crashed, 15-12-36); *K4953-K4955*; *K4957* (crashed while landing at Shawbury, 21-7-38); *K4958*; *K4959*; *K4960* (abandoned in fog near Wittering, 5-11-37); *K4961*; *K4962*; *K4963* (crashed, 27-11-35); *K4964* (crashed at Caynton Manor, Edgemond, 13-10-38); *K4965*; *K4966*; *K4967* (crashed, 23-5-39); *K4968*; *K4969*; *K4970* (crashed while landing at Shawbury, 14-10-38); *K4979-K4981*; *K4982* (crashed, 11-5-40); *K5021*; *K5022*; *K5024*; *K5038*.

No. 12 Flying Training School: *K4948*; *K4961*; *K4977*; *K4978* (crashed at Loughborough, 17-11-39); *K4980*; *K4983*; *K5003*; *K5010* (SOC, 29-3-40); *K5011*; *K5015* (crashed while landing at night at Grantham, 18-12-39).

No. 13 Flying Training School: *K5027*; *K5034*.

No. 14 Flying Training School: *K4893*; *K4966*; *K4971*; *K4974*; *K4981*; *K5034*.

No. 15 Flying Training School: *K4929*; *K4942*; *K5027* (crashed while landing at Evanton, 18-12-39).

Elementary & Reserve Flying Training Schools: No. 2 ERFTS: *K5033*. No. 5 ERFTS: *K4983*. No. 9 ERFTS: *K4953*. No. 13 ERFTS: *K4888*. No. 21 ERFTS: *K4995*. No. 22 ERFTS: *K4988* (crashed at Knapwell, 28-6-39). No. 23 ERFTS: *K4891*. No. 29 ERFTS: *K4945*; *K4959*. No. 31 ERFTS: *K5044*.

Supplied to South African Air Force: *K4889* (5-9-40); *K4891* (5-5-42); *K4936* (9-9-41); *K4940* (23-6-42); *K4941* (4-11-41); *K4942* (14-7-41); *K4943* (16-11-41); *K4946* (29-7-42); *K4962* (8-10-40); *K4968* (26-5-41); *K4974* (9-1-42); *K4975* (7-6-41); *K4981* (26-5-41); *K4995* (7-10-41); *K4999* (12-4-41); *K5001* (22-10-40); *K5004* (6-10-41); *K5009* (4-12-40); *K5018* (7-1-41); *K5022* (15-10-40); *K5028* (19-9-41); *K5033* (11-5-41); *K5034* (6-10-41); *K5035* (7-6-41); *K5039* (3-10-41); *K5042* (3-10-41); *K5047* (15-10-40).

Supplied to Royal Egyptian Air Force: *K4954* (10-7-40); *K5020* (30-3-40); *K5032* (10-7-40).

Ground Instruction Machines: *K4887* (became *2020M*, 7-40); *K4893* (became *2051M*, 8-40); *K4935* (became *1209M*); *K4969* (became *2313M*, 10-40); *K4972* (became *1764M*); *K4990* (became *1526M*, 6-39); *K5003* (became *2314M*, 5-40); *K5011* (became *1862M*, 5-40); *K5016* (became *1771M*); *K5024* (became *2055M*, 8-40); *K5045* (became *2237M*, 10-40).

Other Units and duties, etc.: *K4886* (No. 502 Sqn.; SOC, 2-1-41); *K4888* (R.A.F. College, Cranwell); *K4889* (No. 504 Sqn., No. 610 Sqn., A.A.F.); *K4891* (Northolt Stn. Flt.); *K4900* (Middle East Communications Flt.; crashed while landing at Kolundia, 23-6-42); *K4904* (No. 250 Sqn.); *K4907* (Iraq Communications Flt.; crashed while landing at Habbaniya, 19-8-43); *K4909* (No. 173 Sqn.; crashed near Gaza, Palestine, 21-1-43); *K4916* (No. 71 OTU; SOC, 27-7-44); *K4917* (No. 223 Sqn.; crashed while landing at Ismailia, 22-10-41); *K4919*, *K4938* (School of Army Co-operation); *K4929*, *K5003* (R.A.F. College, Cranwell); *K4943* (CFS); *K4945*, *K4969* (Northolt Stn. Flt.; R.A.F. College, Cranwell); *K4959* (Northolt Stn. Flt.); *K4979* (CFS); *K4998* (Ferry Pilots' Pool; ATA); *K5018* (No. 614 Sqn.; No. 25 (F) Sqn.; No. 601 Sqn.); *K5025* (No. 110 Sqn., RCAF; No. 112 Sqn., RCAF); *K5032* (Northolt Stn. Flt.; RAE); *K5033* (Northolt Stn. Flt); *K5035* (No. 600 Sqn.; No. 604 Sqn.; No. 607 Sqn., A.A.F.); *K5036* (No. 601 Sqn.; crashed in spin, 10-5-37); *K5037* (No. 604 Sqn.; crashed in Pagham harbour, 10-8-36).

The Hawker Hart Trainer (Series 2A). Third production batch of 114 aircraft, *K5784-K5897*, built by Vickers (Aviation) Ltd., Weybridge, Surrey, to Specification 8/35, to Contract No. 410420/35, between February and May 1936. Rolls-Royce Kestrel X and XDR engines. (No aircraft fitted with sand filters during manufacture.)

No. 1 Flying Training School: *K5793*; *K5806* (crashed at Lower Clatford, Andover, 23-2-40); *K5814*; *K5816* (crashed while landing at Shrewton, 18-2-42); *K5819*; *K5820*; *K5823*; *K5826* (crashed at Colworth House, Beds., 31-8-41); *K5827*; *K5839*; *K5847*; *K5861*; *K5870* (SOC, 10-2-41); *K5871* (SOC, 21-3-40); *K5878*; *K5885* (crashed near Leuchars, 2-10-36); *K5886-K5888*; *K5896*.

No. 2 Flying Training School: *K5811*; *K5836* (crashed at Digby, 21-6-37); *K5837* (crashed, 29-11-37); *K5838-K5841*; *K5858*; *K5862* (SOC, 1943); *K5868*.

No. 3 Flying Training School: *K5785-K5788*; *K5789* (crashed, 25-7-36); *K5794* (crashed while landing at Grantham, 3-6-37); *K5797* (SOC, 20-4-40); *K5798* (SOC, 6-4-40); *K5800-K5803*; *K5807*; *K5824* (crashed on barn while landing at Grantham, 12-4-37); *K5825-K5827*; *K5855*; *K5869*; *K5870-K5873*; *K5876*; *K5877*; *K5883*; *K5894*.

No. 5 Flying Training School: *K5816*; *K5825* (crashed, 19-8-37); *K5870*; *K5871.*

No. 6 Flying Training School: *K5810* (crashed while landing at Little Rissington, 10-11-39); *K5818* (crashed while landing at Netheravon, 21-5-36); *K5819-K5823*; *K5842* (crashed, 21-8-36); *K5872.*

No. 7 Flying Training School: *K5797*; *K5799* (crashed at Deeping St. Nicholas, Lincs, 17-8-40); *K5821*; *K5822* (SOC, 28-7-40); *K5826-K5828*; *K5830*; *K5833* (crashed while landing at Hornchurch, 8-6-36); *K5834*; *K5835*; *K5838*; *K5850*; *K5856* (SOC, 4-5-40); *K5857*; *K5858*; *K5860-K5862*; *K5868*; *K5874*; *K5875*; *K5877* (crashed near Alton, Hants, 28-11-39); *K5879*; *K5882*; *K5886* (SOC, 8-3-40); *K5889*; *K5892* (SOC, 2-5-40); *K5894*; *K5897.*

No. 8 Flying Training School: *K5826*; *K5853*; *K5855*; *K5865-K5867*; *K5878-K5880*; *K5894*; *K5897.*

No. 9 Flying Training School: *K5784;* *K5793*; *K5802* (crashed, 3-12-40); *K5804*; *K5805* (collided with *K5813* on the ground at Thornaby and written off, 20-6-36); *K5807*; *K5808*; *K5809* (crashed, 7-12-40); *K5810-K5816*; *K5817* (crashed while landing at Hullavington, 6-9-37); *K5819*; *K5831*; *K5839-K5841*; *K5843*; *K5844* (crashed while landing at Hullavington, 11-2-38); *K5845* (crashed, 2-1-37); *K5846* (crashed at Castle Coombe, 8-2-41); *K5847*; *K5848*; *K5851* (landed on top of Anson *L7057*, 2-7-40); *K5865*; *K5866* (SOC, 20-1-41); *K5869*; *K5873*; *K5878*; *K5881* (SOC, 3-9-39); *K5883* (SOC, 22-9-40); *K5884*; *K5887.*

No. 10 Flying Training Unit: *K5795* (crashed near Market Drayton, Shropshire, 19-12-38); *K5796*; *K5797*; *K5799*; *K5868*; *K5869*; *K5872*; *K5881-K5883*; *K5890* (crashed, 3-5-38); *K5892.*

No. 11 Flying Training School: *K5786* (crashed, 2-10-39); *K5803* (crashed while landing at Wittering, 1-10-37); *K5828-K5830*; *K5887.*

No. 12 Flying Training School: *K5799*; *K5822*; *K5826*; *K5865*; *K5867*; *K5868*; *K5872*; *K5879*; *K5882.*

No. 13 Flying Training School: *K5788*; *K5826*; *K5855*; *K5864* (crashed on landing at Drem, 3-10-39); *K5879.*

No. 14 Flying Training School: *K5788*; *K5811.*

No. 15 Flying Training School: *K5826*; *K5838*; *K5852*; *K5853*; *K5856*; *K5862*; *K5879*; *K5887.*

Elementary & Reserve Flying Training Schools: No. 3 ERFTS: *K5807.* No. 10 ERFTS: *K5816.* No. 11 ERFTS: *K5816.* No. 19 ERFTS: *K5800.* No. 20 ERFTS: *K5798.* No. 28 ERFTS: *K5810.* No. 29 ERFTS: *K5884.* No. 31 ERFTS: *K5797.*

Royal Air Force College, Cranwell: *K5790*; *K5791* (crashed at Cranwell, 20-9-39); *K5792*; *K5793*; *K5801* (SOC, 5-7-40); *K5831*; *K5832* (crashed while landing at Welbourn, 10-10-38); *R5846*; *R5848*; *R5849* (crashed while landing at Cranwell, 4-4-38); *K5853* (SOC, 13-5-40); *K5865*; *K5867*; *K5883*; *K5884* (crashed during night landing at Cranwell, 7-11-39).

Central Flying School: *K5850-K5858*; *K5859* (crashed in night landing at Upavon, 27-1-38); *K5860-K5862*; *K5863* (crashed while landing at Upavon, 6-12-35); *K5864*; *K5877.*

Glider Pilots' Exercise Unit: *K5819*; *K5861*.

Cambridge University Air Squadron: *K5889, K5890*.

Transferred to Admiralty Charge: *K5869* (31-12-41); *K5874* (31-12-41); *K5895* (15-11-39).

Supplied to South African Air Force: *K5784* (15-10-40); *K5787* (15-10-40); *K5788* (4-12-40); *K5790* (8-10-40); *K5792* (22-10-40); *K5793* (6-10-41); *K5804* (22-10-40); *K5807* (10-4-41); *K5814* (12-8-41); *K5821* (8-10-40); *K5827* (6-10-41); *K5831* (17-4-42); *K5835* (18-4-41); *K5838* (26-5-41); *K5848* (15-6-41; but lost at sea in transit); *K5850* (14-7-41); *K5852*; *K5855* (22-10-40); *K5857* (11-5-41); *K5858* (8-10-40); *K5860* (21-6-41; but lost at sea in transit); *K5865* (26-5-41); *K5867* (8-10-40); *K5868* (22-10-40); *K5872* (8-10-40); *K5873* (11-5-41); *K5876* (15-6-41); *K5878* (17-4-42); *K5879* (28-1-41); *K5882* (7-5-41); *K5887* (8-10-40); *K5889* (8-10-40); *K5894* (11-4-41); *K5896* (5-11-41); *K5897* (15-10-40).

Supplied to Royal Egyptian Air Force: *K5880* (30-3-40).

Ground Instruction Machines: *K5796* (became *1770M*); *K5811* (became *2052M*, 8-40); *K5830* (became *1758M*); *K5839* (became *2053M*, 7-40); *K5875* (became *1527M*, 6-39); *K5891* (became *919M*; 11-36).

Other Units and duties, etc.: *K5808* (ATA; SOC, 2-7-43); *K5813* (No. 64 (F) Sqn.; Straits Settlements Volunteer Air Force; No. 274 Sqn.; burnt on the ground at Bu Amud, 25-11-42); *K5819* (No. 296 Sqn.; No. 295 Sqn.; SOC, 9-3-44); *K5821* (Air Armament School); *K5823* (ATA; SOC, 29-1-44); *K5834* (ATA; SOC, 10-7-42); *K5843* (ATA; crashed while landing at Thame, 31-8-43); *K5847* (Electrical & Wireless School; No. 3 Radio School; ATA; SOC, 28-1-44); *K5861* (No. 296 Sqn.; ATA; SOC, 24-1-44); *K5888* (To Iraq, then India; SOC, 5-1-42); *K5891* (No. 604 Sqn., A.A.F.; crashed 30-10-36); *K5893* (No. 601 Sqn., A.A.F.; crashed while landing at Hendon, 1-10-37); *K5895* (Nos. 603 and 610 Sqns., A.A.F.); *K5896* (Nos. 604 and 501 Sqns., A.A.F.).

The Hawker Hart Trainer (Series 2A). Sixth production batch of 136 aircraft, *K6415-K6550*, built by Sir W.G. Armstrong Whitworth Aircraft Ltd., Coventry, to Specification 8-35. Rolls-Royce Kestrel X and XDR (many replaced in service by Kestrel XVI and XVIDR). *K6415-K6425* fitted with sand filters for service in the Middle East. Aircraft delivered between March and October 1936.

No. 1 Flying Training School: *K6439*; *K6448*; *K6449*; *K6455*; *K6462-K6464*; *K6466*; *K6467*; *K6469*; *K6470*; *K6474*; *K6475*; *K6478*; *K6485* (shot down by Messerschmitt Bf 110 over Old Sarum, 21-7-40); *K6491*; *K6499*; *K6500*; *K6501* (crashed at Shrewton landing ground, 15-10-41); *K6502*; *K6507* (crashed while landing at Shrewton, 24-10-41); *K6508*; *K6516*; *K6518*; *K6520-K6522*; *K6526*; *K6531*; *K6534*; *K6540* (crashed while landing at Shrewton, 8-11-40); *K6542*.

No. 2 Flying Training School: *K6439*; *K6440*; *K6441* (crashed, 18-6-36); *K6442* (crashed, 19-5-40); *K6443*; *K6444*; *K6448*; *K6456*; *K6459*; *K5460* (crashed while taking off at Boscombe Down, 22-3-38); *K6461*; *K6462*; *K6468*; *K6472*; *K6485*; *K6489* (crashed while landing at Digby, 23-4-37); *K6502*; *K6506*; *K6511*; *K6531*; *K6536*; *K6540*; *K6545*; *K6549*.

No. 3 Flying Training School: *K6443*; *K6462*; *K6487*; *K6494*; *K6498*; *K6504*; *K6510*; *K6521*; *K6524*; *K6538* (SOC, 1-7-40); *K6539*; *K6541-K6544*.

No. 4 Flying Training School (Egypt, Palestine and Iraq): *K6415-K6418*; *K6419* (crashed while landing at Amman, 30-8-39); *K6420-K6425*.

No. 5 Flying Training Unit: *K6440*; *K6479*; *K6485*; *K6499-K6501*; *K6508*; *K6511*; *K6514*; *K6515*; *K6517*; *K6522*; *K6536*; *K6547*.

No. 6 Flying Training School: *K6427-K6431*; *K6432* (crashed while landing at Bicester, 18-5-36); *K6433-K6436*; *K6474*; *K6476*; *K6493*; *K6498*; *K6513*; *K6523*; *K6528*; *K6539*; *K6541*.

No. 7 Flying Training School: *K6428*; *K6436* (SOC, 1-7-40); *K6448*; *K6449* (crashed, 31-5-40); *K6453*; *K6459* (crashed, 6-6-40); *K6464*; *K6470*; *K6498*; *K6505* (struck another aircraft during take-off at Peterborough and crashed, 21-4-38); *K6507*; *K6511* (crashed while landing at Sibson, 27-9-40); *K6513*.

No. 8 Flying Training School: *K6431* (SOC, 1-7-40); *K6433*; *K6438*; *K6475*; *K6511*; *K6513*.

No. 9 Flying Training School: *K6437* (crashed at Barnard Castle, Co. Durham, 23-1-37); *K6438* (crashed, 29-11-40); *K6439*; *K6444* (crashed, 17-1-41); *K6447* (crashed during night landing at Babdown landing ground, 11-10-40); *K6454-K6458*; *K6462*; *K6463*; *K6466* (crashed at Monkton Farley, Bath, 3-10-40); *K6468*; *K6472*; *K6476*; *K6478*; *K6484*; *K6487* (SOC, 12-6-41); *K6488*; *K6490* (SOC, 26-4-40); *K6491*; *K6496* (crashed, 17-11-40); *K6497* (crashed, 18-11-40); *K6512*; *K6518*; *K6520*; *K6524*; *K6525*; *K6527*; *K6528* (SOC, 19-2-40); *K6530*; *K6534*; *K6537* (crashed at Nailsworth, Glos, 28-10-40); *K6539*; *K6541* (crashed at night, 7-8-40); *K6542*; *K6544*; *K6549* (crashed, 14-5-40).

No. 10 Flying Training School: *K6430*, *K6431*; *K6492* (crashed at Ternhill, 13-5-37); *K6517*; *K6533*.

No. 11 Flying Training School: *K6429* (crashed near Derby, 10-10-39); *K6444*; *K6484*; *K6496*; *K6498*; *K6507*; *K6516*; *K6518*; *K6524*; *K6525*; *K6534*; *K6539-K6541*.

No. 12 Flying Training School: *K6427* (SOC, 1-7-40); *K6428*; *K6440* (SOC, 16-8-40); *K6449*; *K6459*; *K6469* (crashed, 21-6-40); *K6470*; *K6486*; *K6529*; *K6530*.

No. 13 Flying Training School: *K6431*; *K6452* (crashed near Dunblane, Perthshire, 18-9-39); *K6454*; *K6533*.

No. 14 Flying Training School: *K6454*; *K6466*; *K6536*.

No. 15 Flying Training School: *K6467*; *K6475*; *K6516*; *K6518*; *K6521* (crashed while landing at Lossiemouth, 22-6-39).

No. 16 Flying Training School: *K6539*.

Elementary & Reserve Flying Training Schools: No. 1 ERFTS: *K6473*; *K6493*; *K6543*; *K6544*. No. 2 ERFTS: *K6456*; *K6549*; *K6550* (collided with Anson *N5260* while landing at Filton, 17-7-39). No. 3 ERFTS: *K6509*; *K6532* (collided with Swordfish *L2740* and crashed, 25-8-37); *K6535*. No. 4 ERFTS: *K6429*; *K6484*; *K6523*; *K6525*. No. 5 ERFTS: *K6427*; *K6486*; *K6529*; *K6530*. No. 6 ERFTS: *K6494*; *K6542*. No. 7 ERFTS: *K6524*; *K6526*. No. 8 ERFTS: *K6472*; *K6506*. No. 9 ERFTS: *K6539*; *K6541*. No. 10 ERFTS: *K6450*. No. 12 ERFTS: *K6499*; *K6547*; *K6548* (SOC, 1-7-40). No. 13 ERFTS: *K6485*; *K6540*; *K6545*; *K6546*. No. 15 ERFTS: *K6511*; *K6522*. No. 16 ERFTS: *K6527*; *K6528*. No. 19 ERFTS: *K6487*; *K6488*. No. 20 ERFTS: *K6508*; *K6510*; *K6511*. No. 22 ERFTS: *K6451* (SOC, 8-8-40); *K6465*; *K6496*. No. 28 ERFTS: *K6474*; *K6476*; *K6498*. No. 29 ERFTS: *K6468*.

Royal Air Force College, Cranwell: *K6442* (crashed, 19-5-40); *K6445* (crashed while landing, 28-9-39); *K6446* (crashed while landing, 4-5-36); *K6447*; *K6448*; *K6450*; *K6468*; *K6477*; *K6478*; *K6494*; *K6495*; *K6518*; *K6519*.

Central Flying School: *K6452-K6454*.

Oxford University Air Squadron: *K6487-K6489*; *K6498*; *K6511*.

Cambridge University Air Squadron: *K6502*, *K6504*, *K6506*.

University of London Air Squadron: *K6508*; *K6510*.

Supplied to South African Air Force: *K6428* (8-10-40); *K6435* (22-10-40); *K6439* (17-4-42); *K6443* (27-1-41); *K6448* (8-10-40); *K6450* (22-10-40); *K6453* (4-9-42); *K6454* (17-1-41); *K6455* (5-12-41); *K6462* (19-9-41); *K6463* (13-4-42); *K6468* (7-5-41); *K6470* (7-6-41); *K6471* (7-6-41); *K6472* (17-4-42); *K6474* (12-8-41); *K6483* (12-10-40); *K6484* (16-5-41); *K6488* (14-7-41); *K6491* (12-8-41); *K6495* (21-4-41); *K6498* (7-6-41); *K6500* (12-6-42); *K6502* (14-7-41); *K6504* (11-4-41); *K6506* (8-10-40); *K6513* (14-5-41); *K6516* (26-10-41); *K6518* (26-5-41); *K6520* (7-42); *K6524* (14-7-41); *K6527* (9-1-42); *K6530* (26-5-41); *K6530* (26-5-41); *K6531* (14-7-41); *K6535* (15-10-40); *K6542* (12-8-41); *K6544* (1-11-40); *K6545* (22-10-40).

Supplied to Royal Egyptian Air Force: *K6473* (30-3-40);

Ground Instruction Machines: *K6430* (became *1772M*); *K6456* (became *2054M*, 7-40); *K6458* (12-6-36); *K6475* (became *2039M*, 7-40); *K6509* (became *1779M*); *K6510* (became *2043M*, 6-40); *K6514* (became *1598M*, 6-39); *K6517* (became *2189M*, 8-40); *K6529* (became *1954M*, 6-40); *K6536* (became *1945M*, 5-40); *K6546* (became *2019M*, 9-40).

Other Units and duties, etc: *K6417* (Damascus Communications Flt.; SOC, 7-9-42); *K6420* (No. 71 O.T.U.; SOC, 21-5-42); *K6421* (No. 173 Sqn.); *K6422* (No. 71 O.T.U.; No. 26 Anti-Aircraft Co-operation Unit; crashed while landing at Lydda, 14-10-43); *K6423* (No. 71 O.T.U.; SOC, 27-7-44); *K6426* (Straits Settlements Volunteer Air Force; crashed on Penang airfield during aerobatic display, 6-3-38); *K6433* (to Admiralty Charge, 15-11-39; No. 780 Sqn., F.A.A.); *K6435* (Odiham Stn. Flt.); *K6448* (No. 32 (F) Sqn.); *K6449* (No. 17 (F) Sqn.); *K6466* (No. 19 (F) Sqn.); *K6467* (No. 111 (F) Sqn.); *K6468* (No. 56 (F) Sqn.); *K6469* (No. 43 (F) Sqn.); *K6470* (No. 25 (F) Sqn.); *K6471* (No.24 (C) Sqn.); *K6472* (No. 609 Sqn., A.A.F.); *K6473* (No. 610 Sqn., A.A.F.); *K6474* (No. 611 Sqn., A.A.F.); *K6475* (No. 73 (F) Sqn.); *K6476* (No. 80 (F) Sqn.); *K6478* (ATA; SOC, 14-11-43); *K6479* (No. 17 (F) Sqn.; Duxford Stn. Flt.; Tangmere Stn. Flt.; No. 614 Sqn., A.A.F.); *K6480* (No. 54 (F) Sqn.; No. 29 (F) Sqn.; crashed while landing at Debden, 25-8-37); *K6481* (No. 56 (F) Sqn.; No. 604 Sqn., A.A.F.; No. 80 (F) Sqn.; crashed into hangar at Debden, 25-8-37); *K6482* (No. 607 Sqn.; No. 245 (F) Sqn.; No. 152 (F) Sqn.); *K6483* (No. 608 Sqn., A.A.F.); *K6484* (No. 54 (F) Sqn.); *K6485* (No. 501 Sqn., A.A.F.); *K6493* (Farnborough Stn. Flt.); *K6496* (Andover Stn. Flt.; Abingdon Stn. Flt.); *K6503* (Duxford Stn. Flt.; crashed and SOC, 1937); *K6505* (Duxford Stn. Flt.); *K6510* (Northolt Stn. Flt.); *K6522* (No. 602 Sqn., A.A.F.; ATA, crashed while landing at Thame, 2-9-43); *K6534* (ATA; SOC, 24-10-43).

The Hawker Estonian Hart. Eight aircraft, *146-153*, built by H.G. Hawker Engineering Co., Ltd., Kingston, during 1932. Rolls-Royce Kestrel IS engines. First flight by *146*, 19 July 1932, P.E.G. Sayer. Delivered to Estonia during September and October 1932. Interchangeable wheel and float undercarriage.

The Hawker Swedish Hart. Four aircraft, *1301-1304*, built by Hawker Aircraft Ltd., Kingston, during 1933. Bristol Pegasus IM2 radial engines. First flight by *1301*, 6 January 1934. Delivered to Sweden during July 1934. Interchangeable wheel and float undercarriage. A further 42 aircraft built under licence at the State Aircraft Factory, Trollhättan, during 1935-36, powered by licence-built 550 h.p. Nohad (Bristol) Pegasus IU2 radial engines.

The Hawker Tomtit. One prototype built as a private venture under Works Order No. 391/28 and given Company "registration" *H.T.1* by H.G. Hawker Engineering Co. Ltd. Aircraft built between July and September 1928. First flown by P.W.S. Bulman in November that year. 130 h.p. Armstrong Siddeley Mongoose IIA engine., later replaced by 150 h.p. Mongoose IIIC. Taken on Air Ministry Charge under Contract No. 878972/28. To A. & A.E.E., Martlesham Heath, 11-28, for brief handling trials. Displayed by H.G.H.E.L. at the Olympia Show, 16/27-7-29. Allocated Service No. *J9772*. To Martlesham, 8-29 to 4-30. Service trials with No. 3 Flying Training School, Grantham, 6-30; No. 24 (Communications) Sqn., 10-7-30 until 5-33. A.D.G.B. Communications Flt., 12-35 to 1-36.

The Hawker Tomtit. Five sporting aircraft ordered under private Contract, *G-AALL*, *G-AASI*, *G-ABAX*, *G-ABII* and *G-ABOD* (numerous engine installations). Works Order Nos. allocated as suffixes to original 391/28.

G-AALL. Originally flown (c. 3-30) with Mongoose IIIA, but changed to Mongoose IIIC. C. of A. issued 11-6-30. Prepared for H.R.H. the Prince of Wales. Raced in 1930 King's Cup Race (18th), and 1932 King's Cup Race (retired). Scrapped in 1937.

G-AASI. First flown with A.B.C. Cirrus Hermes II engine (later changed to Wolseley A.R.9). Owned by H.G. Hawker Engineering Co., Ltd. C. of A. issued, 30-9-30. To Martlesham Heath for trials under Contract, 1930. Brooklands School of Flying Ltd., 1932-1934. Wolseley Motors Ltd., 1934-1936. Owned by J.G. Hopcraft, 1936. King's Cup Races, 1933 (retired); 1934 (7th); Manx Air Races, 1936 (2nd and 10th). Registered to W. Humble, Firbeck.1942. Scrapped, c.1943.

G-ABAX. First flown with Mongoose IIIA engine (later changed to Wolseley A.R.9). Owned by the Hon F.E. Guest, 1930-32. C. of A. issued, 26-6-30. King's Cup Races, 1930 (12th), 1933 (retired), 1934 (retired). Brooklands School of Flying Ltd., 1932-1933; Wolseley Motors Ltd., 1934-1936; S.U. Carburettor Co., Ltd., 1936. Tollerton Aero Club, c.1938. Scrapped, c. 1940?

G-ABII. Mongoose IIIC. C. of A. issued, 31-1-31. Owned by H. Wilcox, Esq. King's Cup Race, 1932 (retired). Damaged beyond repair, Cowes, 10-4-48.

G-ABOD. Prototype Wolseley test bed. Aircraft flown with Wolseley A.R.2, A.R.7 and A.R.9 (also Aquarius and Aries) engines. Owned by H.G. Hawker Engineering Co. Ltd., 1931-1933. C. of A. issued, 2-1-33. Brooklands School of Flying Ltd., 1933-1934; Wolseley Motors Ltd., 1934-1936; S.U. Carburettor Co. Ltd., 1936. King's Cup Races, 1933 (retired), 1934 (retired). Tollerton Aero Club. Scrapped during the War.

The Hawker Tomtit I. First production batch of 10 aircraft, *J9773-J9782*, ordered from H.G. Hawker Engineering Co. Ltd., Kingston, under Contract No. 910623/29, built during 1929 and 1930. 150 h.p. Armstrong Siddeley Mongoose III radial engines.

No. 3 Flying Training School, Grantham: *J9773* (10-29 to 12-30); *J9774* (5-30 to 9-31); *J9775* (6-30 to 5-31); *J9776* (4-30 to 11-30); *J9777* (from 9-29; struck Siskin *J9190* while taking off at Spittlegate, 14-7-31, and SOC); *J9778* (3-30 to 8-31); *J9779* (from 11-30); *J9780* (5-30 to 6-31); *J9781* (from 11-30); *J9782* (9-30 to 8-31).

No. 3 (F) Sqn.: *J9779* (7-31 to 8-31).

No. 24 (C) Sqn.: *J9776* (12-31 to 6-32); *J9781* (from 4-12-31).

Central Flying School: *J9780* (from 1929); *J9782* (from 7-33).

Civil Registrations: *J9781:* Sold to L.J. Anderson, registered *G-AEXC*, C. of A. issued 5-4-38. Herts and Essex Aero Club, 8-38. Scrapped during Second World War. *J9782:* Sold to C.B. Field, 11-2-37, but registration (*G-AEVP*) not taken up. Re-sold to C.B. Field, C. of A. issued 11-3-38, as *G-AFFL*. Sold to H.D. Rankin, 7-38; aircraft broken up at Southend, 9-39.

The Hawker Tomtit I. Second production batch of six aircraft, K1448-K1453, built by H.G. Hawker Engineering Co. Ltd., during July 1930 under Contract No. 910623/29. Armstrong Siddeley Mongoose IIIC engines.

No. 3 Flying Training School, Grantham: *K1448* (SOC, 20-1-31); *K1449* (SOC, 17-3-32; *K1450-K1452.*

Other aircraft and Civil Registrations: *K1450* (CFS); *K1451* (prepared as demonstration aircraft for Canadian Department of National Defence, c.1932. Became *G-AEVO*, C. of A. issued 1-4-37; scrapped at Redhill, 1946-47); *K1453* (RAE; SOC, 3-7-35).

The Hawker Tomtit I. Third production batch of eight aircraft, *K1779-K1786*, built by H.G. Hawker Engineering Co. Ltd., during November and December 1930 and ordered under Contract No. 27634/30. Delivered in January 1931. 150 h.p. Armstrong Siddeley Mongoose IIIC engines.

Service Units: *K1780* (No. 2 FTS; SOC, 11-1-35); *K1782* (No. 24 (C) Sqn.; sold on civil register; *K1783* ("C" Flt., Gosport; sold on civil register; *K1784* (No. 3 FTS; sold on civil register; *K1785* (CFS; Anti-Aircraft Co-operation Unit; sold on civil register; *K1786* (No. 3 FTS; No. 23 Group Communications Flt.; No. 5 Group Communications Flt.; sold on civil register)

Civil Registrations: *K1781* (became *G-AFIB*; C. of A. issued 15-8-38; Vickers (Aviation) Ltd., 1941; became road block at Chilbolton, 10-43); *K1782* (became *G-AEES*; C. of A. issued 11-5-36; destroyed in hangar fire, Maylands, 6-2-40; *K1783* (became *G-AGEF*; C. of A. issued 8-7-42; scrapped 18-10-43, following accident); *K1784* (became *G-AFVV*; C. of A. issued 4-7-39; owned by Alex Henshaw, 1941); *K1786* (sold 26-8-38; became *G-AFTA*; C. of A. issued 28-4-39; purchased by HAL and restored; preserved with Shuttleworth Collection with original R.A.F. serial, *K1786*).

The Hawker Canadian Tomtit. Two aircraft, numbered *139* and *140*, shipped to Canada in 1930 on order to the Canadian Department of National Defence. Mongoose IIIA engines. These aircraft differed from all others in having a split-axle undercarriage.

The Hawker New Zealand Tomtit. Four aircraft shipped out to New Zealand during 1930-31 for service with the New Zealand Permanent Air Force as elementary trainers. Mongoose IIIC engines.

The Hawker F.20/27 Interceptor. One prototype, *J9123*, designed to Air Ministry Specification F.20/27, and built by H.G. Hawker Engineering Co. Ltd., Kingston, in 1928 under Contract No. 813870/27. 530 h.p. Bristol Jupiter VIIF radial engine. First flight, 8-28, P.W.S. Bulman. To A. & A.E.E., 8-28. Re-engined with Bristol Mercury IIIA engine. To A. & A.E.E., 1-30 to 2-30. To R.A.E., 16-6-30. Re-engined with 520 h.p. Bristol Mercury VI. To A. & A.E.E., 7-30. Aircraft crashed while landing at Farnborough, 14-12-31.

The Hawker Hoopoe. One naval interceptor fighter prototype, *N237*, designed to Specification N.21/26 (as amended in 1927), ordered under Contract No. 858360/27, and first flown by P.W.S. Bulman in about October 1928. Fitted initially with Bristol Mercury II radial (as specified) and two-bay wings. To the M.A.E.E., Felixstowe, for evaluation with twin float undercarriage in 1929 (?). Returned to H.G.H.E.L. to be re-engined with Armstrong Siddeley Jaguar (first with plain Townend ring, later with concentric rings) and single-bay wings; limited deck landing trials in the latter configuration. Armstrong Siddeley Panther III engine fitted in 1930, and wheel spats added. Aircraft written off Company charge in 1932.

The Hawker Hornet. One prototype interceptor fighter prototype, *J9682*, designed as a private venture to Specification F.20/27 with 420 h.p. Rolls-Royce F.XIA (in parallel with Jupiter-powered Hawker F.20/27 Interceptor, *J9123*—see above). First flown in March 1929 by P.W.S. Bulman. Acquired by Air Ministry under Contract No. 887063/28, and re-engined with 480 h.p. Rolls-Royce F.XIS. To A. & A.E.E., 27-5-29. Displayed at Olympia Show, 16/27-5-29. Re-engined with 525 h.p. Rolls-Royce F.XIIS. To A. & A.E.E., 2-30. R.A.E., Farnborough, 3-30. Re-named **Fury**. To No. 1 Sqn., 3-30, for Service trials. Collided with Siskin J9359, near Chichester, Sussex, 11-4-30; lost upper wing and crashed.

The Hawker Fury I. First production batch of 21 aircraft, *K1926-K1946*, to Specification 13/30, ordered under Contract No. 40559/30, and built by H.G. Hawker Engineering Co. Ltd., between October 1930 and March 1931; delivered to R.A.F. in April 1931. Rolls-Royce Kestrel IIS engines.

No. 1 (F) Sqn.: *K1926*; *K1931*; *K1940*; *K1943.*

No. 25 (F) Sqn.: *K1930*; *K1945.*

No. 32 (F) Sqn.: *K1939.*

No. 43 (F) Sqn.: *K1927-K1930*; *K1931* (SOC, 13-5-37); *K1932*; *K1933* (SOC, 28-8-35); *K1934*; *K1935*; *K1936* (collided with *K1933* and damaged beyond repair, 28-1-33); *K1937*; *K1938*; *K1939* (SOC, 8-10-37); *K1940*; *K1941* (crashed while descending through fog, 30-10-36); *K1942-K1944*; *K1945* (SOC, 19-6-35); *K1946.*

Ground Instruction Machines: *K1926* (became *928M*); *K1927* (became *1068M*, 5-38); *K1928* (became *1739M*, 1-40); *K1930* (became *2196M*, 8-40); *K1932* (became *987M*, 10-37); *K1935* (became *1949M*, 6-40); *K1942* (became *749M*, 1-36); *K1943* (became *974M*, 1-37); *K1944* (became *853M*, 6-36); *K1945* (became *1045M*, 3-38).

Other Units and duties: *K1926*, *K1927* (A. & A.E.E; R.A.E.); *K1928* (A. & A.E.E.; No. 3 F.T.S.; No. 1 Air Armament School); *K1929* (No. 3 F.T.S.; to South African Air Force, 6-9-40); *K1934* (R.A.E.; SOC, 12-6-36); *K1935* (became **Fury Mark II** prototype); *K1937* (No. 11 F.T.S.); *K1938* (No. 11 F.T.S.; crashed on take-off at Wolverhampton, 13-7-38); *K1940* (No. 1 Air Armament School); *K1941* (Nos. 5 and 3 F.T.S.).

The Hawker Fury I. Second production batch of 48 aircraft, *K2035-K2082*, built to Specification 13/30 by H.G. Hawker Engineering Co. Ltd., Kingston, between January and March 1932, and ordered under Contract No. 102468/31. Rolls-Royce Kestrel IIS engines.

No. 1 (F) Sqn.: *K2035*; *K2036* (collided with *K2064* near Shoreham, 26-5-32); *K2037*; *K2038* (collided with *K2044*, 5-4-32); *K2039* (SOC, 27-11-37); *K2040*; *K2041-K2043*; *K2044* (collided with *K2047* near Northolt, 23-4-34); *K2045* (crashed, 15-12-36); *K2046*; *K2047* (collided with *K2044* near Northolt, 23-4-34); *K2048*; *K2049* (SOC, 10-8-32); *K2050-K2052*; *K2055*; *K2060*; *K2061* (hit cables near Lewes, 22-2-38); *K2062*; *K2063*; *K2064* (collided with *K2036* near Shoreham, 26-5-32); *K2066*; *K2067*; *K2069*; *K2074*; *K2075*.

No. 25 (F) Sqn.: *K2041*; *K2048*; *K2050*; *K2051-K2053*; *K2054* (SOC, 28-7-32); *K2055*; *K2056* (SOC, 8-5-34); *K2057* (collided with *K2055* near Hawkinge and crashed, 17-9-32); *K2059* (crashed while landing at North Weald, 30-3-36); *K2060*; *K2062*; *K2066-K2072*; *K2073* (crashed at Thorney Island, 25-9-33); *K2076-K2078*; *K2079* (crashed, 3-9-36).

No. 43 (F) Sqn.: *K2035*; *K2050-K2053*; *K2070*; *K2074* (broke up in the air near Chichester, Sussex, 4-4-38); *K2075*; *K2076*; *K2080* (SOC, 7-7-41); *K2081*; *K2082.*

No. 87 (F) Sqn.: *K2052*; *K2062*; *K2066.*

Flying Training Schools: No. 3 FTS: *K2035* (crashed while landing at South Cerney, 29-6-39); *K2058* (crashed while landing at South Cerney, 29-7-38); *K2067* (crashed, 28-1-37); *K2071.* No. 5 FTS: *K2050.* No. 6 FTS: *K2040* (crashed on range near Netheravon, 28-8-36). No. 8 FTS: *K2050.* No. 10 FTS: *K2082* (SOC, 10-10-39). No. 11 FTS: *K2062.*

Supplied to South African Air Force: *K2050* (5-9-40); *K2071* (5-9-40).

Ground Instruction Machines: *K2037* (became *849M*, 5-36); *K2041* (became *947M*, 4-37); *K2042* (became *925M*, 2-37); *K2043* (became *1019M*, 11-37); *K2046* (became *1131M*, 9-38); *K2048* (became *1018M*, 11-37); *K2051* (became *1017M*, 11-37); *K2052* (became *2018M*, 6-40); *K2055* (became *1044M*, 3-38); *K2060* (became *1026M*, 12-37); *K2062* (became *1465M*, 5-39); *K2063* (became *976M*, 8-37); *K2066* (became *992M*, 10-37); *K2069* (became *946M*, 3-37); *K2070* (became *1122M*); *K2075* (became *998M*, 10-37); *K2078* (became *948M*, 2-37); *K2081* (became *1048M*).

The Hawker Fury I. Third production batch of 16 aircraft, *K2874-K2883* and *K2899-K2904*, ordered under Contract No. 184968/32 (Parts I and 2) to Specification 13/30, and built by H.G. Hawker Engineering Co. Ltd., during December 1932 and January 1933. Kestrel IS engines and twin Vickers Mark II machine guns.

No. 1 (F) Sqn.: *K2878*; *K2881*; *K2899*; *K2900* (SOC, 3-1-38); *K2901* and *K2902* (collided over Stansted Park, Essex, 17-12-37); *K2903.*

No. 25 (F) Sqn.: *K2877*; *K2878*; *K2882*; *K2883.*

No. 43 (F) Sqn.: *K2882*; *K2883.*

No. 87 (F) Sqn.: *K2878*; *K2882*; *K2883.*

Flying Training Schools: No. 2 FTS: *K2877*; *K2903.* No. 3 FTS: *K2876*; *K2880* (SOC, 30-7-74); *K2882.* No. 6 FTS: *K2876.* No. 9 FTS: *K2879.* No. 11 FTS: *K2878* (SOC, 3-5-38); *K2883* (crashed while landing at Penrhos, 1-4-38).

Supplied to South African Air Force: *K2875* (7-10-40); *K2877* (5-9-40); *K2899* (7-10-40); *K2903* (7-10-40).

Ground Instruction Machines: *K2874* (became *2239M*, 10-40); *K2876* (became *1719M*, 1-40); *K2879* (became *1911M*, 4-40); *K2881* (became *1049M*, 4-38); *K2882* (became *2241M*, 11-40).

Other Units and duties, etc.: *K2874* (R.A.E.); *K2875* (C.F.S.; R.A.E.); *K2879* (R.A.E.); *K2899* (No. 1 Air Armament School); *K2904* (C.F.S.; crashed while landing at Marlborough landing ground, Wilts, 23-5-39).

The Hawker Fury I. Fourth production batch of 13 aircraft, *K3730-K3742*, ordered under Contract No. 252331/33 to Specification 13-32, and built by Hawker Aircraft Ltd., Kingston, between September and November 1934. Rolls-Royce Kestrel IS engines and Vickers Mark III machine guns.

No. 43 (F) Sqn.: *K3730-K3741*; *K3742* (crashed in sea, 27-6-35).

No. 2 Flying Training School: *K3730* (crashed during gun firing at Sutton Bridge, 20-6-38); *K3731*; *K3732* (crashed, 4-2-36); *K3741.*

No. 3 Flying Training School: *K3731*; *K3740.*

No. 5 Flying Training School: *K3733*; *K3734* (SOC, 21-7-37); *K3735*; *K3736* (crashed while landing at Sealand, 17-3-39).

No. 6 Flying Training School: *K3737* (crashed, 6-1-36); *K3738* (crashed while landing at Little Rissington, 6-9-39); *K3739*.

Supplied to South African Air Force: *K3731* (5-9-40); *K3733* (1-7-40); *K3735* (1-7-40); *K3739* (5-9-40); *K3740* (5-9-40); *K3741* (6-9-40).

Ground Instruction Machine: *K3736* (became *1464M*).

The Hawker Fury I. Fifth production batch of 20 aircraft, *K5663-K5682*, ordered under Contract No. 409396/35 to Specification 13-32, and built by Hawker Aircraft Ltd., Kingston, during November and December 1935. Final standard of preparation.

No. 1 (F) Sqn.: *K5673*; *K5679*.

No. 24 (C) Sqn.: *K5672*.

No. 25 (F) Sqn.: *K5677*.

No. 43 (F) Sqn.: *K5671* (crashed while landing at Andover, 6-7-36); *K5672*; *K5674*; *K5675*.

Royal Air Force College, Cranwell (Advanced Training Squadron): *K5664*; *K5665*; *K5677* (crashed on take-off at Cranwell, 10-5-38); *K5678*; *K5680*; *K5681* and *K5682* (collided in the air, 7-10-36).

Flying Training Schools: No. 3 FTS: *K5673* (crashed while landing at South Cerney, 7-12-38); *K5676*; *K5678*; *K5680*. No. 5 FTS: *K5663*; *K5669*; *K5670*; *K5672*. No. 6 FTS: *K5667*. No. 7 FTS: *K5663*; *K5668* (SOC, 12-10-37); *K5669*; *K5670*. No. 8 FTS: *K5672*. No. 11 FTS: *K5666* (SOC, 12-10-37); *K5679* (SOC, 14-5-37).

Supplied to South African Air Force: *K5663*, *K5669*, *K5670* and *K5672* (1-7-40); *K5674* (5-8-40); *K5675* (6-9-40); *K5676* (5-9-40); *K5678* (6-9-40); *K5680* (7-10-40).

Ground Instruction Machines: *K5664* (became *2246M*); *K5667* (became *1732M*).

Other Unit: *K5664* (No. 9 MU.; crashed while landing at Cosford, 29-6-40).

The Hawker Fury I. Production batch of 89 aircraft, *K8218-K8306*, ordered under Contract No. 419059/35 to Specification 13/32, and built by General Aircraft Ltd., Hanworth, between July 1936 and April 1937. Kestrel IS engines.

No. 1 (F) Sqn.: *K8247-K8249*; *K8255*; *K8272*; *K8275*; *K8276*; *K8278*; *K8279*; *K8281*; *K8291*; *K8296*; *K8303*.

No. 43 (F) Sqn.: *K8250-K8254*; *K8256*; *K8257*; *K8299*.

No. 73 (F) Sqn.: *K8247-K8258*; *K8270-K8272*.

No. 87 (F) Sqn.: *K8256-K8258*; *K8270*; *K8271*; *K8273-K8281*.

Royal Air Force College, Cranwell (Advanced Training Squadron): *K8242*; *K8259*; *K8260*; *K8268*; *K8297*; *K8298*; *K8300-K8302*.

Central Flying School: *K8238-K8240*; *K8241* (crashed near Radstock, Somerset, 9-3-38); *K8243-K8245*; *K8250*; *K8292*.

No. 2 Flying Training School: *K8227*; *K8228*; *K8269*; *K8297*.

No. 3 Flying Training School: *K8231*.

No. 5 Flying Training School: *K8224*; *K8226*.

No. 6 Flying Training School: *K8225*; *K8234*; *K8237*; *K8250*; *K8256*; *K8258* (SOC, 2-38).

No. 7 Flying Training School: *K8224* (crashed while landing at Peterborough, 20-3-39); *K8226*; *K8230*; *K8233*; *K8251* (crashed, 31-10-38); *K8270*; *K8278*; K8288; *K8299*.

No. 8 Flying Training School: *K8226-K8229*; *K8252*; *K8253*; *K8261*; *K8262*; *K8263* (crashed on Tipperweir Hill, Kincardineshire, 18-1-38); *K8265-K8267*; *K8275*; *K8293*; *K8304*.

No. 9 Flying Training School: *K8218-K8221*; *K8222* (crashed on Long Newton range, 20-6-39); *K8223* (collided with gunnery drogue, caught fire and crashed into sea off Chesil Bank, Dorset, 25-5-38); *K8224*; *K8254*; *K8264*; *K8285*; *K8289*; *K8290*; *K8303*; *K8305*.

No. 10 Flying Training School: *K8230-K8233*; *K8282* (crashed while taking off at Penrhos, 28-6-38); *K8283-K8287*; *K8298*; *K8299*.

No. 11 Flying Training School: *K8235*; *K8236*; *K8256*; *K8275*; *K8287*; *K8294* (crashed while landing at Penrhos, 20-3-39); *K8295*; *K8300*; *K8304*.

Other Units and duties, etc.: *K8219* (Aldergrove Stn. Flt.; crashed near Ballygomartin, Ulster,

12-6-37); *K8228* (Waddington Stn. Flt.; SOC, 18-8-37); *K8243* (No. 1 Air Armament School); *K8244* (No. 1 Air Armament School; crashed on Theddlethorpe range, 13-11-39); *K8245, K8246, K8255, K8306* (No. 1 Air Armament School). *K8257* (Northolt Stn. Flt; blown over while taxying, 17-3-40, and damaged beyond repair); *K8273, K8274* and *K8280* (No. 2 Anti-Aircraft Co-operation Unit).

The Hawker Fury Interim Fighter. (Also known as Intermediate Fury). One aircraft, *G-ABSE*, built at Company expense during 1931-32 and flown by P.W.S. Bulman on 13-4-32. Trial installation aircraft fitted in turn with Kestrel IIS, IVS with Goshawk supercharger, Kestrel VI, Goshawk III and Kestrel VI Special. Various TIs incorporated, including wheel spats, cantilever landing gear, Dowty internally-sprung wheels, electro-magnetic bomb gear and Vickers Mark III machine guns. Certificate of Airworthiness issued, 10-5-32. Allocated to Air Service Training, Hamble, for aerobatics, 1936. Scrapped, 1938.

The Hawker Fury II Trial Installation Prototype. One aircraft, previously a Fury I, *K1935*, modified by Hawker Aircraft Ltd. in 1933 up to the standard of preparation currently reached by the Interim Fury *G-ABSE*, i.e. with Kestrel VI and wheel spats. Performance trials with this aircraft at Martlesham Heath resulted in the drafting of Specification 6/35, to which subsequent Fury Mark IIs were built. (Became Ground Instruction Machine, *1949M*, 6-40).

The Hawker Fury II. Production batch of 23 aircraft, *K7263-K7285*, ordered under Contract No. 421941/35 to Specification 6/35, and built by Hawker Aircraft Ltd., Kingston and Brooklands, between October and December 1936. Rolls-Royce Kestrel VI engines.

No. 25 (F) Sqn.: *K7263-K7266; K7267* (SOC, 7-7-37); *K7268-K7278; K7279* (crashed near Dymchurch, 2-8-37); *K7280-K7283*.

No. 41 (F) Sqn.: *K7263-K7266; K7268-K7272; K7273* (crashed at Alwinton, Northumberland, 20-4-38); *K7274-K7277; K7278* (SOC, 26-1-40); *K7280-K7283; K7285.*

Ground Instruction Machines: *K7263* (became *1569M*, 6-39); *K7264* (became *1570M*, 6-39); *K7265* (became *2033M*, 6-40); *K7266* (became *1571M*, 6-39); *K7268* (became *1572M*, 6-39); *K7269* (became *1573M*, 6-39); *K7270* (became *1574M*, 6-39); *K7271* (became *1575M*, 6-39); *K7272* (became *2027M*, 7-40); *K7274* (became *2031M*, 6-40); *K7275* (became *2032M*, 6-40); *K7276* (became *1065M*, 5-38); *K7277* (became *1576M*, 6-39); *K7280* (became *1334M*, 3-39); *K7281* (became *1577M*, 6-39); *K7282* (became *1578M*, 6-39); *K7283* (became *2230M*, 9-40); *K7285* (became *1579M*, 6-39).

Other Unit: *K7284* (Northolt Stn. Flt.; crashed at Fulmer, Bucks, 28-9-39).

The Hawker Yugoslav Fury (Series 1A). Production batch of six aircraft ordered from H.G. Hawker Engineering Co. Ltd., Kingston, under Contract No. 289711/32 for the Royal Yugoslav Air Force and delivered in 1932. Carried temporary manufacturer's Nos. *H.F.1* to *H.F.6. H.F.3* powered by 500 h.p. Hispano-Suiza 12NB engine; remainder with 525 h.p. Rolls-Royce Merlin IIS.

The Hawker Norwegian Fury. One aircraft, *401*, ordered by the Norwegian government in 1932 for competitive evaluation. Powered by 530 h.p. Armstrong Siddeley Panther IIIA. First flown by P.W.S. Bulman, 9 September 1932. At one time was fitted with ski landing gear.

The Hawker Persian Fury (Series I). Production batch of 16 aircraft, *201-216*, ordered in January 1933 by the Persian government under Contract No. 100118/33. Aircr't powered by Pratt & Whitney Hornet S2B1G radial engines driving three-blade Hamilton metal propellers. Deliveries commenced July 1933.

The Hawker Portuguese Fury I. Three aircraft, *50-52*, ordered for the Portuguese Army Air Force in November 1933 under Contract No. 311709/34 (signed in 1934), and built by Hawker Aircraft Ltd. First aircraft flown, 28-5-34. 525 h.p. Rolls-Royce Kestrel IIS engines. All aircraft delivered in June 1934.

The **Hawker Persian Fury (Series II).** Six aircraft ordered in May 1934 by the Persian government under Contract No. 366843/34, to be powered by Bristol Mercury VI SP radial engines. Aircraft numbered from *217* onwards, but several Series I aircraft returned for conversion. First Mercury-powered Fury (No. *203* converted) flew 25-9-34. Deliveries commenced 3-35.

The **Hawker Yugoslav Fury (Special).** One Fury Series IA, previously numbered *H.F.6*, returned to Hawker Aircraft Ltd., for development tests with 720 h.p. Lorraine Petrel Hfrs engine. Delivered to Yugoslavia, 4-35. Subsequent history not known.

The **Hawker Yugoslav Fury (Series II).** Production batch of ten aircraft ordered by the Yugoslav government on 3-10-35 (Contract No. 568281/36, signed in 1936). 745 h.p. Rolls-Royce Kestrel XVI engines, low-drag radiators, provision for four-gun armament, cantilever landing gear and Dowty internally-sprung wheels. First flown, 14-9-36.

The**Hawker Spanish Fury.** Three aircraft, 4-1 to 4-3, ordered by the Spanish Government in October, 1935; 700 h.p. Hispano-Suiza 12Xbrs; two-gun armament, cantilever undercarriage and internally sprung wheels. First flown, 7 April 1936; delivered, July 1936.

The **Hawker High-Speed Fury.** One prototype, *K3586*, designed and built as a private venture to Specification F.14/32, and employed by Hawker Aircraft Ltd. to investigate refinements of the Fury design. Fitted in turn with Kestrel IIS, Kestrel IIIS, Kestrel IVS, Kestrel S, Goshawk III, Goshawk B.41 and P.V.12 (Merlin); parallel-chord and tapered-chord wings, Vee interplane struts, spatted landing gear. Attended numerous flying displays, flown by P.W.S. Bulman. Flown by Rolls-Royce Ltd., and at the R.A.E. (Disposed of to become Ground Instruction Machine *1436M*, 4-39).

The **Hawker Norn.** One company prototype, *H.N.1*, designed and built as private venture in 1930 and submitted for Service evaluation as naval interceptor. Specification 16/30 subsequently prepared around this design. Rolls-Royce F.XIMS engine. A second example was evidently built for deck-landing trials although no record of such trials can be traced. One of the above aircraft was later employed in ditching and flotation trials, probably in 1931. (This project led directly to the design of the Nimrod fleet fighter.)

The **Hawker Nimrod.** One prototype, *S1577*, ordered under Contract No. 102865/31(Part 1) to Specification 16/30, and built by H.G. Hawker Engineering Co. Ltd., on Works Order No. 182/31. Rolls-Royce Kestrel IIS engine. Interchangeable wheel and float undercarriage. First flight, 20-9-31, P.W.S. Bulman.

The **Hawker Nimrod I.** First production batch of 11 aircraft, *S1578-S1588*, ordered under Contract No. 102865/31(Part 2) to Specification 16/30, and built by H.G. Hawker Engineering Co. Ltd. during November and December 1931. Standard of preparation as for prototype *S1577*. First flight by *S1578*, 31-10-31.

The **Hawker Nimrod I.** Second production batch of 26 aircraft, *S1614-S1639*, built to Specification 16/30 (as amended) by H.G. Hawker Engineering Co. Ltd., Kingston, during 1932. Interchangeable wheel and float undercarriage. (Note: *S1638* was compromised by a Supermarine Southampton flying boat.)

   No. 800 Sqn., HMS *Courageous*: *S1619*; *S1621-S1623*; *S1631.*

   No. 801 Sqn., HMS *Courageous*: *S1620*; *S1625-S1627.*

   No. 802 Sqn., HMS *Furious*: *S1615*; *S1616*; *S1630*; *S1634-S1637.*

   Other duties: *S1614* (Seaplane Service trials, M.A.E.E., Felixstowe); *S1629* (catapult trials, Leuchars, 1934).

The **Hawker Nimrod I.** Third production batch of 19 aircraft, *K2823-K2841*, ordered under Contract No. 177993/32 from H.G. Hawker Engineering Co. Ltd., and delivered during January and February 1933.

   No. 702 Sqn., HMS *Glorious*: *K2832* (SOC, 8-1-36); *K2835* (SOC, 18-4-34); *K2837* (SOC, 2-11-34).

   No. 800 Sqn., HMS *Courageous*: *K2826*; *K2827*; *K2829* (crashed during deck landing, 4-11-

36); *K2830* (crashed during deck landing on *Courageous*, 25-9-36); *K2834* (crashed while landing at Worthy Down, 5-9-38); *K2840* (converted to Nimrod II; crashed while landing, Southampton, 31-12-37).

No. 801 Sqn., HMS *Courageous*: *K2825* (crashed into sea, 23-8-35); *K2826*; *K2827*; *K2831*; *K2838*; *K2841* (crashed on take-off from HMS *Furious*, 5-2-36).

No. 802 Sqn., HMS *Furious*: *K2828* (crashed into sea off Malta, 12-11-36); *K2833* (wrecked in gale aboard HMS *Courageous*, 12-3-34); *K2836*; *K2839* (crashed into sea off Malta, 29-8-36).

Transferred to Admiralty Charge: *K2836* (24-5-39); *K2838* (24-5-39).

Ground Instruction Machines: *K2823* (became *1146M*, 10-38); *K2826* (became *1046M*, 3-38); *K2827* (became *1190M*, 12-38); *K2831* (became *894M*, 9-36); *K2833* (became *622M*, 6-34).

Other units and duties: *K2823* (A. & A.E.E., performance trials; No. 17 (F) Sqn., Service trials. Converted to **Nimrod II prototype**).

The Hawker Nimrod II. First production batch of 6 aircraft, *K2909-K2914*, designed to Specification 11/33, ordered from Hawker Aircraft Ltd., Kingston and Brooklands, under Contract No. 252350/33 and built during July and August 1934 on Works Order Nos. 2118 and 2401. *K2909-K2911*, with stainless steel structural components, covered by supplementary Contract No. 163799/32. Rolls-Royce Kestrel IIS engines (some later replaced by Kestrel Vs).

No. 800 Sqn.: *K2909* (SOC, 7-9-37); *K2910*; *K2912* (crashed at sea off the Isle of Wight, 1-9-36); *K2913* (crashed at sea off Bembridge, Isle of Wight, 22-3-37).

No. 801 Sqn.: *K2911*; *K2913*.

No. 802 Sqn.: *K2914* (SOC, 31-8-34).

Other Units: *K2910* (No. 1 FTS; crashed while landing at Netheravon, 21-11-38. Became Ground Instruction Machine *1183M*); *K2911* (Coastal Defence Development Unit; SOC, 28-4-36).

The Hawker Nimrod II. Two aircraft, *K2925* and *K2926*, originally scheduled for stainless steel construction, but completed to standard Mark II configuration under Contract No. 252350/33. (Serial Nos. compromised Vickers Vildebeest II allocation). No in-service details traced.

The Hawker Nimrod II. Second production batch of 9 aircraft, *K3654-K3662*, designed to Specification 11/33, ordered from Hawker Aircraft Ltd. under Contract No. 252350/33 (Part 2). First flight by *K3654*, 31-12-34. Aircraft delivered during January 1935. All aircraft transferred to Admiralty Charge, 24-5-39.

No. 757 Sqn.: *K3656*.

No. 800 Sqn.: *K3655*; *K3656*; *K3659*.

No. 801 Sqn.: *K3656*.

No. 802 Sqn.: *K3654-K3656*; *K3659-K3662*.

Other Units: *K3654* (No. 1 FTS; "C" Flt., Gosport); *K3655* (Worthy Down); *K3656-K3658* (No. 1 FTS); *K3659* ("C" Flt., Gosport).

The Hawker Nimrod II. Third production batch of 10 aircraft, *K4620-K4629*, designed to Specification 11/33 (as amended), ordered from Hawker Aircraft Ltd., Kingston, under Contract No. 252350/33 (Part 3). Most aircraft with Rolls-Royce Kestrel V engines. Delivered during October and November 1935.

No. 800 Sqn.: *K4620* (crashed while landing, Southampton, 8-1-37); *K4621* (crashed while landing at Worthy Down, 21-10-38); *K4625* (crashed after collision with Nimrod *S1631*, 30-4-37); *K4626*; *K4628*; *K4629* (crashed into sea after take-off from HMS *Glorious*, 4-2-37).

No. 801 Sqn.: *K4620*; *K4624* (crashed while landing at Eastleigh, 24-9-36).

No. 802 Sqn.: *K4627*.

No. 803 Sqn.: *K4626*.

Transferred to Admiralty Charge, 24-5-39: *K4626-K2628*.

Other Units: *K4621* (R.A.E., Farnborough); *K4622* ("C" Flt., Gosport; crashed on Upnor range, 15-1-37); *K4623* (No. 1 FTS; crashed on take-off, Leuchars, 20-7-36); *K4625* ("C" Flt., Gosport).

The Hawker Nimrod II. Three replacement aircraft, *K5056-K5058*, to Specification 11/33 ordered from Hawker Aircraft Ltd., Kingston, in 1935 (Contract details not known). Rolls-Royce Kestrel V engines. Serial Nos. said to have compromised Avro Prefects. Delivered in November 1935.

No. 757 Sqn.: *K5057; K5058* (both aircraft transferred to Admiralty Charge, 24-5-39).

No. 800 Sqn.: *K5057; K5058.*

No. 803 Sqn.: *K5057.*

Other Units: *K5056* ("C" Flt., Gosport; crashed while landing at Gosport, 7-2-38); *K5057* ("C" Flt., Gosport; Worthy Down, 1938).

The Hawker Danish Nimrod. Two aircraft, *170* and *171*, supplied to the Danish government early in 1934 as pattern aircraft for proposed licence production. Rolls-Royce Kestrel IIIS engines driving broad-chord Watts wooden propellers. *170* (ff. 25-11-33) delivered with wheel spats; *171* (ff. 8-12-33) delivered without.

The Hawker Japanese Nimrod. One aircraft supplied to the Japanese Navy, believed in 1934. Rolls-Royce Kestrel IIIS engine. Intended as pattern aircraft for proposed licence production, but licence not taken up.

The Hawker Portuguese Nimrod. One aircraft supplied to the Portuguese government, believed in 1934. Flown with both Rolls-Royce Kestrel IIS and Kestrel V engines.

The Hawker O.22/26 Naval Hart. During 1927 design investigations of Specification O.22/26 resulted in modifications to the original Hart prototype, *J9052*, including folding wings, jury struts and, ultimately, twin-float undercarriage. Performance and handling trials led to the preparation of Specification 19/30 and the **Hawker Osprey.** To A. & A.E.E. (No. 22 Sqn.), 1929; deck landing trials, 6-29; No. 405 Flt. (Service trials), 11-29. Trials aboard HMS *Furious*, 1-30. Catapult trials at R.A.E., 2-8-30. Modified fin and rudder and floats added, 11-30. With No. 407 Flt., F.A.A., to South America for sales tour, 1931. Crashed on take-off at Brooklands due to crossed controls, 9-5-31.

The Hawker 19/30 Osprey. Two prototypes, *S1677* and *S1678*, designed to Specification 19/30, ordered under Contract No. 78068/30 (Part 1) from H.G. Hawker Engineering Co. Ltd., and built on Works Order 435(30) at Canbury Park Road, Kingston. *S1677*, with wheel landing gear, underwent trials at A. & A.E.E., Martlesham Heath, and *S1678* (with Short F.45 twin-float undercarriage) performed handling trials at the M.A.E.E., Felixstowe. Rolls-Royce Kestrel IIMS engines.

The Hawker Osprey I. Production batch of 20 aircraft, S1679-S1698 designed to Specification 19/30, and ordered under Contract No. 78068/30 (Part 2) from H.G. Hawker Engineering Co. Ltd., and built on Works Order 477(30) at Canbury Park Road, Kingston. (Original Contract called for 62 aircraft, including prototypes, but production was broken down to include Mark IIs and IIIs (stainless steel), see below.) Interchangeable wheel and float undercarriage (Type I floats, Short F.45).

No. 404 Flt., HMS *Courageous*: *S1683; S1684; S1694.*

No. 803 Sqn., HMS *Eagle*: *S1681; S1682; S1691, S1692; S1696; S1698.*

Other Units and duties: *S1679* (Floatplane Training Squadron, Calshot; *S1685* and *S1687* (later Osprey trainers); *S1690* (one-time company demonstration aircraft).

The Hawker Osprey I. Second production batch of 17 aircraft, *K2774-K2790*, designed to Specification 19/30 and ordered under Contract No. 78068 (Part 3) from H.G. Hawker Engineering Co. Ltd., and built on Works Order 604 (32) at Canbury Part Road, Kingston. Aircraft delivered between September and December 1932. Enlarged fin and rudder incorporated. Rolls-Royce Kestrel IIMS engines.

511

No. 407 Flt.: *K2775* (HMS *Leander*; SOC, 12-12-35); *K2778* (HMS *Achilles*).

No. 444 Flt.: *K2778*.

No. 800 Sqn., HMS *Eagle*: *K2779* (SOC, 24-11-36); *K2781*; *K2785*.

No. 801 Sqn., HMS *Courageous*: *K2781*; *K2785* (lost overboard, HMS *Courageous*, 13-5-38); *K2790*.

No. 802 Sqn.: *K2783*.

No. 803 Sqn., HMS *Hermes*: *K2780*; *K2783*; *K2784* (SOC, 31-12-34); *K2786* (SOC, 30-4-35); *K2788* (crashed at night while landing on HMS *Hermes*, 23-10-35); *K2789* (SOC, 31-10-38); *K2790*.

Transferred to Admiralty Charge, (24-5-39): *K2780-K2783*; *K2790*.

Other Units and duties, etc.: *K2774* (became Ground Instruction Machine, *646M*, 6-35); *K2777* (M.A.E.E., Felixstowe; School of Naval Co-operation); *K2778* (Mount Batten Stn. Flt.); *K2780* (Gosport Stn. Flt.; Worthy Down); *K2781* (Worthy Down); *K2872* (No. 2 Anti-Aircraft Co-operation Unit; "C" Flt., Gosport; Worthy Down); *K2787* (to the Mediterranean; SOC, 27-7-36); *K2790* (Worthy Down).

The Hawker Osprey IIIL. One special aircraft, *K3854* (originally a Hart airframe at AWA, Coventry, brought to Canbury Park Road, Kingston) modified to incoporate stainless steel structural components. Became Mark III and IV prototype. Completed and first flown in January 1934. Assessment by A. & A.E.E., 1934. Rolls-Royce Kestrel V. Tests with various propellers, Brooklands, 1935.

The Hawker Osprey III. First production batch of 39 aircraft, *K3615-K3653*, ordered under Contract No. 249962/33 to Specification 10/33 from Hawker Aircraft Ltd., Kingston., and delivered between March and December 1934. Rolls-Royce Kestrel V engines.

No. 24 (Comms.) Sqn.: *K3616-K3619*.

No. 406 Flt.: *K3630* (SOC, 18-6-36).

No. 407 Flt.: *K3640*.

No. 444 Flt.: *K3634*.

No. 447 Flt.: *K3641*; *K3642* (crashed on take-off at Aboukir, 22-5-36); *K3646*; *K3652*.

No. 711 Sqn.: *K3629* (HMS *Sussex*; SOC, 1-4-36); *K3633* (SOC, 26-2-36); *K3634* (HMS *London*); *K3635* (HMS *London*; crashed, Calshot, 1935; repaired; SOC, 16-9-38); *K3638*; *K3640-K3642*; *K3647*; *K3649*; *K3653*.

No. 715 Sqn.: *K3653* (SOC, 15-12-36).

No. 718 Sqn.: *K3636*; *K3638* (aircraft dropped into sea while being hoisted inboard, HMS *Ajax*, 23-3-37).

No. 758 Sqn.: *K3618* (crashed at Stoneham, Hants, 14-9-39).

No. 801 Sqn.: *K3616* (transferred to Admiralty Charge, 24-5-39); *K3621*; *K3622*; *K3623* (lost overboard, HMS *Furious*, 28-10-37); *K3625* (SOC, 1-9-35); *K3626*; *K3627* (SOC, 5-7-39); *K3640*; *K3648*.

No. 802 Sqn.: *K3628*; *K3637*; *K3643* (crashed, 15-12-37); *K3647*; *K3651*; *K3652* (crashed while alighting at Orkvenica, Yugoslavia, 29-7-38).

"C" Flt., Gosport: *K3621*; *K3622* (lost overboard, HMS *Furious*, 3-9-37); *K3632* (crashed in sea after dinghy broke loose and jammed controls, 5-3-35); *K3637*.

Ground Instruction Machines: *K3631* (became *1953M*); *K3634* (became *1000M*, 10-37); *K3640* (became *922M*, 3-37); *K3648* (became *1228*M, 1-39).

Other Units and duties, etc.: *K3615* (M.A.E.E., Felixstowe); *K3616-K3619* (No. 1 Civil Anti-Aircraft Co-operation Unit); *K3620*, *K3631* (No. 1 FTS); *K3624*, *K3644* and *K3645* (to Far East for Fleet Storage); *K3626* (Coastal Defence Development Unit); *K3637* (No. 1 Coastal Defence Development Flight); *K3653* (M.A.E.E., Felixstowe).

The Hawker Osprey III. Second production batch of 7 aircraft, *K3914-K3920*, designed to Specification 10/33 and built by Hawker Aircraft Ltd., Kingston, in June 1934. Rolls-Royce Kestrel V engines.

No. 407 Flt.: *K3918*.

No. 711 Sqn.: *K3919* (SOC, 14-10-37);

No. 712 Sqn.: *K3918.*

No. 801 Sqn.: *K3916.*

No. 810 Sqn.: *K3916*; *K3917* (crashed while landing at Hal Far, Malta, 7-9-36).

Ground Instruction Machines: *K3914* (became *965M*, 3-37); *K3915* (became *873M*, 7-36); *K3918* (became *971M*, 7-37).

Other Units and duties, etc.: *K3914* ("A" Flt., Calshot); *K3915* (Mediterranean Flt.); *K3916* (Worthy Down; transferred to Admiralty Charge, 24-5-39); *K3918* (Mount Batten Stn. Flt.; "A" Flt., Calshot; School of Naval Co-operation); *K3920* (sold to Hawker Aircraft Ltd., 24-9-34)

The Hawker Osprey III. Third production batch of 14 aircraft, *K4322-K4335*, originally ordered as part of Contract No. 78068/30 (Part 4) as Osprey Mark IIs, but completed as Mark IIIs under Contract No. 324869/34. Interchangeable wheel and float undercarriage (Type II, Short F.51 or F.59 floats). Rolls-Royce Kestrel V engines. Delivered during August and September 1935.

No. 404 Flt., HMS *Courageous*: *K4333.*

No. 407 Flt.: *K4329* (Sold and SOC, 10-2-38)

No. 711 Sqn.: *K4322*; *K4324*; *K4326*; *K4335* (transferred to Admiralty Charge, 24-5-39).

No. 713 Sqn.: *K4322* and *K4324* (to Admiralty Charge, 24-5-39); *K4327.*

No. 714 Sqn.: *K4330.*

No. 718 Sqn.: *K7323* (SOC, 9-4-37).

No. 801 Sqn.: *K4323*; *K4325* (crashed while landing at Donibristle, 31-5-38); *K4326* (crashed while landing at Donibristle, 7-7-38); *K4327* (crashed while landing at Donibristle, 25-7-38); *K4330*; *K4331* (transferred to Admiralty Charge, 24-5-39); *K4332*; *K4333* (crashed, 11-10-37).

No. 802 Sqn.: *K4334* (transferred to Admiralty Charge, 24-5-39).

Other Units and duties, etc.: *K4325* ("C" Flt., Lee-on-Solent; *K4325* (School of Naval Co-operation); *K4328* (to the Middle East); *K4330* and *K4332* (Worthy Down; both aircraft transferred to Admiralty Charge, 24-5-39).

The Hawker Osprey III. Three experimental aircraft, *S1699-S1701*, originally ordered as part of Contract No. 78068/30 to Specification 19/30, but completed to Osprey Mark III standard and with special Admiralty requirements, employing stainless steel primary structure throughout for marine exposure trials at M.A.E.E., Felixstowe, 1935-36. *S1699* and *S1701* fitted with Type II (Short S.59 floats); *S1700* fitted with experimental central float alighting gear (both Armstrong Whitworth and Short designs) with wing-tip stabilizing floats; ultimately became Ground Instruction Machine at R.A.F. College, Cranwell.

The Hawker Osprey III. Three aircraft, *S1702-S1704*, originally ordered as part of Contract No. 78068/30 to Specification 19/30, but completed a standard Mark IIIs. Rolls-Royce Kestrel V, Fairey Reed propeller, Vickers generator and dinghy hatch in top wing.

No. 713 Sqn.: *S1704* (aircraft "069").

The Hawker Osprey IV. Production batch of 26 aircraft, *K5742-K5767*, designed to Specification 26/35 and ordered under Contract No. 402277/35 from Hawker Aircraft Ltd., Kingston. Rolls-Royce Kestrel V engines (some later changed to Kestrel VIs). Delivered between August and October 1935.

No. 407 Flt.: *K5752*; *K5754.*

No. 443 Flt.: *K5745*; *K5746*; *K5751*; *K5755*; *K5760.*

No. 712 Sqn.: *K5752.*

No. 713 Sqn.: *K5758* (crashed while alighting alongside HMS *Penelope* in the Mediterranean, 15-1-37); *K5766.*

No. 714 Sqn.: *K5759.*

No. 716 Sqn.: *K5747* (crashed into mountain in fog, Wynberg, South Africa, 20-1-38); *K5748*; *K5751* (crashed on landing at Simonstown, South Africa, 29-4-37); *K5755.*

No. 718 Sqn.: *K5745* (crashed, 13-11-36); *K5746* (SOC, 23-12-37); *K5760*; *K5761* (aircraft capsized while alighting alongside HMS *Apollo*, 1-2-37); *K5762.*

No. 780 Sqn.: *K5750.*

No. 800 Sqn.: *K5742* ("*108*"); *K5744*; *K5748*; *K5752-K5754*; *K5756* (aircraft abandoned after dinghy came adrift and fouled the controls, 20-9-37); *K5759* (ditched near HMS *Ark Royal*, 12-1-39); *K5764*; *K5765* crashed while landing at Worthy Down, 27-7-39); *K5766*; *K5767.*

No. 801 Sqn.: *K5743*; *K5748*; *K5752*; *K5757*; *K5762-K5765.*

School of Naval Co-operation: *K5750*; *K5752*; *K5754.*

Ground Instruction Machines: *K5755* (became *1229M*, 1-39); *K5760* (became *1172M*).

The Hawker Swedish Osprey. Four aircraft, *2401-2404*, ordered in 1932 from H.G. Hawker Engineering Co. Ltd., and delivered in 1934-35. Interchangeable wheel and float undercarriage (Short F.51 floats). Swedish-built NOHAB-Bristol Mercury engines. First flight by *2401*, 8-9-34.

The Hawker Portuguese Osprey. Two aircraft, *71* and *72*, ordered in 1934 and delivered to Portugal in 1935. First aircraft delivered as landplane, the second a floatplane (Short F.59 floats). Rolls-Royce Kestrel IIMS engines. First flight by *71*, 24-2-35.

The Hawker Spanish Osprey. One aircraft, originally a company demonstrator (*G-AEBD*— which in turn may have originated as *K3920*, purchased from Air Ministry order in 1934) with Kestrel V engine, bought by Spain in 1935. Aircraft returned to Brooklands in January 1936, registered *EA-KAJ*, for installation of Hispano-Suiza 12Xbrs engine. First flight with this installation, 24-2-36. Delivered summer 1936.

The Hawker 15/30 Hart/Demon. Two trial installation Harts, *J9933* and *J9937*, modified to Specification 15/30 with twin forward-firing Vickers machine guns and Rolls-Royce Kestrel IIS engines.

The Hawker Demon. Preliminary production batch of six aircraft, *K1950-K1955*, designed to Specification 15/30, and originally termed Hart Fighters. (See Hawker Hart Fighter).

The Hawker Demon I. Second production batch of 17 aircraft, *K2842-K2858*, to Specification 6/32, ordered from H.G. Hawker Engineering Co. Ltd. under Contract No. 176937/32. Rolls-Royce Kestrel IIS engines. Delivered during February and March 1933.

No. 23 (F) Sqn.: *K2842-K2855*; *K2857*; *K2858.*

No. 25 (F) Sqn.: *K2853.*

No. 29 (F) Sqn.: *K2843* (crashed and SOC, 21-3-38); *K2845* (crashed and SOC, 8-8-36).

No. 41 (F) Sqn.: *K2853*; *K2858* (crashed near Harrow, Middlesex, 20-5-35).

No. 64 (F) Sqn.: *K2850.*

No. 74 (F) Sqn.: *K2850*; K2853.

No. 600 Sqn., A.A.F.: *K2846*; *K2847*; *K2850*; *K2854.*

No. 601 Sqn., A.A.F.: *K2842*; *K2855.*

No. 604 Sqn., A.A.F.: *K2842.*

No. 608 Sqn., A.A.F.: *K2844*; *K2848*; *K2849*; *K2851.*

Ground Instruction Machines: *K2842* (became *1896M*, 4-40); *K2844*; *K2846* (became *1399M*, 4-39); *K2847* (became *1398M*, 4-39); *K2848* (became *1123M*); *K2849*; *K2850* (became *1400M*, 4-39); *K2851*; *K2853* (became *1109M*, 8-38); *K2854* (became *1403M*, 4-39); *K2855* (became *1003M*, 11-37); *K2857* (became *1853M*, 3-40).

Other Units and duties, etc.: *K2842* (A. & A.E.E.); *K2850*, *K2856* and *K2857* (R.A.E.); *K2852* (Boulton Paul Ltd.).

The Hawker Demon I. Third production batch of four aircraft, *K2905-K2908*, to Specification 6/32, ordered from H.G. Hawker Engineering Co. Ltd. under Contract No. 176937/32 (Part 2). Rolls-Royce Kestrel IIB engines. Delivered in March 1933.

No. 25 (F) Sqn.: *K2905; K2906.*

No. 41 (F) Sqn.: *K2905; K2906; K2908.*

No. 64 (F) Sqn.: *K2906; K2907* (crashed while landing at Martlesham Heath, 16-8-37); *K2908.*

No. 74 (F) Sqn.: *K2905-K2907.*

No. 607 Sqn., A.A.F.: *K2906.*

Ground Instruction Machines: *K2906* (became *1394M*, 4-39); *K2908* (became *933M*, 1-37).

Other Unit: *K2905* (A. & A.E.E.; SOC, 20-5-38).

The Hawker Demon I. Fourth production batch of 44 aircraft, *K3764-K3807*, designed to Specification 6/32, ordered from Hawker Aircraft Ltd., Kingston. Rolls-Royce Kestrel IIS (but some later replaced by Kestrel VDR). Aircraft delivered between June and August 1934.

No. 23 (F) Sqn.: *K3786; K3789; K3796-K3802; K3804* (SOC, 9-39).

No. 25 (F) Sqn.: *K3770* (SOC, 25-5-38); *K3791; K3798* (SOC, 21-10-38).

No. 29 (F) Sqn.: *K3766; K3767; K3769* (collided with *K3803* and crashed near North Weald, 30-9-37); *K3770; K3772; K3774; K3775; K3777; K3781* (SOC, 23-12-36); *K3782; K3783; K3785* (crashed, 2-8-38); *K3787; K3791; K3792; K3803* (collided with *K3769* and crashed near North Weald, 30-9-37); *K3805.*

No. 41 (F) Sqn.: *K3765; K3767; K3773; K3777-K3779; K3788; K3790; K3791; K3794; K3798; K3800; K3806.*

No. 64 (F) Sqn.: *K3765; K3773; K3786; K3791.*

No. 65 (F) Sqn.: *K3780* (crashed, 23-7-35); *K3782-K3784; K3788; K3789; K3796; K3800.*

No. 74 (F) Sqn.: *K3767; K3769; K3770; K3772; K3773; K3777; K3784; K3791-K3794.*

No. 600 Sqn., A.A.F.: *K3784; K3793.*

No. 601 Sqn., A.A.F.: *K3796* (crashed taking off at Hendon, 17-6-37); *K3799; K3801; K3802.*

No. 604 Sqn., A.A.F.: *K3786* (SOC, 4-12-39); *K3789; K3797* (SOC, 11-39); *K3800; K3801* (SOC, 1-12-39).

No. 607 Sqn., A.A.F.: *K3765; K3767; K3777; K3792; K3800; K3806.*

No. 608 Sqn., A.A.F.: *K3771* (SOC, 1-3-38); *K3772* (SOC, 29-12-39); *K3779; K3795; K3807.*

Ground Instruction Machines: *K3766* (became *997M*, 10-37); *K3767* (became *1406M*, 4-39); *K3773* (became *1404M*, 4-39); *K3775* (became *949M*, 4-37); *K3776* (became *958M*, 4-37); *K3777* (became *1412M*, 4-39); *K3780* (became *1022M*); *K3782* (became *980M*, 9-37); *K3783* (became *950M*, 4-37); *K3784* (became *1401M*, 4-39); *K3787* (became *957M*, 4-37); *K3788* (became *934M*, 1-37); *K3790* (became *935M*, 1-37); *K3791* (became *2206M*, 8-40); *K3792* (became *1408M*, 4-39); *K3794* (became *979M*, 7-37); *K3495* (became *1687M*, 11-39); *K3799* (became *1414M*, 4-39); *K3800* (became *1532M*, 6-39); *K3802* (became *1005M*); *K3805* (became *961M*, 5-37); *K3806* (became *926M*, 12-36); *K3807* (became *1686M*, 121-39).

Other Units and duties, etc.: *K3764* (A. & A.E.E.; SOC, 20-5-40); *K3771, K3776, K3781, K3787, K3790, K3805* (to Aden); *K3789* and *K3793* (No. 24 ERFTS); *K3795, K3803* and *K3807* (to the Middle East).

The Hawker Demon I. Fifth production batch of 12 aircraft, *K3974-K3985*, to Specification 6/32, ordered from Hawker Aircraft Ltd., Kingston, and delivered during August and September 1934. Rolls-Royce Kestrel IIS engines.

No. 25 (F) Sqn.: *K3976; K3979; K3982; K3983* (collided with Demon *K4538* and crashed near Dover, 5-11-37).

No. 29 (F) Sqn.: *K3974-K3976; K3978* (crashed on take-off at North Weald, 31-8-37); *K3979-K3982; K3985.*

No. 41 (F) Sqn.: *K3974* (crashed while landing at Catterick, 6-9-37); *K3983.*

No. 600 Sqn., A.A.F.: *K3982.*

No. 601 Sqn., A.A.F.: *K3979; K3982.*

No. 604 Sqn., A.A.F.: *K3980; K3985.*

No. 607 Sqn., A.A.F.: *K3984.*

No. 608 Sqn., A.A.F.: *K397*

Ground Instruction Machines: *K3975* (became *1413M*, 4-39); *K3976* (became *1405M*, 4-39); *K3977* (became *1683M*, 11-39); *K3979* (became *1655M*, 1-40); *K3980* (became *2244M*, 10-40); *K3982* (became *2242M*, 10-40); *K3984* (became *713M*, 8-35).

The Hawker Demon I. Sixth production batch of 49 aircraft, *K4496-K4544*, built to Specification 8/34 by Hawker Aircraft Ltd., Kingston and Brooklands, and ordered under Contract No. 325209/34. Delivered between May 1935 and February 1936. Rolls-Royce Kestrel V engines.

No. 23 (F) Sqn.: *K4500.*

No. 25 (F) Sqn.: *K4525*; *K4526* (SOC, 1-7-38); *K4529* (SOC, 21-10-38); *K4532*; *K4538-K4540*; *K4542-K4544.*

No. 29 (F) Sqn.: *K4496*; *K4509*; *K4510.*

No. 41 (F) Sqn.: *K4525*; *K4526*; *K4532*; *K4533* (crashed while landing at Sutton Bridge, 4-3-37); *K4534* (SOC, 27-7-37); *K4535* and *K4536* (collided over Aden, and both crashed, 9-6-36); *K4537-K4540*; *K4541* (crashed at Aden, 18-7-36); *K4542*; *K4543* (SOC, 29-12-39); K4544.

No. 64 (F) Sqn.: *K4507-K4511*; *K4512* (spun and crashed, Martlesham Heath, 28-5-37); *K4515*; *K4516* (crashed, 22-11-37); *K4517* (crashed 29-11-37); *K4518* (SOC, 2-2-37); *K4519* (crashed while landing at Ismailia, 15-5-36); *K4520*; *K4521*; *K4523*; *K4527-K4529*; *K4531*; *K4532*; *K4543.*

No. 600 Sqn., A.A.F.: *K4507*; *K4523* (SOC, 11-39).

No. 601 Sqn., A.A.F.: *K4496*; *K4511*; *K4513*; *K4521*; *K4522*; *K4527*; *K4540.*

No. 604 Sqn., A.A.F.: *K4496*; *K4497*; *K4498* (crashed, 6-2-39); *K4499-K4501*; *K4502* (Crashed on Colindale station, Middlesex, 4-8-35); *K4503-K4505*; *K4506* (SOC, 20-8-40); *K4514*; *K4528* (SOC, 1-5-40); *K4529*; *K4530.*

No. 607 Sqn., A.A.F.: *K4508*; *K4542.*

No. 608 Sqn., A.A.F.: *K4510*; *K4515* (SOC, 29-12-39); *K4543* (SOC, 29-12-39).

No. 24 Elementary Flying Training School: *K4514; K4522.*

Ground Instruction Machines: *K4498* (became *1243M*); *K4499* (became *1759M*, 2-40); *K4500* (became *2298M*, 10-40); *K4501* (became *2029M*, 6-40); *K4503* (became *1397M*, 4-39); *K4504* (became *1682M*, 11-39); *K4505* (became *1760*M, 2-40); *K4507* (became *1761M*, 2-40); *K4508* (became *1407M*, 4-39); *K4509* (became *1409M*, 4-39); *K4510* (became *1684M*, 11-39); *K4511* (became *1416M*, 4-39); *K4513* (became *2028M*, 6-40); *K4520* (became *1484M*, 4-39); *K4521* (became *1395M*, 4-39); *K4525* (became *1694M*, 11-39); *K4527* (became *1396M*, 4-39); *K4530* (became *1212M*, 1-39); *K4531* (became *1410M*, 4-39); *K4532* (became *1693M*, 11-39); *K4537* (became *1001M*, 10-37); *K4538* (became *1038M*, 1-38); *K4540* (became *1415M*, 4-39); *K4542* (became *1402M*, 4-39); K4544 (became *1067M*, 5-38).

Other Units and duties, etc.: *K4496* (R.A.E.; Air Armament School; converted to Turret Demon; SOC, 3-41); *K4497* (Andover Pool); *K4500* (No. 9 Bombing & Gunnery School); *K4505* (School of Photography); *K4514* (crashed at Sydenham, 11-8-40); *K4539* (No. 1 Air Armament School; SOC, 4-12-39).

The Hawker Demon I. First production batch of 59 aircraft, *K5683-K5741*, built by Boulton Paul Aircraft Ltd., Norwich and Wolverhampton, to Specification 6/32 under Contract No. 176937/32 (first three aircraft) and 8/34 under Contract No. 246236/33 (remainder). Rolls-Royce Kestrel VDR engines. Some subsequently fitted with Frazer Nash gun turrets.

No. 23 (F) Sqn.: *K5694*; *K5695*; *K5698*; *K5699*; *K5705* (SOC, 12-2-38); *K5706*; *K5710*; *K5711*; *K5712* (collided with *K5730* and crashed, 3-11-38); *K5718*; *K5719*; *K5725-K5727*; *K5729*; *K5730* (collided with *K5712* and crashed, 3-11-38); *K5731*; *K5732.*

No. 29 (F) Sqn.: *K5699* (crashed near Debden, 21-2-39); *K5725*; *K5733-K5738*; *K5739* (SOC, 3-6-41); *K5740*; *K5741.*

No. 41 (F) Sqn.: *K5693* (crashed at Flaxton, Yorks, 4-2-39).

No. 600 Sqn., A.A.F.: *K5696*; *K5697* (crashed in bad weather, 5-6-37); *K5700-K5704*; *K5707-K5710.*

No. 601 Sqn., A.A.F.: *K5713*; *K5714* (struck mower while landing at West Freugh, 13-8-37); *K5715-K5717*; *K5720*; *K5721*; *K5722* (crashed on take-off at Upavon, 11-2-38); *K5723*; *K5724* (crashed on take-off at Parham Park, 25-7-37); *K5728* (crashed, 10-11-38).

No. 607 Sqn., A.A.F.: *K5683-K5689*; *K5690* (crashed on beach at Dawdon colliery, Co. Durham, 14-5-37); *K5691-K5693.*

No. 9 Bombing and Gunnery School: *K5689*; *K5694* (SOC, 28-9-40); *K5695*; *K5698*; *K5710* (SOC, 10-10-40); *K5719*; *K5725*; *K5729*; *K5731-K5735*; *K5737*; *K5738.*

No. 9 Air Observers' School: *K5706*; *K5710*; *K5725*; *K5731.*

No. 1 Air Armament School: *K5726*; *K5727*; *K5736*; *K5740*; *K5741.*

No. 24 Elementary Flying Training School: *K5689*; *K5698*; *K5702.*

Ground Instruction Machines: *K5683* (became *1411M*, 4-39); *K5684* (became *1680M*); *K5686* (became *2030M*, 10-40); *K5687* (became *2198M*, 8-40); *K5688* (became *1902M*, 1-40); *K5691* (became *1676M*, 11-39); *K5693* (became *1379M*); *K5696* (became *2200M*, 8-40); *K5699* (became *1444M*); *K5700* (became *2199M*, 8-40); *K5701* (became *1897M*, 4-40); *K5702* (became *2507M*, 3-41); *K5704* (became *1678M*, 11-39); *K5707* (became *2245M*, 10-40); *K5708* (became *2197M*, 8-40); *K5709* (became *1681M*, 11-39); *K5711* (became *1056M*, 5-38); *K5713* (became *1417M*, 4-39); *K5714* (became *991M*); *K5715* (became *1418M*, 3-39); *K5716* (became *1419M*, 3-39); *K5717* (became *1677M*, 11-39); *K5718* (became *1030M*, 1-38); *K5719* (became *2213M*, 10-40); *K5720* (became *1420M*, 4-39); *K5721* (became *1421M*, 4-39); *K5723* (became *1422M*, 4-39); *K5725* (became *2299M*, 10-40); *K5727* (became *2008M*); *K5728* (became *1235M*); *K5729* (became *2296M*, 9-40); *K5732* (became *2480M*, 3-41); *K5734* (became *2288M*, 9-40); *K5735* (became *2323M*, 11-40); *K5737* (became *2290M*, 9-40); *K5738* (became *2287M*, 9-40).

Other Units and duties, etc.: *K5685* (No. 2 Ferry Pilots' Pool; crashed near Crediton, Devon, 10-1-40); *K2695* (No. 14 FTS; SOC, 4-12-40); *K5702* (No. 75 Wing); *K5706* (No. 14 FTS; SOC, 4-12-40); *K5735* (No. 3 FTS).

The Hawker Turret Demon. Production batch of ten aircraft, *K5898-K5907*, built by Boulton Paul Aircraft Ltd., Norwich and Wolverhampton, to Specification 8/34, as amended, and delivered in July and August 1937. Rolls-Royce Kestrel X engines.

No. 29 (F) Sqn.: *K5898-K5907.*

No. 64 (F) Sqn.: *K5902*; *K5904.*

No. 1 Air Armament School: *K5900*; *K5902* (SOC, 4-12-40); *K5904* (SOC, 4-12-40); *K5907.*

No. 9 Bombing and Gunnery School: *K5898* (SOC, 17-10-40); *K5905* (ditched off St. Tudwals Island, Caernarvon, 5-8-40); *K5906.*

No. 9 Air Observers' School: *K5899*; *K5905.*

No. 1 Anti-Aircraft Co-operation Unit: *K5904.*

Ground Instruction Machines: *K5899* (became *2293M*, 9-40); *K5900* (became *2400M*, 3-41); *K5901* (became *1197M*, 12-38); *K5906* (became *2291M*, 9-40); *K5907* (became *2297M*, 10-40).

The Hawker Demon I. Third production batch of 37 aircraft, *K8181-K8217*, built by Boulton Paul Aircraft Ltd., Norwich and Wolverhampton, to Specification 8/34, as amended. Rolls-Royce Kestrel VDR, VI, X and XDR engines. Turrets later fitted to some aircraft for training purposes. Delivered between September 1937 and January 1938.

No. 23 (F) Sqn.: *K8194-K8198*; *K8217.*

No. 25 (F) Sqn.: *K8205*; *K8206*; *K8208*; *K8211-K8213.*

No. 64 (F) Sqn.: *K8181-K8185*; *K8186* (SOC, 1-12-38); *K8187-K8189*; *K8194*; *K8195*; *K8198*; K8199 (abandoned in fog and crashed near Duxford, 7-8-38); *K8200* (abandoned in fog and crashed near Wittering, 7-8-38); *K8201* (abandoned in fog and crashed near Duxford, 7-8-38); *K8202*; *K8203*; *K8214*; *K8215*; *K8216.*

No. 600 Sqn., A.A.F.: *K8190*; *K8204.*

No. 601 Sqn., A.A.F.: *K8191* (SOC, 14-4-39).

No. 604 Sqn., A.A.F.: *K8192*; *K8207*.

No. 607 Sqn., A.A.F.: *K8193*.

No. 608 Sqn., A.A.F.: *K8205*; *K8206*; *K8208*; *K8209* (overturned while taxying at Thornaby, 30-4-39); *K8210-K8212*; *K8213* (SOC, 29-12-39).

No. 1 Air Armament School: *K8181*; *K8182*, *K8184* (SOC, 4-12-40); *K8188*; *K8189* (SOC, 1943); *K8194*; *K8196* (SOC, 12-3-40); *K8202* (SOC, 2-12-41); *K8216* (blown over while taxying at Donna Nook, 1-4-40); *K8217* (SOC, 12-40).

No. 9 Bombing and Gunnery School: *K8183*; *K8195*; *K8197* (crashed on take-off at Penrhos, 7-8-40); *K8198*; *K8203*; *K8214* (crashed while landing at Penrhos, 28-8-40).

No. 9 Air Observers' School: *K8198*; *K8203*.

No. 1 Anti-Aircraft Co-operation Unit: *K8182* (SOC, 4-12-40).

Ground Instruction Machines: *K8183* (became *2289M*, 9-40); *K8188* (became *2459M*); *K8193* (became, *1675M*, 11-39); *K8194* (became *2392M*, 3-41); *K8203* (became *2292M*, 9-40); *K8211* (became *1685M*, 11-39); *K8215* (became *1234M*, 1-39).

Other Aircraft: *K8185* (to Rolls-Royce Ltd., Hucknall; SOC, 5-11-38); *K8207* (Andover Pool; SOC, 4-12-39).

The Hawker Australian Demon. Production batch of 18 General Purpose Fighters to Air Ministry (Draft) Specification 1/34, ordered under Contract No. 310586/34; carried Royal Australian Air Force Serial Nos. *A1-1* to *A1-18*. Standard three-gun armament. Rolls-Royce Kestrel VDR engines and limited tropical provisions.

The Hawker Australian Demon. Production batch of 36 Army Co-operation aircraft (with fighter armament and message pick-up hooks, etc.), to Air Ministry (Draft) Specification 1/34 (as amended), ordered under Contract No. 429868/35. Rolls-Royce Kestrel VDR engines. Carried Royal Australian Air Force Serial Nos. *A1-19* to *A1-54*.

The Hawker Australian Demon (also known as Australian Demon Mark II). Production batch of 10 target towing aircraft, *A1-55* to *A1-64*, to Air Ministry Specification 46/36, and ordered under Contract No. 5683346/36. Rolls-Royce Kestrel VDR engines.

The Hawker 7/31 Audax. One prototype, *K1438* (a converted Hart), produced by H.G. Hawker Engineering Co. Ltd., Kingston, to Air Ministry Specification 7/31. First flown as Audax prototype and powered by Rolls-Royce Kestrel IB engine, 29-12-31, by P.E.G. Sayer. To A. & A.E.E. and R.A.E., 1932-1934. Subsequently used by Rolls-Royce Ltd., for tropical Kestrel development. S.O.C., 4-12-39.

The Hawker Audax I. First production batch of 40 aircraft, *K1995-K2034*, designed to Specification 7/31 and ordered under Contract No. 102034/31 from H.G. Hawker Engineering Co. Ltd., Kingston and Brooklands. K1999 and K2020 converted by Hawker to Hart (Special) standard. Kestrel IB engines. First flight by *K1995*, 29-12-31, P.E.G. Sayer. Aircraft delivered between December 1931 and June 1932.

No. 2 (AC) Sqn.: *K1995* (crashed at Hawkinge, 23-5-36); *K2002*; *K2003*; *K2027*; *K2028*.

No. 4 (AC) Sqn.: *K1997* (collided with *K2031* and crashed near Farnborough, 28-5-37); *K1998*; *K1999* (converted to Hart (Special)); *K2000-K2004*; *K2006*; *K2007*; *K2018*; *K2020* (converted to Hart (Special)); *K2021-K2025*; *K2026* (crashed, 6-7-347); *K2031* (collided with *K1997* and crashed near Farnborough, 28-5-37).

No. 13 (AC) Sqn.: *K2001*; *K2009* (crashed on Salisbury Plain, 4-11-36); *K2010-K2019*; *K2027*; *K2028* (crashed while low flying over Salisbury Plain, 5-6-36); *K2029-K2031*; *K2032* (caught fire during engine starting at Odiham, 1-4-37); *K2033*.

No. 16 (AC) Sqn.: *K2025*.

No. 24 (C) Sqn.: *K2008*.

No. 77 (B) Sqn.: *K2006*; *K2021*; *K2022*.

No. 211 (B) Sqn.: *K1998*; *K2001*; *K2011*; *K2013*; *K2014*; *K2016*; *K2018*; *K2019*; *K2024*; *K2029*.

R.A.F. College, Cranwell: *K1996*; *K2034*.

Flying Training Schools: No. 1 FTS: *K2001*; *K2006*; *K2021*; *K2022*. No. 3 FTS: *K2001*. No. 5 FTS: *K2018*; *K2021*. No. 6 FTS: *K1999*; *K2006*; *K2018*; *K2020*. No. 8 FTS: *K2029*. No. 9 FTS: *K1998*; *K2006*; *K2017* (crashed while landing at Hullavington, 16-3-30); *K2018*; *K2019*. No. 11 FTS: *K2011* (crashed on Fenns Moss range, 6-5-40); *K2022*; *K2024*. No. 12 FTS: *K2006*; *K2018*.

Elementary & Reserve Flying Training Schools: No. 9 ERFTS: *K2020*. No. 15 ERFTS: *K2001*; *K2013*. No. 19 ERFTS: *K2017*. No. 22 ERFTS: *K2021*. No. 34 ERFTS: *K2025* (crashed while landing at Southend, 23-6-39). No. 35 ERFTS: *K1998*; *K2029*. No. 39 ERFTS: *K2019*. No. 43 ERFTS: *K2018*. No. 44 ERFTS: *K2024*. No. 45 ERFTS: *K2011*.

Supplied to the South African Air Force: *K2000* (as No. *1936*); *K2018*; *K2029* (22-10-40).

Ground Instruction Machines: *K1996* (became *1141M*, 10-38); *K1999* (became *1769M*, 1-40); *K2012* (became *936M*, 1-37); *K2013* (became *2613M*, 7-41); *K2015* (became *837M*, 1-37); *K2016* (became *1047M*, 4-38); *K2033* (became *929M*, 1-37); *K2034* (became *800M*, 4-36).

Other Units and duties, etc.: *K1996* (converted to Hart Trainer: A & A.E.E.; CFS; R.A.E.); *K1999* (Coastal Command Special Duties Flt.; No. 4 Group Special Duties Flt.); *K2000* (R.A.E.); *K2003* (School of Photography; to India: No. 1 Service Flying Training School (India); No. 1 Air Gunners' School (India); crashed on take-off at Bairagarh, 17-6-43); *K2006* (No. 101 Glider Operational Training Unit); *K2008* (Home Communications Flt.; Northolt Stn. Flt.); *K2012* and *K2015* (School of Army Co-operation); *K2019* (No. 3 Radio School); *K2020* (No. 3 Electrical and Wireless School); *K2022* (No. 2 and 4 Glider Training Schools; crashed while landing at Kidlington, 11-8-42).

The Hawker Audax I. Second production batch of 91 aircraft, *K3055-K3145*, designed to Specification 7/31 and ordered under Contract No. 102034 (2nd Part) from H.G. Hawker Engineering Co. Ltd., Kingston and Brooklands. Delivered between May and October 1933. 18 aircraft, *K3128-K3145*, converted to Hart (Special) while in service.

No. 2 (AC) Sqn.: *K3055* (crashed while landing at Hawkinge, 21-4-36); *K3056*; *K3057*; *K3058* (crashed while landing at Knighton Down landing ground, Larkhill, 21-6-37); *K3059-K3065*; *K3085-K3089*; *K3090* (hit high tension cables and crashed near Hawkinge, 23-5-36); *K3104*; *K3111*; *K3114*; *K3126*.

No. 4 (AC) Sqn.: *K3065*; *K3071*; *K3079*; *K3093*; *K3095*; *K3109*; *K3116*; *K3122*; *K3124*; *K3127*.

No. 13 (AC) Sqn.: *K3079*; *K3081*; *K3083*; *K3103*.

No. 16 (B) Sqn.: *K3082*.

No. 20 Sqn. (India, from 1935): *K3117*.

No. 26 (AC) Sqn.: *K3067*; *K3068*; *K3069* (crashed while landing at Catterick, 25-6-37); *K3070-K3075*; *K3076* (crashed, 9-3-36); *K3077*; *K3078* (crashed on take-off at Hucknall, 25-6-37); *K3079*; *K3091-K3093*; *K3094* (crashed at Filton, 30-4-37); *K3095* (crashed while landing at Catterick, 3-5-37); *K3096*; *K3101*; *K3119* (crashed while landing at Catterick, 30-4-36).

No. 52 (B) Sqn. (Middle East, 1941): *K3107*; *K3111*; *K3124*.

No. 77 (B) Sqn.: *K3081*; *K3083*; *K3103*.

No. 146 Sqn. (India, 1941): *K3098*.

No. 173 (C) Sqn. (Egypt, 1942-43): *K3124* (crashed north of Bilbeis, 10-2-43).

No. 208 (AC) Sqn. (Egypt, from 1935): *K3105-K3108*; *K3110-K3112*; *K3114*; *K3115*; *K3117*; *K3118*; *K3121*; *K3125*; *K3145*.

No. 237 Sqn. (Kenya, from 1940): *K3107*; *K3127* (crashed while taking off at Kermanshah, 23-8-42).

No. 267 (C) Sqn. (Egypt, from 1940): *K3124*.

No. 601 Sqn., A.A.F.: *K3082*.

No. 615 Sqn., A.A.F.: *K3016*.

School of Photography: *K3066*; *K3097*; *K3098*; *K3102*.

Farnborough Station Flight: *K3066*; *K3968*; *K3097*.

Flying Training Schools: No. 1 FTS: *K3059*; *K3064*; *K3085*; *K3101*; *K3103* (crashed, 2-5-41).
No. 2 FTS: *K3065*; *K3086* (crashed while landing at Warmwell, 12-4-38); *K3089*; *K3104*;
K3142; *K3144*. No. 3 FTS: *K3060*; *K3083*; *K3088*; *K3101*; *K3138* (crashed at Stoke
Rochford, 27-11-36); *K3139-K3144*. No. 4 FTS (Middle East): *K3115*; *K3116*; *K3120*;
K3121; *K3122* (crashed at Abu Sueir, 12-11-36); *K3123-K3125*; *K3126* (crashed while
landing at Habbaniya, 3-10-40); *K3127*. No. 5 FTS: *K3067*; *K3087*. No. 6 FTS: *K3077*;
K3087; *K3143*. No. 7 FTS: *K3072* (as Hart (Special); SOC, 23-10-36); *K3073*; *K3079*;
K3093 (crashed at Collingbourne Ducis, 21-6-40); *K3128* (struck bowser while taxying
at Peterborough, 24-10-39); *K3129* (crashed while landing at Peterborough, 30-7-40);
K3130 (crashed while landing at Hamble, 26-9-37); *K3131* and *K3133* (collided while
landing at Peterborough, 6-5-40); *K3132*; *K3134-K3138*; *K3143*. No. 8 FTS: *K3060*;
K3071 (crashed on take-off at Montrose, 26-1-38); *K3083*; *K3085*; *K3096*. No. 9 FTS:
K3059; *K3060*; *K3080*; *K3082*; *K3083*; *K3096*; *K3101*. No. 10 FTS: *K3073*; *K3079*;
K3088; *K3092*; *K3093*; *K3143*. No. 11 FTS: *K3059*; *K3064*; *K3083*; *K3085*; *K3091*
(crashed near Hodnet, Shropshire, 12-4-40); *K3092*. No. 13 FTS: *K3085*; *K3096*. No. 14
FTS: *K3104* No. 15 FTS: *K3060*.

Elementary & Reserve Flying Training Schools: No. 2 ERFTS: *K3103*. No. 5 ERFTS:
K3081 (crashed on take-off at Hanworth, 24-7-39). No. 15 ERFTS: *K3101*. No. 20
ERFTS: *K3143*. No. 23 ERFTS: *K3073*; *K3092*. No. 32 ERFTS: *K3079*; *K3093*. No. 33
ERFTS: *K3082*. No. 34 ERFTS: *K3080*. No. 35 ERFTS: *K3096*. No. 38 ERFTS: *K3060*.
No. 42 ERFTS: *K3087*. No. 45 ERFTS: *K3091*. No. 50 ERFTS: *K3083*.

Supplied to South African Air Force: *K3060* (24-8-42); *K3068* (10-4-41); *K3073* (20-12-40);
K3079 (22-10-40); *K3085* (22-10-40); *K3096* (1941); *K3101* (15-1-42); *K3104* (22-10-
40); *K3114* (22-10-40); *K3134* (6-9-42); *K3137* (30-5-42).

No. 1 Service Flying Training School (India): *K3077* (crashed while landing at Ambala, 13-
11-41); *K3082*; *K3088* (crashed and burned, Patiala, 15-9-42); *K3097* (crashed while
landing at Ambala, 27-1-42); *K3098* (damaged while taxying at Miramshah, 9-9-43, and
SOC); *K3102* (crashed while Landing at Ambala, 25-6-42); *K3105*.

Supplied to Southern Rhodesian Air Force: *K3108* (1-11-40); *K3117*.

Ground Instruction Machines: *K3057* (became *989M*, 9-37); *K3061* (became *1052M*, 4-38);
K3063 (became *729M*, 11-35); *K3067* (became *2004M*, 6-40); *K3087* (became *1907M*,
5-40); *K3100* (became *748M*, 1-36); *K3139* (became *2025M*, 6-40); *K3141* (became
1170M, 11-38).

Other Units and duties, etc.: *K3061* (No. 615 Sqn., A.A.F.); *K3064* (struck picketing blocks
while landing at Hullavington, 6-11-40); *K3067* (R.A.E.); *K3068* (School of Army Co-
operation); *K3080* (Special Duties Flt.); *K3084* (Iraq); *K3105* (No. 3 Sqn., IAF); *K3107*
(Iraq Comms. Flt); *K3109* (R.A.E.); *K3114* (No. 1 School of Army Co-operation); *K3125*
(Iraq Comms. Flt.).

The Hawker Audax I. Third production batch of 43 aircraft, *K3679-K3721*, to Specification
7/31, ordered from Hawker Aircraft Ltd., Kingston and Brooklands in July 1933. Delivered
between November 1933 and January 1934. Rolls-Royce Kestrel IB engines. First flight by
K3679, 22 November 1933.

No. 2 (AC) Sqn.: *K3718* (crashed on take-off at Hawkinge, 11-1-37.

No. 4 (AC) Sqn.: *K3689*; *K3708*; *K3710*.

No. 5 Sqn. (India): *K3720* (SOC, 12-41).

No. 13 (AC) Sqn.: *K3711*.

No. 16 (AC) Sqn.: *K3691-K3697*; *K3698* (crashed at Old Sarum, 29-5-37); *K3699-K3702*;
K3707; *K3709*; *K3711*; *K3712*.

No. 41 (F) Sqn.: *K3701*.

No. 52 Sqn. (Iraq): *K3717*.

No. 77 (B) Sqn.: *K3710* (crashed while landing at Castle Bromwich, 23-8-37).

No. 146 Sqn. (India): *K3686* (crashed in Calcutta, 1-12-41); *K3693*.

No. 208 (AC) Sqn. (Middle East): *K3713*; *K3714*.

No. 211 (B) Sqn.: *K3689; K3708.*

School of Army Co-operation: *K3679-K3688; K3690; K3703-K3706.*

Flying Training Schools: No. 1 FTS: *K3699; K3721.* No. 2 FTS: *K3690.* No. 3 FTS: *K3693; K3697; K3699.* No. 4 FTS: *K3713; K3715* (crashed at Abu Sueir, 10-9-37); *K3716* (force landed on north shore of Dead Sea, 31-8-39); *K3717.* No. 5 FTS: *K3696.* No. 7 FTS: *K3691.* No. 9 FTS: *K3690; K3694; K3695; K3702-K3704; K3711; K3712; K3721.* No. 11 FTS: *K3689; K3707.* No. 13 FTS: *K3691.* No. 15 FTS: *K3691.*

Elementary & Reserve Flying Training Schools: No. 3 ERFTS: *K3693; K3697.* No. 9 ERFTS: *K3696.* No. 18 ERFTS: *K3695; K3699; K3712.* No. 20 ERFTS: *K3689.* No. 23 ERFTS: *K3708* (ditched in River Swale, near Faversham, Kent, 21-5-38). No. 24 ERFTS: *K3691.* No. 30 ERFTS: *K3707.* No. 31 ERFTS: *K3711.* No. 33 ERFTS: *K3702.*

No. 3 Radio School: *K3683* (aircraft abandoned over Dreghorn, Ayrshire, 13-5-42); *K3703; K3709.*

Supplied to South African Air Force: 22-11-40: *K3679; K3680; K3682; K3702; K3707. K3685* (1-11-40); *K3690* (15-1-42); *K3697* (26-5-41); *K3705* (1-11-40, as No. *1842*); *K3721* (16-11-41).

Ground Instruction Machines: *K3688* (became *1020M*, 12-37); *K3692* (became *1133M*, 9-38); *K3696* (became *2017M*, 5-40); *K3701* (became *1177M*, 11-38); *K3719*, became *1062M* as **Hector** prototype; see below).

Other Units and Duties, etc.: *K3684* (No. 2 and 4 GTS); *K3693* and *K3706* (No. 1 SFTS (India)); *K3706* (No. 225 Group Comms. Flt.; crashed while landing at Royakatai, India, 28-11-43); *K3714* (Heliopolis Comms. Flt.; SOC, 15-5-41); *K3719* (Converted to **Hawker Hector** prototype; first flight 14 February 1936). *K3720* (prepared as **Audax (Singapore)** for service with the Straits Settlements Volunteer Air Force, c.1935).

The Hawker Audax I. First production batch of 25 aircraft, *K4838-K4862*, built by Gloster Aircraft Co. Ltd., Brockworth, to Air Ministry Specification 19/34 under Contract No. 333990/34, and prepared for service in India; aircraft sometimes, semi-officially, referred to as the Audax (India). Rolls-Royce Kestrel IB and X engines.

No. 20 Sqn. (India): *K4838; K4842* (crashed while landing at Peshawar, 24-4-40); *K4843-K4845; K4846* (pilot wounded by small-arms fire over NW Frontier and abandoned near Razmak, 7-1-41); *K4847; K4849; K4851; K4852; K4853* (crashed during message drop, Isha, 16-8-40); *K4854; K4859; K4862.*

No. 28 Sqn. (India): *K4838; K4840; K4843; K4844; K4849; K4850; K4853; K4854; K4855* (crashed while landing at Miramshah, 25-2-39); *K4856-K4858; K4860* (crashed on take-off at Kohat, 16-7-39); *K4861.*

No. 39 Sqn. (India, 1938): *K4862* (crashed near Risalpur, 17-5-39).

No. 60 Sqn. (India): *K4844; K4845; K4861.*

No. 1 Sqn., Indian Air Force: *K4838; K4852; K4856; K4857.*

No. 2 Sqn., Indian Air Force: *K2843; K2861* (aircraft damaged by small-arms fire and crash landed at Miramshah, 6-10-41).

No. 3 Sqn., Indian Air Force: *K4840; K4843* (crashed on take-off at Kohat, 23-3-42); *K4844; K4845; K4848* (crashed on take-off at Miramshah, 13-5-42); *K4849* (crashed at Miramshah, 2-42); *K4850* (crashed at Razmak, 21-8-43); *K4854* (crashed at Kohat Pass, 15-6-43); *K4856* (crashed while landing at Miramshah, 30-7-42).

No. 1 Service Flying Training School, India: *K4838; K4840; K4845; K4851; K4857* (burnt on ground at Ambala, 7-6-42).

No. 1 Armament Training Unit, India: *K4851* (damaged beyond repair in gale, Bairagarh, 21-4-43); *K4858* (crashed near Bairagarh, 28-8-42).

Other Units and duties, etc.: *K4838* (Delhi Comms. Flt.; crashed while landing at Palam, 20-7-43); *K4839* (Lahore Comms. Flt; crashed in River Indus near Mianwali, 20-7-38); *K4845* (No. 353 Sqn., R.A.F.); *K4851* and *K4853* (Lahore Comms. Flt.).

The Hawker Audax I Trainer. First production batch of 56 aircraft, *K5201-K5256*, to Specification 34/34, ordered from the Bristol Aeroplane Co. Ltd., Filton, Bristol, and delivered between January and April 1936. Rolls-Royce Kestrel X engines. (10 aircraft, *K5231-K5340*, prepared for service in the tropics with sand filters and Kestrel XDR engines.)

No. 1 Flying Training School: *K5214*; *K5226*; *K5243*; *K5248* (crashed near Kettering, 11-6-41); *K5252*.

No. 3 Flying Training School: *K5218* (crashed while landing at South Cerney, 27-9-37); *K5219* (crashed at Aston Down, 8-10-37); *K5220*; *K5221*; *K5222* (crashed at sea during weather test, 7-9-436); *K5223* (crashed while landing at South Cerney, 12-1-39); *K5224* (crashed while landing at Grantham, 25-2-38); *K5226*; *K5227* (crashed on Theddlethorpe ranges, North Coates, 13-7-36).

No. 4 Flying Training School, Middle East: *K5231*; *K5232* (broke up in the air near Kantara, Egypt, 20-1-37); *K5233* (crashed near Habbaniya, 22-3-41); *K5234* (crashed near Abu Sueir, 17-5-39); *K5235*; *K5236* (crashed, 5-6-36); *K5237*; *K5238* (crashed, 5-6-36); *K5239*; *K5340.*

No. 5 Flying Training School: *K5228* (crashed on take-off at Catfoss, 8-9-36); *K5229*; *K5230* (crashed at Sealand, 29-9-37); *K5241* (crashed while taking off at Sealand, 4-1-38); *K5242-K5244*; *K5245* (crashed, 14-3-38); *K5246* (crashed on take-off at Sealand, 12-4-38).

No. 6 Flying Training School: *K5253* (crashed on landing at Sutton Bridge, 4-8-37); *K5254*; *K5255*; *K5256* (crashed while landing at night at Netheravon, 19-6-37).

No. 8 Flying Training School: *K5201* (crashed while landing at Dysart landing ground, 19-3-36); *K5202* (crashed in Lunen Bay, 14-10-37); *K5203*; *K5214*; *K5242.*

No. 9 Flying Training School: *K5203* (crashed, 17-1-41); *K5211* (crashed near Chippenham, Wilts, 29-12-40); *K5215* (crashed while landing at Hullavington, 25-10-40); *K5242*; *K5247* (crashed at Lostwithiel, Cornwall, 29-11-38); *K5248*; *K5249* (crashed while landing at night at Thornaby, 2-10-36); *K5250* (crashed, 15-8-39); *K5251* (crashed on take-off at Thornaby, 22-9-36); *K5252.*

No. 10 Flying Training School: *K5204* (crashed, 10-1-39); *K5205*; *K5206* (crashed at Madeley, Cheshire, 9-9-36); *K5207* (crashed while landing at night at Kinloss, 15-9-39); *K5225* (crashed, 25-9-36).

No. 11 Flying Training School: *K5208* (crashed while landing at Penrhos, 13-2-40); *K5209* (crashed, 10-10-39); *K5210* (crashed, 31-1-38); *K5211*; *K5212* (crashed, 27-2-36); *K5213* (crashed on take-off at Wittering, 28-6-37); *K5214*; *K5215*; *K5216* (crashed, 16-7-40); *K5217* (crashed at Hathern, Loughborough, 23-9-37.

No. 12 Flying Training School: *K5342*; *K5243.*

No. 13 Flying Training School: *K5203*; *K5214.*

No. 15 Flying Training School: *K5203*; *K5214.*

Supplied to South African Air Force: *K5205* (20-10-40); *K5226* (9-4-41); *K5252* (5-12-41); *K5254* (22-10-40).

Ground Instruction Machines: *K5225* (became *904M*, 9-36); *K5238* (became *876M*, 6-36); *K5244* (became *15287M*, 6-39); *K5247* (became *1236M*, 12-38).

Transferred to Admiralty Charge, 5-41: *K5214*; *K5221.*

Other Units and duties, etc.: *K5205* (No. 1 School of Army Co-operation); *K5220* (Desford Stn. Flt.); *K5221* (R.A.F. College, Cranwell); *K4231* (No. 52 Sqn., Habbaniya, Iraq; Western Desert Comms. Flt.); *K5237* (No. 1 S.F.T.S.(I); No. 3 Sqn., I.A.F.); *K5239* (No. 84 Sqn.); *K5244* (Hucknall Stn. Flt.); *K5255* (No. 1 S.F.T.S.(I); crashed while landing at Ambala, 20-12-41).

The Hawker Audax (India). First production batch of 25 aircraft, *K5561-K5585*, built by A.V. Roe & Co. Ltd., Manchester, for service in India. Enlarged radiators and sand filters; Rolls-Royce Kestrel IB engines. Aircraft delivered between April and May 1936.

No. 20 Sqn. (India): *K5567*; *K5568*; *K5573*; *K5577*; *K5580*; *K5585* (crashed while landing at Kohat, 30-9-40).

No. 28 Sqn. (India): *K5561-K5564*; *K5565* (abandoned after engine failure at night, 12-11-37); *K5566* (crashed near Miramshah, 7-11-41); *K5567* (crashed in Hangu Valley, 25-7-40); *K5568*; *K5569*; *K5570* (crashed while message dropping on NW Frontier, 29-4-37); *K5571*; *K5574*; *K5575*; *K5578-K5583*; *K5584* (crashed while landing at Ambala, 18-2-39); *K5585*.

No. 1 Sqn., I.A.F.: *K5564* (crashed near Miramshah, 7-11-41); *K5571*; *K5572*; *K5576*; *K5578* (crashed at Spinwan, 10-4-41); *K5582* (crashed on take-off at Miramshah, 30-5-41).

No. 2 Sqn., I.A.F.: *K5562*; *K5564*; *K5575*; *K5577* (crashed on Kohat bombing range, 18-9-41); *K5579*.

No. 3 Sqn., I.A.F.: *K5561*; *K5563*; *K5573-K5575*; *K5581* (crashed on take-off at Miramshah, 18-9-42); *K5583*.

No. 1 Armament Training Unit (India): *K5562*; *K5563*; *K5568* (crashed at Pempora, 25-7-42).

No. 1 S.F.T.S., (India): *K5571*; *K5572* (crashed at Babial, near Ambala, 2-6-42); *K5575*.

The Hawker Audax I. Second production batch of 18 aircraft, *K5586-K5603*, to Specification 34/34, ordered under Contract No. 389426/35 from A.V. Roe & Co. Ltd., Manchester, and delivered between March and April 1937. Rolls-Royce Kestrel Xs, some de-rated. Some aircraft fitted with sand filters and enlarged radiators and shipped to India in 1939-1940 (Note. These were not to full Audax (India) standard.)

No. 2 (AC) Sqn.: *K5586*; *K5587*.

No. 63 (F) Sqn.: *K5589-K5595*.

No. 105 (B) Sqn.: *K5590*; *K5591*; *K5593*; *K5594*.

No. 226 (B) Sqn.: *K5596-K5602*.

Royal Air Force College, Cranwell: *K5589*; *K5592* (crashed while landing at Cranwell, 20-9-39); *K5595* (crashed at Cranwell, 24-10-38); *K5603*.

Flying Training Schools: No. 1 FTS: *K5591*; *K5599*. No. 2 FTS: *K5587*. No. 3 FTS: *K5586*; *K5597*. No. 5 FTS: *K5596*; *K5598* (crashed while landing at night at Sealand, 6-5-38). No. 7 FTS, *K5588*. No. 8 FTS: *K5591*; *K5602*. No. 9 FTS: *K5597*; *K5599*; *K5601* (crashed while landing at Hullavington, 3-4-40). No. 12 FTS: *K5596*. No. 15 FTS: *K5591*.

Elementary & Reserve Flying Training Schools: No. 2 ERFTS: *K5599*. No. 4 ERFTS: *K5594*. No. 5 ERFTS: *K5586*. No. 10 ERFTS: *K5591*. No. 15 ERFTS: *K5590* (crashed in poor visibility at Oldbury-on-Severn, 6-3-38); *K5593* (collided with Battle *K7649* on the ground at Redhill and SOC). No. 19 ERFTS: *K5601*. No. 21 ERFTS: *K5596*.

No. 1 Service Flying Training School (India): *K5589* (crashed while landing at Ambala, 6-6-42); *K5594* (crashed at Ambala, 16-1-43); *K5597* (crashed while landing at Ambala, 3-10-42); *K5603* (caught fire and burnt out on ground at Ambala, 31-7-42).

Other Units and duties, etc.: *K5586* (No. 615 Sqn., A.A.F.); *K5588* (No. 1 Armament Training Unit, India); *K5591* (School of Photography); *K5594* (Northolt Stn. Flt.); *K5600* (School of Photography).

The Hawker Audax (including **Audax Trainer, Audax (India), Audax (Singapore) etc.**). Third production batch of 162 aircraft, *K7307-K7468*, to Specification 34/34, as amended, under Contract No. 437224/35, ordered from A.V. Roe & Co. Ltd., Manchester. *K7312*, *K7315* and *K7316* were Audax (Singapore). Rolls-Royce Kestrel IB, X and XDR engines. Aircraft delivered between July and November 1936.

No. 2 (AC) Sqn.: *K7381*.

No. 5 Sqn. (India, 1941-42): *K7315* (crashed while landing at Imphal, 18-6-42); *K7316*; *K7333*.

No. 13 (AC) Sqn.: *K7426*; *K7454*.

No. 24 (C) Sqn.: *K7383*.

No. 26 (AC) Sqn.: *K7383*.

No. 61 (B) Sqn.: *K7427-K7431*.

No. 63 (B) Sqn.: *K7464-K7468*.

No. 66 (F) Sqn.: *K7329* (crashed, 3-11-36).

No. 77 (B) Sqn.: *K7391; K7426; K7433; K7454.*

No. 105 (B) Sqn.: *K7409-K7414; K7438; K7439.*

No. 114 (B) Sqn.: *K7409-K7414.*

No. 144 (B) Sqn.: *K7415-K7419.*

No. 146 (F) Sqn.: *K7333; K7356* (crashed on Kobo range, Assam, 28-4-42); *K7372.*

No. 148 (B) Sqn.: *K7432; K7434-K7437.*

No. 226 (B) Sqn.: *K7403-K7408.*

No. 237 (Rhodesia) Sqn.: *K7420.*

R.A.F. College, Cranwell: *K7374; K7375* (crashed at Ancaster, Lincs, 14-9-38); *K7376; K7377* and *K7458* (collided and both aircraft crashed at Stubton, Lincs, 8-5-39); *K7378-K7380; K7422; K7423* (crashed during night take-off at Cranwell, 13-12-39); *K7424; K7465-K7467.*

No. 1 Flying Training School: *K7323* (crashed while landing at Netheravon, 23-11-40); *K7325; K7327* (crashed on take-off at Stormy Down, 26-6-41); *K7328; K7331; K7336; K7338* (crashed, 21-4-39); *K7342; K7348; K7382; K7384* (crashed at Great Somerford, near Malmesbury, 1-10-40); *K7390* (crashed while landing at Shrewton, 11-10-41); *K7391; K7393; K7414; K7421; K7424; K7463.*

No. 2 Flying Training School: *K7325; K7342; K7343; K7344* (crashed while landing at Kelmscott, 6-2-39); *K7348; K7349; K7350* (crashed near Penrhos, 6-8-37); *K7351; K7352; K7353* (crashed while landing at night at Brize Norton, 21-11-38); *K7354* (crashed on take-off at Brize Norton, 11-7-38); *K7363* (crashed on landing at Digby, 9-11-36); *K7364* (crashed, 12-10-37); *K7365; K7366* (crashed at Clanfield, Oxon, 16-2-39); *K7367; K7392* (crashed, 29-11-37); *K7393; K7398* (crashed, 12-10-37); *K7422.*

No. 3 Flying Training School: *K7309; K7325; K7331; K7332* (crashed after take-off at Grantham, 26-10-36); *K7333; K7334; K7335* (crashed on landing at Grantham, 7-6-37); *K7336-K7341; K7382; K7399; K7404; K7405; K7410; K7412; K7439* (crashed while landing at South Cerney, 25-5-40); *K7443* (crashed near Stroud, Glos, 21-12-37); *K7444* (crashed, 11-10-39); *K7445; K7446; K7447* (crashed at Purton, Wilts, 2-10-39); *K7449* (crashed at Atwick, Yorks, 17-2-39); *K7455; K7463.*

No. 5 Flying Training School: *K7309; K7323; K7328; K7389* (crashed while landing at Sealand, 11-4-39); *K7426; K7428; K7441; K7442; K7454; K7468.*

No. 6 Flying Training School: *K7345; K7346* (crashed, 28-1-38); *K7355-K7357; K7358* (crashed while landing at Netheravon, 1-7-37); *K7359* (crashed while landing at Netheravon, 5-4-37); *K7360; K7361* (crashed at Bourton-on-the-Water, Glos., 21-11-39); *K7362; K7368* (crashed at Cranfield, 6-2-39); *K7369-K7371; K7384; K7401; K7411; K7421; K7436; K7450; K7451; K7454.*

No. 7 Flying Training School: *K7336; K7340; K7369; K7371; K7374; K7379* (crashed while landing at Peterborough, 7-6-40); *K7385-K7388; K7403; K7437; K7456* (crashed while landing at Peterborough, 28-11-39); *K7457* (crashed while landing at night at Peterborough, 4-1-40).

No. 8 Flying Training School: *K7314; K7322; K7323; K7326; K7376* (crashed on Edendocher Hill, Kincardineshire, 5-5-39); *K7385* (crashed while low flying, Dysart, Fife, 29-2-40); *K7390; K7394; K7395; K7397* (crashed while landing at Montrose, 21-3-40).

No. 9 Flying Training School: *K7307* (crashed at Hullavington, 7-4-38); *K7308* (crashed while landing at Babdown landing ground, 17-4-40); *K7309; K7310* (struck ambulance while taking off at Thornaby, 4-5-37); *K7311; K7317* (crashed, 19-8-37); *K7318* (crashed while landing at Kemble, 17-4-39); *K7319* (crashed while landing at Newton Down landing ground, 1-5-40); *K7322* (crashed at Hockley Heath, 19-11-40); *K7327; K7328; K7329* (crashed, 3-11-36); *K7330; K7334* (crashed near Hullavington, 7-10-39); *K7341; K7348; K7373; K7391; K7393; K7402* (damaged beyond repair in gale, 21-8-40); *K7405; K7412* (crashed at night at Babdown Farm, 23-10-40); *K7414; K7421; K7422; K7425; K7430; K7431* (crashed while landing at Hullavington, 10-9-39); *K7432* (crashed while landing at Hullavington, 3-1-41); *K7434; K7440* (burnt on ground at Hullavington, 28-

8-40); *K7445* (struck balloon cable and crashed at Longbridge, Birmingham, 12-12-40); *K7452* (crashed while landing at Babdown Farm, 1-11-40); *K7454*; *K7462*; *K7468*.

No. 10 Flying Training School: *K7324*; *K7325*; *K7369*; *K7396* (collided with Audax *K5149* and crashed near Penrhos, 10-10-38); *K7397*; *K7402*; *K7452*.

No. 11 Flying Training School: *K7320*; *K7321* (crashed while landing at Shawbury, 15-8-39); *K7327*; *K7347* (crashed on Theddlethorpe ranges, 26-4-37); *K7402*; *K7407*; *K7414*; *K7427* (crashed while landing at Shawbury, 8-1-40); *K7435* (abandoned after loss of control, Acton Heath, 11-10-38); *K7446* (crashed on West Moors, Dorset, 2-12-38).

No. 12 Flying Training School: *K7309*; *K7328*; *K7339*; *K7341*; *K7348*; *K7370* (crashed while landing at Grantham, 22-4-40); *K7393*; *K7421*; *K7454*; *K7468*.

No. 13 Flying Training School: *K7324*; *K7336*; *K7369*; *K7448*.

No. 14 Flying Training School: *K7311* (crashed while landing at Kinloss, 5-2-40); *K7343*; *K7351*; *K7352*; *K7365*; *K7367* (crashed at Harrold, Beds, 29-5-40); *K7422*.

No. 15 Flying Training School: *K7324*; *K7336*; *K7369*; *K7448* (crashed, 11-11-39).

No. 2 Glider Training School: *K7328*; *K7342*; *K7352*; *K7380*; *K7393*; *K7455*; *K7466*; *K7467*.

No. 4 Glider Training School: *K7328*; *K7331*; *K7342*; *K7352*; *K7380*; *K7393*; *K7405*; *K7422*; *K7424* (crashed while landing at Kidlington, 6-10-42); *K7426*; *K7455*; *K7466*; *K7567*.

School of Photography: *K7372*; *K7432*.

School of Army Co-operation: *K7410*; *K7417*; *K7452*;

No. 20 (Pilots) Advanced Flying Unit: *K7328*; *K7331*; *K7405*; *K7422*; *K7426*; *K7466*; *K7467*.

No. 101 Glider Operational Training Unit: *K7468*.

No. 102 Glider Operational Training Unit: *K7331*.

Elementary & Reserve Flying Training Schools: No. 1 ERFTS: *K7381* (crashed on houses at Edmonton, London, while low flying, 4-9-38). No. 2 ERFTS: *K7373*; *K7382*. No. 4 ERFTS: *K7355* (crashed while landing at Brough, 12-6-38). No. 5 ERFTS: *K7439*. No. 6 ERFTS: *K7407*. No. 7 ERFTS: *K7421*. No. 9 ERFTS: *K7409*. No. 19 ERFTS: *K7373*; *K7459* (crashed at Brighton, 11-2-39); *K7460* (crashed at Loxwood, Sussex, 19-2-39); *K7461* (crashed at Stamford, Lincs, 10-6-39); *K7462*. No. 15 ERFTS: *K7463*. No. 20 ERFTS: *K7415* (crashed into trees during aerobatics over Sevenoaks, Kent, 9-4-39); *K7416* (crashed, 21-1-38); *K7418* (crashed while landing at Gravesend, 7-5-38); *K7427*; *K7428*; No. 21 ERFTS: *K7454*. No. 23 ERFTS: *K7357*. No. 47 ERFTS: *K7323*.

Elementary Flying Training Schools: No. 1 EFTS: *K7464*. No. 3 EFTS: *K7405*; *K7406* (suffered taxying accident at Hamble, 15-6-39); *K7413* (crashed at Lymington, 2-8-38); No. 9 EFTS: *K7403*; *K7408*. No. 10 EFTS: *K7404*, *K7412*. No. 21 EFTS: *K7468*.

No. 1 Service Flying Training School (India): *K7313* (crashed during aerobatics at Lahore, 9-3-43); *K7336*; *K7357* (abandoned when pilot became lost near Delhi, 14-11-41); *K7372*; *K7374*; *K7442* (crashed, 11-9-42); *K7465* (crashed while landing at Ambala, 15-9-42).

Supplied to South African Air Force: *K7314* (22-10-40); *K7320* (22-10-40); *K7330* (21-4-41); *K7337* (11-42; lost at sea in SS *City of Hankow*); *K7339* (20-12-40); *K7341*; *K7343* (22-10-40); *K7348*; *K7362* (11-40, as No. *1843*); *K7365* (5-41); *K7373* (11-40, as No. *1838*); *K7378* (10-4-41); *K7386* (6-40); *K7388* (22-10-40); *K7399* (4-42); *K7404* (11-40, as No. *1835*); *K7407* (10-40); *K7409* (5-41); *K7410* (10-40); *K7414* (8-10-42); *K7417* (10-40); *K7420*; *K7428* (15-6-41); *K7430* (29-9-41); *K7436* (17-4-42); *K7437* (4-12-40, as No. *1834*); *K7441* (1-11-40, as No. *1841*); *K7463* (8-10-41).

Ground Instruction Machines: *K7324* (became *1908M*, 5-40); *K7349* (became *1132M*, 9-38); *K7383* (became *2218M*, 9-40); *K7400* (became *2219M*, 9-40); *K7429* (became *2035M*, 10-40); *K7433* (became *1039M*, 1-38); *K7451*; *K7453*; *K7464* (became *2037M*, 6-40).

Other Units and duties, etc.: *K7314* (Ternhill Stn. Flt.); *K7316* (Delhi Comms. Flt.; struck by Dominie at Dum Dum and damaged beyond repair, 16-11-43); *K7320* (Odiham Stn. Flt.); *K7373* and *K7381* (No. 615 Sqn., A.A.F.); *K7391* (No. 613 Sqn., A.A.F.); *K7400* (ATA; crashed while landing at Cardiff, 5-9-40); *K7414* (Cambridge University Air Squadron);

K7429 (Duxford Stn. Flt.; Abingdon Stn. Flt.); *K7448* (No. 8 Armament Training Camp).

The Hawker Audax I. Second production batch of 85 aircraft, *K7469-K7553*, to Specification 34/34, built by the Bristol Aeroplane Co. Ltd., Filton, Bristol, and delivered between July and November 1936. Rolls-Royce Kestrel X and XDR engines. 48 aircraft, *K7502-K7549*, prepared for tropical service with enlarged radiators and sand filters.

No. 14 Sqn. (Palestine and Egypt): *K7503.*

No. 33 (F) Sqn. (Palestine and Egypt): *K7515.*

No. 52 Sqn. (Iraq): *K7503*; *K7504* (caught fire and burnt on ground at Habbaniya, 1-9-41); *K7512*; *K7514*; *K7515*; *K7521*; *K7525*; *K7526*; *K7528*; *K7530.*

No. 146 (F) Sqn., (India): *K7480.*

No. 173 (C) Sqn., (Egypt): *K7512* (crashed 60 miles west of Tobruk, 21-3-43); *K7525.*

No. 208 Sqn. (Middle East): *K7506*; *K7508*; *K7520-K7523*; *K7527*; *K7528*; *K7531*; *K7544-K7549.*

No. 237 (Rhodesia) Sqn. (Middle East): *K7531*; *K7534*; *K7540-K7542*; *K7544* (crashed at Mosul, 5-8-42); *K7545*; *K7546* (force landed at El Wak and abandoned, 18-6-40); *K7548*; *K7549.*

No. 1 Sqn., Southern Rhodesian Air Force: *K7546.*

No. 4 Sqn., South African Air Force: *K7540* (crashed in poor visibility 5 miles south of Nyeri, Kenya, 11-7-41); *K7549* (crashed in poor visibility 20 miles south of Nyeri, Kenya, 11-7-41).

No. 3 Sqn., Indian Air Force: *K7482.*

R.A.F. College Cranwell: *K7489*; *K7499.*

No. 1 Flying Training School: *K7482*; *K7484*; *K7489*; *K7595*; *K7496*; *K7550.*

No. 2 Flying Training School: *K7469* (crashed while landing at night at Digby, 23-2-37); *K7470* (crashed, 29-22-37); *K7486* (crashed in sea, 12-7-39).

No. 4 Flying Training School (Middle East): *K7502-K7504*; *K7505* (crashed at Rutbah, Iraq, 30-8-39); *K7506-K7508*; *K7509* (crashed while landing at Jif Jaffa, Sinai, 3-1-38); *K7510* (crashed while landing at night at Abu Sueir, 12-1-38); *K7511*; *K7512*; *K7513* (crashed on Abu Sueir ranges, 22-7-38); *K7514*; *K7515*; *K7516* (crashed while landing at Abu Sueir, 3-5-39); *K7517* (collided with Audax *K7523*, and crashed 15 miles north of Baghdad, 12-9-40); *K7518*; *K7519*; *K7520* (crashed while landing at Abu Sueir, 6-7-38); *K7521*; *K7522* (crashed at Abu Sueir, 6-5-38); *K7523* (collided with Audax *K7517* and crashed 15 miles north of Baghdad, 12-9-40); *K7524-K7526*; *K7527* (crashed while landing at Abu Sueir, 31-3-39); *K7528-K7530*; *K7532-K7535*; *K7536* (crashed while landing near Abu Sueir, 25-11-38); *K7537* (crashed at Abu Sueir, 17-6-37); *K7538* (crashed while landing at Abu Sueir, 25-10-38); *K7539-K7543*; *K7547.*

No. 5 Flying Training School: *K7474*; *K7493* (crashed while landing at night at Sealand, 10-7-39); *K7494* (crashed on landing at Sealand, 25-8-38); *K7495*; *K7550.*

No. 6 Flying Training School: *K7475*; *K7483*; *K7551* (crashed while landing at Netheravon, 11-10-37).

No. 7 Flying Training School: *K7482*; *K7484*; *K7496*; *K7498* (crashed while landing at Peterborough, 11-3-40).

No. 8 Flying Training School: *K7471* (struck HT cables over River Tay and crashed, 24-5-37); *K7472-K7475*; *K7476* (crashed at Dysart landing ground, 17-9-37); *K7477* (crashed, 9-2-38); *K7478* (crashed while landing at Montrose, 22-4-38); *K7487* (crashed, 30-7-37); *K7488* (crashed during night landing at Montrose, 14-12-36); *K7489.*

No. 9 Flying Training School: *K7485*; *K7500*; *K7553.*

No. 10 Flying Training School: *K7479*; *K7481* (crashed near Kidderminster, 1-1-39); *K7482-K7484*; *K7490*; *K7491* (crashed during night landing at Ternhill, 4-2-37); *K7492*; *K7496*; *K7497* (crashed at Hodnet, Shropshire, 9-9-37); *K7498*; *K7499.*

No. 11 Flying Training School: *K7482*; *K7492* (crashed at Cheswardine, Staffs, 26-1-40); *K7500*; *K7501* (collided with Audax *K7435* and crashed, 25-10-37).

No. 12 Flying Training School: *K7489* (crashed on night cross country flight, 10-10-39); *K7550* (crashed at Coalville Grammar School, Leics, 17-11-39).

No. 13 Flying Training School: *K7479* (crashed at East Linton, E. Lothian, 14-9-39); *K7484*; *K7490*; *K7496*; *K7498.*

No. 15 Flying Training School: *K7490*; *K7496*; *K7498.*

Nos. 2/4 Glider Training Schools: *K7475*; *K7495.*

Straits Settlements Volunteer Air Force: *K7480*; *K7515.*

Western Desert Communications Flt.: *K7514* (crashed near Maaten Bagush, 20-12-41); *K7528.*

Middle East Communications Flt.: *K7515* (crashed on take-off at Lydda, 5-12-42); *K7541* (ditched off Syrian coast, 21-5-42); *K7542.*

No. 4 Sqn., South African Air Force: *K7540* (crashed in poor visibility 5 miles south of Nyeri, Kenya, 11-7-41); *K7549* (crashed in poor visibility 20 miles south of Nyeri, Kenya, 11-7-41).

No. 1 Sqn., Southern Rhodesian Air Force: *K7546.*

No. 1 Service Flying Training School (India): *K7480*; *K7484* (crashed near Delhi, 10-6-42); *K7503* (crashed near Kasauli, 23-2-43); *K7529* (crashed near Ambala, 20-5-42); *K7530*; *K7539* (crashed at Ambala, 16-6-42); *K7547* (crashed while landing at Ambala, 3-10-42).

Elementary & Reserve Flying Training Schools: No. 19 ERFTS: *K7553.* No. 26 ERFTS: *K7552.* No. 47 ERFTS: *K7474.*

Supplied to the South African Air Force: *K7474* (26-5-41); *K7500* (5-11-40); *K7533* (22-10-40).

Supplied to Southern Rhodesian Air Force: *K7534* (1-11-40); *K7548* (1-11-40).

Other Units and duties, etc.: *K7495* (No. 102 Glider Operational Training Unit); *K7526* (No. 3 Middle East Training School); *K7528* (El Adem Communications Flt.; No. 51 Repair & Servicing Unit; crashed while landing at Qasaba, 5-2-42); *K7531* (Pilots & Aircrew Pool, Eastleigh, Kenya; No. 108 M.U.; aircraft overturned during engine starting, LG.222, 15-1-43); *K7542* and *K7544* (Iraq Comms. Flt.).

The Hawker Audax I. Fourth production batch of 25 aircraft, *K8311-K8335*, to Specification 34/34, ordered from A.V. Roe & Co. Ltd., Manchester, under Contract No. 389426/35, and delivered between March and June 1937. All aircraft prepared as trainers for home service, but several shipped out to India for transfer to the Indian Air Force in 1942-43.

No. 97 (B) Sqn.: *K8330.*

No. 144 (B) Sqn.: *K8312.*

No. 146 (F) Sqn. (India): *K8328.*

No. 148 (B) Sqn.: *K8335.*

R.A.F. College, Cranwell: *K8311.*

Flying Training Schools: No. 1 FTS: *K8318*; *K8324*; *K8325* (crashed near Aylesbury, Bucks, 6-2-41); *K8331.* No. 2 FTS: *K8314.* No. 3 FTS: *K8318-K8320*; *K8322*; *K8324*; *K8325*; *K8327*; *K8332* (crashed 7 miles west of Tewkesbury, 10-1-40); *K8334* (crashed while landing at South Cerney, 4-3-40). No. 5 FTS: *K8321*; *K8331.* No. 8 FTS: *K8313*; *K8330*; *K8335.* No. 9 FTS: *K8312*; *K8315* (crashed at Beversbrook bombing range, Calne, Wiltshire, 13-5-40); *K8316*; *K8321*; *K8322* (crashed at Compton Bassett, Wiltshire, 24-11-40); *K8327*; *K8329* (crashed at Sopworth, Wiltshire, 5-8-40). No. 11 FTS: *K8316.* No. 12 FTS: *K8321.* No. 14 FTS: *K8314.* No. 15 FTS: *K8330.*

Elementary & Reserve Flying Training Schools: No. 1 ERFTS: *K8320*; *K8324*; *K8329.* No. 2 ERFTS: *K8318*; *K8319.* No. 4 ERFTS: *K8317* (crashed while landing at Brough, 1-7-38); *K8326*; *K8330.* No. 5 ERFTS: *K8334.* No. 7 ERFTS: *K8321*; *K8331.* No. 8 ERFTS: *K8316.* No. 12 ERFTS: *K8323.* No. 13 ERFTS: *K8322*; *K8325*; *K8327*; *K8328.* No. 22 ERFTS: *K8333.* No. 34 ERFTS: *K8329.* No. 35 ERFTS: *K8330.*

Supplied to South African Air Force: *K8313* (21-10-40); *K8314* (1-11-40 as No. *1844*); *K8316* (5-12-41); *K8318* (8-4-42); *K8330* (22-10-40); *K8333* (22-10-40).

Other Units and duties, etc.: *K8319* (No. 1 S.F.T.S.(India); crashed near Ambala, 10-9-42); *K8320* (No. 3 Photographic Reconnaissance Unit; SOC, 30-11-43); *K8321* (No. 2 Glider Training School; No. 4 Glider Training School; crashed at Kingston Bagpuize, Oxon, 18-2-43); *K8324* (No. 102 Glider Operational Training Unit; No. 4 G.T.S.); *K8327* (Nos. 2 and 4 G.T.S.); *K8328* (Northolt Stn. Flt.; No. 3 Sqn., I.A.F.; No. 7 Sqn., I.A.F.; crashed while landing at Miramshah, 17-12-43); *K8335* (No. 5 Sqn., R.A.F., India; crashed at Ghopal, Assam, 9-9-42).

The Hawker Persian Audax (Series I). Production batch of 30 aircraft for Persia, *401-430*, built by H.G. Hawker Engineering Co. Ltd., Kingston and Brooklands, in 1933. Pratt & Whitney Hornet S2B1G radial engines driving three-blade Hamilton Hydromatic propellers (two-blade Watts also flown on test). First flight by *401*, 22 August 1933.

The Hawker Persian Audax (Series 2). Production batch of 26 aircraft for Persia, *431-456*, built by Hawker Aircraft Ltd., Kingston and Brooklands, during 1934-35. *431-436* with Bristol Pegasus IIM radial engines; *437-456* with Pegasus IIM2 engines. Final aircraft first flown 20 March 1935.

The Hawker Iraqi Audax. Production batch of 34 aircraft for Iraq built by Hawker Aircraft Ltd., Kingston, and Brooklands, during 1935-36. The first 24 aircraft were delivered with Bristol Pegasus IIM2 radial engines, the remainder with Pegasus VIP8 engines. At least one aircraft was flown with a Bristol Mercury radial, and another was fitted temporarily with a Pratt & Whitney Hornet S2B1G radial. Aircraft believed registered as *28-61*. (Some aircraft known to be flying in 1945-46).

The Hawker Canadian Audax. Single aircraft delivered for evaluation in Canada during 1934, conforming to Air Ministry Specification 34/34, powered by Rolls-Royce Kestrel XDR.

The Hawker Egyptian Audax. Single aircraft, *K400*, believed built by Hawker Aircraft Ltd., powered by an Armstrong Siddeley Panther X radial engine and delivered to Egypt in 1936 (?). Further production batch (of unknown extent) to similar specification prepared by Sir W.G. Armstrong Whitworth Aircraft Ltd., Coventry, delivered in 1937 (?).

The Hawker G.23/33 Hardy. One prototype, *K3013*, originally built as a Hart by Vickers (Aviation) Ltd., Weybridge, under Contract No. 198868/32. Aircraft returned to Brooklands from R.A.F. Kenley in 1933 and progressively modified to conform to Air Ministry Specification G.23/33 under Contract No. 279525/33. First flown as Hardy prototype on 7 September 1934 by P.E.G. Sayer. Performance and handling trials at Brooklands, A. & A.E.E., 1934-35; R.A.E., 1935-36. Ultimately became Ground Instruction Machine, *1448M*, at No. 6 S. of T.T., 4-39.

The Hawker Hardy I. First production batch of 21 aircraft, *K4050-K4070*, to Specification G.23/33, built by Gloster Aircraft Co., Ltd., Brockworth, Glos, under Sub-Contract No. 288988/33. First aircraft flown in October 1934 (?). First aircraft delivered to No. 30 Squadron, Mosul, Iraq, in April 1935.
    No. 6 Sqn., Ramleh, Palestine: *K4050-K4053*; *K4054* (crashed at Tulkarm, Palestine, 27-7-38); *K4055*; *K4056*; *K4057* (blown over in squall at Sulaimaniya landing ground, 9-7-38); *K4059*; *K4060* (SOC, 15-3-41); *K4062-K4065*; *K4066* (crashed 20 miles south of Ma'an, Transjordan, 2-5-38); *K4067*; *K4068*; *K4070* (crashed while landing 6 miles west of Ramleh, 15-11-39).
    No. 30 Sqn., Mosul, Iraq: *K4050-K4057*; *K4058* (SOC, 27-7-38); *K4059*; *K4060*; *K4061* (crashed, 19-5-36); *K4062-K4068*; *K4069* (crashed while landing at Habbaniya, 12-10-37); *K4070*.

No. 237 (Rhodesia) Sqn., Nairobi, Kenya: *K4053* and *K4055* (both aircraft destroyed in Italian air raid on Goz Regeb, Sudan, 12-12-40); *K4062* (attacked and damaged by Gladiator 6 miles south of Cub Cub landing ground, 25-2-41; SOC); *K4065*; *K4067*.
Supplied to Southern Rhodesian Air Force: *K4050*; *K4065*.
Other Units: *K4050* (No. 70 O.T.U.; Training Unit and Reserve Pool, Middle East).

The Hawker Hardy I. Second production batch of 16 aircraft, *K4306-K4321*, built by Gloster Aircraft Co. Ltd., Brockworth, Glos, to Specification G.23/33 under Contract No. 323238/ 34, and delivered between May and July 1935.

No. 6 Sqn., Ramleh, Palestine: *K4306-K4316*; *K4317* (crashed, 26-8-38); *K4318-K4321*.
No. 30 Sqn., Mosul, Iraq: *K4306-K4321*.
No. 237 (Rhodesia) Sqn., Nairobi, Kenya: *K4307* and *K4308* (both aircraft destroyed in Italian air raid on Goz Regeb, Sudan, 12-12-40); *K4310* (crashed on take-off at Sarum, 3-1-41); *K4311*; *K4313* (shot down by Fiat C.R.42 over Cheren, Ethiopia, 7-2-41); *K4314-K4316*; *K4318*; *K4319*.
Other Units: *K4314* (Training Unit & Reserve Pool, Middle East; SOC, 10-2-41); *K4320* (crashed while landing at Abu Sueir, 30-5-40).

The Hawker Hardy I. Third production batch of 10 aircraft, *K5914-K5823*, built by Gloster Aircraft Co. Ltd., Brockworth, Glos, to Specification G.23/33 under Contract No. 413880/ 35, and delivered in February 1936.

No. 6 Sqn., Ramleh, Palestine: *K5914-K5918*; *K5920-K5922*.
No. 30 Sqn., Mosul, Iraq: *K5914*; *K5920*.
No. 237 (Rhodesia) Sqn., Nairobi, Kenya: *K5914* (missing from patrol, 16-5-40); *K5915* (crashed at Atbara, Sudan, 16-11-40); *K5916*; *K5917*; *K5921*; *K5922* (shot down by Fiat C.R.42s over Tessener, Ethiopia, 12-1-42); *K5923*.
Communications Flt., Hinaidi: *K5914-K5918*.
Supplied to Southern Rhodesian Air Force: *K5916*; *K5917*.
Other Units and duties, etc.: *K5919* (remained in U.K.; A. & A.E.E. for trials with low pressure tyres and additional desert equipment; to R.A.F. Watchfield; became Ground Instruction Machine, 10-43); *K5923* (Summit Stn. Flt.; SOC, 5-42).

The Hawker F.7/30 — P.V.3. One prototype, registered *IPV-3*, designed as private venture to meet requirements of Air Ministry Specification F.7/30 for four-gun day-and-night fighter. Powered initially by Rolls-Royce Goshawk III steam-cooled engine. First flight, 15 June 1934 . To A. & A.E.E. for initial evaluation and handling. Fitted with Goshawk B.41 (first flown, 26 June 1935), and with Goshawk B.43 driving three-blade Fairey Reed propeller (first flown 9 July 1935). To Rolls-Royce Ltd., October 1935.

The Hawker G.4/31 — P.V.4. One prototype, registered *IPV-4*, designed as private venture to meet requirements for general purpose light bomber of Air Ministry Specification G.4/31. Powered initially by Bristol Pegasus III and first flown on 6 December 1934. Pegasus X fitted in 1935, and aircraft registered *K6926*; to A. & A.E.E. for initial evaluation. To Bristol Aeroplane Co. Ltd., Filton. Flown with Bristol Perseus and Bristol Taurus radial engines. S.O.C., 29-3-39.

The Hawker 22/34 Hartbees. Four pattern aircraft, *801-804*, built by Hawker Aircraft Ltd., Kingston, to Specification 22/34 on behalf of the South African Air Force during 1934-35. *801* flown on 28 June 1935; *803*, first flown on the same day, featured additional armour protection for the crew. Delivered to South Africa in 1935.

The Hawker Hartbees I. Production batch of 65 aircraft, *805-869*, built under licence at the Roberts Heights factory, South African Air Force Depot, Pretoria, South Africa, during 1936-38. Based at Waterkloof airfield until deployed to Kenya on the outbreak of the Second World War. At least two aircraft served at Habbaniya, Iraq, in 1943.

The Hawker G.7/34 Hind. One prototype, *K2915*, originally commenced manufacture to Specification 25/31 as a modified Hart, but further modified by Hawker Aircraft Ltd., Kingston and Brooklands, to meet requirements of Specification G.7/34 under Contract No. 159690/34. First flight, 12 September 1934. Rolls-Royce Kestrel V engine. Underwent evaluation, performance and handling trials at A. & A.E.E., Martlesham Heath, and the R.A.E., 1934-36. (Ultimately supplied to the South African Air Force, 8-5-41).

The Hawker Hind I. First production batch of 20 aircraft, *K4636-K4655*, to Specification G.7/34, ordered under Contract No. 333273/34, and built by Hawker Aircraft Ltd., Kingston and Brooklands. Rolls-Royce Kestrel V engir.es. Delivered during December 1935 and January 1936.

No. 18 (B) Sqn.: *K4640.*

No. 21 (B) Sqn.: *K4638-K4640*; *K4644*; *K4645*; *K4649*; *K4650.*

No. 34 (B) Sqn.: *K4642-K4645.*

No. 49 (B) Sqn.: *K4652.*

No. 83 (B) Sqn.: *K4652.*

No. 98 (B) Sqn.: *K4638*; *K4641*; *K4646* (crashed, 27-1-37); *K4647*; *K4648* (crashed near Hucknall, 15-6-37); *K4651.*

No. 104 (B) Sqn.: *K4641*; *K4646-K4648*; *K4651.*

No. 107 (B) Sqn.: *K4653*; *K4654*; *K4655* (crashed while taking off at Perham Down, 30-10-36).

R.A.F. College, Cranwell: *K4652.*

Flying Training Schools: No. 1 FTS: *K4651* (crashed st Shrewton landing ground, 12-10-41); *K4652* (crashed while landing at Stormy Down, 4-8-40). No. 9 FTS: *K4644.* No. 10 FTS: *K4651.* No. 12 FTS: *K4650.*

Elementary & Reserve Flying Training Schools. No. 26 ERFTS: *K4644.* No. 32 ERFTS: *K4650.* No. 47 ERFTS: *K4651.*

No. 2 Air Observers' School: *K4652-K4654.*

No. 10 Bombing & Gunnery School: *K4651*; *K4652*; *K4653* (damaged while taxying at Warmwell, 2-4-40, and SOC).

Supplied to South African Air Force: *K4636*; *K4638* (30-4-40); *K4640* (21-4-41); *K4643* (8-41); *K4645* (16-6-40); *K4647* (11-6-40); *K4649* (19-7-40); *K4653* (23-4-41).

Supplied to the Royal New Zealand Air Force: *K4642* (21-8-40); *K4650* (4-7-41).

Other Units and duties, etc.: *K4636* (A. & A.E.E., performance and handling trials; Northolt Stn. Flt.); *K4638* (Duxford Stn. Flt.); *K4639* (University of London Air Squadron); *K4640* (No. 610 Sqn., A.A.F.); *K4641* (No. 19 M.U.; crashed 2 miles south of Cheddar, Somerset, 18-12-39); *K4642* (No. 603 Sqn., A.A.F.); *K4643* (No. 500 Sqn., A.A.F.); *K4645* (No. 602 Sqn., A.A.F.); *K4650* (No. 1 Parachute Flying Unit); *K4653* and *K4654* (No. 7 Armament Training Station).

The Hawker Hind I. Second production batch of 193 aircraft, *K5368-K5560*, prepared to Air Ministry Specification 11/35, and ordered under Contract No. 404654/35. Built by Hawker Aircraft Ltd., Kingston and Brooklands, and delivered between January and August 1936. Rolls-Royce Kestrel V engines. Many later modified as dual-control trainers.

No. 12 (B) Sqn.: *K5394* (crashed at Calshot, 1-4-37); *K5395* (crashed while landing at Andover, 16-7-37); *K5396*; *K5399*; *K5501*; *K5526*; *K5548*; *K5549* (crashed while landing at Andover, 13-3-37); *K5550-K5554*; *K5555* (abandoned in severe icing conditions, 10-1-38).

No. 15 (B) Sqn.: *K5401*; *K5413*; *K5414*; *K5421*; *K5428* (crashed while landing at Upper Heyford, 25-11-37); *K5430-K5433*; *K5439*; *K5440*; *K5449*; *K5450*; *K5459*; *K5460*; *K5461* (crashed, 22-6-36); *K5462*; *K5463* (crashed while landing at Hullavington, 22-10-36); *K5559*; *K5560.*

No. 18 (B) Sqn.: *K5400*; *K5451*; *K5452* (crashed at Cottisford, Oxon, 10-8-37); *K5453* (crashed, 21-4-37); *K5454* (crashed, 11-2-38); *K5471*; *K5472* (crashed on take-off at Upper Heyford, 22-3-37); *K5473*; *K5474* (crashed at Cottisford, Oxon, 30-12-36); *K5475*; *K5481*; *K5483-K5486*; *K5487* (crashed, 24-4-37); *K5488*.

No. 21 (B) Sqn.: *K5373*; *K5377*; *K5386*; *K5388* (crashed in low cloud, 24-2-37); *K5397*; *K5441*; *K5446*; *K5512*; *K5513*; *K5518* (crashed on night cross country, 26-8-37).

No. 24 (C) Sqn.: *K5421*.

No. 34 (B) Sqn.: *K5393*; *K5397*; *K5398*; *K5441*; *K5512*; *K5513*.

No. 40 (B) Sqn.: *K5422*; *K5423*; *K5424* (crashed while landing at Abingdon, 19-3-36); *K5425-K5427*; *K5428* (crashed, 17-7-36); *K5429-K5431*; *K5436*; *K5437* (crashed while taking off at Abingdon, 16-6-37); *K5438*; *K5447*; *K5448*; *K5465-K5470*; *K5495*.

No. 44 (B) Sqn.: *K5400-K5403*; *K5404* (crashed on take-off at Waddington, 29-7-37); *K5405* (crashed while landing at Waddington, 8-7-37); *K5407*; *K5415*; *K5417-K5420*; *K5434*; *K5435*.

No. 49 (B) Sqn.: *K5372*; *K5382-K5384*; *K5385* (crashed in fog, 2-2-37); *K5402*; *K5412*; *K5442*; *K5443*; *K5455*.

No. 50 (B) Sqn.: *K5403*; *K5407*.

No. 52 (B) Sqn.: *K5406-K5410*; *K5411* (crashed while landing at Upwood, 10-5-37); *K5412*; *K5470* (crashed as pilot tried to avoid HT cables, 28-4-37).

No. 57 (B) Sqn.: *K5390*; *K5406*; *K5409*; *K5455-K5458*; *K5477*; *K5478*; *K5479* (crashed, 4-3-38); *K5480*; *K5481*; *K5482* (crashed at Halton, 12-8-36).

No. 62 (B) Sqn.: *K5415*.

No. 82 (B) Sqn.: *K5408*; *K5410*.

No. 83 (B) Sqn.: *K5374*; *K5375*; *K5525* (crashed, 10-1-39); *K5527*; *K5528* (crashed in cloud, 13-6-37); *K5529* (crashed at Loftus, Yorks, 3-8-37); *K5530*; *K5556*.

No. 88 (B) Sqn.: *K5451*; *K5496-K5499*; *K5542*.

No. 98 (B) Sqn.: *K5368*; *K5376*; *K5378* (crashed on beach in poor visibility near North Coates, 13-5-36); *K5379*; *K5380* (crashed while landing at Hucknall, 2-7-37); *K2381*; *K5434*; *K5444* (crashed, 5-6-37); *K5445* (crashed, 1-4-37); *K5515*.

No. 103 (B) Sqn.: *K5519-K5524*.

No. 104 (B) Sqn.: *K5514* (crashed on take-off at Hucknall, 9-4-37); *K5515*.

No. 106 (B) Sqn.: *K5408*; *K5413*; *K5439*; *K5440*; *K5449*; *K5450*; *K5559*.

No. 107 (B) Sqn.: *K5419*; *K5435*; *K5543*; *K5544*; *K5545* (crashed while landing at Andover, 19-1-37); *K5558* (crashed in night landing at Harwell, 13-12-37).

No. 113 (B) Sqn.: *K5371*; *K5420*; *K5430*; *K5443*; *K5462*; *K5548* (crashed while landing in Suez Canal Zone, 15-2-39); *K5552*; *K5554*; *K5556*.

No. 114 (B) Sqn.: *K5400-K5405*;

No. 134 (F) Sqn.: *K5422* (damaged while taxiing at Kasfareet, Egypt, 30-12-39; SOC, but brought back on charge and preserved).

No. 139 (B) Sqn.: *K5369*; *K5370* (crashed at Beccles, Suffolk, 4-5-37); *K5371*; *K5372*; *K5374-K5476*.

No. 142 (B) Sqn.: *K5371*.

No. 185 (B) Sqn.: *K5423*; *K5426*; *K5427*; *K5495*.

No. 211 (B) Sqn.: *K5389*; *K5408*; *K5409*; *K5430*; *K5456-K5458*; *K5477*; *K5483*; *K5484*; *K5520*; *K5554*.

No. 218 (B) Sqn.: *K5371*; *K5372*; *K5389*; *K5390*; *K5391* (crashed, 28-7-38); *K5392*; *K5409*; *K5441*; *K5516* (crashed on Theddlethorpe ranges, Lincs, 6-10-36); *K5517*.

No. 296 (GT) Sqn.: *K5468*.

No. 500 Sqn., A.A.F.: *K5393*.

No. 501 Sqn., A.A.F.: *K5396*; *K5398*; *K5399*; *K5410*; *K5550*; *K5551* (crashed, 23-7-38); *K5560*.

No. 502 Sqn., A.A.F.: *K5417*.

No. 503 Sqn., A.A.F.: *K5481*; *K5485*.

No. 504 Sqn., A.A.F.: *K5492*.

No. 602 Sqn., A.A.F.: *K5418; K5460; K5500; K5502-K5509; K5510* (crashed while approaching to land at Renfrew, 27-7-37); *K5511; K5513.*

No. 603 Sqn., A.A.F.: *K5392; K5498* (crashed after hitting HT cables, 26-3-38); *K5499.*

No. 605 Sqn., A.A.F.: *K5431; K5531-K5541.*

No. 609 Sqn., A.A.F.: *K5421; K5451; K5492; K5496; K5497; K5519; K5542.*

No. 610 Sqn., A.A.F.: *K5400; K5476.*

No. 611 Sqn., A.A.F.: *K5379; K5390; K5401; K5406; K5414; K5433; K5478; K5480; K5490; K5493; K5500.*

No. 612 Sqn., A.A.F.: *K5460.*

No. 613 Sqn., A.A.F.: *K5379; K5406; K5433; K5473; K5478; K5490; K5493.*

No. 614 Sqn., A.A.F.: *K5379; K5478; K5493.*

No. 616 Sqn., A.A.F.: *K5473; K5481; K5485; K5488.*

R.A.F. College, Cranwell: *K5368* (crashed in night landing at Barkston Heath, 30-7-40); *K5376; K5382* (crashed as pilot tried to avoid HT cables, Lytchett Maltravers, Dorset, 26-4-40); *K5401* (crashed, 27-8-40); *K5408* (crashed after striking HT cables near Caythorpe, Lincs, 4-12-40); *K5413* (crashed into the River Trent near Clifton while low flying, 6-7-40); *K5416; K5419* (crashed while landing at West Freugh, 17-12-39); *K5432* (crashed while landing at Barkston Heath, 23-7-40); *K5438; K5441; K5447; K5448; K5450; K5455* (damaged in taxying accident at Cranwell, 10-4-40, and SOC); *K5468; K5506; K5512* (crashed while landing at night at Barkston Heath, 26-8-40); *K5515; K5527; K5531; K5537; K5541; K5543; K5547* (crashed while landing at night at Cranwell, 8-4-40).

No. 1 Flying Training School: *K5369; K5372; K5374; K5376; K5393; K5399; K5435; K5441; K5447; K5450; K5468; K5471; K5475; K5486; K5491* (crashed on Otmoor bombing range, 18-5-40); *K5503* (crashed while landing at Netheravon, 17-7-40); *K5506* (crashed while landing at Netheravon, 17-8-41); *K5522* (crashed at Netheravon, 23-7-41); *K5524; K5527; K5542.*

No. 3 Flying Training School: *K5501* (crashed, 17-2-38).

No. 5 Flying Training School: *K5384; K5446; K5502; K5505; K5512; K5553; K5559.*

No. 6 Flying Training School: *K5407.*

No. 8 Flying Training School: *K5439; K5465; K5475; K5524.*

No. 9 Flying Training School: *K5377; K5383; K5439; K5449; K5465; K5495; K5517; K5523.*

No. 10 Flying Training School: *K5386; K5393; K5397; K5427; K5450; K5491; K5503; K5506; K5522; K5524; K5530* (collided with Anson *L7059* while landing at Ternhill, 9-11-39); *K5532.*

No. 11 Flying Training School: *K5393; K5396; K5398; K5450; K5491; K5503; K5550;*

No. 12 Flying Training School: *K5368; K5369; K5372; K5374; K5402; K5440; K5442; K5468; K5469; K5471; K5486; K5515; K5522; K5547; K5559.*

No. 14 Flying Training School: *K5532; K5535.*

No. 15 Flying Training School: *K5381; K5384; K5416; K5438; K5447; K5448; K5502; K5531; K5557*

Elementary & Reserve Flying Training Schools: No. 1 ERFTS: *K5382; K5416; K5455; K5531.* No. 3 ERFTS: *K5397; K5526.* No. 4 ERFTS: *K5475; K5524.* No. 6 ERFTS: *K5512.* No. 7 ERFTS: *K5434; K5543.* No. 8 ERFTS: *K5471; K5505.* No. 9 ERFTS: *K5532; K5553.* No. 12 ERFTS: *K5535.* No. 13 ERFTS: *K5377; K5419; K5438; K5441.* No. 15 ERFTS: *K5372; K5480.* No. 16 ERFTS: *K5374; K5486.* No. 18 ERFTS: *K5369; K5423; K5449; K5495.* No. 20 ERFTS: *K5368; K5423.* No. 21 ERFTS: *K5381; K5413; K5448.* No. 22 ERFTS: *K5442; K5450; K5522.* No. 23 ERFTS: *K5466* (crashed at Bredhurst, 18-6-39); *K5511.* No. 26 ERFTS: *K5465; K5557.* No. 27 ERFTS: *K5401.* No. 30 ERFTS: *K5447; K5547.* No. 31 ERFTS: *K5402.* No. 32 ERFTS: *K5440; K5468; K5469.* No. 33 ERFTS: *K5435; K5439; K5491.* No. 34 ERFTS: *K5393.* No. 35 ERFTS: *K5377; K5384; K5502; K5505.* No. 39 ERFTS: *K5517; K5523.* No. 42 ERFTS: *K5407.* No. 43 ERFTS: *K5446.* No. 44 ERFTS: *K5427; K5506.* No. 45 ERFTS: *K5503.* No. 46

ERFTS: *K5396*; *K5398*; *K5550*. No. 56 ERFTS: *K5386*; *K5530*. No. 60 ERFTS: *K5515*.

Supplied to the South African Air Force: *K5369* (15-6-41; lost in transit); *K5372* (16-6-41); *K5374* (10-6-41); *K5375* (11-6-40); *K7376* (7-10-41); *K7379* (6-5-40); *K7393* (9-7-42); *K7396* (16-6-40); *K7400* (29-5-40); *K5407* (22-7-40); *K5410* (25-7-40); *K5417* (6-6-40); *K5435* (12-4-41); *K5436* (6-6-40); *K5460* (25-4-40); *K5467* (6-6-40); *K5471* (9-6-42); *K5473* (29-5-40); *K5475* (14-7-41); *K5478* (30-4-40); *K5481* (16-6-40); *K5485* (6-6-40); *K5486* (31-5-42); *K5488* (29-5-40); *K5490* (6-5-40); *K5493* (6-5-40); *K5495*-*K5497* (4-41); *K5505* (22-7-40); *K5507*-*K5509* (6-6-40); *K5513* (30-6-40); *K5517* (22-7-40); *K5519* (19-7-40); *K5521* (6-6-40); *K5524* (9-6-42); *K5527* (15-6-41); *K5532*, *K5535* (7-5-41); *K5539*-*K5541* (25-7-40).

Supplied to Royal New Zealand Air Force: *K5390*, *K5392* (5-9-40); *K5402*, *K5406* (27-8-40); *K5423* (13-10-40); *K5431*, *K5433* (14-8-40); *K5441* (4-7-41); *K5449* (13-10-40); *K5451* (28-11-40); *K5465* (14-2-41); *K5476* (21-8-40); *K5492* (28-11-40); *K5499* (9-8-40); *K5500* (13-10-40); *K5502* (6-12-40); *K5504* (14-8-40); *K5523* (10-10-40); *K5533* (21-8-40); *K5534* (30-7-40); *K5536* (21-8-40); *K5550* (14-8-40); *K5553* (13-10-40); *K5560* (5-9-40).

Supplied to Royal Afghan Air Force: *K5409*; *K5457*; *K5554*.

Supplied to Irish Air Corps: *K5415*; *K5446*; *K5559*.

Ground Instruction Machines: *K5377* (became *2622M*); *K5381* (became *1860M*, 4-40); *K5386* (became *2624M*); *K5394* (became *968M*, 4-37); *K5397*; *K5412* (became *1433M*); *K5414* (became *1592M*, 6-39); *K5434* (became *1378M*, 3-39); *K5438* (became *18612M*, 4-40); *K5442* (became *1931M*, 5-40); *K5459* (became *964M*, 7-39); *K5464* (became *972M*, 11-36); *K5480* (became *2106M*, 7-40); *K5525* (became *1371M*); *K5531* (became *1863M*, 4-40); *K5538* (became *1609M*, 7-39); *K5551* (became *1366M*, 8-38); *K5557* (became *1864M*, 4-40).

Other Units and duties, etc.: *K5369* (Catterick Stn. Flt.); *K5373*, *K5387*, *K5418*, *K5504* (Oxford University Air Squadron); *K5384* (No. 110 Sqn., R.C.A.F.); *K5386*, *K5397*, *K5506* (Parachute Flying Unit); *K5399* (No. 7 Pilots' Advanced Flying Unit); *K5412*, *K5491* (Rolls-Royce Ltd.); *K5421* (Yeadon Stn. Flt; Northolt Stn. Flt.; No. 1 Glider Training School; Glider Instructors' School); *K5425* (No. 2 Air Observers' School); *K5430* (Heliopolis Stn. Flt.); *K5440*, *K5447* (A.T.A.); *K5467* (Northolt Stn. Flt.); *K5468* (A.T.A.; crashed while landing at Thame, 17-9-43); *K5507* (Duxford Stn. Flt.); *K5515* (Nos. 1, 2 and 4 Glider Training Schools); *K5520* (Heliopolis Stn. Flt.; crashed near Qasaba, 27-2-40); *K5546* (No. 13 MU Parachute Section; damaged in air raid on Henlow, 26-9-40, and SOC.); *K5552* (Training Unit and Reserve Pool [Middle East]); No. 2 P.R.U.; SOC, 30-9-42).

The Hawker Hind I. Third production batch of 244 aircraft, *K6613*-*K6856*, to Specification 11/35 ordered under Contract No. 424497/35, signed 4 August 1935 and built by Hawker Aircraft Ltd., Kingston and Brooklands. Delivered between October 1936 and June 1937. Total of 124 aircraft subsequently modified by General Aircraft Ltd. as dual control trainers. Rolls-Royce Kestrel V, VDR, X and XDR engines.

No. 9 (B) Sqn.: *K6710*.

No. 12 (B) Sqn.: *K6834*.

No. 15 (B) Sqn.: *K6760*.

No. 18 (B) Sqn.: *K6633*; *K6835*; *K6836* (crashed while landing at Sawbridgeworth, 2-9-37).

No. 21 (B) Sqn.: *K6627*-*K6629*; *K6684* (collided with Hind *K4638* near Lympne and crashed, 29-5-37); *K6686*-*K6688*; *K6714*; *K6756*; *K6757*-*K6759*; *K6776*; *K6837*; *K6838*.

No. 24 (C) Sqn.: *K6706* (SOC, 21-10-40); *K6814* (SOC, 17-10-40).

No. 34 (B) Sqn.: *K6630*-*K6632*; *K6688*; *K6689* (crashed, 6-12-37); *K6690*; *K6727*; *K6756*; *K6757*; *K6838*.

No. 39 (B) Sqn.: *K6826*.

No. 40 (B) Sqn.: *K6805*.

No. 44 (B) Sqn.: *K6776.*

No. 49 (B) Sqn.: *K6616; K6641; K6642; K6643* (collided with Hind *K6753* over Scampton, 31-3-38, and crashed); *K6644; K6645; K6646* (crashed while landing at Worthy Down, 29-5-37); *K6647; K6713; K6752; K6753* (collided with *K6643* over Scampton, 31-3-38, and crashed); *K6800; K6806; K6939.*

No. 50 (B) Sqn.: *K6671; K6679; K6737; K6739; K6740* (crashed while landing, 20-10-38); *K6741-K6743; K6744* (crashed at New Ollerton, Notts, 14-12-37); *K6746* (collided with *K6748*, also of No. 50 Sqn., and crashed near Woodhall Spa, Lincs, 16-8-37); *K6747; K6749; K6750; K6780; K6812; K6813; K6820; K6821.*

No. 52 (B) Sqn.: *K6731; K6732; K6733* (crashed while landing at Upwood, 23-9-37); *K6735; K6736.*

No. 57 (B) Sqn.: *K6713; K6778.*

No. 62 (B) Sqn.: *K6772; K6773* (crashed while landing at Warmwell, 22-11-37); *K6774-K6784.*

No. 82 (B) Sqn.: *K6822* and *K6825* (collided while approaching to land at Cranfield, 5-11-37); *K5823, K5824; K5826-K5829; K5930* (crashed during night landing at Cranfield, 12-10-37); *K6831-K6833; K6842.*

No. 83 (B) Sqn.: *K6634* (crashed at Little Queensberry Hall, near Dumfries, 7-4-37); *K6635; K6636* (crashed in cloud, 12-8-38); *K6637; K6638* (struck cars while landing, Turnhouse, 22-7-37); *K6639; K6640; K6754; K6806; K6810; K6840; K6841.*

No. 88 (B) Sqn.: *K6843-K6850.*

No. 90 (B) Sqn.: *K6737-K6744; K6745* (crashed while landing at Bicester, 14-5-37); *K6746-K6750.*

No. 98 (B) Sqn.: *K6613* (crashed near Port William, Wigtownshire, 18-8-37); *K6614* (crashed near Ulverston, Lancs, 5-6-37); *K6615; K6616; K6617* (crashed, 19-4-37); *K6618; K6619; K6710; K6716-K6718; K6719* (crashed 24-9-37); *K6720; K6721.*

No. 103 (B) Sqn.: *K6677-K6683; K6719; K6720; K6736; K6849.*

No. 104 (B) Sqn.: *K6620-K6626; K6711; K6712; K6721-K6723; K6852.*

No. 106 (B) Sqn.: *K6760.*

No. 107 (B) Sqn.: *K6692-K6696; K6697* (crashed while landing, 19-8-38); *K6698; K6725; K6731; K6751.*

No. 108 (B) Sqn.: *K6670-K6676; K6724; K6726-K6730; K6734; K6775.*

No. 110 (B) Sqn.: *K6809-K6821.*

No. 112 (F) Sqn.: *K6824* (crashed while taking off in soft sand at Port Said, Egypt, 17-9-39).

No. 113 (B) Sqn.: *K6732; K6734; K6796-K6800; K6801* (crashed while taking off at Abingdon, 24-6-37); *K6802-K6808; K6823; K6824; K6826.*

No. 139 (B) Sqn.: *K6683; K6711-K6715; K6734.*

No. 142 (B) Sqn.: *K6631; K6654; K6655; K6656* (crashed while landing at night at Andover, 15-6-37); *K6657-K6660; K6661* (crashed on take-off at Hendon, 11-6-37); *K6662* (crashed near Andover, 9-8-37); *K6663-K6666; K6667* (crashed 21-12-37); *K6668; K6669; K6715; K6735.*

No. 185 (B) Sqn.: *K6805.*

No. 211 (B) Sqn.: *K6675; K6696; K6832; K6833; K6842; K6851-K6855.*

No. 216 (B) Sqn.: *K6797.*

No. 218 (B) Sqn.: *K6627; K6628* (crashed, 16-9-37); *K6629; K6630* (crashed at Kirkby Bellars, Leics, 15-7-37); *K6631; K6632* (crashed into sea in cloud, 26-11-37); *K6633; K6736; K6755.*

No. 500 Sqn., A.A.F.: *K6699; K6700* (crashed while taking off at Tangmere, 19-8-37); *K6701-K6709.*

No. 501 Sqn., A.A.F.: *K6690; K6747; K6782* (damaged beyond repair in ground collision, 12-6-38); *K6823; K6827-K6829; K6831.*

No. 502 Sqn., A.A.F.: *K6761; K6762; K6763* (struck radio mast at Aldergrove and crashed, 14-11-37); *K6764-K6771; K6838.*

No. 503 Sqn., A.A.F.: *K6727; K6838.*

No. 504 Sqn., A.A.F.: *K6716; K6720; K6785-K6795.*

No. 600 Sqn., A.A.F.: *K6661.*

No. 603 Sqn., A.A.F.: *K6627; K6629; K6755; K6809; K6811; K6814-K6817; K6819* (crashed in poor visibility, Bishopshill, Kinloss, 18-2-39); *K6843; K6844; K6847.*

No. 605 Sqn., A.A.F.: *K6625; K6626; K6672; K6674; K6676; K6726.*

No. 609 Sqn., A.A.F.: *K6728; K6730; K6736; K6790; K6820; K6845; K6846; K6848* (crashed while taking off at Yeadon, 18-6-39); *K6850.*

No. 610 Sqn., A.A.F.: *K6615; K6654; K6659; K6660; K6663; K6664; K6718; K6721.*

No. 613 Sqn., A.A.F.: *K6666.*

No. 614 Sqn., A.A.F.: *K6735.*

No. 616 Sqn., A.A.F.: *K6727; K6757* (crashed on take-off at Doncaster, 22-9-37).

R.A.F. College, Cranwell: *K6622; K6635* (crashed while landing at night at Barkston Heath landing ground, 20-6-40); *K6641; K6670; K6678-K6680; K6682; K6692-K6694; K6706; K6707; K6720; K6731* (crashed while landing at night at Barkston Heath, 30-7-40); *K6749; K6760* (crashed while landing at Cranwell, 24-10-39); *K6762; K6766; K6770; K6784; K6785; K6792; K6794; K6800; K6806; K6834; K6843; K6849.*

No. 1 Flying Training School: *K6615; K6619; K6622; K6633* (crashed near Pucklechurch, Glos, 22-4-40); *K6644* (crashed while landing at Shrewton, 12-4-41); *K6648; K6651; K6652* (crashed while landing at Netheravon, 20-2-41); *K6653* (crashed while landing at Stormy Down, 8-11-41); *K6658* (crashed near Shepton Mallet, 14-7-40); *K6659* (crashed at Crickhowell, Brecon, 2-5-41); *K6670; K6678; K6679; K6685; K6693; K6694; K6707; K6713* (crashed while landing at Stormy Down, 1-11-40); *K6720; K6728; K6730* (crashed on take-off at Netheravon, 18-6-41); *K6736; K6751* (crashed near Netheravon, 29-5-40); *K6756; K6759; K6762* (crashed on landing at Stormy Down, 8-12-40); *K6766; K6770; K6772* (crashed while landing at Stormy Down, 14-6-40); *K6775; K6777* (crashed near Shepton Mallet, 17-5-40); *K6783; K6784; K6791; K6794; K6806* (caught fire on the ground at Netheravon, 22-10-41); *K6827; K6838; K6845* (crashed 3 miles north of Andover, 6-4-41); *K6846; K6852.*

No. 5 Flying Training School: *K6687; K6712; K6727; K6758* (crashed on Hoylake beach, Cheshire, 4-3-40); *K6793; K6818; K6829.*

No. 6 Flying Training School: *K6695.*

No. 8 Flying Training School: *K6633; K6772* (crashed while landing at Stormy Down, 14-6-40); *K6779; K6783; K6787.*

No. 9 Flying Training School: *K6655.*

No. 10 Flying Training School: *K6619; K6633; K6637; K6639* (crashed on take-off at Ternhill, 2-1-40); *K6657; K6672; K6685; K6714; K6776; K6783; K6821; K6823; K6827; K6837; K6852.*

No. 11 Flying Training School: *K6615; K6623; K6657; K6714; K6726; K6756; K5659; K6788; K6789; K6791; K6827.*

No. 12 Flying Training School: *K6639; K6658; K6679; K6713; K6716; K6720; K6725; K6751; K6770; K6774; K6775; K6786; K6794; K6795; K6798.*

No. 14 Flying Training School: *K6642; K6777; K6793.*

No. 15 Flying Training School: *K6641; K6680; K6687; K6749; K6785; K6800; K6849.*

No. 16 Flying Training School: *K6650.*

Cambridge University Air Squadron: *K6742* (crashed on take-off at Duxford, 28-7-39).

University of London Air Squadron: *K6690.*

No. 1 Air Armament School: *K6648-K6653; K6756.*

No. 1 Parachute Flying Unit: *K6637; K6685; K6714; K6818; K6821; K6823; K6837* (crashed while landing at Aston Down, 15-4-40).

No. 2 Air Observers' School: *K6644; K6670; K6806; K6839.*

Elementary & Reserve Flying Training Schools: No. 1 ERFTS: *K6616* (crashed at Hillend, St. Albans, 13-7-37); *K6645* (crashed while landing at Hatfield, 8-5-39); *K6784; K6792;*

K6800. No. 3 ERFTS: *K6726; K6789.* No. 4 ERFTS: *K6633; K6772; K6779; K6783; K6787.* No. 5 ERFTS: *K6788.* No. 7 ERFTS: *K6641; K6692; K6731.* No. 8 ERFTS: *K6720; K6774.* No. 9 ERFTS: *K6777.* No. 11 ERFTS: *K6642; K6724; K6829.* No. 12 ERFTS: *K6669; K6677; K6793.* No. 13 ERFTS: *K6622; K6849.* No. 15 ERFTS: *K6713; K6716.* No. 16 ERFTS: *K6639; K6725; K6795.* No. 18 ERFTS: *K6711; K6729.* No. 19 ERFTS: *K6698* (crashed approaching to land at Gatwick, 20-8-39); *K6751; K6786; K6794.* No. 20 ERFTS: *K6775.* No. 21 ERFTS: *K6658; K6693; K6694.* No. 22 ERFTS: *K6620* (crashed on landing at Cambridge, 13-5-39); *K6657; K6752* (crashed during aerobatics near Chatteris, Cambs, 5-2-39). No. 23 ERFTS: *K6623; K6723* (crashed while landing at Luton, 21-5-39); *K6791; K6852.* No. 24 ERFTS: *K6818.* No. 25 ERFTS: *K6834.* No. 26 ERFTS: *K6680.* No. 27 ERFTS: *K6678; K6682; K6749; K6760; K6834.* No. 28 ERFTS: *K6785.* No. 29 ERFTS: *K6765.* No. 31 ERFTS: *K6679.* No. 33 ERFTS: *K6805.* No. 35 ERFTS: *K6687; K6712.* No. 38 ERFTS: *K6758.* No. 40 ERFTS: *K6685; K6837.* No. 42 ERFTS: *K6695.* No. 43 ERFTS: *K6727.* No. 45 ERFTS: *K6714; K6756; K6759.* No. 46 ERFTS: *K6827.* No. 47 ERFTS: *K6619; K6823.* No. 50 ERFTS: *K6635; K6637.* No. 56 ERFTS: *K6821.*

Supplied to South African Air Force: *K6621* (16-7-40); *K6623* (29-4-40); *K6624* (7-5-40); *K6625* (23-5-40); *K6640* (19-7-40); *K6642* (7-6-41); *K6648* (9-6-42); *K6650* (11-5-41); *K6654* (9-7-41); *K6660* (29-4-40); *K6663* (30-6-40); *K6664* (16-6-40); *K6669* (19-7-40); *K6670* (26-5-41); *K6671* (29-4-40); *K6673* (10-6-40); *K6674* (29-5-40); *K6676* (6-6-40); *K6677* (21-4-41); *K6678* (21-6-41, but lost at sea); *K6680* (7-10-41); *K6683, K6688* (6-6-40); *K6690* (29-5-40); *K6695* (16-6-40); *K6699* (7-5-41); *K6704* (18-5-41); *K6707* (15-6-41); *K6709* (10-6-40); *K6711* (24-5-41); *K6715; K6718* (29-4-40); *K6722; K6726* (7-5-40); *K6729* (19-7-40); *K6736, K6738, K6739, K6741* (26-4-40); *K6743* (6-6-40); *K6759* (7-10-41); *K6765* (6-6-40); *K6767* (16-6-40); *K6769; K6770* (9-7-42); *K6771; K6775* (15-6-41); *K6776* (7-10-41); *K6783* (11-5-41); *K6788* (7-5-40); *K6789; K6790* (13-5-41); *K6798* (8-5-41); *K6805* (15-6-41, but lost at sea); *K6811* (22-7-40); *K6813* (26-4-40); *K6816* (16-6-40); *K6818* (27-2-41); *K6823* (9-7-42); *K6831* (7-5-40); *K6840, K6841* (29-9-40); *K6843, K6846* (30-5-42); *K6850* (11-4-41); *K6852* (26-5-41).

Supplied to the Royal New Zealand Air Force: *K6622* (4-7-41); *K6626* (5-9-40); *K6629* (14-8-40, but lost at sea); *K6649* (14-2-41); *K6666* (5-9-40); *K6672* (30-7-40); *K6679* (4-7-41); *K6687* (20-8-40); *K6692* (21-8-42); *K6693* (10-10-40); *K6701, K6702* (9-8-40); *K6703* (10-10-40); *K6705* (30-7-40); *K6708* (9-8-40); *K6710* (6-12-40, but lost at sea); *K6717* (20-8-40); *K6720* (4-7-41); *K6721* (5-9-40); *K6735* (30-7-40); *K6749* (27-8-40); *K6761* (9-8-40); *K6764* (14-8-40, but lost at sea); *K6768* (9-8-40); *K6774, K6785* (14-8-40, but lost at sea); *K6786* (14-2-41); *K6787* (20-8-40); *K6792* (28-22-40); *K6793* (5-9-40); *K6800* (13-10-40); *K6809* (14-8-40, but lost at sea); *K6810* (10-10-40); *K6815* (6-12-40, but lost at sea); *K6817* (14-8-40, but lost at sea); *K6820* (20-8-40); *K6821* (6-12-40, but lost at sea); *K6829* (5-9-40); *K6844* (28-11-40); *K6849* (5-9-40).

Supplied to the Royal Afghan Air Force: *K6668* (4-39); *K6675* (7-39); *K6832* (7-39); *K6842* (7-39); *K6853* (7-39); *K6855* (7-39).

Supplied to the Irish Air Corps: *K6755* (1-6-40); *K6781* (1-6-40).

Ground Instruction Machines: *K6627* (became *2170M*, 5-40); *K6635* (became *2044M*, 7-40); *K6641* (became *1865M*, 4-40); *K6681* (became *1140M*); *K6686* (became *1117M*, 9-38); *K6694* (became *1866M*, 4-40); *K6725* (became *1943M*, 1-40); *K6727* (became *1944M*, 5-40); *K6772* (became *2040M*, 7-40); *K6828* (became *1427M*, 4-39); *K6847* (became *2003M*, 6-40); *K6856* (became *1193M*, 1-39).

Other Units and duties, etc.: *K6644, K6670, K6806* (No. 10 Bombing & Gunnery School); *K6657, K6691, K6856* (R.A.E.); *K6681* (No. 2 Armament Training Camp); *K6686* (No. 4 Armament Training Camp); *K6699, K6703, K6810* (Duxford Stn. Flt); *K6717* (Special Duties Flt.); *K6734* (Heliopolis Comms. Flt.); *K6790, K6820* (Yeadon Stn. Flt.); *K6826* (Western Desert Comms. Flt.; crashed on take-off, LG.18, 2-4-42); *K6827* (Glider Pilots' Exercise Unit; crashed while approaching to land at Shrewton, 13-9-42); *K6834* (A.T.A.;

crashed while landing at Thame, 3-6-43).

The Hawker Hind I. Fourth production batch of 50 aircraft, *L7174-L7223*, to Specification 13/37, built by Hawker Aircraft Ltd., Kingston and Brooklands, between September 1937 and January 1938. Rolls-Royce Kestrel V or VDR engines. Most aircraft completed as bombers, but many subsequently modified as trainers with rear gun removed.

No. 12 (B) Sqn.: *L7182*; *L7183*.

No. 15 (B) Sqn.: *L7177*; *L7187*.

No. 18 (B) Sqn.: *L7186*; *L7189*; *L7190*; *L7193*.

No. 21 (B) Sqn.: *L7175*; *L7191-L7193*.

No. 24 (C) Sqn.: *L7185*.

No. 40 (B) Sqn.: *L7176*.

No. 49 (B) Sqn.: *L7194* (crashed, 24-1-38).

No. 50 (B) Sqn.: *L7195*; *L7196*.

No. 57 (B) Sqn.: *L7186*; *K7187*.

No. 82 (B) Sqn.: *L7197*.

No. 83 (B) Sqn.: *L7198*.

No. 98 (B) Sqn.: *L7199*; *L7200*.

No. 103 (B) Sqn.: *L7183*; *L7188*.

No. 104 (B) Sqn.: *L7201*.

No. 108 (B) Sqn.: *L7184*; *L7185*.

No. 211 (B) Sqn.: *L7174-L7181*.

Nos. 296 and 297 (GT) Sqns: *L7185*.

No. 501 Sqn., A.A.F.: *L7182*; *L7197*.

No. 503 Sqn., A.A.F.: *L7193*.

No. 504 Sqn., A.A.F.: *L7179*; *L7199*.

No. 600 Sqn., A.A.F.: *L7215* (crashed while avoiding Oxford during landing at Hendon, 18-2-39).

No. 605 Sqn., A.A.F.: *L7204*.

No. 609 Sqn., A.A.F.: *L7177*; *L7185*; *L7188*.

No. 610 Sqn., A.A.F.: *L7186*; *L7187*.

No. 611 Sqn., A.A.F.: *L7214*.

No. 616 Sqn., A.A.F.: *L7193*.

R.A.F. College, Cranwell: *L7175*; *L7176* (damaged beyond repair in taxying accident at Cranwell, 16-7-40); *L7179*; *L7192* (crashed at Roxholm Hall, Leasingham, Lincs, 7-3-40).

Flying Training Schools. No. 1 FTS: *L7175*; *L7183*; *L7186*; *L7188-L7190*; *L7205* (crashed from spin near Shrewton, 26-7-41); *L7212*; *L7219* (crashed at Collingbourne Ducis, Wilts, 6-2-41). No. 2 FTS: *L7179*. No. 3 FTS: *L7193*. No. 5 FTS: *L7184*; *L7210*; *L7220*. No. 6 FTS: *L7196*. No. 10 FTS: *L7189*; *L7193*; *L7195*; *L7207*; *L7213*; *L7216*; *L7219*. No. 11 FTS: *L7206*; *L7208*; *L7211*; *L7212*; *L7221*. No. 12 FTS: *L7176*; *L7201*; *L7223*.

Elementary & Reserve Flying Training Schools: No. 4 ERFTS: *L7189*. No. 7 ERFTS: *L7175*; *L7221*. No. 8 ERFTS: *L7209*; *L7211*. No. 12 ERFTS: *L7210*. No. 13 ERFTS: *L7203*. No. 14 ERFTS: *L7176*. No. 18 ERFTS: *L7201*. No. 19 ERFTS: *L7184*; *L7193*; *L7200*. No. 20 ERFTS: *L7179*; *L7223*. No. 22 ERFTS: *L7206*. No. 23 ERFTS: *L7216*. No. 24 ERFTS: *L7220*. No. 25 ERFTS: *L7205*; *L7207*. No. 26 ERFTS: *L7192*; *L7218*; *L7222*. No. 27 ERFTS: *L7218*. No. 30 ERFTS: *L7202* (crashed while landing at Derby, 20-5-39). No. 34 ERFTS: *L7208*; *L7212*. No. 42 ERFTS: *L7196*. No. 44 ERFTS: *L7213*. No. 47 ERFTS: *L7219*.

Supplied to South African Air Force: *L7175* (7-42); *L7177* (4-41); *L7179* (5-41); *L7186*; *L7196* (19-7-40); *L7197* (16-6-40); *L7203* (24-5-40); *L7209* (22-7-40); *L7213* (3-9-42).

Supplied to the Royal New Zealand Air Force: *L7184* (5-9-40); *L7195* (21-8-40); *L7210* (13-10-40); *L7218, L7220* (10-10-40); *L7221* (30-7-40).

Supplied to the Royal Afghan Air Force (7-39): *L7180, L7181, L7191.*

Ground Instruction Machines: *L7183* (became *2869M*, 1-42); *L7189* (became *2870M*, 1-42); *L7201; L7205* (became *1383M*, 4-39, temporarily; brought back on charge); *L7215* (became *1389M*, 2-39); *L7222* (became *1257M*, 2-39).

Other Units and duties, etc: *L7174* (No. 202 Group Comms. Flt.; No. 1 Sqn., S.A.A.F.; Levant Comms. Flt.; Heliopolis Comms. Flt.); *L7178* (sold to Indian govt., 4-39); *L7185* (Glider Pilots' Exercise Unit); *L7190* (No. 20 (Pilots') Advanced Flying Unit); *L7198* (No. 4 Ferry Pilots' Pool; crashed at Neston, Cambs, 23-9-40); *L7204* (Nos. 101 and 102 Glider Operational Training Units; No. 1 Glider Training School; Glider Instructors' School); *L7211* (A.T.A.; crashed while landing at Thame, 6-8-43); *L7212, L7216* (No. 1 Air Armament School).

The Hawker Hind Trainer. Fifth production batch of 20 aircraft, *L7224-L7243*, built by Hawker Aircraft Ltd., Kingston and Brooklands, with dual controls and all armament deleted. Rolls-Royce Kestrel VDR and XDR engines. Delivered between February and June 1938.

No. 296 (GT) Sqn.: *L7235.*

No. 500 Sqn., A.A.F.: *L7230.*

No. 501 Sqn., A.A.F.: *L7226* (crashed near Henlow, 24-2-41); *L7228* (crashed, 12-6-38).

No. 503 Sqn., A.A.F.: *L7226.*

No. 602 Sqn., A.A.F.: *L7229.*

No. 605 Sqn., A.A.F.: *L7237.*

No. 609 Sqn., A.A.F.: *L7232.*

No. 610 Sqn., A.A.F.: *L7227.*

No. 613 Sqn., A.A.F.: *L7238* (crashed at Magon, Mon, 3-9-39).

No. 614 Sqn., A.A.F.: *L7239* (crashed near Cardiff, 3-8-39).

No. 616 Sqn., A.A.F.: *L7229.*

Flying Training Schools. No. 1 FTS: *L7231* (crashed, 15-3-39); *L7233* (crashed while landing at night at Netheravon, 10-5-40); *L7234; L7235.* No. 10 FTS: *L7224; L7235;* No. 11 FTS: *L7224; L7225; L7230.* No. 12 FTS: *L7243.* No. 16 FTS: *L7242.*

Elementary & Reserve Flying Training Schools: No. 3 ERFTS: *L7234.* No. 6 ERFTS: *L7235.* No. 7 ERFTS: *L7241* (crashed near Desford, 23-6-39). No. 23 ERFTS: *L7236* (crashed, 15-10-38). No. 25 ERFTS: *L7243.* No. 26 ERFTS: *L7242.* No. 27 ERFTS: *L7240.*

Supplied to South African Air Force: *L7229* (4-41); *L7230* (6-42); *L7232* (6-5-40); *L7234* (16-7-40); *L4242* (8-8-41, but lost at sea).

Supplied to Royal New Zealand Air Force: *L7224* (21-8-40); *L7225* (30-7-40).

Ground Instruction Machines: *L7233; L7237* (became *1108M*, 7-38).

Other Units and duties, etc: *L7224, L7225* (No. 14 EFTS); *L7231* (Debden Stn. Flt.); *L7233* (Church Fenton Stn. Flt.); *L7234* (North Weald Stn. Flt.); *L7235* (A.T.A., SOC, 7-12-43); *L7238* (Andover Stn. Flt.); *L7241* (Duxford Stn. Flt.); *L7243* (Parachute Flying Unit).

The Hawker Swiss Hind. One aircraft, *HB-HAL*, ordered by the Swiss government in 1935 from Hawker Aircraft Ltd., Kingston. First flown, 23 January 1936, and delivered later that year. Rolls-Royce Kestrel V.

The Hawker Yugoslav Hind. Three aircraft ordered by Yugoslav government during 1936. Aircraft No. *1* (first flight, 7 June 1937) and No. *2* powered by Rolls-Royce Kestrel XVI engine; No. *3* powered by Gnome-Rhône K-9 engine.

The Hawker Portuguese Hind. Four aircraft ordered from Hawker Aircraft Ltd., Kingston, by the Portuguese government during February 1937. First flight, 5 June 1937. Rolls-Royce Kestrel V engines.

The Hawker Afghan Hind. Eight aircraft ordered during 1937 from Hawker Aircraft Ltd., Kingston (in addition to ex-R.A.F. aircraft, see above), and delivered to Afghanistan during 1938. The first four aircraft were powered by Rolls-Royce Kestrel Vs, the others by Kestrel VDRs.

The Hawker Persian Hind. Production batch of 35 aircraft, *601-635*, ordered from Hawker Aircraft Ltd., Kingston, and built during 1938. First flight by *601*, 28 April 1938. Bristol Mercury VIII radial engines.

The Hawker Latvian Hind. Three aircraft, *176-178*, ordered by the Latvian government from Hawker Aircraft Ltd., Kingston, in January 1938. First flight by *176*, 4 May 1938. All aircraft delivered with Bristol Mercury IX radial engines, but at one time *178* flew with a Bristol Pegasus radial.

The Hawker 14/35 Hector. One prototype, *K3719* (formerly an Audax I), designed and prepared to Air Ministry Specification 14/35 for an interim army co-operation aircraft, by Hawker Aircraft Ltd., Kingston and Brooklands, during 1935—drawing on experience with the Dagger test bed, Hart *K2434*. First flight, 14 February 1936. Napier Dagger III engine. Handling and performance trials, A. & A.E.E., R.A.E., and Westland Aircraft Ltd., Yeovil, during 1936. Ultimately disposed of as Ground Instruction Machine, *1062M*, May 1938.

The Hawker Hector I. First production batch of 78 aircraft, *K8090-K8167*, built by Westland Aircraft Ltd., Yeovil, under Sub-contract No. 497301/36 to Air Ministry Specification 14/35. Deliveries commenced February 1937; completed June 1937. 805 h.p. Napier Dagger IIIMS engines.

No. 4 (AC) Sqn.: *K8091-K8099*; *K8106-K8108*; *K8112-K8114*; *K8119*; *K8120*; *K8124* (crashed while avoiding display crowd at Odiham, 28-5-38); *K8125* (crashed while landing at North Coates, 22-7-38); *K8126*; *K8131-K8133*; *K8137*; *K8138*; *K8141-K8143*; *K8145*; *K8146*.

No. 13 (AC) Sqn.: *K8091*; *K8092* (crashed while landing at Odiham, 8-5-37); *K8093*; *K8094* (crashed near Farnborough, *15-6-37*, having run out of fuel); *K8095-K8099*; *K8106* (crashed at Porton landing ground, 13-11-38); *K8107*; *K8108*; *K8112*; *K8113* (crashed while landing at Sealand, 26-3-38); *K8114*; *K8118*; *K8140*; *K8144*.

No. 53 (AC) Sqn.: *K8139*; *K8147-K8150*.

No. 296 (GT) Sqn.: *K8099*; *K8108* (crashed at Croydon Hall, Washford, Somerset, 1-7-42); *K8112*; *K8134*; *K8146*; *K8154*.

No. 612 Sqn., A.A.F.: *K8100*; *K8101*; *K8104* (crashed while taking off at Dyce, 29-5-39).

No. 613 Sqn., A.A.F.: *K8102*; *K8108*; *K8116* (probably damaged by flak over Calais, 27-5-40, and crashed on Shakespeare Cliff, Dover); *K8127*; *K8138*.

No. 614 Sqn., A.A.F.: *K8109-K8111*.

No. 615 Sqn., A.A.F.: *K8102*; *K8103*; *K8105*; *K8115-K8117*; *K8127*; *K8128* (crashed while landing at Kenley, 24-7-38); *K8129*; *K8134*; *K8135*.

R.A.F. College, Cranwell: *K8115-K8117*; *K8121-K8123*; *K8130*.

No. 1 School of Army Co-operation: *K8110*; *K8112*; *K8121* (crashed on take-off at Old Sarum, 29-8-40); *K8122*; *K8131*; *K8132*; *K8150*;

No. 1 Glider Training School: *K8097*; *K8111*; *K8119* (undercarriage damaged and aircraft abandoned in the air, 3-7-41); *K8122*; *K8132*; *K8137*; *K8140*; *K8143*; *K8152*; *K8161*; *K8164*; *K8166*; *K8167*.

No. 2 Glider Training School: *K8108*; *K8111*; *K8126* (crashed in low cloud at Weston-on-the-Green, Oxon, 11-4-42); *K8134*; *K8140*; *K8142*; *K8146*.

No. 4 Glider Training School: *K8122*; *K8123*; *K8135*; *K8142*; *K8145* (crashed while landing at Kidlington, Oxon, 16-8-42); *K8150*; *K8151* (crashed at Hill House Farm, Comerton, 30-7-42); *K8152*; *K8155* (crashed while landing at Kidlington, 27-8-42); *K8156-K8158*;

K8161-K8164; K8166; K8167 (struck another aircraft while taking off at Kidlington and crashed, 22-1-43).

No. 101 Glider Operational Training Unit: *K8093* (crashed while landing at Kidlington, 22-6-42); *K8099; K8134; K8139* (crashed at Hook Horton, Oxon, 2-9-42); *K8145; K8150; K8155; K8156; K8163.*

No. 102 Glider Operational Training Unit: *K8151; K8157; K8158; K8161; K8166.*

Glider Pilots' Exercise Unit: *K8097; K8099; K8103; K8111; K8112; K8134; K8154* (crashed while landing at Shrewton, 31-8-42); *K8163.*

Glider Instructors' School: *K8097* (crashed while landing at Thame, 13-10-42); *K8142* (crashed at Thame, 9-12-42).

Airborne Forces Experimental Establishment: *K8108; K8111; K8112; K8134; K8139; K8140; K8142; K8145; K8146; K8152; K8156; K8161; K8164; K8166.*

Parachute Flying Unit: *K8100* (crashed at Auchentyre, Moray, 1-8-40); *K8103; K8105; K8117; K8118; K8120; K8129; K8142; K8143; K8146-K8149.*

Central Landing Establishment: *K8119; K8137.*

Central Landing School: *K8126.*

No. 2 Anti-aircraft Co-operation Unit: *K8127; K8135; K8136* (crashed into the sea off Harwich, 11-7-41); *K8150; K8155; K8165.*

Supplied to the Irish Air Corps (1-42): *K8098; K8102; K8105; K8114; K8115; K8117; K8130; K8148; K8159.*

Ground Instruction Machines: *K8091* (became *2407M*, 12-40); *K8095* (became *2401M*, 12-40); *K8101* (became *2416M*, 12-40); *K8107* (became *2402M*, 12-40); *K8109* (became *1111M*, 8-38); *K8118* (became *2403M*, 12-40); *K8120* (became *2404M*, 12-40); *K8128* (became *1125M*, 7-38); *K8131; K8138* (became *1941M*, 6-40); *K8144* (became *2400M*, 12-40); *K8147* (became *2405M*, 12-40).

Other Units and duties, etc.: *K8090* (A. & A.E.E. and R.A.E.); *K8119* (Watchfield Stn. Flt.); *K8112* (R.A.E.); *K8133* (Swanton Morley Stn. Flt.); K8137 (Newtownards Stn. Flt.).

The Hawker Hector I. Second production batch of 100 aircraft, *K9687-K9786*, to Air Ministry Specification 14/35 (as amended) under Contract No. 521856/36 and sub-contracted to Westland Aircraft Ltd., Yeovil. Deliveries commenced July 1937 and completed December 1937. Napier Dagger III engines.

No. 2 (AC) Sqn.: *K9737-K9742; K9748-K9757.*

No. 4 (AC) Sqn.: *K9758; K9782.*

No. 13 (AC) Sqn.: *K9737; K9759* (crashed in the Pennines, 6-8-38).

No. 26 (AC) Sqn.: *K9715-K9723; K9724* (crashed while landing at Catterick, 13-5-38); *K9725; K9726; K9730-K9732; K9736; K9738.*

No. 53 (AC) Sqn.: *K9687; K9688; K9695-K9697; K9701; K9702* (crashed while landing at Odiham, 4-5-38); *K9703; K9707; K9708; K9711; K9712* (crashed while landing at Harwell, 17-2-39).

No. 59 (AC) Sqn.: *K9689; K9690* (crashed on take-off at Andover, 19-5-39); *K9691-K9694; K9698* (blown off runway at Aldergrove and SOC, 20-3-39); *K9704-K9706; K9709; K9710; K9713; K9714; K9739.*

No. 296 (GT) Sqn.: *K9689; K9711; K9727; K9740* (crashed into tank on approaching to land at Netheravon, 23-7-42); *K9746; K9757; K9768; K9769; K9770* (crashed while landing at Shrewton, 14-5-42).

No. 602 Sqn., A.A.F.: *K9733; K9734; K9749-K9757; K9761; K9765; K9777; K9778.*

No. 612 Sqn., A.A.F.: *K9757; K9763* (crashed at Methlick, Aberdeenshire, 2-10-38); *K9786.*

No. 613 Sqn., A.A.F.: *K9713; K9717; K9727; K9731; K9732; K9735; K9740; K9762; K9781.*

No. 614 Sqn., A.A.F.: *K9727-K9729; K9735; K9740; K9741; K9742; K9748; K9762; K9766; K9779; K9784* (crashed while landing at Cardiff, 3-4-38).

No. 615 Sqn., A.A.F.: *K9785.*

Central Flying School: *K9760; K9764; K9768; K9769.*

Central Landing Establishment: *K9711; K9716; K9723; K9750; K9752; K9755; K9765; K9768; K9771.*

No. 1 School of Army Co-operation: *K9691; K9695* (crashed while landing at Old Sarum, 8-2-40); *K9696; K9708* (crashed on take-off at Old Sarum, 22-5-40); *K9711; K9717; K9726* (crashed Maddington Down, Wilts, 15-11-40); *K9732* (crashed while landing at Old Sarum, 14-8-40); *K9734; K9740; K9749* (crashed at Stockton, Wilts, 14-5-40); *K9758* (crashed at Old Sarum, 6-3-40); *K9762; K9771; K9776; K9777* (crashed while landing at Old Sarum, 27-10-40); *K9778* (crashed at Broad Chalk, near Salisbury, 3-3-40); *K9780.*

No. 1 Glider Training School: *K9687; K9716; K9718; K9723* (crashed on take-off at Thame, 6-7-41); *K9734; K9735; K9744; K9750; K9751; K9755* (crashed at Thame after losing wheel on take-off, 29-6-42); *K9762* (crashed at Thame, 22-9-41); *K9765* (crashed on landing at Thame, 26-4-42); *K9771; K9773.*

No. 2 Glider Training School: *K9703; K9706; K9713; K9764; K9785.*

No. 4 Glider Training School: *K9706* (crashed on take-off at Kidlington, 15-9-42); *K9711; K9713; K9716; K9729; K9734-K9737; K9743; K9744* (crashed while landing at Kingston Bagpuize, Oxon, 5-2-43); *K9745; K9752; K9756; K9764* (crashed on night exercise, 1-12-42); *K9767; K9771; K9772; K9780* (crashed on landing at Kidlington, 12-9-42).

No. 101 Glider Operational Training Unit: *K9713; K9736; K9737; K9738* (crashed while taking off with two Hotspur gliders in tow at Kelmscott, 13-4-42); *K9745; K9752; K9770; K9781.*

No. 102 Glider Operational Training Unit: *K9703; K9706; K9711; K9742; K9743; K9747* (crashed while landing at Kindlington, 19-5-42); *K9752; K9780.*

Glider Pilots' Exercise Unit: *K9687; K9689; K9696* (crashed while landing at night at Shrewton); *K9703; K9713; K9727; K9742; K9743; K9747; K9757; K9768; K9769; K9781* (crashed at Shrewton, 9-11-42); *K9785.*

Glider Instructors' School: *K9743.*

Airborne Forces Experimental Establishment: *K9699; K9704; K9711; K9718; K9721; K9727; K9736-K9738; K9740; K9745; K9760; K9770; K9781.*

Parachute Flying Unit: *K9697; K9699; K9704; K9720; K9729; K9742; K9748; K9760; K9765; K9785.*

Central Landing Establishment: *K9711; K9716; K9723; K9750; K9752; K9765; K9768; K9771.*

No. 2 Anti-aircraft Co-operation Unit: *K9696; K9714;* K9719 (crashed on landing at Roborough, 4-9-41); *K9746. K9753; K9764; K9766; K9772; K9783* (crashed on take-off at Roborough, 27-2-42).

Supplied to the Irish Air Corps (1-42): *K9697; K9715; K9725; K9761.*

Ground Instruction Machines: *K9688* (became *2406M*, 12-40); *K9691* (became *2356M*, 10-40); *K9692* (became *2418M*, 10-40); *K9693* (became *1173M*, 12-38); *K9694* (became *2408M*, (12-40); *K9700* (became *2414M*, 12-40); *K9701* (became *2411M*, 12-40); *K9705* (became *2409M*, 12-40); *K9709* (became *2410M*, 12-40); *K9710* (became *2413M*, 12-40); *K9717* (became *2338M*, 10-40); *K9720* (became *2412M*, 12-40); *K9732* (became *2208M*, 8-40); *K9739* (became *1612M*, 7-39); *K9777* (became *2357M*, 11-40); *K9786* (became *2415M*, 12-40).

Other Units and duties, etc.: *K9699* (Service Ferry Pilots' Pool); *K9707* (No. 41 O.T.U.); *K9714* (No. 2 School of Photography; No. 7 Bombing & Gunnery School; Aircraft Gun Mounting Establishment); *K9722, K9725* (Stoke Orchard Stn. Flt.); *K9730* (crashed at Bishops Cleeve, Cheltenham, while with No. 20 MU., 11-10-40); *K9733* (No. 6 Ferry Pilots' Pool; crashed while landing at Henlow, 15-11-40); *K9740* (No. 3 Ferry Pilots' Pool); *K9752* (R.A.E.); *K9774* (Thame A.T.A. Ferry Pool); *K9779* (Sywell Stn. Flt.).

The Hawker F.36/34 ("Interceptor Monoplane") Hurricane. One prototype, *K5083*, designed and built to Air Ministry Specification F.36/34 (as modified by provisions of F.5/34) and ordered under Contract No. 357483/34 from Hawker Aircraft Ltd., Kingston. First flown by

P.W.S. Bulman on 6 November 1935, powered by 1,025 h.p. Rolls-Royce Merlin "C" engine, without armament. Evaluation, handling and performance trials at A. & A.E.E., R.A.E. and Rolls-Royce Ltd., 1936. Eight Colt-Browning machine guns fitted and flown in August 1936. Service trials at Martlesham Heath commenced March 1936 (first flown by F/Sgt. S. Wroath on 16-3-36). Employed for air sequences in film *Shadow of the Wing* at Martlesham, August-October 1937). Allocated for Ground Instruction Machine, *1211M*, 5-39, but taken on charge by H.A.L. (said to have remained airworthy until 1942.)

Note: Space permits the full Service allocation of only the first production batch of Hurricanes to be shown (as being the aircraft which provided the main strength of R.A.F. Fighter Command during the first year of the Second World War). Thereafter representative allocations within each production batch are shown.

The Hawker Hurricane I. First production batch of 600 aircraft, *L1547-L2146*, built by Hawker Aircraft Ltd., Kingston and Brooklands, to Specification 15/36 under Contract No. 527112/36. 430 aircraft completed with fabric-covered wings; 170 with metal-clad wings; some aircraft retrospectively fitted with metal wings. 1,030 h.p. Rolls-Royce Merlin II and III engines; Merlin IIs with Watts two-blade wooden propellers; Merlin IIIs with either D.H. or Rotol three-blade propellers. Works Orders: No. 3002 covered *L1547*; No. 3010, *L1548-L1597*; No. 3021, *L1598-L1647*; No. 3032, *L1648-L1697*; No. 3043, *L1698-L1747*; No. 3054, *L1748-L1797*; No. 3065, *L1798-L1847*; No. 3076, *L1848-L1897*; No. 3087, *L1898-L1947*; No. 3098, *L1948-L1997*; No. 3109, *L1998-L2047*; No. 3113, *L2048-L2097*; No. 3124, *L2098-L2145*; No. 3002, *L2146*. Deliveries commenced 15-12-37; completed 6-10-39. First flight by *L1547*, 12 October 1937, flown by P.G. Lucas.

No. 1 (F) Sqn.: *L1590*; *L1671* (lost in France, 5-40); *L1673*; *L1676* (lost in France, 5-40); *L1677* (crashed at Tangmere, 16-2-39); *L1678* (crashed at Tangmere, 16-2-39); *L1679* (lost in France); *L1680* (crashed on Hayling Island, Hants, 4-7-39); *L1681* (lost in France, 5-40); *L1682* (crashed near Debden, 7-2-39); *L1685*; *L1686* (lost in France, 5-40); *L1687*; *L1688* and *L1689* (lost in France, 5-40); *L1690* (crashed at night near Tangmere, 5-1-39); *L1692* (crashed while landing at Tangmere, 13-3-39); *L1694* (crashed on take-off at Tangmere, 4-4-39); *L1757* (burnt at Château Bougon, France, on evacuation, 18-6-40); *L1813*; *L1842*; *L1843* (lost in France, 5-40); *L1855* (crashed in night landing at Tangmere, 26-6-39); *L1856* (shot down by flak, St. Quentin, 18-5-40); *L1925* (lost in France, 5-40); *L1927*; *L1943* (shot down by Bf 110s, 15-5-40, over France); *L1959-L1970*; *L1971* (crashed at Fenetrange (2-3-40); *L1972-L1979*; *L2061*.

No. 3 (F) Sqn.: *L1565-L1573*; *L1576-L1578*; *L1579* (crashed while landing at Kenley, 10-5-38); *L1580*; *L1582*; *L1583*; *L1585-L1588*; *L1591* (Missing, 15-5-40, over France); *L1609* (abandoned over Merville, 17-5-40); *L1610* (crashed and abandoned, Wevelghem, 15-5-40); *L1644*; *L1645* (Missing in France, 15-5-40); *L1649* (abandoned in France, 5-40); *L1722*; *L1723*; *L1742*; *L1781* (SOC, 3-7-40); *L1898*; *L1899* (abandoned at Vitry-en-Artois, 17-5-40); *L1901* (Missing, 13-5-40, over France); *L1902*; *L1903* (crashed on take-off at Kenley, 25-3-40); *L1904* (crashed on take-off at Kenley, 24-3-40); *L1907* (crashed into sea, 1-2-40); *L1908* (abandoned in France, 14-5-40); *L1917*; *L1923* (shot down near Fiefs, France, 10-5-40); *L1924*; *L1926*; *L1928*; *L1932* (shot down near Louvain, 14-5-40); *L1933-L1936*; *L1937* (control lost and abandoned near Dorking, Surrey, 10-10-39); *L1938* (crashed while landing, Biggin Hill, 30-6-39); *L1939* (crashed in poor visibility near Sittingbourne, Kent, 10-9-39); *L1940* (SOC, 3-7-40); *L2067*; *L2123* (crashed on Folkestone golf course, 11-3-40).

No. 17 (F) Sqn.: *L1590-L1592*; *L1594*; *L1600*; *L1601*; *L1605*; *L1607-L1611*; *L1636*; *L1645*; *L1727*; *L1742*; *L1746*; *L1808*; *L1829*; *L1830*; *L1915*; *L1921* (Missing near Dover, 18-8-40); *L1975*; *L1976* (crashed while landing at Kenley, 8-9-39); *L2034*; *L2035*; *L2080-L2084*; *L2086-L2089*; *L2091*; *L2092*; *L2100*; *L2102*.

No. 29 (F) Sqn.: *L2048* (SOC, 26-1-40); *L2080-L2084*; *L2086-L2092*; *L2100*.

No. 32 (F) Sqn.: *L1567* (SOC, 8-39); *L1572*; *L1647* (collided with tractor, Sutton Bridge, 2-5-39); *L1655*; *L1659*; *L1660*; *L1661* (abandoned 5 miles south of Herne Bay, Kent, 9-7-39); *L1662* (crashed in low cloud at Tatsfield, Kent, 11-8-39); *L1663-L1668*; *L1670*; *L1672* (crashed while approaching to land at Biggin Hill, 6-4-39); *L1674*; *L1675* (crashed while approaching to land at Biggin Hill, 26-2-39); *L1841*; *L1970*; *L1972*; *L2049*; *L2050*; *L2062* (lost, 1-9-40); *L2063*; *L2075*; *L2086* (to Admiralty charge, 22-4-41).

No. 43 (F) Sqn.: *L1577*; *L1592*; *L1594*; *L1608* (shot down, 7-6-40); *L1671*; *L1685* (lost in France, 5-40); *L1686*; *L1687*; *L1689*; *L1704*; *L1722*; *L1723*; *L1725* (abandoned over Northumberland, 5-12-39); *L1726* (abandoned, 7-6-40); *L1727*; *L1728*; *L1729* (crashed on take-off at Acklington, 21-2-40); *L1730-L1734*; *L1735* (crashed while landing at Tangmere, 24-1-39); *L1736* (abandoned near Tangmere, 18-8-40); *L1737* (crashed while landing at Rouen/Boos, 7-6-40); *L1738* (crashed while landing at Tangmere, 22-4-39); *L1739* (shot down by He 111 over English Channel, 14-8-40); *L1742*; *L1744* (crashed into sea off Northumberland coast, 9-2-40); *L1758* (shot down over Dunkirk, 1-6-40); *L1824* (crashed on landing, Tangmere, 9-7-40); *L1825*; *L1835*; *L1847* (shot down, 7-6-40); *L1849* (suffered engine fire and abandoned south of Tangmere, 7-7-40); *L1898*; *L1931* (shot down by Bf 109s near Abbeville, 7-6-40); *L1955* (crashed near Ashford, Kent, 29-7-40); *L1958*; *L1959*; *L1963* (crashed at Cragburn Dean, near Usworth, 27-10-40); *L1968* (crashed into sea off Acklington, 4-2-41); *L1970*; *L1974*; *L1983*; *L2047*; *L2066* (collided with Hurricane *L1734* and crashed, 18-1-40); *L2116* (shot down near Abbeville, 7-6-40); *L2143*.

No. 46 (F) Sqn.: *L1601*; *L1750*; *L1791*; *L1792* (crashed at night near Corby, Northants, 29-3-39); *L1794* (shot down by Ju 88 over Narvik, 29-5-40); *L1795* (crashed while landing at Digby, 24-2-39); *L1796*; *L1797* (crashed on landing at Digby, 19-6-39); *L1801* (pilot lost control and abandoned near Leadenham, Lincs, 18-4-40); *L1802*; *L1803*, *L1808*; *L1812* (SOC, 5-40); *L1813*; *L1814*; *L1816* (shot down by Ju 88 over Norway, 29-5-40); *L1817*; *L1854*; *L1857* (crashed on take-off at Digby, 6-3-40); *L1892*; *L1988* (Missing from patrol, Harstad, Norway, 29-5-40); *L2071*; *L2083*. Aircraft lost in HMS *Glorious*, 10-6-40: *L1793*, *L1804-L1806*; *L1815*; *L1853*; *L1961*; *L1980*.

No. 56 (F) Sqn.: *L1565*; *L1584*; *L1590-L1596*; *L1597* (landed wheels-up at North Weald, 6-2-39); *L1598* (collided with Hurricane *L1611* and crashed near North Weald, 12-6-39); *L1599* (crashed near Chelmsford, 24-4-39); *L1600*; *L1601*; *L1602* (crashed while landing at Filton, 2-6-39); *L1603* (crashed while landing at night at Northolt, 29-9-38); *L1604* (crashed while landing at Debden, 12-12-38); *L1605*; *L1607-L1611*; *L1645*; *L1715*; *L1742*; *L1764* (shot down near Portland, 30-9-40); *L1828* (crashed while landing at North Weald, 23-3-39); *L1829*; *L1830*; *L1972* (Missing, 29-5-40); *L1975*; *L1976*; *L1980-L1983*; *L1984* (crashed at Playford, Suffolk, 29-1-40); *L1985* (shot down by Spitfires near Ipswich, 6-9-39); *L1986-L1992*; *L1998-L2005*; *L2076*.

No. 71 (F) Sqn.: *L1715*; *L1796*; *L1935*; *L1989*.

No. 73 (F) Sqn.: *L1565*; *L1566* (crashed while landing at Sutton Bridge, 9-5-39); *L1568*; *L1569* (crashed while landing at Norrent-Fontes, France, 8-10-39); *L1570* (crashed on take-off at Digby, 21-4-39); *L1571*; *L1572*; *L1573* (crashed near Newark, Notts, 23-6-39); *L1576* (crashed while landing at Digby, 9-3-39); *L1577*, *L1578*; *L1582* (crashed while landing at Digby, 4-8-39); *L1585*; *L1586*; *L1633* (crashed at night while landing at Digby, 18-4-39); *L1657*; *L1673* (shot down at Betheniville, France, 13-5-40); *L1683*; *L1687*; *L1693* (lost in France, 5-40); *L1766*; *L1808*; *L1826* (lost in France, 7-6-40); *L1827*; *L1844* (SOC, 1-7-40); *L1864*; *L1891* (lost in France, 5-40); *L1927*; *L1958*; *L1959* (force landed in Luxembourg, 11-9-39, and interned); *L1960* (SOC, 3-6-42); *L1962* (crashed at St. Privat, France, 12-3-40); *L1965*; *L1967* (shot down by Bf 109s near Metz, 22-12-39); *L1968*; *L1975*; *L1981*; *L2036* (shot down by Bf 109s over Thames Estuary, 23-9-40); *L2039*; *L2047*; *L2076*.

No. 79 (F) Sqn.: *L1585*; *L1586* (crashed at Pett, Sussex, 21-11-39); *L1587* (SOC, 27-2-40); *L1588* (crashed on beach, 29-9-39); *L1593* (crashed at Ditchling Common, East Sussex,

20-6-39); *L1594*; *L1617*; *L1624*; *L1697*; *L1698*; *L1699* (crashed into sea off Reculver, Kent, 16-2-40); *L1700*; *L1701*; *L1705*; *L1707* (crashed at Chelsham, Surrey, 11-9-39); *L1709* (crashed from spin at Three Bridges, Sussex, 26-4-40); *L1712*; *L1714-L1716*; *L1718*; *L1719* (landed wheels-up at Biggin Hill, 13-4-40); *L1720-L1722*; *L1771*; *L1781*; *L1782* (abandoned in the air one mile north of Bekesbourne, Kent, 27-2-39); *L1784*; *L1841*; *L1846*; *L1906* (crashed on take-off at Manston, 25-11-39); *L1929* (crashed, 10-10-39); *L1942*; *L1945*; *L1986*; *L2049* (lost in France, 5-40); *L2050*; *L2065* (lost in France, 5-40); *L2068* (lost in France, 5-40); *L2145* (Missing over France, 20-5-40).

No. 85 (F) Sqn.: *L1575* (crashed on landing at Debden, 3-1-39; *L1590*; *L1604* (crashed while landing at Debden, 12-12-38); *L1632* (lost in France, 5-40); *L1634* (crashed near Debden, 20-12-38); *L1635* (lost in France, 5-40); *L1636*; *L1637* (crashed in France, 18-4-40); *L1639*; *L1640* (lost in France, 5-40); *L1641* (lost in France); *L1642*; *L1643* (crashed on take-off at Debden, 12-4-39); *L1644*; *L1648* (crashed while landing at Debden, 6-10-38); *L1649*; *L1650* (crashed on take-off at Debden, 12-1-39); *L1651* (crashed while landing at Aldergrove, 27-10-38); *L1653*; *L1656* (crashed on landing at Debden, 9-11-38); *L1715*; *L1765* (crashed at Le Touquet, France, 23-12-39); *L1773*; *L1774*; *L1774* (lost in France, 5-40); *L1775* (lost in France, 5-40); *L1778* (destroyed in France, 10-5-40); *L1779* (lost in France, 5-40); *L1796*; *L1833-L1835*; *L1854* (crashed near Church Fenton, 25-9-40); *L1889*; *L1898* (lost in France, 5-40); *L1900*; *L1915* (shot down by Bf 109s over Kent, 29-8-40); *L1933* (hit by British AA and crash landed at Hawkinge, 24-8-40); *L1935*; *L1978* (6-3-40); *L1979* (Missing over France, 13-5-40); *L2071* (shot down by Bf 109 near Kenley, 1-9-40).

No. 87 (F) Sqn.: *L1592*; *L1605* (destroyed in France, 30-5-40); *L1612*; *L1613* (crashed at Plechatel, France, 12-2-40); *L1614-L1617*; *L1618* (pilot, dazzled by searchlight, lost control and abandoned aircraft, Steeple Morden, Cambs, 18-8-39); *L1619* (force landed in Belgium and interned, 10-11-39); *L1620* (crashed into sea off Holbeach, Lincs, 14-9-38); *L1621* (crashed while landing at Debden, 7-3-39); *L1622* (landed wheels-up at Debden, 6-2-39); *L1623* (abandoned over the sea off Felixstowe, 17-7-39); *L1624*; *L1625* (crashed on take-off at Bury St. Edmunds landing ground, 11-11-39); *L1626* (crashed on take-off at Debden, 11-7-39); *L1627* (crashed on landing at Debden, 11-7-39); *L1628* (force landed at La Panne, Belgium, 14-11-39, and interned); *L1629* (crashed near Debden, 11-7-39); *L1630* (lost in France, 5-40); *L1646* (lost in France, 5-40); *L1722* (damaged in ground accident in France, 20-4-40, and abandoned); *L1743*; *L1768*; *L1776* (crashed from spin, Forêt de Nieppe, 5-10-39); *L1777*; *L1813* (force landed at Coxyde, Belgium, 14-11-39, and interned); *L1831* (landed wheels-up at Debden, 23-5-39); *L1832*; *L1930* (Missing over France, 13-5-40); *L1963*; *L1964* (lost in France, 5-40); *L1965*; *L1970* (Missing over France, 12-5-40); *L2036*; *L2047*.

No. 111 (F) Sqn.: *L1548*; *L1549* (crashed at Hillingdon while approaching to land at Northolt, 20-7-38); *L1550* (crashed at Colnbrook, Bucks, 18-7-38); *L1551* (crashed at Ickenham, Middlesex, 19-5-38); *L1552*; *L1553* (landed wheels-up at Northolt, 6-10-38); *L1554* (crashed on landing at Northolt, 24-4-39); *L1555*; *L1556* (crashed at Uxbridge, 1-2-39); *L1557* (crashed near Biggin Hill after take-off, 9-8-39); *L1558* (crashed near Alton, Hants, 17-1-39); *L1559* (crashed near Dorking, Surrey, 17-1-39); *L1560*; *L1561* (crashed on Harrow golf course, Middlesex, 17-2-39); *L1563*; *L1564* (crashed into sea, 2-6-40); *L1581*; *L1583*; *L1584*; *L1589*; *L1607* (shot down by Bf 110 over France, 18-5-40); *L1631* (crashed while landing at night at Northolt, 8-9-39); *L1638*; *L1654*; *L1660*; *L1704*; *L1716*; *L1718* (lost in France, 5-40); *L1720* (shot down by Bf 110 over France, 19-5-40); *L1730* (lost in France, 6-40); *L1733* (force landed in France, 19-5-40, and abandoned); *L1740*; *L1741*; *L1774* (shot down by Bf 110 over France, 19-5-40); *L1820-L1823*; *L1830*; *L1833*; *L1892* (shot down over Kent, 6-9-40); *L1973*; *L2001* (crashed while landing at Hatfield, 19-6-40); *L2051* (shot down by Bf 109 over France, 18-5-40); *L2052*; *L2055*.

No. 151 (F) Sqn.: *L1601*; *L1606* (crashed while landing at North Weald, 6-11-39); *L1654*; *L1745* (crashed while landing at North Weald, 20-3-39); *L1746-L1750*; *L1753* (crashed while landing at night at North Weald, 15-4-39); *L1754* (crashed while landing at North Weald, 28-2-39); *L1755* (lost in France, 5-40); *L1756-L1758*; *L1764*; *L1766*; *L1767* (crashed while landing at North Weald, 14-4-39); *L1768*; *L1769*; *L1777*; *L1798*; *L1799* (crashed into the North Sea, 2-4-40); *L1850*; *L1959*; *L1961*; *L1962*; *L1975*; *L1977*; *L2005* (shot down by Bf 109s, 28-8-40); *L2047* (crashed while landing at Digby, 25-10-40); *L2087*; *L2092*; *L2146*.

No. 152 (F) Sqn.: *L1592*; *L1608*.

No. 213 (F) Sqn.: *L1584*; *L1600*; *L1605*; *L1770-L1772*; *L1777*; *L1780*; *L1783*; *L1784*; *L1785* (crashed near Wittering, 20-5-39); *L1789*; *L1790*; *L1800* (crashed while landing at Wittering, 4-7-39); *L1808*; *L1809* (abandoned near Grantham, 10-3-39); *L1810* (crashed while landing at Wittering, 29-3-39); *L1911* (crashed on take-off at Wittering, 3-8-39); *L1812*; *L1817* (lost in France, 5-40); *L1818*; *L1819*; *L1829*; *L1851*; *L1852*; *L1854*; *L1889*; *L1914*; *L1982*; *L2057*; *L2060*; *L2062*; *L2142*; *L2146* (lost in France, 6-40).

No. 229 (F) Sqn.: *L1770*; *L1780*; *L1783*; *L1786*; *L1790* (crashed into the sea 30 miles off Grimsby, 9-4-40); *L1802*; *L1803*; *L1808*; *L1812*; *L1817*; *L1829* (lost 15-8-42); *L1852*; *L1854*; *L1889*; *L1951*; *L1961*; *L1980*; *L1982* (Missing over France, 31-5-40); *L1988*; *L1998*; *L2000*; *L2060*; *L2071*; *L2090* (crashed, 30-9-40); *L2142*; *L2146*.

No. 232 (F) Sqn.: *L1952*.

No. 236 (F) Sqn.: *L1998*.

No. 238 (F) Sqn.: *L1702* (collided with Hurricane *N2474* over Shaftesbury, Dorset, 30-9-40); *L1827*; *L1889*; *L1998*; *L2089*.

No. 242 (F) Sqn.: *L1572*; *L1584*; *L1595*; *L1638*; *L1654*; *L1665* (Missing over France, 18-5-40); *L1666*; *L1746* (Missing over France, 28-5-40); *L1747*; *L1748*; *L1749* (lost in France, 5-40); *L1756* (crashed on take-off at Manston, 29-5-40); *L1757*; *L1766*; *L1922*; *L1948* (lost over France, 1-6-40); *L1972*; *L1981*; *L1983*; *L1992*; *L2002* (crashed at night near Bolton Percy, Tadcaster, Yorks, 3-3-40); *L2003*; *L2004* (Missing over France, 1-6-40); *L2039*; *L2087*.

No. 249 (F) Sqn.: *L1595* (crashed near Bulford Camp, Amesbury, Wilts, 20-9-40); *L1715*; *L1764*; *L1832*; *L1998*; *L2067*.

No. 253 (F) Sqn.: *L1565* (Missing over France, 1-6-40); *L1600*; *L1609*; *L1611*; *L1615*; *L1645*; *L1653*; *L1655* (lost in France, 5-40); *L1660*; *L1663*; *L1666*; *L1667* (Missing over France, 18-5-40); *L1668* (pilot lost control and abandoned aircraft near Rickmansworth, Herts, 26-4-40); *L1674* (Missing over France, 19-5-40); *L1701*; *L1712*; *L1771*; *L1818*; *L1830* (shot down by Bf 109 near Biggin Hill, 31-8-40); *L1841*; *L1928* (crashed after oxygen failure, 10-10-40); *L1965* (Missing, 30-8-40); *L2020*; *L2071*.

No. 257 (F) Sqn.: *L1585*; *L1659*; *L1703* (pilot abandoned aircraft after engine fire; aircraft crashed at Watford Way, Edgware, Middlesex, 15-8-40); *L1706*; *L1868*; *L2101*; *L2102*.

No. 263 (F) Sqn.: *L1583*; *L1864*; *L2062*.

No. 303 (Polish) Sqn.: *L1696* (Missing, 27-9-40); *L1770*; *L1825*; *L2026*.

No. 306 (Polish) Sqn.: *L1687*; *L1700*; *L1717* (crashed 3 miles south of Shrewsbury, 26-11-40); *L1771*; *L1870*; *L1895*; *L1956*; *L1969*; *L2011*.

No. 308 (Polish) Sqn.: *L2092*.

No. 310 (Czech) Sqn.: *L1825*; *L1842*; *L1848*.

No. 312 (Czech) Sqn.: *L1547* (pilot abandoned aircraft which crashed in the River Mersey off Ellesmere Port, 10-10-40); *L1644* (abandoned after fire in the air near Cambridge, 10-9-40); *L1701*; *L1740*; *L1748*; *L1841*; *L1926*.

No. 315 (Polish) Sqn.: *L1740*; *L1959*.

No. 317 (Polish) Sqn.: *L1969*.

No. 318 (Polish) Sqn.: *L1752* (crash landed at Detling after engine fire, 2-7-43); *L1723*; *L1742*; *L1747*.

No. 501 Sqn., A.A.F.: *L1572*; *L1578* (shot down near Ashford, Kent, 2-9-40); *L1600*; *L1605*; *L1609*; *L1624* (lost, 21-6-40); *L1636*; *L1657*; *L1659*; *L1829*; *L1864*; *L1865* (shot down by Bf 109 over Dover, 24-8-40); *L1866* (abandoned in France, 5-40); *L1767* (crashed while landing at night at Tangmere, 18-1-40); *L1868*; *L1869* (crashed while landing at Filton, 26-3-39); *L1870-L1872*; *L1910*; *L1911* (lost, 21-6-40); *L1949*; *L1953*; *L1991* (abandoned in France, 5-40); *L2037* (lost in France, 5-40); *L2038*; *L2039*; *L2045*; *L2046*; *L2050* (lost in France, 5-40); *L2052*; *L2053* (crashed at Mezières, France, 12-5-40); *L2054* (crashed at Beauvillers, 12-5-40); *L2055*; *L2056* (crashed while landing at Anglure, 31-5-40); *L2124*.

No. 504 Sqn., A.A.F.: *L1583*; *L1595*; *L1615* (shot down near Faversham, Kent, 7-9-40); *L1638*; *L1639*; *L1877*; *L1911*; *L1912* (lost in France, 5-40); *L1913* (damaged by British AA and abandoned near Nuneaton, 29-9-40); *L1915*; *L1916* (lost in France, 5-40); *L1922*; *L1931*; *L1941* (lost, 14-5-40); *L1942*; *L1943*; *L1944* (lost in France, 5-40); *L1945*; *L1946*; *L1947* (crashed near Bungay, Suffolk, 30-4-40); *L1948*; *L1950-L1952*; *L1954* (crashed while landing at Metheringham landing ground, 9-9-39); *L1956*; *L1957*; *L1999*.

No. 601 Sqn., A.A.F.: *L1664*; *L1670*; *L1750*; *L1772*; *L1789*; *L1819*; *L1877*; *L1894* (aircraft hit gun post on take-off at Exeter and crashed, 21-9-40); *L1914* (lost in France, 5-40); *L1917*; *L1936* (crashed near Lewes, Sussex, 4-7-40); *L1987*; *L1990* (shot down by Bf 109s near Portsmouth, 18-8-40); *L1998*; *L2034* (lost in France, 6-40); *L2035*; *L2057* (shot down off Portland, 11-8-40); *L2080*; *L2081*; *L2084*; *L2088* (Missing, 21-5-40); *L2099* (crashed near Middle Wallop, 1-6-40); *L2102*; *L2141*; *L2143*.

No. 605 Sqn., A.A.F.: *L1601*; *L1611*; *L1789*; *L1830*; *L2012* (collided with Do 17 near Marden, Kent, and crashed, 15-9-40); *L2013*; *L2014*; *L2018*; *L2020*; *L2058* (Missing, 22-5-40); *L2059* (shot down near Odiham, 9-9-40); *L2061* (shot down by Bf 109 near Tunbridge Wells, 8-9-40); *L2098*; *L2100*; *L2101*; *L2103* (crashed into the sea off Dunbar, East Lothian, 9-8-40); *L2115* (crashed near Dunbar, East Lothian, 24-6-40); *L2117* (crashed 6 miles north of Folkestone, 31-5-40); *L2119* (Missing, 27-5-40); *L2120* (22-5-40); *L2121* (Missing, 23-5-40); *L2122* (shot down by Bf 109s over West Malling, 15-9-40).

No. 607 Sqn., A.A.F.: *L1577* (crashed at Middle Moneynut, East Lothian, 1-2-41); *L1728* (lost 7-10-40); *L1957*; *L1968*;

No. 610 Sqn., A.A.F.: *L2115-L2122*.

No. 615 Sqn., A.A.F.: *L1592*; *L1983*; *L1992*; *L2003*; *L2075*; *L2098*; *L2123*.

No. 616 Sqn., A.A.F.: *L2101-L2103*.

No. 5 Operational Training Unit: *L1571*; *L1572*; *L1653*; *L1664*; *L1683*; *L1698*; *L1716*; *L1786*; *L1798*; *L1808*; *L1821*; *L1827*; *L1836*; *L1852*; *L1896*; *L1902*; *L1934*; *L1946* (crashed at Beachley, Glos, 1-10-40); *L1958*; *L1973*; *L1975*; *L1977*; *L2067*; *L2076*; *L2080*; *L2098*; *L2100*; *L2124*.

No. 6 Operational Training Unit: *L1548*; *L1555*; *L1574*; *L1654* (collided with Hurricane *L1833* and crashed, 3-9-40); *L1660*; *L1704*; *L1705* (crashed at Sutton Bridge, 4-10-40); *L1713*; *L1714* (crashed near Wisbech, Lincs, 29-7-40); *L1732*; *L1741*; *L1766* (crashed at Walpole St. Andrew, Lincs, 5-10-40); *L1669*; *L1789*; *L1814*; *L1820*; *L1833* (collided with Hurricane *L1654* and crashed, 3-9-40); *L1851*; *L1864*; *L1895* (crashed on landing at Sutton Bridge, 12-6-40); *L1896*; *L1897* (crashed at Upwell, Norfolk, 25-6-40); *L1910*; *L1924*; *L1927*; *L1942*; *L1986* (abandoned near Marholm, Northants, 30-9-40); *L2003* (crashed on landing at Sutton Bridge, 16-10-40); *L2011*; *L2045*; *L2052*; *L2063* (crashed at Holbeach, Lincs, 30-8-40); *L2064*; *L2070*; *L2073*; *L2082* (collided with Canadian Hurricane *324* and crashed near Sutton Bridge, 18-8-40); *L2083*; *L2084*; *L2091*.

No. 7 Operational Training Unit: *L1653*; *L1704*; *L1713*; *L1716*; *L1721*; *L1732*; *L1786*; *L1791* (crashed at Holt, near Wrexham, 25-7-40); *L1798*; *L1821*; *L1825*; *L1833*; *L1870*; *L1896*; *L1946*; *L1986*; *L1989*; *L2020* (crashed at Hawarden, 22-7-40); *L2063*; *L2076*; *L2082*; *L2100*; *L2124*.

No. 41 Operational Training Unit: *L1563* (crashed on landing at Andover, 4-3-44); *L1571*; *L1574*; *L1740*; *L1742*; *L1768*; *L1821*; *L1958*; *L1983*; *L2143*.

No. 51 Operational Training Unit: *L1568*.

No. 52 Operational Training Unit: *L1653*; *L1657*; *L1748*; *L1945*; *L2087*.

No. 54 Operational Training Unit: *L1771*.

No. 55 Operational Training Unit: *L1571*; *L1596* (crashed at Aston Down, 27-12-40); *L1653*; *L1660*; *L1670* (crashed at Keld, Yorks, 10-4-41); *L1698*; *L1700* (crashed at Saul, Glos, 28-12-40); *L1701*; *L1716*; *L1721*; *L1740*; *L1742*; *L1747*; *L1748*; *L1768*; *L1786*; *L1789*; *L1798* (crashed at Combe Down, near Yatesbury, 10-9-40); *L1807* (crashed at Usworth, 8-3-41); *L1808*; *L1819*; *L1832*; *L1836* (crashed at Bournmoor, Co. Durham, 28-4-41); *L1841* (crashed at Great Stainton, Co. Durham, 1-5-41); *L1852* (crashed on take-off at Moreton-in-the-Marsh, 2-1-41); *L1864*; *L1889*; *L1896*; *L1902* (crashed at Andoversford, Glos, 17-12-40); *L1926* (crashed on landing at Ouston, 15-4-41); *L1934*; *L1957*; *L1977* (crashed near Stroud, Glos, 9-10-40); *L1983*; *L1992*; *L1999* (crashed at Tetbury, Glos, 29-11-40); *L2067*; *L2070* (crashed near Annan, 11-3-43); *L2072* (crashed near Sutton Bridge, 22-3-40); *L2075*; *L2076* (crashed on take-off at Aston Down, 22-2-41); *L2080*; *L2089*; *L2092*; *L2098* (crashed at Aston Down, 26-12-40); *L2101*; *L2102*; *L2124* (crashed at Moreton-in-Marsh, Glos, 5-12-40).

No. 56 Operational Training Unit: *L1552* (crashed on Terrington Marsh, Norfolk, 17-12-40; *L1555* (crashed at Long Sutton, Norfolk, 17-4-41); *L1563*; *L1568*; *L1574*; *L1581*; *L1594*; *L1617*; *L1638*; *L1659* (crashed on landing at Sutton Bridge, 19-11-40); *L1663*; *L1664*; *L1666*; *L1695*; *L1704*; *L1706*; *L1712*; *L1713* (crashed at Sutton Bridge, 15-10-40); *L1731*; *L1740*; *L1741* (crashed 3 miles south of Downham Market, 4-1-41); *L1777*; *L1783*; *L1808*; *L1814*; *L1820* (crashed at Sutton Bridge, 17-12-40); *L1851*; *L1864* (crashed at Sutton Bridge, 12-12-40); *L1868* (crashed at Sutton Bridge, 17-1-41); *L1877*; *L1889*; *L1917*; *L1935*; *L1951*; *L1973*; *L1989*; *L1998*; *L2006*; *L2011*; *L2026*; *L2055* (crashed from spin, West Walton, 11-6-41); *L2070*; *L2073* (collided with Hurricane *P3650* and crashed at sea off Leuchars, 23-6-43); *L2083* (crashed near Sutton Bridge, 8-10-40); *L2091*; *L2100*.

No. 59 Operational Training Unit: *L1574*; *L1664*; *L1715*; *L1727* (crashed at Gedney Dye, Lincs, 8-9-40); *L1771*; *L1796*; *L1808*; *L1818* (crashed near Longtown, 5-4-41); *L1870* (crashed at Watch Hill, Aspatria, Cumberland, 29-7-41); *L1877*; *L1910*; *L1924*; *L1952*; *L2052*; *L2075*; *L2089*; *L2143*.

No. 63 Operational Training Unit: *L1664*.

No. 81 Operational Training Unit: *L1668*; *L1877*.

No. 151 Operational Training Unit (India): *L1848*; *L1935* (crashed at Risalpur, 11-12-43).

No. 5 Flying Training School: *L1571*; *L1594*; *L1638*; *L1653*; *L1683*; *L1695* (crashed at Eaton Constantine, near Shrewsbury, 3-1-42); *L1704*; *L1716*; *L1721*; *L1747*; *L1768*; *L1770*; *L1788* (crashed on take-off at Ternhill, 30-9-41); *L1819*; *L1848*; *L1864*; *L1951*; *L1981*; *L1983*; *L2052*; *L2064*; *L2075*; *L2080*; *L2101*.

No. 6 Flying Training School: *L1846*.

No. 8 Flying Training School: *L1568*; *L1572*; *L1712*; *L1723*; *L1731* (crashed while landing at Montrose, 13-9-41); *L1777*; *L1827*; *L1927* (crashed while landing at Montrose, 23-12-41); *L1934*; *L1935*; *L1958*; *L2073*; *L2089*; *L2092*.

No. 9 Flying Training School: *L1594*; *L1601*; *L1660*; *L1666*; *L1683*; *L1687*; *L1695*; *L1701*; *L1703*; *L1706*; *L1742*; *L1747*; *L1784*; *L1821*; *L1822* (fire in the air and pilot abandoned aircraft at Dursley, Glos, 10-9-41); *L1825*; *L1832* (crashed while landing at Castle Coombe, 8-7-41); *L1846*; *L1942*; *L1951* (crashed at Park Farm, Chipping Sodbury, Glos, 11-2-42); *L2038* (crashed at Rudloe, Somerset, 31-10-41); *L2045*; *L2087*; *L2102*.

Allocated for shipment to Canada: Works Order No. 6243 covered: *L1759* (as *310*); *L1760* (as *311*); *L1761* (as *312*); *L1762* (as *313*); *L1763* (as *314*); *L1878* (as *315*); *L1879* (as *316*); *L1880* (as *317*); *L1881* (as *318*); *L1882* (as *319*); *L1883* (as *320*); *L1884* (as *321*; later returned to U.K. to become the Hillson F.H. 40 Slip-wing Hurricane); *L1885* (as *322*); *L1886* (as *323*); *L1887* (as *324*); *L1888* (as *325*); *L1890* (as *326*); *L2021* (as *327*); *L2022* (as *320*); *L2023* (as *329*); *L2144* (as *330*, but lost at sea in transit). Works Order No. 6251 covered *L1848* (despatched as pattern aircraft, 2-3-39). Works Order No. 6639 covered *L2144* (despatched 28/9/39 as sample aircraft for proposed production of Hurricane in Canada).

547

Shipped to Yugoslavia from 15-12-38 after manufacture under Works Order No. 6132: *L1751* (as *1-205*); *L1752* (as *2-206*); *L1837* (as *3-291*); *L1838* (as *4-292*); *L1839* (as *5-293*); *L1840* (as *6-294*); *L1858* (as *7-312*); *L1859* (as *8-313*); *L1860* (as *9-314*); *L1861* (as *10-315*); *L1862* (as *11-316*); *L1863* (as *12-317*).

Supplied to Belgium from 4-39 after manufacture under Contract No. B.655029/37 and Works Order No. W.O. 6725: *L1918* (as *1*); *L1919* (as *2*); *L1920* (as *3*); *L1993* (as *4*); *L1994* (as *5*); *L1995* (as *6*); *L1996* (as *7*); *L1997* (as *8*); *L2040* (as *9*); *L2041* (as *10*); *L2042* (as *11*); *L2043* (as *12*); *L2044* (as *13*); *L2045* (as *14*); *L2105* (as *14*); *L2106* (as *15*); *L2107* (as *16*); *L2108* (as *17*); *L2109* (as *18*); *L2110* (as *19*); *L2111* (as *20*). Licence production negotiated with Avions Fairey and several aircraft completed and flown by date of German invasion, 10-5-40, in addition to at least two R.A.F. Hurricanes (see above) which had force landed in Belgium and had been "interned".

Supplied to Romania from 28-8-39 after manufacture under Works Order No. 7368: *L2077*; *L2078*; *L2085*; *L2093-L2097*; *L2104*; *L2112-L2114* (12 aircraft).

Supplied to Turkey from 14-9-39 after manufacture under Works Order No. 7432: *L2125-L2139* (15 aircraft). Delivery completed, 1-5-40.

Supplied to Poland: *L2048* (aircraft shipped 24-7-38; unloaded at Gdynia, 4-8-39; then returned to U.K., 25-8-39. Served with No. 29 (F) Sqn.).

Supplied to South African Air Force: *L1708* (11-38); *L1710* and *L1711* (11-38); *L1874-L1876* (3-39); *L1909* (4-39).

Supplied to Persia, 10-39: *L2079* (as *251*).

Converted to Hurricane Mark IIs (1940-41): *L1581* (became *BV157*); *L1636* (became *DG640*); *L1684* (became *DG354*); *L1769* (became *DR359*); *L1989* (became *DG649*).

Ground Instruction Machines: *L1548* (became *3273M*, 7-42); *L1551* (became *2307M*); *L1552* (became *2643M*); *L1553* (became *1430M*); *L1554* (became *1493M*); *L1559* (became *1539M*); *L1560* (became *1191M*); *L1561* (became *1368M*); *L1568* (became *4534M*, 2-44); *L1575* (became *1380M*); *L1597* (became *1242M*); *L1600* (became *4862M*, 4-44); *L1602* (became *1703M*); *L1603* (became *1181M*); *L1604* (became *1468M*); *L1621* (became *1431M*); *L1622* (became *1237M*); *L1625* (became *1370M*); *L1634* (became *1358M*); *L1643* (became *1474M*); *L1650* (became *1365M*); *L1651* (became *1215M*); *L1656* (became *1232M*); *L1657* (became *2834M*, 12-40); *L1659* (became *3222M*, 7-42); *L1660* (became *3587M*, 3-43); *L1663* (*4501M*, 1-44); *L1672* (became *1466M*); *L1675* (became *1426M*); *L1677* (became *1226M*); *L1683* (became *3589M*, 3-43); *L1691* (became *1373M*, 2-39); *L1697* (became *3202M*, 7-42); *L1698* (became *3174M*, 7-42); *L1701* (became *3586M*, 3-43); *L1727* (became *3368M*); *L1727* (became *3368M*, 9-40); *L1731* (became *2797M*, 9-41); *L1735* (became *1363M*, 2-39); *L1745* (became *1439M*, 4-39); *L1754* (became *1424M*, 3-39); *L1771*(10-44); *L1780* (became *3441M*, 11-42); *L1783* (became *3084M*, 5-42); *L1784* (became *3285M*, 5-42); *L1785* (became *2141M*, 6-39); *L1791* (became *2172M*, 8-40); *L1795* (became *1388M*); *L1798* (became *3576M*); *L1809* (became *1442M*); *L1810* (became *1454M*, 4-39); *L1814* (became *3579M*, 3-43); *L1818* (became *2577M*, 4-41); *L1867* (became *1843M*, 1-40); *L1869* (became *1467M*, 4-39); *L1873* (became *3244M*, 7-42); *L1896* (became *2984M*, 6-42); *L1903* (became *1884M*, 3-40); *L1910* (became *4321M*, 11-43); *L1952* (became *3369M*, 1-43); *L1957* (became *3274M*, 7-42); *L1969* (became *3672M*); *L1999* (became *2466M*); *L2006* (became *4343M*, 11-43); *L2010* (became *1611M*, 7-39); *L2018* (became *3194M*, 2-41); *L2020*; *L2046* (became *3573M*, 3-43); *L2067* (became *3581M*, 2-43); *L2072*; *L2084* (became *3575M*, 3-43); *L2098*; *L2101* (became *3582M*, 3-43); *L2102* (became *3592M*, 3-43).

Other Units and duties, etc.: *L1547*, *L1562*, *L1574*, *L1669*, *L1695*, *L1696* (slotted wings), *L1702*, *L1780*, *L2006* to A. &.A.E.E. for various trials. *L1560*, *L1695*, *L1696*, *L1702*, *L1713*, *L1717*, *L1780*, *L1788* to R.A.E. for various trials. *L1562*, *L1592* (Special Duties Flt.); *L1563* (Air Fighting Development Unit); *L1592*, *L1653* (No. 9 Air Observers' School; Nos. 5 and 9 Pilots' Advanced Flying Unit; crashed near Castle Coombe, 24-7-

42); *L1582* (experimental colour schemes with H.A.L.); *L1601, L1846, L1958, L1981* (R.A.F. College, Cranwell); *L1606* (returned to H.A.L. for repair, but purchased by the Company and registered *G-AFKX* for demonstrations and T.I.s); *L1636; L1670* (No. 4 Ferry Pilots' Pool); *L1638* (No. 6 Ferry Pilots' Pool); *L1664* (No. 1422 Flt.); *L1669* (First tropical trials Hurricane, 1939-40; Nos. 80 and 274 Sqns. in Middle East; crashed on landing at Amriya, 30-9-40); *L1683* (Empire Central Flying School); *L1684* (Northolt Stn. Flt.); *L1697, L1700, L1713* (Rolls-Royce Ltd.); *L1706, L1934* (No. 1622 Flt.); *L1712* (No. 17 and 5 Pilots' Advanced Flying Unit); *L1715, L1796* (No. 2 Sqn., RCAF); *L1715* (No. 691 (AAC) Sqn.; damaged beyond repair, 17-4-44); *L1716* (No. 1 Air Armament School); *L1721* (Nos. 9 and 7 Pilots' Advanced Flying Unit); *L1750* (trials with additional armour by H.A.L.; fitted with two 20-mm. cannon for trials with A.& A.E.E.; flew with Nos. 46 and 151 Sqn. thus armed during the Battle of Britain); *L1768* (Tactical Air Force Comms. Flt.; No. 1665 Heavy Conversion Unit); *L1808* (Tactical Exercise Unit); *L1846* (No.1623 Flt.); *L1856* (fitted with Merlin XII engine by H.A.L. under Works Order No. 6297, but returned to standard before delivery to R.A.F.); *L1864, L1917* (No. 1480 Flt.); *L1870-L1872, L2006-L2011, L2064, L2069, L2070, L2072-L2075* (No. 11 Group Pool); *L1783* (Central Flying School); *L1808, L1877* (No. 2 Tactical Exercise Unit; No. 1665 Heavy Conversion Unit); *L1896* (Ferry Training Unit); *L1935* (No. 667 (TT) Sqn.); *L2060* (Fighter Command Comms. Flt.; lost in France, 5-40); *L2089* (No. 2 Fighter Instructors' School); *L1893* (Second tropical trials Hurricane; to Middle East, c.9-39; Nos. 33 and 112 Sqns.; SOC, 18-3-40).

The Hawker Hurricane I. Second production batch of 300 aircraft built by Hawker Aircraft Ltd., Kingston and Brooklands, under Contract No. 751458/38. Rolls-Royce Merlin III engines driving Rotol or D.H. three-blade propellers. *N2318-N2367; N2380-N2409; N2422-N2441; N2453-N2502; N2520-N2559; N2582-N2631; N2645-N2729.* Deliveries commenced 29-9-39; completed 1-5-40. Average rate of production, approx. two aircraft per day. Aircraft fought with R.A.F. squadrons in Battle of France and Battle of Britain. Numerous aircraft later converted to Sea Hurricane IA etc., and to Mark IIA. Twelve aircraft (*N2718-N2729*) shipped to Yugoslavia; these aircraft replaced on R.A.F. Contract. Some aircraft tropicalised and despatched to the Middle East late in 1940.

The Hawker Hurricane I. First production batch of 500 aircraft built by Gloster Aircraft Co. Ltd., Brockworth, Glos., under Contract No. 962371/38/C.23a. Rolls-Royce Merlin III engines. *P2535-P2584; P2614-P2653; P2672-P2701; P2713-P2732; P2751-P2770; P2792-P2836; P2854-P2888; P2900-P2924; P2946-P2995; P3030-P3069; P3080-P3124; P3140-P3179; P3200-P3234; P3250-P3264.* Deliveries commenced, 11-39; completed 4-40. Average rate of production approx. three aircraft per day. Majority of aircraft fought with R.A.F. squadrons in Battle of France and Battle of Britain. Numerous aircraft converted to Sea Hurricane IA, Hurricane IIA and IIB (some of the latter being shipped to Russia in 1941). *P2968* supplied to Irish Air Corps as "*107*", 29-11-43.

The Hawker Hurricane I. Third production batch of 500 aircraft (plus 44 attrition replacements) built by Hawker Aircraft Ltd., Kingston, Brooklands and Langley, under Contract No. 962371/38. Rolls-Royce Merlin III engines. *P3265-P3279; P3300-P3324; P3345-P3364; P3380-P3429; P3448-P3492; P3515-P3554; P3574-P3623; P3640-P3684; P3700-P3739; P3755-P3789; P3802-P3836; P3854-P3903; P3920-P3944; P3960-P3984.* Replacement aircraft: *P8809-P8818; R2680-R2689; T9519-T9538; W6667-W6670.* Deliveries commenced, 21-2-40; completed, 20-7-40; average rate of production, approx. three aircraft per day. Majority of aircraft served with R.A.F. squadrons during Battle of France and Battle of Britain. Many subsequently converted to Sea Hurricane IA etc., Hurricane IIA and IIB (some being shipped to Russia late in 1941). Many also tropicalised and shipped to Mediterranean and Middle East from late 1940. *P3269* was the prototype Hurricane Mark II with Rolls-

Royce Merlin XX engine. *P3416* was supplied to the Irish Air Corps as "*108*", 29-11-43, and *P3720* was supplied to Persia, c.11-40, as "*252*".

The Hawker Canadian Hurricane I. Pilot production batch of 40 aircraft, *P5170-P5209*, built by the Canadian Car & Foundry Corporation, Montreal, during 1939-40. Powered by Rolls-Royce Merlin IIs and IIIs shipped from Britain. All aircraft shipped to Britain between 2-40 and 8-40, and served with R.A.F. and R.C.A.F. squadrons during the Battle of Britain. A small number converted to Sea Hurricane IAs. *P5176* force landed in Eire during 1942 and transferred to the Irish Air Corps as "*93*". *(Note: These aircraft were not re-designated Canadian Hurricane Mark Xs, and were always officially termed Canadian Hurricane Is to differentiate British-built engines.)*

The Hawker Hurricane I. Second production batch of 100 aircraft built by Gloster Aircraft Co. Ltd., Brockworth, under Contract No. 19773/39/23a. *R4074-R4123; R4171-R4200; R4213-R4232.* Rolls-Royce Merlin III engines. Deliveries commenced c.5-40; completed c.7-40; average rate of production, 2-3 aircraft per day. Almost all aircraft served on R.A.F. Fighter Command squadrons during the Battle of Britain. *R4103* and *R4104* shipped to South African Air Force. Several aircraft later converted to Sea Hurricane IAs (e.g. *R4178*) and Hurricane IIAs (e.g. *R4091*, became *DR373* and was shipped to Russia, c.9-41). Some aircraft (e.g., *R2418*), converted to Mark IIA, tropicalised and shipped to the Middle East. All aircraft with metal wings.

The Hawker Hurricane I and II. Third production batch of 1,700 aircraft built by Gloster Aircraft Co. Ltd., under Contract No. 85730/40/23a. Rolls-Royce Merlin III and XX engines and either Rotol (majority) or D.H. three-blade propellers. Part 1 (500 aircraft, all Mark Is): *V6533-V6582; V6600-V6649; V6665-V6704; V6722-V6761; V6776-V6825; V6840-V6889; V6913-V6962; V6979-V7028; V7042-V7081; V7099-V7138; V7156-V7195.* Part 2: (200 aircraft, all Mark Is): *W9110-W9159; W9170-W9209; W9125-W9244; W9260-W9279; W9290-W9329; W9340-W9359.* Part 3 (400 aircraft, all Mark Is): *Z4022-Z4071; Z4085-Z4119; Z4161-Z4205; Z4223-Z4272; Z4308-Z4327; Z4347-Z4391; Z4415-Z4434; Z4482-Z4516; Z4532-Z4581; Z4603-Z4652.* Part 4 (600 aircraft: Mark Is, IIAs and IIBs): Marks Is: *Z4686-Z4720; Z4760-Z4809; Z4832-Z4876; Z4920-Z4939;* Mark IIAs: *Z4940-Z4969; Z4987-Z4989;* Mark IIBs: *Z4990-Z5006; Z5038-Z5087; Z5117-Z5161; Z5202-Z5236; Z5252-Z5271; Z5302-Z5351; Z5376-Z5395; Z5434-5483; Z5529-Z5563; Z5580-Z5629; Z5649-Z5693.* Deliveries commenced between July 1940; completed August 1941. Average rate of production, approximately five aircraft per day.

The Hawker Hurricane I. Fourth production batch of 500 aircraft built by Hawker Aircraft Ltd., Langley, under Contract No. 62305/39. Rolls-Royce Merlin III engines. *V7200-V7209; V7221-V7260; V7276-V7318; V7337-V7386; V7400-V7446; V7461-V7510; V7533-V7572; V7588-V7627; V7644-V7690; V7705-V7737; V7741-V7780; V7795-V7838; V7851-V7862; AS987-AS990.* Deliveries commenced, 2-7-40; completed 5-2-41; average rate of production, approx. two aircraft per day. First 25 aircraft delivered with fabric-covered wings, remainder with metal-clad wings (some of the early aircraft retrospectively modified). Aircraft served during the Battle of Britain, many later being modified as Sea Hurricane IA and Hurricane Mark IIs. *V7260* and *V7360* armed with four 20-mm cannon; the latter flown by No. 46 Sqn. in Battle of Britain. *V7411, V7435, V7463* and *V7540* supplied to the Irish Air Corps as "*104*", "*112*", "*114*" and "*105*" respectively. *V7480* employed in towed-fighter experiments by Flight Refuelling Ltd., from 3-41. Many aircraft tropicalised and despatched to the Middle East from 10-40 onwards. Several fought in Greek and Crete campaigns.

The Hawker Hurricane IIA, IIB and IIC. Fifth production batch of 1,000 aircraft built by Hawker Aircraft Ltd., Langley, under Contract No. 62305/39 (Part 2). Rolls-Royce Merlin

XX engines. *Z2308-Z2357; Z2382-Z2426; Z2446-Z2465; Z2479-Z2528; Z2560-Z2594; Z2624-Z2643; Z2661-Z2705; Z2741-Z2775; Z2791-Z2480; Z2882-Z2931; Z2959-Z2999; Z3017-Z3036; Z3050-Z3099; Z3143-Z3187; Z3221-Z3276; Z3310-Z3359; Z3385-Z3404; Z3421-Z3470; Z3489-Z3523; Z3554-Z3598; Z3642-Z3691; Z3740-Z3784; Z3826-Z3845; Z3885-Z3919; Z3969-Z4018.* Deliveries commenced, 14-1-41; completed, 28-7-41; average rate of production, approx. five aircraft per day. Aircraft served with Fighter Command squadrons as fighter-bombers (principally Mark IIBs) and as night fighters (Mark IICs) during 1941; many tropicalised and shipped to Middle and Far East, 1941-42. *Z2326* underwent trials with two Rolls-Royce and Vickers 40-mm anti-tank guns at A. & A.E.E. (as prototype Hurricane Mark IID); *Z2905* underwent trials with 90-gallon underwing ferry tanks; *Z3092* underwent trials with rocket projectiles at A.& A.E.E., from 4-41. *Z3687* underwent trials with A.W.A. laminar-flow wings at R.A.E., from 1946. *Z4015* converted to tropicalised Sea Hurricane IC with four-cannon wings. Numerous converted Sea Hurricanes fought in North Cape and Malta convoy battles, 1941-42.

The Hawker Canadian Hurricane X. Second production batch of 340 aircraft built by the Canadian Car & Foundry Corporation, Ontario, Canada, during 1940-41. First part of Contract (20 aircraft), *AE958-AE977,* shipped to U.K., 6-40. Second part (300 aircraft), *AF945-AG344,* shipped to U.K. between 8-40 and 4-41. Third part (20 aircraft), *AG665-AG684,* shipped to U.K., 4-41. All aircraft in Parts 1 and 2 originally completed with eight-gun wings and Packard Merlin 28 engines (some subsequently modified by No. 13 M.U., Henlow, with 12-machine gun or four-cannon wings (remaining Mark Xs), and other refitted with Merlin XXs—becoming Marks IIBs and IICs. Many aircraft in Part 3 shipped to Russia. *AE971-AE974* lost at sea in transit to U.K. Many aircraft subsequently converted to Sea Hurricane IBs and ICs.

The Hawker Canadian Hurricane X. Third production batch of 100 aircraft, *AM270-AM369,* built by the Canadian Car & Foundry Corporation, Ontario, Canada, during 1941. Revised manufacturing tolerances and procedures to conform to British standards. All aircraft shipped to Britain during 1941-42 with eight-gun wings and Packard Merlin 28 engines. Most were re-engined with Merlin XXs and fitted with Mark IIB or IIC wings (many of the "Mark IIBs" being shipped to Russia in the North Cape convoys). Those that served with R.A.F. Squadrons (mostly No. 1 (F) Sqn. and the Turbinlite Squadrons) were Mark IIC night fighters and intruders plumbed for underwing fuel tanks.

The Hawker Hurricane IIB, IIC and IID. Sixth production batch of 1,350 aircraft built by Hawker Aircraft Ltd., Langley, during 1941-42. Rolls-Royce Merlin XX engines: *BD696-BD745; BD759-BD793; BD818-BD837; BD855-BD899; BD914-BD963; BD980-BD986; BE105-BE117; BE130-BE174; BE193-BE242; BE274-BE308; BE323-BE372; BE394-BE428; BE468-BE517; BE546-BE590; BE632-BE651; BE667-BE716; BM898-BM936; BM947-BM996; BN103-BN142; BN155-BN189; BN203-BN242; BN265-BN298; BN311-BN337; BN346-BN389; BN399-BN435; BN449-BN497; BN512-BN547; BN559-BN603; BN624-BN654; BN667-BN705; BN719-BN759; BN773-BN802; BN818-BN846; BN859-BN882; BN896-BN940; BN953-BN987.* Deliveries commenced, 24-7-41; completed 18-3-42; average rate of production, approximately six aircraft per day. Majority of aircraft completed as tropicalised Mark IIBs which were shipped to the Middle and Far East. *BN797* and *BN841-861* were Mark IID anti-tank aircraft with 40-mm guns and were issued to No. 6 Squadron in the Western Desert. Most of the remaining home-based aircraft were night fighters and intruders with cannon armament.

The Hawker Hurricane IIA, IIB and IIC. Fourth production batch of 450 aircraft built by Gloster Aircraft Co. Ltd., Brockworth, Glos. Rolls-Royce Merlin XX engines. *BG674-BG723; BG737-BG771; BG783-BG832; BG844-BG888; BG901-BG920; BG933-BG977;*

BG990-BG999; BH115-BH154; BH167-BH201; BH215-BH264; BH277-BH296; BH312-BH361. Deliveries commenced, 9-41; completed 12-41; average rate of production, approximately five aircraft per day. The majority of aircraft were completed for tropical service, being shipped mostly to the Middle and Far East (as well as a number to Russia—including all the final 100 aircraft). Some took part in the defence of Ceylon against attacks by Japanese carrier-borne aircraft, and in the defence of Calcutta. Others, originally diverted to Singapore, were used in the defence of Java and Sumatra early in 1942.

The Hawker Hurricane IIB, IIC and IID. Seventh production batch of 1,888 aircraft built by Hawker Aircraft Ltd., Langley, during 1942. Rolls-Royce Merlin XX engines. *BN988-BN992; BP109-BP141; BP154-BP200; BP217-BP245; BP259-BP302; BP316-BP362; BP378-BP416; BP430-BP479; BP493-BP526; BP538-BP566; BP579-BP614; BP628-BH675; BP692-NBP711; BP734-BP772. HL544-HL591; HL603-HL634; HL654-HL683; HL698-HL747; HL767-HL809; HL828-HL867; HL879-HL913; HL925-HL941; HL953-HL997; HM110-HM157; HV275-HV317; HV333-HV370; HV396-HV445; HV468-HV516; HV534-HV560; HV577-HV612; HV634-HV674; HV696-HV745; HV768-HV799; HV815-HV868; HV873-HV921; HV943-HV989; HW115-HW146; HW167-HW207; HW229-HW278; HW291-HW323; HW345-HW373; HW399-HW444; HW467-HW501; HW533-HW572; HW596-HW624; HW651-HW686; HW713-HW757; HW779-HW808; HW834-HW881.* Deliveries commenced, 17-3-42; completed, 23-11-42; average rate of production, approximately eight aircraft per day. Comprised home-based Mark IIC night fighters and intruders and large numbers of tropicalised Mark IIB fighter bombers, Mark IIC night fighters, and tropicalised Mark IID anti-tank aircraft for service in the Western Desert and in India and Burma. A small number of aircraft was equipped with A.I. Mark IV radar, serving with No. 245 (F) Sqn. at Middle Wallop for a short period.

The Hawker Hurricane IIB, IIC, IID and IV. Eighth production batch of 1,200 aircraft built by Hawker Aircraft Ltd., Langley, during 1942-43 under Contract No. 62305/39/C/Va (Parts 1-6). Rolls-Royce Merlin XX and 27 engines. *KW745-KW777; KW791-KW832; KW846-KW881; KW893-KW936; KW949-KW982; KX102-KX146; KX161-KX202; KX220-KX261; KX280-KX307; KX321-KX369; KX382-KX425; KX452-KX491; KX521-KX567; KX579-KX621; KX691-KX736; KX749-KX784; KX796-KX838; KX851-KX892; KX922-KX967; KZ111-KZ156; KZ169-KZ201; KZ216-KZ250; KZ266-KZ301; KZ319-KZ356; KZ370-KZ412; KZ424-KZ470; KZ483-KZ526; KZ540-KZ582; KZ597-KZ612.* Deliveries commenced, 20-11-42; completed 19-4-43 (excluding conversion of some Sea Hurricanes). Average rate of production, approx. eight aircraft per day. 24 aircraft between *KW770* and *KW930* converted to Sea Hurricane IIC (and re-registered between *NF668* and *NF703*). *KX405* and *KZ193* converted as first two prototype Hurricane Mark Vs. *KZ706* was employed on trials with Long Tom rocket projectile. Majority of aircraft tropicalised and flown by R.A.F. squadrons in Mediterranean theatre and South-east Asia. Home-based squadrons flew fighter-bomber and rocket-armed aircraft on cross-Channel operations; No. 184 Squadron was the only U.K.-based unit to fly the Mark IID anti-tank aircraft on operations. Many of the Mark IIs were shipped to Russia.

The Hawker Hurricane IIC and IV. Ninth production batch of 1,205 aircraft built by Hawker Aircraft Ltd., Langley, during 1943 under Contract No. 62305/39/Vb (Parts 7 to 12). Rolls-Royce Merlin XX and 27 engines. *KZ613-KZ632; KZ646-KZ689; KZ702-KZ750; KZ766-KZ801; KZ817-KZ862; KZ877-KZ920; KZ933-KZ949; LA101-LA144; LB542-LB575; LB588-LB624; LB639-LB687; LB707-LB744; LB769-LB801; LB827-LB862; LB873-LB913; LB927-LB973; LB986-LB999; LD100-LD131; LD157-LD185; LD199-LD219; LD232-LD266; LD287-LD315; LD334-LD351; LD369-LD416; LD435-LD470; LD487-LD508; LD524-LD539; LD557-LD580; LD594-LD632; LD651-LD695; LD723-LD749; LD772-LD809; LD827-LD866; LD885-LD905; LD931-LD979; LD993-LD999.* Deliveries commenced 18-4-43; completed 29-9-43; average rate of production, slightly over seven aircraft per day. Majority completed in tropical configuration and shipped to Mediterranean and Far Eastern theatres. Many shipped to Russia or transferred to the Indian Air Force. Mark IVs armed with 40 mm guns flown by No. 137 Sqn. (U.K.-based) on cross-Channel operations, and No. 6 Sqn. (based in Italy) flew Mark IVs armed with R.P.s. Many Mark IVs supported the Fourteenth Army in Burma during 1944.

The Hawker Hurricane IIB, IIC and IV. Tenth and final production batch of 1,357 aircraft built by Hawker Aircraft Ltd., Langley, during 1943-44 under Contract No. 62305/39/Vc (Parts 13-19). Part 20 was for 143 Hurricane IVs and Vs, but was cancelled, 1-12-43. Rolls-Royce Merlin XX, 24 and 27 engines. *LE121-LE146; LE163-LE183; LE201-LE214; LE247-LE273; LE291-LE309; LE334-LE368; LE387-LE405; LE432-LE449; LE456-LE484; LE499-LE535; LE552-LE593; LE617-LE665; LE679-LE713; LE737-LE769; LE784-LE816; LE829-LE867; LE885-LE925; LE938-LE966; LE979-LE999; LF101-LF135; LF153-LF184; LF197-LF237; LF256-LF298; LF313-LF346; LF359-LF405; LF418-LF435; LF451-LF482; LF494-LF516; LF529-LF542; LF559-LF601; LF620-LF660; LF674-LF721; LF737-LF774. MW335-MW373. PG425-PG456; PG469-PG499; PG512-PG554; PG567-PG610; PZ730-PZ778; PZ791-PZ835; PZ848-PZ865.* Deliveries commenced, 29-9-43; completed (excluding *PZ865*), 24-5-44. Average rate of production, approx. six aircraft per day. Most operational aircraft were flown in Italy and the Balkans, and in South-east Asia; many aircraft transferred to the Indian Air Force. Home-based aircraft used primarily for training. About 30 aircraft (all Mark IICs) refurbished and sold to Portugal in 1945. *LF536, LF541, LF566, LF624, LF770* and *PZ796* sold to the Irish Air Corps in 1945. *LF363* was the last Hurricane built to be flown by an operational R.A.F. squadron (No. 309 (Polish) Sqn.) and, with *PZ865* "The Last of the Many", has been preserved in flying condition, both aircraft being operated by the R.A.F. Battle of Britain Memorial Flight. (*PZ865* was also for a time owned by Hawker Aircraft Ltd., registered *G-AMAU*; C. of A. issued 23-5-50).

The Hawker Hurricane IIB and IIC. Single production batch of 300 aircraft built by the Austin Motor Co. Ltd., Longbridge, Birmingham, during 1941. Rolls-Royce Merlin XX engines. *AP516-AP550; AP564-AP613; AP629-AP648; AP670-AP714; AP732-AP781; AP801-AP825; AB849-AP898; AP912-AP936.* Approximately 200 of this batch were shipped to Russia. The remainder served operationally with home-based squadrons and in the Middle and Far East. *AP920*, for example, was a Tropical Met. Mark IIC which served with No. 1414 (Met.) Flt. at Mogadishu, Italian Somaliland, in 1943. Others flew in defence of Calcutta, Chittagong and Ceylon.

The Hawker Hurricane V. One prototype, *NL255* (in addition to conversions, *KX405* and *KZ193*, see above), undertaken as joint Hawker/Rolls-Royce venture and ultimately covered by Ministry Contract as proposed "low attack" Hurricane. Rolls-Royce Merlin 32 (ground-boosted) engine. A subsequent production contract was cancelled. Original cost of *NL255* believed offset against loss of *LD182* (crashed during manufacturers' flight test, 16-7-43).

Lend-Lease Financed Canadian Hurricane Production:

The Hawker Canadian Hurricane X. Fourth production batch of 50 aircraft, *BW835-BW884*, built by the Canadian Car & Foundry Corporation, Montreal, during 1941. Packard Merlin 28 engines and Hamilton Standard propellers. The majority were shipped to Russia; some retained for service with R.C.A.F. in Canada. Eight-gun armament.

The Hawker Canadian Hurricane XI. Fifth production batch of 150 aircraft, *BW885-BX134*, built by the Canadian Car & Foundry Corporation, Montreal, during 1941-42. Packard

Merlin 28 engines and Hamilton Standard propellers. Most aircraft shipped to Britain and onwards to Russia; some retained in Britain as night fighters (with 12-gun wing), serving with the Turbinlite squadrons (e.g. *BW962, BW973* and *BX115*).

The Hawker Canadian Hurricane XI and XII. Sixth production batch of 248 aircraft, *JS219-JS371, JS374-JS468*, built by the Canadian Car & Foundry Corporation, Montreal, during 1942. Packard Merlin 28 (Mark XI) and 29 (Mark XII). Many aircraft shipped to Russia, but some retained for service with the R.C.A.F., R.C.N., R.A.F. and Fleet Air Arm (converted as Sea Hurricanes). 185 aircraft with 12-gun wings (Mark XIB and XIIB) and 63 with four-cannon wings (Mark XIIC). Interesting examples included (*inter alia*) *JS253*, a Sea Hurricane XIIB in American markings (which served with No. 800 Sqn. aboard H.M.S. *Biter* during Torch landings); *JS330*, a Hurricane N.F. Mark XIIC with No. 245 Sqn. in Britain; and *JS465*, a "tropical" Hurricane N.F. Mark XIIC with No. 79 Sqn. in defence of Chittagong.

The Hawker Canadian Hurricane XIIA. Seventh production batch of 150 aircraft built by the Canadian Car & Foundry Corporation, Montreal, during 1942-43. Packard Merlin 29 engines. *PJ660-PJ695; PJ711-PJ758; PJ779-PJ813; PJ842-PJ872*. Majority shipped to Russia; others retained in Canada for shipborne duties as Sea Hurricane XIIAs with the Royal Canadian Navy. A small number served with the R.A.F. in Burma during 1943-44.

The Hawker P.4/34 Henley. Two prototypes, *K5115* and *K7554*, built by Hawker Aircraft Ltd., Kingston and Brooklands, during 1936 and 1937, under Contract No. 370869/34 to meet requirements of Air Ministry Specification P.4/34. *K5115* was powered by a Rolls-Royce Merlin "F" engine, being completed as the dive bomber prototype and first flown at Brooklands on 10 March 1937. Underwent handling and performance trials at A. & A.E.E. in 1938 and then delivered to Rolls-Royce Ltd. to become Vulture engine test bed. SOC, 25-3-41. *K7554* was completed as a target tug with Merlin II engine and first flown on 26 May 1938. Trials at A. & A.E.E., 1938-39; Service trials with No. 1 Anti-aircraft Co-operation Unit as target tug; to R.A.E., c.1940; became Ground Instruction Machine *3674M*, 7-43.

The Hawker Henley III. One production batch of 200 aircraft, *L3243-L3642*, built by Gloster Aircraft Co. Ltd., Brockworth, Glos. (Original order for 350 aircraft was reduced in 1938 when rôle was changed from light bomber to target tug; *L3443-L3642* cancelled). Rolls-Royce Merlin II or III engines. Deliveries began in November 1938; completed in September 1940.

   No. 1 Anti-Aircraft Co-operation Unit: *L3243*; *L3244*; *L3245* (ditched in sea off Bude, Cornwall, 1-4-40); *L3246*; *L3249-L3260*; *L3266*; *L3268*; *L3270*; *L3271* (caught fire and crashed near Carew Cheriton, 4-2-41); *L3272*; *L3274*; *L3275* (crashed near Andover, 2-5-39); *L3276*; *L3277* (lost in air raid on Weston Zoyland, 18-10-40); *L3278-L3280*; *L3281* (crashed while landing at Bircham Newton, 12-4-39); *L3282*; *L3283*; *L3284* (crashed near Towyn, 3-6-41); *L3285* (crashed taking-off at Cark, 10-8-39); *L3286-L3288*; *L3289* (crashed while landing at Squires Gate, 2-7-41); *L3290* (lost in air raid on Penrhos, 9-7-40); *L3291* (landed wheels-up on beach at Weybourne, Norfolk, 12-6-39); *L3292*; *L3293* (ditched off Cornish coast, 17-4-42); *L3294* (landed wheels-up at Squires Gate, 7-6-39); *L3295-L3297*; *L3298* (crashed near Weybourne, Norfolk, 23-5-41); *L3300*; *L3301* (struck AA gun and crashed in sea off Anglesey, 26-9-42); *L3304*; *L3307*; *L3311*; *L3312* (ditched off Towyn, 29-10-40); *L3313*; *L3314* (crashed while landing at Weston-super-Mare, 5-2-40); *L3316-L3321*; *L3322* (crashed on landing at Cark, 11-11-42); *L3323-L3328*; *L3330*; *L3331*; *L3334-L3338*; *L3341-L3343*; *L3344* (crashed at Lydstep, Pembroke, 3-5-40); *L3345* (crashed while landing at Yeovil, 26-9-39); *L3346* (crashed near

Carew Cheriton,3-4-40); *L3347*; *L3350*; *L3351* (crashed in cloud at Llanaelhaiarn, Caernarvon, 17-10-40); *L3353-L3356*; *L3357* (crashed at Bootle, Lancs, 8-7-42); *L3358*; *L3359* (lost in air raid on Penrhos, 9-7-40); *L3360-L3362*; *L3363* (crashed on Blakeney Marshes, Norfolk, 11-12-41); *L3364*; *L3366* (crashed while landing at Bodorgan, 28-4-42); *L3367-L3374*; *L3378*; *L3381-L3389*; *L3390* (hit HT cables and crashed near St. Austell, Cornwall, 7-2-43); *L3393-L3400*; *L3403*; *L3405* (crashed at Hill Farm, Playford, Suffolk, 31-7-42); *L3406*; *L3407*; *L3409*; *L3410*; *L3412*; *L3415* (crashed at Llandwrog, 24-12-41); *L3418* (dived into sea off Malltreath Bay, Anglesey, 6-7-40); *L3419-L3422*; *L3423* (crashed in sea off Watchet, Somerset, 20-6-41); *L3424* (crashed at Cannington, Somerset, 17-12-40); *L3425*; *L3426* (crashed on take-off at Cleave, Bude, 28-3-40); *L3427* (crashed west of Carew Cheriton, 23-4-40); *L3428* (crashed on take-off at Weston Zoyland, 15-11-40); *L3429*; *L3431* (crashed in Shrinkle Bay, Manorbier, 21-12-40); *L3432* (crashed near Rhosneigr, Anglesey, 10-6-40); *L3433* (crashed on landing at Cleave, 31-7-41); *L3434*; *L3435* (crashed in sea off Towyn, 5-5-42); *L3436-L3440*; *L3441* (crashed near Aberporth, 26-5-42); *L3442*.

No. 1489 Flt.: *L3247*; *L3267*; *L3310*; *L3320*.

No. 1490 Flt. *L3376*.

No. 1600 Flt.: *L3262*; *L3325*; *L3362*.

No. 1601 Flt.: *L3247*; *L3249*; *L3266* (crashed on landing at Weston Zoyland, 26-10-43); *L3267*; *L3287*; *L3310*; *L3315*; *L3319*; *L3396*; *L3429*; *L3442* (crashed on landing at Weston Zoyland, 25-10-43).

No. 1602 Flt.: *L3254*; *L3270*; *L3282*; *L3292* (crashed into sea off Penhale Point, Cornwall, 9-8-43); *L3317*; *L3324* (crashed in Fistral Bay, Newquay, 20-4-43); *L3347* (crashed at Cleave, 28-10-43; *L3395*; *L3412*; *L3420*; *L3434*.

No. 1603 Flt.: *L3255*; *L3262*; *L3268*; *L3272*; *L3286*; *L3328*; *L3371*; *L3389*; *L3397*.

No. 1604 Flt.: *L3300*; *L3326* (struck on the ground by *L3349* at Cleave, 5-3-41); *L3349* (swung on landing at Cleave and struck *L3326*, 5-3-41); *L3350*; *L3355* (damaged by *L3300* on the ground at St. Mawgan, 25-2-43); *L3395*; *L3437*; *L3439*.

No. 1605 Flt.: *L3243*; *L3251*; *L3288*; *L3297*; *L3321*; *L3325*; *L3334* (hit mountain near Penygroes, Caernarvon, 20-11-42); *L3393*; *L3410*; *L3425* (crashed on landing at Towyn, 2-2-43); *L3438*.

No. 1606 Flt.: *L3394*.

No. 1607 Flt.: *L3252*; *L3274*; *L3279*; *L3283*; *L3311*; *L3335*; *L3336*; *L3369*; *L3407*; *L3439*.

No. 1608 Flt.: *L3386*; *L3403*; *L3438*; *L3439*.

No. 1609 Flt.: *L3248*; *L3287*; *L3306*; *L3364*; *L3387*; *L3399*; *L3403*; *L3409*; *L3422*; *L3440* (crashed at Llanbrynmaer, Montgomery, 2-12-42).

No. 1611 Flt.: *L3260*; *L3313*; *L3320*; *L3331*; *L3372*; *L3407*; *L3436*.

No. 1612 Flt.: *L3256*; *L3296*; *L3330*; *L3331* (crashed at Gorleston, Norfolk, after fire in the air, 19-9-43); *L3341*; *L3354*; *L3378*; *L3388*; *L3420*; *L3421*.

No. 1613 Flt.: *L3258*; *L3259*; *L3327*; *L3338*; *L3342*; *L3343*; *L3353*; *L3360*; *L3394*; *L3442*.

No. 1614 Flt.: *L3287*; *L3295*; *L3323*; *L3380*; *L3383*.

No. 1616 Flt.: *L3248*; *L3249* (crashed at St. Osyth, Essex, 30-7-43); *L3280*; *L3286*; *L3295*; *L3304*; *L3321* (crashed on landing at Ipswich, 12-11-43); *L3558*; *L3360*; *L3373*; *L3374*; *L3380*; *L3381*; *L3383*; *L3419*; *L3429*.

No. 1617 Flt.: *L3258*; *L3268*; *L3304*; *L3323*; *L3336*; *L3337*; *L3380*; *L3382*; *L3400*.

No. 1623 Flt.: *L3442*.

No. 1628 Flt.: *L3276*; *L3323*; *L3337*; *L3382*; *L3400*.

(Henleys also served in a number of rôles on various other units, including Nos. 291, 587, 595, 631, 639 and 679 (Target Towing) Squadrons, No. 2 Anti-Aircraft Co-operation Unit, General Reconnaissance units, Air Observers' Schools, Observers' Advanced Flying Units, Bombing and Gunnery Schools and Air Armament Schools, Armament Training Stations and Armament Practice Camps.)

The Hawker F.9/35 Hotspur. One prototype, *K8309*, designed to meet the demands of Air Ministry Specification F.9/35 for two-seat turret fighter by Hawker Aircraft Ltd., Kingston, and built under Contract No. 453461/35 dated 10 December 1935. First flight, 14 June 1938, by P.G. Lucas. Wooden gun turret mock-up fitted initially and powered by 1,030 h.p. Rolls-Royce Merlin "E" engine. Turret mock-up later removed and engine changed to Merlin II. Production order placed for 389 aircraft (*L3643-L4031*) with A.V. Roe & Co. Ltd., Manchester, but cancelled early in 1937. Prototype spent its entire life on an intensive trials programme with various flap configurations at the R.A.E. Aircraft crashed at Yateley Common, Hampshire, 12-2-42, and struck off charge.

The Hawker F.18/37 Tornado. Two prototypes, *P5219* and *P5224*, designed to Specification F.18/37, ordered under Contract No. 815124/38 and built under Works Order No. 5264 by Hawker Aircraft Ltd., Kingston and Langley, during 1938-39. Rolls-Royce Vulture engines.
P5219 ff. 6-10-39, P.G. Lucas. Rolls-Royce Vulture II No. 12. Ventral radiator. First flight with nose radiator, 6-12-39. Wheel flaps added, 1-40. Suffered engine failure and force landed, 31-7-40. Vulture V No. 164, 3-41.
P5224 ff. 15-12-40, P.G. Lucas. Vulture II No. 132. Extended trials on radiator fairing, 2-41, at D. Napier & Son and Rolls-Royce Ltd. Returned to HAL, Langley, 3-41. Engine failure and forced landing, 31-3-41. Vulture V, No. 126, 6-41; Vulture V, No. 132, 8-41.

The Hawker Tornado I. Order for one prototype, *R7936*, and 199 aircraft, between *R7937* and *R8197*, ordered from A.V. Roe & Co. Ltd., Manchester, in 1939, but cancelled in 1941. Rolls-Royce Vulture V engines. Only *R7936* completed and flown (*R7937* and *R7938* completed except for engine installation, and subsequently used to complete an additional prototype, *HG641*, see below). (Cancelled aircraft were *R7939-R7975; R7992-R8036; R8048-R8091; R8105-R8150; R8172-R8197*).
R7936 ff (at Langley), 31-8-41, P.G. Lucas. Vulture V No. 4252. Performance tests at Langley, 8-41 to 3-42. Thereafter trials at A. & A.E.E., R.A.E., and Rolls-Royce Ltd. Trials as propeller test bed with de Havilland and Rotol.

The Hawker Tornado. Additional prototype, *HG641*, assembled from components of *R7937* and *R7938* (see above) and first flown at Langley by P.G. Lucas, 23-10-41, powered by Bristol Centaurus CE4S No. 19. Underwent development of engine installation; fitted with Centaurus IV No. 27 with modified cowling, oil cooler and exhaust system; first flown in this configuration, 23-12-42, by P.G. Lucas. Subsequently to Bristols, Filton.

The Hawker F.18/37 Typhoon. Two prototypes, *P5212* and *P5216*, designed to Air Ministry Specification F.18/37, ordered under Contract No. 815124/38 and built under Works Order No. 5232 dated 3 March 1938 by Hawker Aircraft Ltd. at Langley during 1938-40.
P5212 ff. 24-2-40, P.G. Lucas. Nose radiator; part of radiator fairing lost on 2nd flight, 1-3-40; Sabre I No. 95009. Structural failure in flight, 9-5-40, flying with Sabre No. 95007; Sabre No. 95013, 8-40; Sabre No. 95018, 9-40; Sabre No. 95015, 2-41; Sabre No. 95022, 2-41; Sabre No. 95026, 8-41; production Sabre II No. S. 322, 5-42. Provision for twelve Browning machine guns.
P5216 ff. 3-5-41, P.G. Lucas. First flown with extended wing tips, 9-11-41. Sabre No. 95018, 15-6-41; production Sabre II No. S.322, 27-4-42. Four 20-mm. Hispano cannon.

The Hawker F.18/37. One additional prototype, *LA594*, ordered under Contract No. 21392/41 and commenced manufacture under Works Order No. 3862 powered by Bristol Centaurus IV. Provisionally designated Centaurus Typhoon II, this aircraft was not completed, but components were employed in the Tempest II prototype *LA602* (see below).

[Note: All Typhoon production was centred on Gloster Aircraft Co. Ltd., Brockworth, Glos.

However a small pilot production batch of 15 aircraft (employing components common to the Typhoon and the Avro-built Tornado) was produced at Langley, being intended as development and trials aircraft; most were, however, delivered to the R.A.F. Although these Typhoons were not completed until the Gloster deliveries were well under way, they are shown first for convenient reference.]

The Hawker Typhoon IA and IB. Pilot production batch of 15 aircraft, *R8198-R8200, R8220-R8231*, built by Hawker Aircraft Ltd., Langley. First flight by *R8198*, 26-11-41. (Mk. IA, *R8198-R8200, R8220, R8221*; remainder Mk. IBs.)

No. 56 (F) Sqn.: *R8199; R8200* (shot down by Spitfires of No. 401 Sqn., 1-6-42); *R8220; R8223; R8224; R8227.*

No. 181 (F) Sqn.: *R8229.*

No. 182 (F) Sqn.: *R8221* (struck balloon cable and force landed near Salisbury, 13-2-43).

No. 197 (F) Sqn.: *R8227.*

No. 245 (F) Sqn.: *R8230* (hit by flak and crashed near Loningen, 11-4-45)

No. 486 (NZ) Sqn.: *R8227* (Struck by another Typhoon while on the ground at Tangmere, 23-5-43).

No. 609 Sqn.: *R8220; R8221; R8222; R8224* (overstressed in aerobatics, 13-9-43).

Ground Instruction Machine: *R8222* (became *4400M*, 12-43).

The Hawker Typhoon IA and IB. First production batch of 250 Mark IAs and IBs built by Gloster Aircraft Co. Ltd., Brockworth. Napier Sabre II engines and three-blade propellers. *R7576-R7599, R7613-R7655; R7672-R7721; R7738-R7775; R7792-R7829; R7845-R7890; R7913-R7923.* Deliveries commenced, September 1941; completed June 1942. Rate of production, approx. one air per day. First flight by R7576, 27-5-41, at Brockworth by Michael Daunt.

No. 1 (F) Sqn.: *R7851; R7856* (crashed 3 miles NW of Tangmere, 23-8-43); *R7861* (Missing off Amble, Northumberland, 21-10-42; assumed to have collided with *R7867*); *R7862* (crashed near Charterhall, 21-11-42); *R7863* (Missing, 19-5-43); *R7864* (crashed at Danehills, Sussex, 13-2-43); *R7865; R7867* (Missing off Amble, Northumberland, 21-10-43; assumed to have collided with *R7861*); *R7868; R7876* (Missing over Channel, 29-3-43); *R7877; R7919; R7921-R7923.*

No. 3 (F) Sqn.: R7649; R7869.

No. 56 (F) Sqn.: *R7576; R7580; R7582-R7584; R7585* (collided with tractor at Matlaske, 24-8-42); *R7586-R7589; R7591; R7592* (crashed near East Harling, 1-11-41); *R7593-R7599; R7613; R7615; R7616; R7620; R7621; R7629; R7633* (crashed at Oulton, 27-8-42); *R7641; R7643; R7644* (lost tail in dive near Spalding, Lincs, 18-8-42); *R7646; R7648; R7652* (crashed on landing at Matlaske, 20-9-42); *R7653; R7675; R7678* (shot down by Spitfires off Dover, 1-6-42); *R7679; R7680; R7682-R7684; R7694; R7702* (crashed while landing at Matlaske, 4-11-42); *R7711* (crashed on landing at Coltishall, 1-10-42); *R7714; R7739* (crashed 3 miles east of Oulton, 12-4-43); *R7752; R7823* (crashed at Matlaske, 24-4-43); *R7824-R7826; R7846* (abandoned in spin near Fordham, Suffolk, 8-12-42); *R7849; R7853* (shot down by Spitfire off Dungeness, 30-7-42); *R7854* (lost tail during aerobatics near Brinton, Norfolk, 17-1-43); *R7869.*

No. 181 (F) Sqn.: *R7589; R7627; R7631; R7649; R7676* (spun into the ground near Duxford, 27-9-42); *R7696; R7825; R7889.*

No. 182 (F) Sqn.: *R7621; R7624; R7629* (crashed on landing at Martlesham Heath, 30-9-42); *R7653; R7677; R7681; R7683; R7688; R7691* (crashed on take-off at Martlesham Heath, 13-11-42); *R7706; R7771* (shot down by flak near Osnabrück, 28-2-45); *R7914.*

No. 183 (F) Sqn.: *R7631; R7649; R7869.*

No. 184 (F) Sqn.: *R7825.*

No. 193 (F) Sqn.: *R7627; R7684.*

No. 195 (F) Sqn.: *R7688; R7914.*

No. 197 (F) Sqn.: *R7651; R7681; R7706.*

No. 198 (F) Sqn.: *R7653* (crashed at Acklington, 26-2-43); *R7690*; *R7696*; *R7698*.

No. 245 (F) Sqn.: *R7880* (crashed on take-off at Lydd, 24-9-43).

No. 247 (F) Sqn.: *R7820* (shot down by flak near Vimoutiers, 18-8-44);

No. 257 (F) Sqn.: *R7879*.

No. 266 (F) Sqn.: *R7589*; *R7590*; *R7618* (crashed in poor visibility near Welney, Cambs, 13-6-42); *R7619*; *R7622-R7624*; *R7626*; *R7627*; *R7630*; *R7631*; *R7634-R7636*; *R7637* (crashed near Duxford, 8-3-42); *R7639*; *R7641*; *R7642*; *R7645* (abandoned over Channel after engine failure, 15-9-42); *R7649*; *R7654* (crashed at Great Casterton, Rutland, 24-4-42); *R7655* (crashed near Duxford, 4-6-42); *R7672* (crashed while landing at Duxford, 29-6-42); *R7674*; *R7676*; *R7686* (ditched 15 miles east of Torquay, 3-2-43); *R7687* (crashed in Hampshire, 28-11-42); *R7689*; *R7695* (crashed with structural failure at Wooton Glanville, Dorset, 24-10-42); *R7696*; *R7704*; *R7707*; *R7715* (crashed on landing at Exeter, 13-2-43); *R7800*; *R7913* (Missing from Dieppe, 19-8-42); *R7814* (collided with Spitfire, 16-9-42); *R7815* (shot down by Spitfires south of Dungeness during Dieppe operation, 19-8-42); *R7819* (crashed at Warmwell, 8-11-42); *R7820*; *R7821* (crashed at Morebath, Devon, 2-2-43); *R7822*; *R7829*; *R7847* (crashed while landing at Ibsley, 15-9-42); *R7882*; *R7915* (ditched 25 miles south-east of Start Point, Devon, 17-6-43).

No. 486 (NZ) Sqn.: *R7631*; *R7766*; *R7866* (crashed at Durrington, Sussex, 24-11-42).

No. 609 Sqn., A.A.F.: *R7581*; *R7595*; *R7624*; *R7628* (wheels-up landing at Duxford, 10-6-42); *R7630*; *R7640*; *R7647* (abandoned near Ely, Cambs, 29-5-42); *R7651*; *R7677*; *R7680*; *R7681*; *R7688*; *R7689* (shot down over the Channel, 15-12-42); *R7690*; *R7691*; *R7698*; *R7703*; *R7706*; *R7708* (shot down by British AA fire at Pegwell Bay, Kent, 31-10-42); *R7710* (collided with *R7817* on take-off at Duxford, 26-6-42); *R7713*; *R7752*; *R7816* (crashed at Catwater Farm, Cambridge, 30-7-42); *R7817* (collided with *R7710* on take-off at Duxford, 26-6-42); *R7818* (flew into Dover balloon barrage and crashed, 5-11-42); *R7845*; *R7849*; *R7855* (crashed on landing at Manston, 16-4-43); *R7872* (shot down by Fw 190s off Cap Gris Nez, 14-2-43); *R7880*; *R7883* (landed wheels-up at Duxford, 1-8-42).

No. 55 Operational Training Unit: *R7651*; *R7681*; *R7789*.

No. 56 Operational Training Unit: *R7615*.

No. 59 Operational Training Unit: *R7580* (crashed from spin near Milfield, 13-6-43); *R7591*; *R7621*; *R7630* (crashed while landing at Milfield, 26-6-43); *R7649*; *R7683*; *R7696*; *R7706*.

Other Units and duties: *R7576*, *R7589*, *R7595*, *R7617*, *R7881* (R.A.E.); *R7577*, *R7614*, *R7617*, *R7646*, *R7673*, *R7700* (A. & A.E.E.); *R7579* (C.F.S.); *R7580*, *R7581*, *R7595* (Air Fighting Development Unit); *R7590* (crashed while landing with No. 8 M.U., Little Rissington, 22-6-42); *R7591* (Fighter Leaders' School); *R7595*, *R7822*, *R7881* (No. 3 Tactical Exercise Unit); *R7630*, *R7651*, *R7881* (Fighter Interception Unit); *R7578*, *R7638*, *R7643*, *R7694*, *R7697*, *R7712*, *R7771*, *R7850* (D. Napier & Sons, Ltd.); *R7684*, *R7698* (Duxford Stn. Flt.); *R7881* (experimentally equipped with AI Mark IV radar as **Typhoon N.F. Mark IB**; SOC, 16-9-45). Note: 67 aircraft of this batch were relegated as Ground Instruction Machines, the majority between 6-43 and 11-43, and many as the result of minor accidents.

The Hawker Typhoon IA and IB. Second production batch of 250 aircraft built by Gloster Aircraft Co. Ltd., Brockworth, Glos., during 1942. *R8630-R8663; R8680-R8722; R8737-R8781; R8799-R8845; R8861-R8900; R8923-R8947; R8966-R8981.* Napier Sabre IIA and IIB engines. Deliveries commenced April 1942; completed November 1942; average rate of production, slightly more than one aircraft per day. Total of nineteen Mark IAs distributed throughout batch; remainder Mark IBs.

No. 1 (F) Sqn.: *R8630*; *R8631*; *R8634* (crashed at Pevensey, Sussex, 28-4-43); *R8690* (crashed north of Longtown, 5-9-42); *R8708*; *R8752*; *R8942* (collided with Typhoon *DN615* in cloud and crashed at Benenden, Kent, 6-3-43).

No. 3 (F) Sqn.: *R8835* (shot down by Fw 190s near Poix, 18-5-43); *R8836*; *R8879* (shot down by Fw 190s near Poix, 18-5-43); *R8895* (ditched after take-off at Bradwell Bay, 22-3-44); *R8926*; *R8946* (Missing after convoy attack off Holland, 1-7-43); *R8977*; *R8979* (shot down by Fw 190s near Poix, 18-5-43).

No. 56 (F) Sqn.: *R8715*; *R8721*; *R8745*; *R8822* (collided with *DN433* and crashed near Blickling, Norfolk, 20-1-43); *R8824*; *R8825* (crashed at Barton Lamas, Norfolk, 28-4-43); *R8827*; *R8865* (crashed with battle damage near The Hague, Holland, 13-1-43); *R8873*; *R8876* (shot down by flak over The Hague, 13-1-43); *R8899*; *R8940*.

No. 164 (F) Sqn.: *R8781*; *R8840*; *R8926*; *R8969*.

No. 168 (FR) Sqn.: *R8696* (9-44).

No. 175 (F) Sqn.: *R8687*; *R8843*; *R8884*; *R8933*; *R8943*; *R8976*; *R8978*.

No. 181 (F) Sqn.: *R8742*; *R8746*; *R8772*; *R8802*; *R8828-R8830*; *R8833* (shot down by Bf 109 off the Pas de Calais, 30-7-43); *R8835*; *R8836*; *R8840*; *R8843* (shot down by flak near Goch, 29-9-44); *R8862*; *R8863*; *R8866* (missing, 15-7-43); *R8867*; *R8868*; *R8871*; *R8875* (wheels-up landing at Detling, 25-9-43); *R8877*; *R8879*; *R8880* (missing off Dutch coast, 19-2-43); *R8896*; *R8900*; *R8927*; *R8929*; *R8932*; *R8947*; *R8976*; *R8977*.

No. 182 (F) Sqn.: *R8799*; *R8826*; *R8834* (shot down by flak, Tricqueville, 16-4-43); *R8839* (crashed on take-off at Ridgewell, 22-1-43); *R8842*; *R8862*; *R8863*; *R8892*; *R8893* (crashed in Forêt d'Hardelot, 28-4-43); *R8924* (shot down by flak near Hesdin, 25-4-43); *R8927*; *R8928*; *R8930*; *R8945*; *R8947*; *R8966*; *R8974*; *R8975*; *R8981* (damaged by flak and crashed near Ford, 13-5-43).

No. 183 (F) Sqn.: *R8884-R8886*; *R8926*; *R8933*; *R8944* (ran out of fuel and ditched in Channel, 14-5-43); *R8970* (shot down near Evreux, 17-8-44); *R8973*; *R8976*; *R8978*; *R8979*.

No. 184 (F) Sqn.: *R8687*; *R8843*.

No. 193 (F) Sqn.: *R8651*; *R8702*; *R8890*.

No. 195 (F) Sqn.: *R8660*; *R8760* (air bottle exploded in flight and aircraft S.O.C., 25-2-43); *R8781*; *R8819*; *R8938*.

No. 197 (F) Sqn.: *R8885*; *R8886*.

No. 198 (F) Sqn.: *R8707*; *R8709*; *R8840*; *R8894* (hit by flak off Boulogne, and assumed ditched, 10-2-44); *R8935* (crashed near Radcliffe, Northumberland, 11-3-43); *R8939*; *R8966*.

No. 245 (F) Sqn.: *R8636*; *R8687*.

No. 247 (F) Sqn.: *R8687*; *R8688* (shot down by P-47 north-east of Arnhem, 14-1-45); *R8693*; *R8841*; *R8844*; *R8867*; *R8932* (crashed after engine failure at Achmer, 17-4-45); *R8943*.

No. 257 (F) Sqn.: *R8632*; *R8633* (lost tail and crashed at High Ercall, 29-7-42); *R8636*; *R8637* (crashed on landing at Zeals, 24-1-43); *R8638*; *R8639*; *R8642*; *R8650* (crashed near Linstead, Hants, 29-11-42); *R8652-R8656*; *R8658*; *R8659*; *R8661* (Mark IA); *R8663* (crashed at Chilframe, Dorset, 15-12-42); *R8680*; *R8685*; *R8691*; *R8703*; *R8710*; *R8711* (hit radar mast while landing at Bolt Head, 29-9-42); *R8768*; *R8832*; *R8872* (crashed while landing at Exeter, 22-12-42); *R8923*; *R8980*.

No. 263 (F) Sqn.: *R8923*.

No. 266 (F) Sqn.: *R8638* (crashed at Portreath, 30-7-43); *R8693*; *R8694*; *R8743* (ditched south-east of Torquay, 20-2-43); *R8767* (spun into sea during fight with Fw 190s, Guipavas, 15-8-43); *R8772* (crashed at Whimple, Devon, 28-2-43); *R8781*; *R8802* (crashed near Etaples, France, 11-1-43); *R8803*; *R8804* (hit by flak and ditched off French coast, 9-7-43); *R8811* (abandoned after being damaged by Spitfires near Exeter, 17-4-43); *R8813*; *R8823* (crashed on landing at Warmwell, 27-10-42); *R8861* (crashed into sea 3 miles south of Bolt Head, Devon, 15-4-43); *R8864* (crashed in night landing at Warmwell, 12-10-42); *R8878*; *R8934*; *R8936*; *R8937* (crashed near Topsham, Devon, 30-4-43); *R8939*.

No. 438 (Canadian) Sqn.: *R8971*.

No. 439 (Canadian) Sqn.: *R8897*; *R8971* (crashed near New Cumnock, Ayrshire, 20-2-44);

No. 486 (NZ) Sqn.: *R8660*; *R8681*; *R8682* (collided with Lancaster while taking off at Tangmere, 24-2-43); *R8683* (missing, 2-10-42); *R8684*; *R8692*; *R8696*; *R8697* (collided with Typhoon *DN611* on ground at Tangmere, 3-8-43); *R8698* (crashed at Battle, Sussex, following fire in the air, 16-10-42); *R8699*; *R8700*; *R8701* (crashed into sea 6 miles south-east of Selsey Bill, 31-10-42); *R8704*; *R8706*; *R8712*; *R8744* (crashed at Tangmere, 14-3-43); *R8768*; *R8781*; *R8800* (Missing, 18-12-42); *R8801* (damaged in action and S.O.C., 31-10-42); *R8814* (crashed from spin at Willesborough, Kent, 25-10-42); *R8816* (crashed on take-off at Tangmere, 24-2-43); *R8843*; *R8881*; *R8885*; *R8886*; *R8936*; *R8941* (crashed while landing at Tangmere, 8-1-43);

No. 609 Sqn., A.A.F.: *R8715*; *R8781*; *R8810*; *R8812* (crashed near Battle, Sussex, 23-10-42); *R8815*; *R8826*; *R8837* (crashed into sea 15 miles south of South Foreland, Kent, 23-12-42); *R8841*; *R8845* (shot down by P-47s near Doullens, 21-12-43); *R8874*; *R8883* (crashed into sea off Dover, 30-4-43); *R8888* (crashed at Marston, Kent, 29-3-43); *R8898*; *R8899*; *R8940*; *R8972* (shot down by flak near Hottot, 11-7-44); *R8977*.

No. 54 Operational Training Unit: *R8882*.

No. 55 Operational Training Unit: *R8968*.

No. 59 Operational Training Unit: *R8652* (crashed while landing at Rearsby, 15-8-43); *R8661*; *R8705*; *R8709* (crashed while taking off at Milfield, 20-5-43); *R8867* (crashed while taking off at Milfield, 18-4-43); *R8878*.

Other Units and duties, etc.: *R8635* (R.A.E.; crashed on Meadfoot Beach, Torquay, 21-5-43); *R8687*, *R8707*, *R8715* (Duxford Stn. Flt.); *R8688*, *R8693* (R.A.E.); *R8720* (No. 9 Ferry Pilots' Pool; crashed, Brockworth, 30-8-42); *R8762* (Glosters; Napiers; A. & A.E.E.); *R8809* (hood development; HAL; A. & A.E.E.); *R8828* (Snailwell Stn. Flt.); *R8878* (Fighter Leaders' School); *R8882*, *R8926*, *R8968* (No. 3 Tactical Exercise Unit); *R8889* (HAL; A. & A.E.E.; tropical trials aircraft; to North Africa and Western Desert; Service trials with No. 451 (Australian) Sqn., 6-43); *R8897* (No. 83 Ground Support Unit); *R8943* (R.A.E.; de Havillands); *R8967* (Fighter Leaders' School; crashed near Lowick, Northumberland, 30-9-44).

The Hawker Typhoon IB. Third production batch of 700 aircraft built by Gloster Aircraft Co. Ltd., Brockworth, Glos. Napier Sabre IIA and IIB engines. Part 1 (300 aircraft): *DN241-DN278*; *DN293-DN341*; *DN356-DN389*; *DN404-DN453*; *DN467-DN513*; *DN529-DN562*; *DN576-DN623*. Part 2 (400 aircraft): *EJ900-EJ934*; *EJ946-EJ995*; *EK112-EK152*; *EK167-EK197*; *EK208-EK252*; *EK266-EK301*; *EK321-EK348*; *EK364-EK413*; *EK425-EK456*; *EK472-EK512*; *EK535-EK543*. Deliveries commenced, 20-9-42; completed 5-4-43; average rate of production, approximately 24 aircraft per week.

No. 1 (F) Sqn.: *DN241* (crashed at Southend, 9-2-43); *DN335*; *DN385*; *DN432*; *DN451*; *DN490*; *DN502*; *DN585* (shot down by a Fw 190A off Brighton, 13-3-43); *DN615* (collided with Typhoon *R8942* and crashed near Tonbridge, 6-3-43); *EJ974*; *EJ982*; *EJ983*; *EJ992*; *EK113*; *EK176*; *EK210*; *EK228* (lost tail and crashed, 15-7-43).

No. 3 (F) Sqn.: *DN246* (shot down by Fw 190s over Poix, 16-5-43); *DN253*; *DN589* (shot down by Fw 190s off Holland, 7-43); *DN590*; *DN609* (crash landed near Billericay, 28-4-43, and S.O.C.); *EJ914* (shot down by Fw 190s over Eu, 18-5-43); *EJ930*; *EJ950*; *EJ958*; *EJ961* (shot down by flak off Dunkirk, 29-6-43); *EJ964*; *EJ968*; *EJ970* (shot down by Fw 190s off Holland, 7-43); *EJ987*; *EJ989*; *EK149*; *EK187*; *EK217* (shot down by Fw 190s over Eu, 18-5-43); *EK227* (shot down, 2-6-43); *EK371*; *EK495*.

No. 4 (FR) Sqn.: (FR Mark IB): *EJ929*; *EJ955*; *EK247*; *EK390*; *EK427*; *EK436*; *EK440* (shot down by flak near Bocholt, 18-11-44).   **(PR Mark IB):** *EK180*; *EK380*; *EK429*.

No. 56 (F) Sqn.: *DN265*; *DN270*; *DN277*; *DN307*; *DN317*; *DN330*; *DN374* (hit by flak off Dutch coast and abandoned, 15-3-43); *DN380*; *DN406*; *DN411* (crashed into sea from spin, 24-2-43); *DN447*; *DN478*; *DN488*; *DN491*; *DN535*; *DN583*; *EJ962*; *EJ978*; *EK144*; *EK179*; *EK181*; *EK183*; *EK189*; *EK209*; *EK268*; *EK269*; *EK285*; *EK321*; *EK326*.

No. 137 (F) Sqn.: *DN429*; *DN492*; *EJ972*; *EK128*; *EK270*.

No. 164 (F) Sqn.: *DN432*; *EJ987*; *EK115*.

No. 168 (F) Sqn.: *EK219*; *EK233*; *EK382*; *EK384*; *EK432*.

No. 174 (F) Sqn.: *DN537; DN538; DN553; DN580; EJ993; EK128; EK134; EK369; EK379.*

No. 175 (F) Sqn.: *DN263; DN267; DN408* (crashed at Lydd after engine failure on take-off, 1-7-43); *DN548; DN578; DN606; DN610; EJ901; EJ902; EJ910; EJ934; EJ946; EJ947; EJ979; EJ980; EJ984* (shot down over Dieppe, 19-6-43); *EJ995; EK133; EK138; EK139; EK153; EK171; EK382* (aircraft crashed during attack on train near Münster, 30-3-45); *EK447; EK455.*

No. 181 (F) Sqn.: *DN259; DN337; DN358; DN421; EK184; EK221; EK280.*

No. 182 (F) Sqn.: *DN246; DN261; DN319; DN484; DN597; EJ952; EK226; EK388; EK395* (shot down by flak over Dunkirk harbour, 2-8-43).

No. 183 (F) Sqn.: *DN248; DN249; DN268; DN271; DN273; DN275; DN278* (crashed, 21-2-43); *DN297; DN334; DN377; DN405; EK497* (shot down at Chievres by U.S. P-51 during Operation Bodenplatte, 1-1-45); *EK498.*

No. 184 (F) Sqn.: *DN471; EJ926; EK220; EK497.*

No. 193 (F) Sqn.: *DN256; EJ967.*

No. 195 (F) Sqn.: *DN266; DN306; DN314; DN315; DN316; DN328; DN331; DN358; DN361; DN370; DN373; DN375; DN389; DN412; DN434* (aircraft crashed during low-flying exercise, 9-4-43); *DN441; DN474* (crashed, 9-3-43); *EJ910; EJ921; EK273.*

No. 197 (F) Sqn.: *DN264; DN301; DN309; DN320; DN321; DN362; DN363; DN371; DN376; DN407; DN410; DN443; DN473; DN494; DN497; DN536; DN545; DN548; DN558; DN559; DN576; EJ928; EK505.*

No. 198 (F) Sqn.: *DN341; DN438* (crashed into sea off St. Annes, 1943); *EK187.*

No. 245 (F) Sqn.: *DN293; DN435; DN591; DN599; EJ971.*

No. 247 (F) Sqn.: *DN252; DN278; DN338; DN381; DN382; DN404; DN420; DN429-DN431; DN444* (crashed at Madeley, Shropshire, 19-3-43); *DN453; DN487; DN493; DN531; DN534; DN539; DN540; DN543; EJ911; EJ991; EK190; EK270; EK371.*

No. 257 (F) Sqn.: *DN245; DN295* (crashed at Beddington, 28-2-43); *DN318; DN333; DN442; EJ919; EJ926; EJ927; EK172; EK322.*

No. 266 (F) Sqn.: *DN262; DN296; DN359; DN562; EJ917; EJ924; EJ925; EJ931* (crashed into sea 12 miles east of Berry Head, 21-6-43); *EJ932; EJ955; EJ986; EK245.*

No. 268 (FR) Sqn. (FR Mark IB): *EK180; EK191; EK196; EK212; EK240; EK247; EK267; EK272; EK372; EK428; EK436;* **(PR Mark IB):** *EJ905; EK272; EK380.*

No. 438 (Canadian) Sqn.: *DN619.*

No. 439 (Canadian) Sqn.: *EK219; EK383; EK481.*

No. 486 (NZ) Sqn.: *EJ948; EJ973; EK511.*

No. 609 Sqn., A.A.F.: *DN406; DN582; DN601; EK121; EK187.*

Other Units and duties, etc.: *DN323, EJ906* (tropical trials in the Middle East with No. 451 (Australian) Sqn.; 6-43—with *R8889*); *EK122* (H.A.L.; trials with pressure plotting wing, 2-43); *EK229, EK497* (H.A.L., A. & A.E.E.; extended trials with external stores; drop tanks, rockets, bombs and smoke generators, supply containers, etc.).

The Hawker Typhoon IB. Fourth production batch of 600 aircraft built by Gloster Aircraft Co. Ltd., Brockworth, during 1943. Napier Sabre IIA engines fitted from new, but many aircraft modified with Sabre IIB engine in 1944. *JP361-JP408; JP425-JP447; JP480-JP516; JP532-JP552; JP576-JP614; JP648-JP689; JP723-JP756; JP784-JP802; JP836-JP861; JP897-JP941; JP961-JP976; JP125-JR152; JP183-JR223; JR237-JR266; JR289-JR338; JR360-JR392; JR426-JR449; JR492-JR535.* Later aircraft in this batch were fitted with sliding hoods from new; some early aircraft were retrospectively modified. Deliveries commenced, 5-4-43; completed, 12-43. Average rate of production, about 18 aircraft per week.

No. 1 (F) Sqn.: *JP483; JP498; JP592; JP679; JP680; JP685; JP738; JP795; JP847; JP961; JR126; JR144* (Missing, 21-12-43); *JR237* (Missing, 22-12-43).

No. 3 (F) Sqn.: *JP408; JP426* (shot down over Cap Gris Nez, 10-11-43); *JP585* (shot down over Holland, 5-9-43); *JP684* (Missing over Holland, 8-2-44); *JP733* (Missing, 5-10-43);

JP741; *JP744* (shot down over Cap Gris Nez, 10-11-43); *JP756* (shot down over Cap Gris Nez, 10-11-43); *JP842* (shot down over Cap Gris Nez, 10-11-43); *JP847*; *JP857* (Missing, 5-10-43); *JP921* (Missing, 4-10-43); *JP926* (Missing, 5-10-43); *JR188* (ditched during operations following engine failure, 3-2-44); *JR314*; *JR446*; *JR448*; *JR497*.

No. 4 (FR) Sqn.: (FR Mark IB): *JP373*; *JP389*; (PR Mark IB): *JP372*.

No. 56 (F) Sqn.: *JP446*; *JP606*; *JP651*; *JP681*; *JP682*; *JP728*; *JP749*; *JP754*; *JP915*; *JR197*; *JR262*; *JR263*; *JR360*; *JR442*; *JR503*; *JR504*; *JR532*; *JR535*.

No. 137 (F) Sqn.: *JP583*; *JP663*; *JR247*; *JR261*; *JR305*; *JR327*; *JR437*; *JR497*; *JR500*; *JR504*; *JR505*; *JR516*; *JR530*; *JR533*; *JR535*.

No. 164 (F) Sqn.: *JP367*; *JP407*; *JP443*; *JP446*; *JP489*; *JP607*; *JP849*; *JR139*; *JR222*; *JR243*; *JR363*; *JR377*; *JR428*; *JR514*; *JR515* (shot down by flak near Fruges, 28-5-44).

No. 168 (F) Sqn.: *JP919*; *JP920*; *JR244*; *JR308*; *JR332*; *JR508*;

No. 174 (F) Sqn.: *JP443*; *JP444* (shot down by flak at Amiens/Glissy, 16-8-43); *JP445*; *JP480*; *JP484*; *JP535*; *JP541*; *JP549*; *JP550*; *JP602*; *JP671*; *JP918*; *JR195*; *JR495*; *JR526*.

No. 175 (F) Sqn.: *JP369* (shot down by flak near Evreux, 5-2-44); *JP376*; *JP378*; *JP379*; *JP382*; *JP385* (shot down by flak near Evreux, 5-2-44); *JP387*; *JP394*; *JP396*; *JP429*; *JP441*; *JP496*; *JP512*; *JP577* (shot down over France while escorting bombing raid, 16-8-43); *JP584* (crashed into sea during offensive operations, 26-10-43); *JP614*; *JP736*; *JP753*; *JR194*; *JR308*; *JR327*; *JR360*; *JR376* (Missing, 27-2-45); *JR501*; *JR502* (shot down by flak south of St. Lô, 9-7-44); *JR517* (Missing in action, 2-2-45).

No. 181 (F) Sqn.: *JP515*; *JP551*; *JP579*; *JP604* (shot down by flak near Caen on D-day, 6-6-44); *JP739*; *JP917*; *JP920*; *JP923*; *JP968* (crashed from spin during attack in Pas de Calais, 25-1-44); *JR137*; *JR244*; *JR261*; *JR292*; *JR294*; *JR297*; *JR317*; *JR381*.

No. 182 (F) Sqn.: *JP370*; *JP380*; *JP381*; *JP389*; *JP391*; *JP395*; *JP397*; *JP400*; *JP401*; *JP403*; *JP480*; *JP540*; *JP552* (Missing from sweep over Amiens, 19-8-43); *JP612*; *JP654*; *JP688*; *JP913*; *JR127*; *JR193*; *JR220*; *JR255*; *JR293*; *JR427*; *JR517*; *JR524*; *JR528*.

No. 183 (F) Sqn.: *JP382*; *JP601*; *JP743*; *JP793*; *JP856* (shot down by Bf 109Gs in Evreux area, 17-8-44); *JP969*; *JP970*; *JR128*; *JR209*; *JR260*; *JR263*; *JR392*; *JR431*; *JR535*.

No. 184 (F) Sqn.: *JP367*; *JP440*; *JP511*; *JP656*; *JP659*; *JR189* (shot down near Trun, France, 18-8-44); *JR194*; *JR310*; *JR337*; *JR449*; *JR493*; *JR510*; *JR525*.

No. 186 (F) Sqn.: *JR131*; *JR132*; *JR148*; *JR199*; *JR200* (collided with Spitfire while landing, 11-43); *JR218*; *JR240*; *JR249*; *JR250*; *JR264*; *JR298*; *JR313*; *JR318*; *JR324*; *JR335*.

No. 193 (F) Sqn.: *JP802*; *JP919*.

No. 195 (F) Sqn.: *JP407*; *JP437*; *JP503*; *JP607*; *JP648*; *JP849*; *JP855*; *JP908*; *JR149*; *JR223*.

No. 197 (F) Sqn.: *JP504*; *JP743*; *JP843*; *JP900*; *JP967*; *JR138*; *JR214*; *JR248*; *JR318*; *JR336*; *JR338*; *JR376*.

No. 198 (F) Sqn.: *JP503* (aircraft shot down during attack on Jobourg radar station, 24-5-44); *JP579*; *JP655*; *JP667*; *JP844*; *JP963* (crashed on take-off at Martragny, 31-7-44); *JR141* (shot down by Bf 109Gs, 17-8-44); *JR150* (shot down by flak over Ligecourt, 3-1-44); *JR197*; *JR241*; *JR298*; *JR366*; *JR512*; *JR517*; *JR527*.

No. 245 (F) Sqn.: *JP432*; *JP660*; *JP802*; *JR214*; *JR311*; *JR501*.

No. 247 (F) Sqn.: *JP482*; *JP487*; *JP488* (collided with *JP661* while landing at Hurn, 8-5-44); *JP505*; *JP538*; *JP544*; *JP578*; *JP581*; *JP588*; *JP649*; *JP653* (crashed off Hythe following attack on St. Omer, 29-3-43); *JP661*; *JP672*; *JP675*; *JP688*; *JP730* (crashed in Channel, 28-2-44); *JP785*; *JP786*; *JR205*; *JR207*; *JR208*; *JR326*; *JR372*; *JR384*; *JR513*; *JR524*.

No. 257 (F) Sqn.: *JP447* (crashed into sea following engine failure, 7-11-43); *JP490*; *JP491*; *JP494*; *JP510* (missing from operation near Fécamp, 16-3-44); *JP742*; *JP919*; *JR320*.

No. 263 (F) Sqn.: *JR196*; *JR251*; *JR253*; *JR304*; *JR330*; *JR382*; *JR434*; *JR440*; *JR531*; *JR552*.

No. 266 (F) Sqn.: *JP441*; *JP512*; *JP752*; *JP853*; *JP934*; *JP974*; *JR135*; *JR288*; *JR303*; *JR368*.

No. 268 (FR) Sqn. (FR Mark IB): *JP371*; *JP373*; *JP389*.

No. 439 (Canadian) Sqn.: *JP401*; *JP931*; *JP299*; *JR362*; *JR444*; *JR506*; *JR521*.

No. 486 (NZ) Sqn.: *JP532*; *JP689*; *JP853*; *JP901*; *JR152*; *JR217*; *JR329*; *JR334*.

No. 609 Sqn., A.A.F.: *JP425*; *JP851*; *JP974*; *JR294*; *JR312*; *JR379*; *JR534*.

Other Units and duties: *JP689* (Fighter Leaders' School); *JP859, JR185; JR443* (No. 55 O.T.U.); *JR149* (No. 56 O.T.U.); *JR265* (No. 1 A.P.S.); *JR371* (No. 59 O.T.U.).

The Hawker Typhoon IB. Fifth production batch of 800 aircraft, built by Gloster Aircraft Co. Ltd., Brockworth. Most aircraft with Napier Sabre IIB engines, sliding hoods, faired cannon and four-blade propellers: *MM951-MM995; MN113-MN156; MN169-MN213; MN229-MN269; MN282-MN325; MN339-MN381; MN396-MN436; MN449-MN496; MN513-MN556; MN569-MN608; MN623-MN667; MN680-MN720; MN735-MN779; MN791-MN823; MN851-MN896; MN920-MN956; MN968-MN999; MP113-MP158; MP172-MP203.* Deliveries commenced 8-12-43; completed 15-6-44; average rate of production, slightly more than four aircraft per day.

No. 1 (F) Sqn.: *MN115; MN124; MN242; MN252; MN513.*

No. 3 (F) Sqn.: *MN188; MN209; MN515; MN779.*

No. 56 (F) Sqn.: *MM992; MN182; MN198; MN206; MN304.*

No. 137 (F) Sqn.: *MM966; MM969; MM972; MN117* (crashed on take-off at Manston, 24-4-44); *MN191; MN198; MN306; MN374; MN421; MN429* (Missing from anti-shipping patrol off Danish coast, 1-4-44); *MN455; MN533; MN575; MN584; MN627; MN822; MN863; MN922; MN955* (shot down by Fw 190s near Goch, 24-9-44); *MN990; MP195.*

No. 164 (F) Sqn.: *MN113; MN172; MN177; MN523; MN535; MN550; MN572; MN604; MN631; MN794; MN885.*

No. 168 (F) Sqn.: *MM993; MN122; MN366; MN639; MN993; MN999.*

No. 174 (F) Sqn.: *MM952; MM954; MN141; MN194; MN253; MN371; MN496; MN577; MN683.*

No. 175 (F) Sqn.: *MM966; MN138; MN202-MN204; MN353; MN362; MN470; MN471; MN481; MN582; MN594; MN606; MN717; MN874; MN972; MN983* (Missing after rocket attack, 11-9-44); *MP176; MP184.*

No. 181 (F) Sqn.: *MN199; MN205; MN208; MN304; MN681; MN775; MN992.*

No. 182 (F) Sqn.: *MM995; MN303; MN340; MN472; MN531; MN575; MN681; MN891* (shot down by flak oner Normandy, 25-7-44); *MN995.*

No. 183 (F) Sqn.: *MN130* (shot down by Bf 109Gs near Evreux, 17-8-44); *MN260; MN265* (shot down by Bf 109Gs over Allied landing beaches, D-day, 6-6-44); *MN413; MN419; MN454* (shot down by Fw 190s over Normandy, D-day, 6-6-44); *MN478* (shot down by Bf 109Gs over Normandy, D-day, 6-6-44); *MN549; MN642* (shot down by flak south of Caen, 7-6-44); *MN681; MN802; MN862; MN868; MN923.*

No. 184 (F) Sqn.: *MN131* (shot down by flak south of Aunay, 30-7-44); *MN141; MN174; MN194; MN255; MN288; MN299; MN301; MN323; MN360; MN425; MN485; MN529; MN590; MN667; MN692; MN873; MN924; MN956; MN985; MN997; MP133; MP146* (shot down by flak near Trun, 18-8-44).

No. 186 (F) Sqn.: *MN486.*

No. 193 (F) Sqn.: *MN252; MN712; MN716; MN886; MN926; MN970; MP151.*

No. 197 (F) Sqn.: *MN324; MN423; MN491; MN689; MN752; MN881; MN893; MN921; MN925; MN996; MP113; MP119; MP123; MP143; MP157; MP188; MP190; MP194; MP199.*

No. 198 (F) Sqn.: *MN132; MN143* (Missing in action, 23-5-44); *MN192* (shot down by flak near Dieppe, 2-6-44); *MN195; MN234; MN293; MN410* (shot down in attack on Jobourg radar station, 24-5-44); *MN526; MN537; MN546; MN570; MN735; MN884; MN985; MP115; MP132.*

No. 245 (F) Sqn.: *MN121; MN267; MN371; MN812; MN813; MN993.*

No. 247 (F) Sqn.: *MM961; MM963; MM975; MM979; MN299; MN317; MN363; MN371; MN373; MN421; MN430; MN451; MN542* (abandoned off Dieppe, 22-5-44); *MN585; MN647; MN710; MN823; MN949; MN951; MN979; MP126.*

No. 257 (F) Sqn.: *MN118; MN291; MN354; MN367; MN376; MN381; MN396; MN405; MN408; MN416; MN452; MN492; MN541; MN598* (lost in accident, 13-1-45); *MN645;*

MN991; MP115; MP116; MP124.

No. 263 (F) Sqn.: *MN139; MN187; MN295; MN407; MN477; MN769; MN823; MN883; MN989.*

No. 266 (F) Sqn.: *MN133; MN184* (shot down by flak in attack on tanks at Argentan, 15-8-44); *MN264; MN320; MN343; MN353; MN364* (destroyed on the ground at Deurne, 1-1-45); *MN400; MN493; MN518; MN587; MN600* (shot down by flak near Falaise, 9-8-44); *MN739* (damaged on ground at Deurne, 1-1-45, and S.O.C.); *MN889; MN932; MN989; MN993; MP174; MP180.*

No. 438 (Canadian) Sqn.: *MM957* (crash landed in France following engine failure, 8-5-44; pilot, Wg. Cdr. R.T.P. Davidson, evaded capture); *MM959; MN283; MN321; MN345; MN347; MN375; MN398; MN402; MN417; MN424* (damaged on ground at Eindhoven, 1-1-45); *MN426; MN482; MN547; MN626; MN758.*

No. 439 (Canadian) Sqn.: *MN210; MN308; MN310; MN316; MN352; MN356; MN370; MN379; MN401; MN417; MN427; MN435; MN464; MN516; MN529; MN553; MN574; MN581; MN589; MN626; MN663; MN665; MN691; MN765* (damaged on ground at Eindhoven, 1-1-45, and S.O.C.); *MN870* (damaged on ground at Eindhoven, 1-1-45, and believed written off); *MP134* (damaged on ground at Eindhoven, 1-1-45, and believed written off); *MP136.*

No. 440 (Canadian) Sqn.: *MN115; MN171; MN257; MN298; MN307; MN348; MN366; MN378; MN403; MN428* (shot down south of Caen, D-day, 6-6-44); *MN457; MN535; MN547; MN548; MN555; MN577; MN583; MN603; MN635; MN664; MN691; MN777; MP130.*

No. 486 (NZ) Sqn.: *MN282.*

No. 609 Sqn., A.A.F.: *MM986* (as *"DS-J"*, flown by Wg. Cdr. D.J. Scott, Wing Leader, No. 123 Wing); *MN131* (shot down by flak south of Aunay, 30-7-44); *MN178; MN305; MN306; MN521; MN701; MN868.*

Other Units and duties, etc.: *MN148* (A.F.D.U.); *MN229, MN418* (Fighter Leaders' School; later Ground Instruction Machine, *5553M*); *MN240, MN956* (No. 56 O.T.U.); *MN266, MN400, MP118* (No. 55 O.T.U.); *MN315* (modified as prototype **Typhoon P.R. Mark IB**); *MN466, MN661, MN861* (miscellaneous armament and stores trials, H.A.L.); *MN587* (flown by Gp. Capt. D.E. Gillam as *"ZZII"*, Wing Leader, No. 146 Wing); *MN753, MN804* (No. 54 O.T.U.); *MN941* (flown as *"DJ-S"* by Gp. Capt. D.J. Scott, Wing Leader, No. 123 Wing).

The Hawker Typhoon IB. Sixth production batch of 400 aircraft built by Gloster Aircraft Co. Ltd., Brockworth, Glos. Napier Sabre IIA and IIB engines. *PD446-PD480; PD492-PD536; PD548-PD577; PD589-PD623; RB192-RB235; RB248-RB289; RB303-RB347; RB361-RB408; RB423-RB459; RB474-RB512.* Deliveries commenced, 15-6-44; completed, 5-1-45; average rate of production, approx. two aircraft per day.

No. 137 (F) Sqn.: *PD551; PD611; RB193; RB252; RB254; RB318; RB504.*

No. 164 (F) Sqn.: *PD511; RB264; RB332; RB484.*

No. 168 (F) Sqn.: *PD613* (badly damaged on the ground at Eindhoven, 1-1-45, and S.O.C.); *RB209* (struck by another Typhoon on the ground at Eindhoven and S.O.C., 2-1-45); *RB427; RB499.*

No. 174 (F) Sqn.: *RB303; RB457.*

No. 175 (F) Sqn.: *PD494; PD559; PD560; RB214* (shot down by flak, 19-3-45); *RB215; RB216; RB304; RB347; RB492; RB511.*

No. 183 (F) Sqn.: *PD500; PD516* (Missing from rocket attack NE of Ede, 19-11-44); *PD606; RB222; RB258; RB448.*

No. 181 (F) Sqn.: *RB341.*

No. 183 (F) Sqn.: *RB453.*

No. 184 (F) Sqn.: *PD496; RB200; RB383; RB400; RB408.*

No. 193 (F) Sqn.: *PD500; RB227; RB254; RB259.*

No. 197 (F) Sqn.: *PD447; PD460; PD471; PD477; PD507; PD531; PD534; RB211, RB212; RB228; RB230; RB251; RB316; RB474.*

No. 198 (F) Sqn.: *PD456; PD466; PD497; PD499; PD508; PD605; PD618; RB223.*

No. 245 (F) Sqn.: *RB380.*

No. 247 (F) Sqn.: *PD495; RB225; RB344; RB378; RB459.*

No. 257 (F) Sqn.: *PD521.*

No. 266 (F) Sqn.: *PD473; PD501; PD504; PD514; PD521* (destroyed by V-2 rocket on Deurne, 25-10-44); *PD527; PD528; PD553; PD576; RB219* (damaged on the ground at Eindhoven, 1-1-45, and S.O.C.); *RB223; RB248; RB260; RB426; RB451; RB478.*

No. 438 (Canadian) Sqn.: *RB207; RB391.*

No. 439 (Canadian) Sqn.: *PD451; PD492; PD564; PD608; RB198* (badly damaged on the ground at Eindhoven, 1-1-45, and S.O.C.); *RB232* (badly damaged on the ground at Eindhoven, 1-1-45, and S.O.C.); *RB255* (badly damaged on the ground at Eindhoven, 1-1-45, and S.O.C.); *RB262; RB281; RB324; RB326; RB369; RB402; RB441; RB477.*

No. 440 (Canadian) Sqn.: *PD452; PD510; PD589; RB203; RB205* (flown as *"FGG"* by Wg. Cdr. F.G. Grant, Wing Leader, No. 143 (Canadian) Wing, until written off in German attack on Eindhoven, 1-1-45); *RB310; RB377; RB389; RB440; RB445; RB475; RB485; RB494; RB495; RB506.*

No. 609 Sqn., A.A.F.: *PD449; PD466; PD519; RB250; RB311; RB431.*

Other Units and duties, etc.: *PD521* (flown as *"JB-II"* by Wg. Cdr. J.R. Baldwin, Wing Leader, No. 146 Wing); *RB379* (was the only Typhoon shipped to Russia, c.12-44). *RB431* (flown as *"JCB"* by Wg. Cdr. J.C. Button, Wing Leader, No. 123 Wing).

The Hawker Typhoon IB. Seventh and final production batch of 300 aircraft built by Gloster Aircraft Co. Ltd., Brockworth (299 built). Napier Sabre IIB engines. *SW386-SW428; SW443-SW478; SW493-SW537; SW551-SW596; SW620-SW668; SW682I-SW716; SW728-SW772.* Deliveries commenced, 5-1-45; completed, 13-11-45; average rate of production, slightly under one aircraft per day.

No. 137 (F) Sqn.: *SW403; SW426; SW473; SW510; SW561.*

No. 164 (F) Sqn.: *SW410.*

No. 175 (F) Sqn.: *SW399; SW407; SW450; SW464; SW529; SW564.*

No. 183 (F) Sqn.: *SW414; SW454; SW455; SW459; SW463; SW466; SW503; SW509.*

No. 184 (F) Sqn.: *SW413; SW421; SW444; SW512; SW515; SW587.*

No. 198 (F) Sqn.: *SW472; SW478; SW520; SW556.*

No. 263 (F) Sqn.: *SW419; SW570; SW586; SW588.*

No. 247 (F) Sqn.: *SW461; SW504.*

No. 438 (Canadian) Sqn.: *SW398; SW414.*

No. 439 (Canadian) Sqn.: *SW423; SW446; SW459; SW460; SW537.*

No. 440 (Canadian) Sqn.: *SW401; SW428; SW452; SW462; SW641.*

No. 609 Sqn., A.A.F.: *SW501; SW504; SW536; SW566.*

No. 55 Operational Training Unit: *SW627; SW628.*

No. 56 Operational Training Unit: *SW474; SW523; SW621; SW622; SW624; SW625.*

No. 59 Operational Training Unit: *SW531; SW562; SW568; SW572; SW575; SW591; SW593; SW628; SW629; SW631-SW636.*

Other Aircraft: *SW408* (Deleted from Contract).

The Hawker P.1005. Two prototypes, *HV266* and *HV270*, designed to Air Ministry Specification B.11/41, powered by two Napier Sabre NS.8SM engines, ordered under Contract No. 1712/C.23a. To be built under Works Order No. 9616 (*HV266*) and No. 9960 (*HV270*), dated 28-1-41 and 15-4-41 respectively. Mock-up of this twin-engine bomber was almost complete, and *HV266* was about 40 per cent complete when the project was cancelled on 3 July 1942.

The Hawker F.10/41 Tempest (Mark V and VI prototype). One prototype, formerly referred to as the Typhoon II, *HM595*. Designed to Air Ministry Specification F.10/41 and ordered under Contract No. 1986/C.23a. Napier Sabre II (No. S1001) driving D.H. four-blade propeller (No. 50004). First flight, 2 September 1942, P.G. Lucas. With modified fin, 24-9-42; with fully extended dorsal fin, 17-11-42. Modified as Tempest VI prototype with 2,340 h.p. Napier Sabre V (No. S.5055); first flight, 9 May 1944, W. Humble. With Sabre V No. S.5063 driving Rotol four-blade propeller, 23-9-44; with engine No. S.5-73, 9-2-45.

The Hawker Tempest I prototype. One prototype, formerly referred to as Typhoon II, *HM599*. Designed to Air Ministry Specification F.10/41 and ordered under Contract No. 1640/23a. Works Order No. 2100, dated 21-11-41. Napier Sabre IV (No. S.75) driving D.H. four-blade propeller No. 50004. First flight, 24 February 1943, P.G. Lucas. With engine No. S.76, 26-3-43; with engine No. S.72, 4-6-43; with (production) engine No. S.2904, 19-8-43.

The Hawker Tempest II prototypes. Two prototypes, *LA602* and *LA607*. Original design commenced as Centaurus project scheme employing Typhoon airframe under Air Ministry Specification F.18/37 but, amalgamating Centaurus installation in Tornado *HG641* with Typhoon II, being designed to Air Ministry Specification F.10/41, emerged as Tempest II. First prototype, *LA602*, ordered under Contract No. 1986/23a and covered by Works Order No. 720006 dated 27-10-42. First flight, 28 June 1943, P.G. Lucas, with Centaurus IV No. C.80023, driving Rotol four-blade propeller No. EH.294; with engine No. C.80133, 9-7-43; engine No. C.80191, 5-12-43; dorsal fin added, 17-2-44. Second prototype, *LA607*, covered by Works Order No. 720015, dated 6-11-42. First flight, 18 September 1943, P.G. Lucas, with Centaurus IV No. C.80145 driving Rotol four-blade propeller No. EH.282. Rotol five-blade propeller No. EH.318, 13-11-43; engine No. C.80421 with auto-gills, 5-5-44; Centaurus V No. V.80171, 7-7-44; engine No. C.80060, 28-12-44. (Note: A third prototype, *LA610*, was ordered under Contract No. 1986/23a but completed as a prototype F.2/43 Fury with Rolls-Royce Griffon 85 driving Rotol contraprops. See below.)

The Hawker Tempest V. First production batch of 100 aircraft built by Hawker Aircraft Ltd., Langley. *JN729-JN773; JN792-JN822; JN854-JN877*. Most aircraft completed as Series 1 (with long-barrel Hispano Mark II cannon) and some as Series 2 (with short-barrel Hispano Mark V cannon); some aircraft retrospectively modified to Series 2 standard. One aircraft, JN750, completed as Mark II. Deliveries commenced , 12-43; completed, 5-44; average rate of production, approximately four aircraft per week. First flight by JN729, 21-6-43, W. Humble.

> **No. 3 (F) Sqn.:** *JN733-JN736; JN738; JN739; JN742; JN743; JN745; JN748; JN749; JN752-JN755; JN759* (crashed while chasing V-1 flying bomb, 6-8-44); *JN760-JN762; JN768* (shot down in Rheine area, 12-10-44; pilot, Wg. Cdr. R.P. Beamont made P.O.W.); *JN769; JN793; JN808; JN812* (shot down by flak near Volkel, 1-10-44); *JN815; JN821; JN822* (shot down by flak near Rheine airfield, 26-11-44); *JN857; JN862; JN865; JN868* (lost in action against V-1, 1-7-44).

> **No. 56 (F) Sqn.:** *JN808* (Missing from ground attack sortie, 2-2-45); *JN816; JN856; JN864; JN867; JN869; JN875; JN877*.

> **No. 80 (F) Sqn.:** *JN870*.

> **No. 222 (F) Sqn.:** *JN801; JN766; JN792; JN801; JN805; JN807; JN809*.

> **No. 486 (NZ) Sqn.:** *JN751; JN766; JN792; JN801; JN805; JN807; JN809*.

> **Other Units and duties, etc.:** *JN751* (flown as "*R-B*" by Wg. Cdr. R.P. Beamont as Wing Leader of Newchurch Wing; was the first Tempest to fly a ground attack sortie (28-5-44); the first Tempest to shoot down enemy aircraft (a Bf 109G on 8-6-44); and the first Tempest to shoot down a V-1 flying bomb, (16-6-44). *JN798* (store trials with A. & A.E.E.; evaluation as night fighter, 8-44); *JN799* (bombing trials at A. & A.E.E., 1944); *JN807, JN871* (converted to Tempest T.T. Mark 5, 1949-50); *JN867* (No. 17 O.T.U, 1947); *JN874* (propeller trials with Rotol Ltd., 1944); *JN876* (allocated for use by Air

Marshal Sir Roderick Hill, 1944).

The Hawker Tempest V Series 2. Second production batch of 300 aircraft built by Hawker Aircraft Ltd., Langley. *EJ504; EJ518-EJ560; EJ577-EJ611; EJ616-EJ672; EJ685-EJ723; EJ739-EJ788; EJ800-EJ846; EJ859-EJ896.* Naper Sabre IIA or IIB engines, short-barrel cannon and spring-tab ailerons. Deliveries commenced, 5-44; completed 9-44. Average rate of production, approximately 18 aircraft per week.

No. 3 (F) Sqn.: *EJ504; EJ521; EJ540; EJ549; EJ587; EJ610; EJ667; EJ690; EJ700; EJ760; EJ766; EJ786; EJ803* (Missing from patrol, 28-12-44); *EJ845; EJ865; EJ884.*

No. 33 (F) Sqn.: *EJ525* (Missing from sortie near Lübeck, 24-4-45); *EJ866; EJ868* (Missing from fighter sweep near Rheine, 25-2-45); *EK869; EJ880; EJ886.*

No. 56 (F) Sqn.: *EJ522; EJ526* (force landed in enemy territory following engine failure, 3-4-45); *EJ532* (hit high ground in cloud, 29-7-44); *EJ533; EJ534; EJ536* (shot down by flak while escorting raid on Roermond, 5-11-44); *EJ539; EJ541* (crashed during low level attack on enemy MT, 20-1-45); *EJ543; EJ544* (shot down by Fw 190s near Clopenburg, 22-2-45); *EJ545-EJ547; EJ548* (crashed during attack on German train, 16-1-45); *EJ550; EJ552; EJ559* (ditched off Beachy Head following engine failure, 7-44); *EJ578; EJ579; EJ585; EJ593; EJ601; EJ663* (Flt. Lt. F.L. MacLeod shot down Me 262 near Paderborn, 23-12-45); *EJ692; EJ700; EJ703; EJ708* (Missing from sortie near Münster, 26-3-45); *EJ718; EJ721; EJ739-EJ742; EJ761; EJ772; EJ773; EJ775; EJ777; EJ778; EJ780; EJ800; EJ804.*

No. 80 (F) Sqn.: *EJ519* (shot down by flak off Walcheren, 17-9-44); *EJ549; EJ607* (shot down in anti-flak sweep in Flushing area, 18-9-44); *EJ609; EJ633* (shot down by flak near Diepholz, 30-3-45); *EJ641; EJ643; EJ649* (shot down by flak near Oldenburg, 6-4-45); *EJ650; EJ657* (crashed after engine failure, 17-9-44); *EJ658-EJ660; EJ662* (shot down by flak north of Arnhem, 16-9-44); *EJ663; EJ665* (crash landed at Volkel, 11-2-45); *EJ666-EJ670; EJ691; EJ695* (Missing from sortie near Hildesheim, 14-2-45); *EJ696; EJ705; EJ713; EJ714; EJ722; EJ723* (shot down by flak near Flushing and crashed into the sea, 18-9-44); *EJ764; EJ774* (shot down by flak south of Stavelot, 13-1-45); *EJ776* (Missing from patrol near Hildesheim, 14-2-45); *EJ814; EJ830; EJ896.*

No. 222 (F) Sqn.: *EJ608; EJ871.*

No. 274 (F) Sqn.: *EJ525; EJ555; EJ595; EJ604; EJ609; EJ611* (force landed in enemy territory, 27-9-44); *EJ628; EJ632* (shot down, believed by Fw 190s, during patrol, 7-11-44); *EJ633; EJ634; EJ636; EJ637* (crashed into hill in low cloud near Elham, Kent, 13-8-44); *EJ638-EJ640; EJ642* (shot down by flak during attack on Leeuwarden and crashed into sea, 10-9-44); *EJ647; EJ648; EJ687* (Missing after train strike near Bielefeld, 21-2-45); *EJ688; EJ709* (crash landed in No Man's Land during sortie to Münster, 5-10-44); *EJ744; EJ751; EJ762* (crashed in Hamm-Gütersloh area, 1-2-45); *EJ771* (shot down by Bf 109s and Fw 190s near Rheine, 28-2-45); *EJ781; EJ783* (shot down by Bf 109Gs near Minden, 8-2-45); *EJ801; EJ813; EJ814; EJ864; EJ865; EJ876; EJ893.*

No. 501 Sqn., A.A.F.: *EJ520; EJ527; EJ538; EJ551; EJ555; EJ585; EJ591; EJ592; EJ597; EJ600; EJ603; EJ605; EJ608; EJ626; EJ702; EJ763.*

Converted to Tempest T.T. Mark 5, 1949-50: *EJ580; EJ581; EJ585; EJ599; EJ643; EJ660; EJ663; EJ667; EJ669; EJ744; EJ753; EJ758; EJ786; EJ801; EJ805; EJ807; EJ839; EJ846; EJ862; EJ875; EJ879; EJ880.*

Other Units and duties, etc.: *EJ518* (to D. Napier & Sons, Ltd., for installation and trials of annular radiator); *EJ585; EJ846; EJ879* (Armament Practice Stn., Sylt, 1954); *EJ590* (hood jettison trials, Langley, 7-44); *EJ592* (trials with unpainted aircraft, Langley, 7-44); *EJ599, EJ667; EJ669; EJ805; EJ839* (No. 233 Operational Conversion Unit); EJ759 (tropicalised aircraft; ff, 25-9-44); *EJ846* (No. 56 O.T.U.).

The Hawker Tempest V Series 2. Third production batch of 199 aircraft built by Hawker Aircraft Ltd., Langley. *NV639-NV682; NV695-NV735; NV749-NV793; NV917-NV948; NV960-*

NV996. Napier Sabre IIB engine and spring-tab ailerons. Deliveries commenced, 9-44; completed 2-45; average rate of production, approximately twelve aircraft per week.

No. 3 (F) Sqn.: *NV664* (shot down by flak, 10-2-45); *NV669; NV676; NV703; NV713; NV721; NV749; NV767; NV776;NV926; NV960; NV989; NV994.*

No. 16 (F) Sqn.: *NV968.*

No. 33 (F) Sqn.: *NV653; NV664; NV671; NV678; NV679; NV695; NV731* (Missing from sortie near Lübeck, 24-4-45); *NV754* (Missing from sortie near Lübeck, 24-4-45); *NV757; NV764; NV770; NV775; NV783* (shot down near Hamburg, 12-4-45); *NV792; NV919* (shot down during sortie near Hamburg, 12-4-45).

No. 56 (F) Sqn.: *NV640; NV641; NV649; NV659; NV667; NV728* (crashed following engine failure, 3-4-45); *NV771; NV786* (shared with *NV968* in the destruction of Me 262 south of Hamburg, 15-4-45); *NV927; NV928; NV963; NV965; NV968* (shared with *NV786* in the destruction of one Me 262 south of Hamburg, 15-4-45); *NV970; NV973* (Missing from sorties near Osnabrück, 28-3-45); *NV974* (shot down over enemy territory, 1-5-45); *NV980; NV987.*

No. 80 (F) Sqn.: *NV646* (shot down by flak while escorting Typhoons, 25-2-45); *NV654* (force landed after engine failure, 10-2-45, and S.O.C.); *NV657; NV700; NV703; NV704; NV719; NV725; NV789; NV938; NV945; NV960; NV964; NV982* (shot down by flak between Rheine and Osnabrück, 2-4-45); *NV983; NV991* (shot down by Fw 190s near Gravesmühlen, 17-4-45).

No. 222 (F) Sqn.: *NV682; NV939.*

No. 274 (F) Sqn.: *NV639; NV645* (Sqn. Ldr. D.C. Fairbanks, RCAF, shot down one Me 262 over Rheine, 11-2-45); *NV697; NV702; NV722; NV758; NV920* (shot down by flak near Plantlunne, 24-3-45); *NV942* (shot down by flak near Plantlunne, 24-3-45); *NV943* (Missing after combat with Bf 109s and Fw 190s near Rheine, 28-2-45); *NV947; NV977.*

No. 486 (NZ) Sqn.: *NV651; NV706; NV791; NV986.*

Converted to Tempest T.T. Mark 5, 1949-50: *NV661; NV665; NV669; NV671; NV669; NV704; NV712; NV723; NV725; NV763; NV778; NV780; NV781; NV793; NV917; NV922; NV923; NV928; NV937; NV940; NV960; NV962; NV965; NV975; NV978; NV992; NV994-NV996.*

Other Units and duties, etc.: *NV668* (trials with adjustable undercarriage leg flap, H.A.L., 1-45); *NV669* (No. 229 O.C.U.); *NV708* (as "*JCB*" flown by Wg. Cdr. J.C. Button, No. 123 Wing); *NV768* (annular radiator and ducted spinner installation by D. Napier & Sons Ltd.); *NV923* (No. 226 O.C.U.).

The Hawker Tempest V Series 2. Fourth and final production batch of 201 aircraft built by Hawker Aircraft Ltd., Langley. *SN102-SN146; SN159-SN190; SN205-SN238; SN253-SN296; SN301-SN355.* Napier Sabre IIB engines and universal armament provision and drop tank plumbing. Deliveries commenced, 1-45; completed 6-45. Average rate of production, approximately nine aircraft per week. (*SN368-SN416* cancelled in mid-1945).

No. 3 (F) Sqn.: *SN168; SN212; SN220; SN295; SN330; SN339; SN344; SN347; SN352.*

No. 16 (F) Sqn.: *SN135; SN345.*

No. 33 (F) Sqn.: *SN127; SN128; SN134; SN161; SN173* (Missing from patrol in Husumn-Kiel area, 23-4-45); *SN180; SN182; SN187; SN210; SN213; SN228; SN266; SN268; SN315; SN342.*

No. 56 (F) Sqn.: *SN127; SN128; SN131; SN137; SN140; SN186.*

No. 222 (F) Sqn.: *SN178; SN182; SN188.*

No. 274 (F) Sqn.: *SN107; SN118; SN145; SN162; SN179; SN181; SN183; SN210.*

No. 287 (AAC) Sqn.: *SN106; SN116; SN119.*

No. 486 (NZ) Sqn.: *SN146; SN166; SN168.*

Converted to Tempest T.T. Mark 5, 1949-50: *SN209; SN215; SN219; SN227; SN232; SN259-SN264; SN271; SN273; SN274; SN293; SN317; SN321; SN326; SN329* (prototype conversion); *SN3312-SN333; SN340; SN350; SN353; SN354.*

Other Units and duties, etc.: *SN109* (Day Fighter Leaders' School); *SN209* (Armament Practice Station, Sylt); *SN226* (No. 3 Armament Practice Station, Charter Hall); *SN236* (No. 1 Armament Practice Station, Fairwood Common); *SN262* (C.F.E.); *SN320* (R.A.E.); *SN321* (Central Gunnery School, Leconfield); *SN354* (experimental 40-mm. "P"-gun installation, H.A.L., Langley; to A. & A.E.E., 1945).

The Hawker Tempest VI (F. Mark 6). Single production batch of 142 aircraft ordered in 1945 and built by Hawker Aircraft Ltd., Langley, during 1946-47. *NV997-NV999; NX113-NX156; NX169-NX209; NX223-NX268; NX281-NX288.* (Original order was for 300 aircraft, but *NX289-NX325; NX338-NX381; NX394-NX435* and *NX448-NX482* were cancelled in 1945.) Napier Sabre V engines and preparation for service in the tropics.

No. 6 (F) Sqn.: *NX134; NX135; NX138; NX139; NX147; NX149; NX156; NX187; NX191; NX194; NX195; NX203; NX242; NX251; NX257; NX261; NX263.*

No. 8 (F) Sqn.: *NX130; NX131; NX140; NX148; NX152; NX156; NX169; NX180; NX196; NX198; NX202; NX228; NX237.*

No. 39 (F) Sqn.: *NX172; NX185; NX186; NX190; NX197; NX201; NX205; NX207; NX225.*

No. 213 (F) Sqn.: *NX136; NX153; NX180; NX181; NX183; NX184; NX192; NX206; NX227; NX229; NX241; NX244; NX248; NX252; NX256; NX260.*

No. 249 (F) Sqn.: *NX120; NX125; NX126; NX132; NX135; NX141; NX142; NX143; NX170; NX171; NX177; NX182; NX200; NX209; NX232; NX245; NX263; NX284.*

Other Units and duties, etc.: *NV997-NV999, NX113-NX118;* (performance trials at H.A.L. and A. & A.E.E.); *NX119* (first Mark VI gyro gunsight installation, to A. & A.E.E., 1947); *NX121* (engine handling trials, R.A.E.); *NX122* (engine handling, A. & A.E.E.); *NX124* (trials with spring tabs, H.A.L.); *NX133* (trial installations, H.A.L.); *NX144* (target towing trials, A. & A.E.E., 19467-47); *NX188* (propeller trials, Rotol Ltd., 1947); *NX262, NX268* (trials with modified cooling system, H.A.L. and D. Napier & Sons, Ltd.).

The Hawker Tempest II (F and FB Mark 2). Single production batch of 50 aircraft, *MW374-MW423*, built by the Bristol Aeroplane Co. Ltd., Weston-super-Mare, Somerset. Bristol Centaurus V engines. Delivered 1945-46. 27 aircraft transferred to the Royal Indian Air Force from R.A.F. stocks. First flight by MW374, 4 October 1944.

No. 26 (F) Sqn. (Fassberg, Germany): *MW416; MW423.*

No. 33 (F) Sqn. (Fassberg, Germany): *MW416; MW423.*

No. 54 (F) Sqn. (Chilbolton): *MW379; MW387; MW398.*

No. 247 (F) Sqn. (Chilbolton): *MW381; MW390; MW392; MW395; MW396; MW400; MW404.*

Supplied to the Royal Indian Air Force: *MW376* (as "*HA564*"); *MW377* ("*HA568*"); *MW378* ("*HA627*"); *MW379* ("*HA632*"); *MW380* ("*HA628*"); *MW381* ("*HA630*"); *MW382* ("*HA590*"); *MW383* ("*HA631*"); *MW385* ("*HA533*"); *MW386* ("*HA595*"); *MW387* ("*HA592*"); *MW388* ("*HA635*"); *MW389* ("*HA625*"); *MW390* ("*HA620*"); *MW391* ("*HA626*"); *MW392* ("*HA585*"); *MW393* ("*HA634*"); *MW395* ("*HA589*"); *MW396* ("*HA596*"); *MW397* ("*HA611*"); *MW398* ("*HA588*"); *MW399* ("*HA533*"); *MW400* ("*HA604*"); *MW401* ("*HA604*"); *MW402* ("*HA581*"); *MW403* ("*HA575*"); *MW404* ("*HA557*").

Other Units and duties, etc.: *MW374* (Handling and performance trials, Langley and Filton, Bristol); *MW378* (engine trials, Filton, Bristol); *MW409* (assessment of modified ailerons, Langley, 1945).

The Hawker Tempest II (F and FB Mark 2). First production batch of 100 aircraft built by Hawker Aircraft Ltd., Langley. Bristol Centaurus V engines. *MW735-MW778; MW790-MW835; MW847-MW856.* Majority of aircraft completed as fighters, and many subsequently modified to incorporate wiring for underwing bomb racks and rocket hardpoints. 55 aircraft transferred to the Royal Indian Air Force.

No. 54 (F) Sqn.: *MW747; MW755; MW760; MW772* (written off in taxying accident, 19-5-46); *MW773; MW774; MW800; MW820; MW849.*

No. 183 (F) Sqn.: *MW747; MW755; MW763; MW768; MW772; MW773; MW790; MW799* (crashed 29-11-46); *MW811; MW812* (crashed 21-5-46).

No. 247 (F) Sqn.: *MW756; MW760; MW768; MW769; MW793-MW796; MW798* (crashed 11-7-46).

Air Fighting Development Sqn.: *MW743; MW744; MW754.*

Empire Test Pilots' School: *MW775; MW791; MW813* (crashed, 14-7-46); MW818.

Trials at A. & A.E.E., Boscombe Down: *MW736; MW801* (crashed 18-10-45); *MW802-MW806.*

No. 13 Operational Training Unit: *MW750; MW776; MW777; MW797.*

Supplied to the Royal Indian Air Force: *MW739 (as "HA574"); MW741 ("HA622"); MW742 ("HA566"); MW743 ("HA561"); MW745 ("HA587"); MW746 ("HA600"); MW748 ("HA565"); MW750 ("HA601"); MW751 ("HA555"); MW752 ("HA584"); MW754 ("HA597"); MW756 ("HA616"); MW758 ("HA580"); MW759 ("HA602"); MW760 ("HA567"); MW761 ("HA573"); MW762 ("HA594"); MW763 ("HA586"); MW764 ("HA554"); MW767 ("HA624"); MW768 ("HA609"); MW769 ("HA615"); MW770 ("HA562"); MW771 ("HA629"); MW773 ("HA577"); MW775 ("HA607"); MW777 ("HA579"); MW791 ("HA614"); MW793 ("HA603"); MW795 ("HA608"); MW796 ("HA606"); MW797 ("HA610"); MW807 ("HA570"); MW808 ("HA563"); MW809 ("HA598"); MW810 ("HA591"); MW814 ("HA605"); MW817 ("HA569"); MW819 ("HA571"); MW822 ("HA599"). MW823 ("HA583"); MW824 ("HA572"); MW828 ("HA621"); MW829 ("HA612"); MW830 ("HA578"); MW831 ("HA582"); MW847 ("HA559"); MW848 ("HA623"); MW850 ("HA593"); MW851 ("HA560"); MW852 ("HA619"); MW853 ("HA576"); MW854 ("HA558"); MW855 ("HA618"); MW856 ("HA582").*

Other Units and duties, etc.: *MW735, MW736, MW739, MW740, MW741, MW762, MW765, MW766* (miscellaneous trials at Langley and Filton); *MW737* (test bed aircraft for Centaurus XV engine); *MW778* (crashed at Chilbolton, 29-11-45); *MW792* (No. 2 A.P.U.).

The Hawker Tempest II (F and FB Mark 2). Second production batch of 302 aircraft built by Hawker Aircraft Ltd., Langley. Bristol Centaurus V engines. *PR525-PR567; PR581-PR523; PR645-PR689; PR713-PR758; PR771-PR815; PR830-PR876; PR889-PR921.* All aircraft prepared as fighter-bombers, and majority tropicalised for service in the Far East. Seven aircraft supplied to the Royal Indian Air Force from home stocks (and others transferred from the R.A.F. in India); 24 aircraft sold to Pakistan and delivered from home stocks.

No. 5 (F) Sqn. (India): *PR529; PR530; PR532; PR535; PR540; PR559-PR561; PR564; PR594; PR607; PR623; PR646; PR656; PR677; PR680* (damaged in accident near Wagaon, 3-8-46, and S.O.C.); *PR714; PR715; PR718; PR723; PR754; PR815.*

No. 16 (F) Sqn. (Germany): *PR682; PR736; PR776; PR853.*

No. 20 (F) Sqn. (India): *PR551-PR553; PR602; PR801; PR804; PR807.*

No. 26 (F) Sqn. (Germany): *PR865; PR782; PR853.*

No. 30 (F) Sqn. (India): *PR565; PR566; PR583; PR593; PR837; PR840; PR842.*

No. 33 (F) Sqn. (Germany and Singapore): *PR528; PR531; PR599; PR676; PR753; PR774; PR777-PR779; PR782; PR785-PR788; PR797; PR804; PR807; PR845; PR852; PR854; PR859; PR864; PR873; PR895; PR916; PR921.*

No. 152 (F) Sqn. (India): *PR536; PR544-PR546; PR814.*

Empire Test Pilots' School: *PR867; PR919.*

No. 226 Operational Conversion Unit: *PR555; PR811; PR846; PR870.*

Supplied to Royal Indian Air Force. From Home stocks: *PR525 (as "HA617"); PR869 ("HA551"); PR874 ("HA547"); PR890 ("HA552"); PR893 ("HA549"); PR902 ("HA550");*

PR907 ("*HA548*"). From R.A.F. stocks in India: *PR593; PR714.*

Sold to Pakistan: *PR615* (as "*A143*"); *PR649* ("*A138*"); *PR806* ("*A133*"); *PR809* ("*A139*"); *PR865* ("*A135*"); *PR866* ("*A128*"); *PR872* ("*A134*"); *PR875* ("*A144*"); *PR876* ("*A136*"); *PR889* ("*A148*"); *PR891* ("*A147*"); *PR892* ("*A131*"); *PR894* ("*A132*"); *PR897* ("*A146*"); *PR898* ("*A129*"); *PR899* ("*A151*"); *PR900* ("*A140*"); *PR906* ("*A130*"); *PR909* ("*A145*"); *PR910* ("*A142*"); *PR912* ("*A150*"); *PR914* ("*A137*"); *PR915* ("*A149*"); *PR917* ("*A141*").

Other Units and duties: *PR533, PR554, PR662* (trials at Langley and A. & A.E.E.); *PR550* (trials with 90-gallon belly tank, H.A.L., 1946-47); *PR718, PR723, PR754* (with No. 5 Sqn., carried out counter-insurgency operations from R.A.F. Miramshah, 11-46).

[Note: In 1947 a further 498 Tempest IIs were cancelled from the Contract placed with Hawker Aircraft Ltd.: *PR922-PR928; PR941-PR967; PR979-PR999; PS115-PS157; PS173-PS215; PS229-PS273; PS287-PS329; PS342-PS387; PS408-PS449; PS463-PS507; PS520-PS563; PS579-PS625; PS637-PS681.* 30 further aircraft, ordered from the Bristol Aeroplane Co. Ltd., *VA386-VA395* and *VA417-VA436*, were also cancelled.]

The Hawker F.2/43 Fury. Four prototypes designed to Air Ministry Specification F.2/43, built by Hawker Aircraft Ltd., Kingston and Langley. The first two aircraft, *NX798* and *NX802*, were covered by Contract No. 264430/43. *NX798*, first flown 1 September 1944 with Bristol Centaurus XII; later fitted with Centaurus XVIII and sold to Egypt (registered *G-AKRY* for ferry purposes. *NX802*, first flown with Centaurus XII on 25 July 1945, was later fitted with Centaurus XVIII and sold to Pakistan as *K875*. *LA610* (originally covered by the Tempest prototype Contract) was first flown on 27 November 1944 powered by a Rolls-Royce Griffon 85 driving a Rotol six-blade contraprop; later fitted with a Bristol Centaurus XV and ultimately a Napier Sabre VII. The fourth Fury prototype was *VP207*, completed from stock parts in c.1947 and flown with a Napier Sabre VII.

The Hawker N.7/43 Naval Fury (later Sea Fury). Specification F.2/43 adapted to meet Admiraly requirement for shipboard fighter and re-issued as N.7/43. Three prototypes, *SR661, SR666* and *VP857*, covered by Contract No. 27022/44: *SR661*, first flown 21 February 1945, was "semi-navalised" with arrester hook but fixed wings. Powered initially by Bristol Centaurus XII, later replaced by Centaurus XVIII. *SR666*, first flown 12 October 1945, fully navalised with arrester hook and folding wings. Centaurus XV, later replaced by Centaurus XVIII. *VB857*, built by Boulton Paul Aircraft Ltd., Wolverhampton, but assembled by Hawker Aircraft Ltd., Langley. First flown, 31 January 1946, with Centaurus XV, and later with Centaurus XVIII; became the T.I. aircraft for the Sea Fury F.B. Mark XI.

The Hawker Sea Fury F. Mark X. Naval interceptor fighter. One production batch of 50 aircraft, *TF895-TF928* and *TF940-TF955*, prepared to Specification N. 22/43, and built by Hawker Aircraft Ltd., under Contract No. 3682/44 dated 7 July 1944.

No. 778 Sqn.: *TF905; TF906* (crashed, 20-6-47); *TF907.*

No. 802 Sqn.: *TF913; TF918, TF925-TF927.*

No. 803 Sqn.: *TF912; TF913; TF916; TF918-TF920; TF924; TF925; TF940; TF943; TF944* (burnt, 5-4-48); *TF945-TF947.*

No. 805 Sqn.: *TF910; TF911; TF925-TF927; TF943; TF952; TF953.*

No. 807 Sqn.: *TF910; TF911; TF915* (crashed, 21-8-47); *TF921; TF926-TF928; TF948* (crashed, 22-7-47); *TF949* (crashed, 1948); *TF950-TF953; TF954* (crashed 20-1-49).

Re-purchased by H.A.L. in 1957-58. From R.N.A.S. Donibristle: *TF902; TF916.* From R.N.A.S. Anthorn: *TF911; TF913; TF951; TF945.*

OtherUnits and duties, etc.: *TF985, TF987* (performance and handling trials, H.A.L.; *TF903, TF904* (R.D.U., R.N.A.S. Culham); *TF914* (R.D.U., R.N.A.S. Anthorn); *TF955* (R.D.U., R.N.A.S. Culdrose); *TF898, TF899* (fleet trials, H.M.S. *Illustrious*); *TF900* (trials with spring tabs, H.A.L.); *TF923* (armament trials, H.A.L. and A. & A.E.E.); *TF896* (force

571

landed, 3-13-46, and S.O.C.); *TF942* (crashed, 29-6-47); *TF902, TF908, TF923* (miscellaneous trials, A. & A.E.E., 1946-47); *TF908* (I.F.D.U.); *TF917* (No. 52 T.R.A.G.); *TF922, TF941, TF946* (N.A.F.D.U.). *TF909* (delivered to Canada, 1947, for evaluation).

The Hawker Sea Fury F.B. Mark 11. Naval fighter-bomber. First production batch of 50 aircraft, built by Hawker Aircraft Ltd., Langley, under Contract No. 3682/44. *TF956-TF973; TF985-TF999; TG113-TG129.* Design based on third N.7/43 prototype, *VB857*, but with lengthened arrester hook. One 2,480 h.p. Bristol Centaurus IX radial engine driving Rotol five-blade propeller. Provision for external ordnance and drop tanks.

No. 802 Sqn.: *TF959* (crashed, 1947); *TF963; TF970; TF986.*
No. 803 Sqn.: *TF993-TF999; TF113-TG116; TG121; TG122.*
No. 805 Sqn.: *TF956; TF972; TF973; TF990-TF992; TF999.*
No. 807 Sqn.: *TF961; TF964; TF966; TF967; TF9721; TF973; TF987* (crashed 21-8-48).
Supplied to the Royal Canadian Navy, 1948-49: *TF985; TF993-TF995; TF997-TF999; TG113-TG129.*
Re-purchased by H.A.L. in 1957-59. From R.N.A.S. Donibristle: *TF991.* From R.N.A.S. Anthorn: *TF966; TF988; TF989.* From R.N.A.S. Abbotsinch: *TF957; TF969; TF986.*
Other Units and duties, etc.: *TF969* (No. 8 T.U.); *TF988* (No. 52 T.R.A.G.); *TF958, TF968, TF970, TF989* (R.D.U., R.N.A.S. Culdrose); *TF960* (crashed, 26-7-50), *TF970* (R.D.U., R.N.A.S., Anthorn); *TF972* (R.D.U., R.N.A.S. Stretton). *TF957, TF962, TF965, TF986* (A. & A.E.E., Boscombe Down).

The Hawker Sea Fury F.B. Mark 11. Second production batch of 35 aircraft, *VR918-VR952*, built by Hawker Aircraft Ltd., Langley, under Contract No. 657/46, dated 23 October 1946. Bristol Centaurus 18 radial engines driving Rotol five-blade propellers. Full ground attack store provision.

No. 738 Sqn.: *VR920; VR933; VR934.*
No. 802 Sqn.: *VR922; VR924-VR928; VR930; VR934; VR940; VR945-VR947.*
No. 805 Sqn.: *VR950.*
No. 806 Sqn.: *VR932; VR941.*
No. 807 Sqn.: *VR936-VR939; VR943; VR944; VR951; VR952.*
No. 1831 Flt.: *VR951; VR952.*
Supplied to the Royal Canadian Navy, 1948: *VR918; VR919.*
Re-purchased by H.A.L. in 1957-58: From R.N.A.S. Anthorn: *VR924; VR928; VR938; VR943; VR946; VR952.* From R.N.A.S. Abbotsinch: *VR921; VR933.* From R.N.A.S. Donibristle: *VR926; VR947; VR949; VR950.*
Other Units and duties, etc.: *VR921, VR931, VR933, VR935, VR942* (crashed, 1948), *VR948* (R.D.U., R.N.A.S. Culham); *VR945* (R.D.U., R.N.A.S. Lossiemouth); *VR951* (S.A.M., R.N.A.S., Yeovilton); *VR920* (trials at R.A.E. and A. & A.E.E.); *VR923* (Rotol propeller test bed); *VR929* (handling trials and performance measurement, H.A.L. Langley).

The Hawker Sea Fury F.B. Mark 11. Third production batch of 147 aircraft built by Hawker Aircraft Ltd., Kingston and Langley, under Contract No. 1584/47, dated 19 December 1947. *VW224-VW243; VW541-VW590; VW621-VW670; VW691-VW718.* Bristol Centaurus 18 radial engines driving Rotol five-blade propellers. Full ground attack store provision.

No. 736 Sqn.: *VW569; VW588; VW700; VW705; VW714; VW717.*
No. 802 Sqn.: *VW232; VW236-VW238; VW240; VW544; VW566; VW578; VW580; VW700; VW711; VW641.*
No. 803 Sqn.: *VW225; VW227; VW228; VW237; VW543; VW547.*
No. 804 Sqn.: *VW662; VW670; VW694; VW697; VW703; VW705; VW709.*
No. 805 Sqn.: *VW232; VW243; VW543; VW622-VW624; VW626; VW627; VW629-VW632; VW634-VW640; VW642-VW648; VW660.*
No. 807 Sqn.: *VW226; VW228; VW234; VW241; VW546; VW547.*

No. 883 Sqn.: *VW552.*

R.D.U.s: R.N.A.S. Anthorn: *VW558; VW565, VW574-VW576; VW579; VW583; VW585-VW588; VW590; VW 628; VW649-VW651; VW654-VW659; VW661-VW663; VW665-VW669; VW691, VW693; VW695; VW696; VW698; VW699; VW701; VW702; VW704; VW712-VW718.* R.N.A.S. Culham: *VW235; VW239; VW 242; VW541; VW542; VW545; VW548-VW551; VW556; VW557; VW559; VW562; VW567; VW572; VW573; VW577.* R.N.A.S. Stretton: *VW229.*

Supplied to the Royal Canadian Navy: *VW230; VW231; VW563; VW571.*

Re-purchased by H.A.L. in 1957-58: From R.N.A.S. Abbotsinch: *VW569, VW579; VW588; VW653; VW657; VW699.* From R.N.A.S. Anthorn: *VW228, VW229; VW237; VW542; VW543; VW547; VW549; VW551; VW553; VW556; VW560; VW562; VW566; VW568; VW572; VW575; VW577; VW581; VW585; VW649; VW650; VW656; VW667; VW692; VW693; VW694; VW700; VW702, VW704; VW705; VW714; VW715; VW717.* From R.N.A.S. Donibristle: *VW559; VW561; VW564; VW570; VW576; VW663; VW707.*

Other Units and duties, etc.: *VW233, VW553, VW581, VW633; VW653* (No. 52 T.R.A.G.); *VW547, VW564, VW568* (N.A.F.D.U.); *VW582* (S.N.A.W.); *VW692* (No. 21 C.A.G.); *VW621* (Culdrose Fighter School); *VW224, VW554, VW555, VW560, VW625* (miscellaneous trials, H.A.L.); *VW561* (Bristol engine trials); *VW664* (Rotol propeller test bed); *VW569* (crashed, 14-9-48); *VW584* (damaged in barrier accident, 12-7-49); *VW589* (lost overboard, HMS *Glory*, 1950); *VW562* (HMAS *Sydney*, 1950).

The Hawker Sea Fury F.B. Mark 11. Fourth production batch of 136 aircraft built by Hawker Aircraft Ltd., Kingston and Langley, under Contract No. 2576/48, dated 5 July 1948. *VX608-VX 643; VX650-VX696; VX707-VX711; VX724-VX730; VX748-VX764; WF590-WF595; WF610-WF627.* Bristol Centaurus 18 radial engines driving Rotol five-blade propellers. Full ground attack store provision.

No. 738 Sqn.: *VX647-VX649; VX652; VX654; VX660; VX661.*

No. 802 Sqn.: *VX615; VX637; VX638; VX640; VX641; VX664; VX668; VX673.*

No. 805 Sqn.: *VX627; VX631; VX633; VX661.*

No. 883 Sqn.: *VX695.*

No. 1831 Flt.: *VX628; VX631; VX657; VX658.*

R.D.U., R.N.A.S. Anthorn: VX608-VX611; VX614; VX616-VX626; VX629-VX634; VX636; VX639; VX643; VX650; VX651; VX653-VX655; VX658; VX660; VX662; VX666; VX667; VX669-VX672; VX674-VX676; VX678-VX691; VX693; VX694; VX696;VX707-VX711; VX730; VX753; VX754; WF590-WF593; WF610-WF613; WF619;WF623; WF625; WF627.

No. 52 T.R.A.G.: *VX635; VX642; VX656; VX659; VX663; VX665; VX667; VX670; VX676-VX679; VX681; VX689.*

No. 17 C.A.G.: *WF594; WF595; WF620-WF622; WF624; WF626; WF614-WF618.*

No. 21 C.A.G.: *VX692.*

Delivered to the Royal Australian Navy, 1951: *VX724-VX729; VX749-VX752; VX755-VX764.*

Re-purchased by H.A.L., 1957-58: From R.N.A.S. Abbotsinch: *VX611; VX637; VX659; VX684; WF624.* From R.N.A.S. Anthorn: *VX608; VX614; VX615; VX619; VX622; VX624; VX628; VX631; VX632; VX634; VX635; VX640; VX643; VX652; VX654-VX656; VX658; VX666; VX667; VX669; VX671; VX680; VX681; VX693; VX696; VX711; WF595; WF610; WF612; WF615; WF619; WF621; WF623; WF625.* From R.N.A.S. Donibristle: *VX639; VX672; VX678; VX679; WF592; WF594; WF616; WF617.*

Other Units and duties, etc.: *VX612* (C.S.(A) aircraft, Bristol Engine Co. Ltd.); *VX613* (C.S.(A) aircraft, Rotol Ltd.); *VX682* (delivered to Canada, 1951); *VX748* (crashed, 4-9-50); *VX762* (R.N.A.S. Abbotsinch, 1950).

The Hawker Sea Fury F.B. Mark 11. Fifth production batch of 93 aircraft built by Hawker

Aircraft Ltd., Kingston and Langley, under Contract No. 3794/49, dated 15 September 1949. *WE673-WE694; WE708-WE736; WE785-WE806; WM472-WM482; WM487-WM495.* Bristol Centaurus 18 radial engines driving Rotol five-blade propellers. Full ground attack store provision.

No. 801 Sqn.: *WE711-WE714; WE716; WE717; WE726; WE729; WE730: WE735.*

No. 808 Sqn.: *WE677.*

R.D.U. Anthorn: *WE680-WE694; WE708-WE710; WE715; WE718-WE725; WE727; WE728; WE731; WE733; WE734; WE785-WE795; WE787-WE806.*

No. 1 C.A.G.: *WE732; WE736.*

Delivered to the Royal Australian Navy, 1951: *WE675; WE676; WE678; WE796.*

Re-purchased by H.A.L., 1957-58. From R.N.A.S. Abbotsinch: *WE719; WM476.* From R.N.A.S. Anthorn: *WE687; WE710; WE711; WE712; WE713; WE715; WE717; WE718; WE720; WE721; WE727; WE729; WE732; WE788; WE789; WE790; WE792; WE798; WE800; WE802; WE805; WE806; WM488; WM489; WM493; WM494.* From R.N.A.S. Donibristle: *WE681; WE682; WE693; WE723; WE725; WE735; WE785; WE787; WM492.*

The Hawker Sea Fury F.B. Mark 11. Sixth production batch of 37 aircraft built by Hawker Aircraft Ltd., Kingston and Langley, under Contract No. 5042/50, dated 18 August 1950. *WG564-WG575; WG590-WG604; WG621-WG6630.* Bristol Centaurus 18 radial engines driving Rotol five-blade propellers. Full ground attack store provision.

No. 17 C.A.G.: WG591.

R.D.U., R.N.A.S. Anthorn: *WG564-WG575; WG590; WG592-WG604; WG621-WG630.*

Re-purchased by H.A.L., 1957-58: From R.N.A.S. Abbotsinch: *WG593; WG597; WH598.* From R.N.A.S. Anthorn: *WG594; WG602; WG622; WH623; WG625; WG626.* From R.N.A.S. Donibristle: *WG621; WG629.*

The Hawker Sea Fury F.B. Mark 11. Seventh production batch of 78 aircraft built by Hawker Aircraft Ltd., Kingston and Langley, under Contract No. 5042/50 (3rd Part), dated 18 August 1950. *WH581-WH594; WH612-WH623; WJ221-WJ248; WJ276-WJ292; WJ294-WJ297; WJ299-WJ301.* Bristol Centaurus 18 radial engines driving five-blade Rotol propellers. All aircraft in this batch were delivered to R.D.U., R.N.A.S. Anthorn.

Delivered to the Royal Canadian Navy, 1952: *WJ299-WJ301.*

Re-purchased by H.A.L., 1957-58: From R.N.A.S. Abbotsinch: *WH592; WJ222; WJ234; WJ241; WJ243; WJ246; WJ247; WJ286.* From R.N.A.S. Anthorn: *WH585; WH593; WH613; WH614; WH617; WH619; WH621; WJ229; WJ232; WJ276; WJ280; WJ290; WJ291.* From R.N.A.S. Donibristle: *WH584; WJ221; WJ223; WJ228; WJ233; WJ236; WJ242; WJ277; WJ283; WJ292.*

The Hawker Sea Fury F.B. Mark 11. Eighth production batch of 10 aircraft built by Hawker Aircraft Ltd., Kingston and Dunsfold, under Contract No. 6298/51, dated 17 April 1951. *WN474-WN479, WN484-WN487.* Bristol Centaurus 18 radial engines.

Delivered to the Royal Canadian Navy, 1952: *WN474; WN479.*

R.D.U., R.N.A.S. Anthorn: *WN475-WN478; WN484-WN487.*

Re-purchased by H.A.L., 1957-58. From R.N.A.S. Anthorn: *WN477; WN478; WN484; WN486.*

The Hawker Sea Fury F.B. Mark 11. Ninth production batch of 30 aircraft built by Hawker Aircraft Ltd., Kingston and Dunsfold, under Contract No. 7408/51, dated 9 November 1951. *WX627-WZ656.* Bristol Centaurus 18 engines.

Delivered to the Royal Australian Navy, 1954: WZ638-WZ640.

R.D.U., R.N.A.S. Abbotsinch, 1953-54: WZ642-WZ652.

R.D.U., R.N.A.S. Anthorn: *WZ627-WZ637; WZ641; WZ653-WZ656.*

Re-purchased by H.A.L., 1957-58: From R.N.A.S. Abbotsinch: *WZ628-WZ630.* From R.N.A.S. Anthorn: *WZ627; WZ632; WZ654-WZ656.* From R.N.A.S. Donibristle: *WX631.*

The Hawker Sea Fury Two-seat Trainer. One prototype, *VX818,* originally designed and commenced construction as part of an order for four aircraft for Iraq. Owing, however, to interest expressed by the British Admiralty, the aircraft was converted to M.O.S. requirements under Contract No. 1998/47. Bristol Centaurus XVIII, Rotol five-blade propeller and Hawker periscopic sight over the rear cockpit.

The Hawker Sea Fury T. Mark 20. First production batch of 27 aircraft built by Hawker Aircraft Ltd., Kingston and Langley, to Specification N.19/47 under Contract No. 1674/48 dated 15 April 1948. *VX280-VX292; VX297-VX310.* Bristol Centaurus 18 engines driving five-blade Rotol propellers.
N.A.F.D.U.: *VX283.*
Re-purchased by H.A.L., 1957-58: From R.N.A.S. Anthorn: *VX280; VX281; VX290-VX292; VX298; VX300; VX302; VX309.* From R.N.A.S. Donibristle: *VZ299; VX307; VX308.*

The Hawker Sea Fury T. Mark 20. Second production batch of 21 aircraft built by Hawker Aircraft Ltd., Kingston and Langley, under Contract No. 2577/48 dated 21 August 1948. *VZ345-VZ355; VZ363-VZ372.* Bristol Centaurus 18 engines and Rotol five-blade propellers.
Re-purchased by H.A.L., 1957-58: From R.N.A.S. Anthorn: *VZ345; VZ346; VZ349-VZ354; VZ363-VZ365; VZ368; VZ370-VZ372.* From R.N.A.S. Donibristle: *VZ366.*

The Hawker Sea Fury T. Mark 20. Third production batch of 7 aircraft built by Hawker Aircraft Ltd., Kingston and Langley, under Contract No. 3794/49 dated 15 September 1949. *WE820-WE826.* Bristol Centaurus 18 engines and Rotol five-blade propellers.
Re-purchased by H.A.L., 1957-58: From R.N.A.S. Anthorn: *WE820; WE823; WE824; WE826.*

The Hawker Sea Fury T. Mark 20. Fourth production batch of 5 aircraft built by Hawker Aircraft Ltd., Kingston and Langley, under Contract No. 5042/50 dated 18 August 1950. *WG652-WG656.* Bristol Centaurus 18 engines and Rotol five-blade propellers.
Re-purchased by H.A.L., 1957-58: From R.N.A.S. Abbotsinch: *WG656.* From R.N.A.S. Anthorn: *WG652; WG655.*

The Hawker Netherlands Sea Fury F. (and F.B.) Mark 50. Production batch of 10 fighters built by Hawker Aircraft Ltd., Langley, under Contract No. N/SF/2001, dated 21 October 1946, as *10-1* to *10-10.* Further batch of 12 fighter-bombers built under Contract No. N/SF/3001, dated 12 January 1950.

The Hawker Iraqi Fury (or "Baghdad Fury"). Production batch of 30 single-seat fighters and fighter-bombers ordered on 4 December 1946, and built by Hawker Aircraft Ltd., Langley, during 1947-48. An order for four Fury Trainers was placed at the same time, but was subsequently reduced to two (one of these became the prototype Sea Fury T. Mark 20, *VX818;* see above under M.O.S. Contract No. 1998/47; the other was transferred to Contract No. 2203/SS/854 for Pakistan as *K850*). A further order for 25 single-seat Furies was placed by Iraq on 21 July 1951, and for three Fury Trainers on 7 March 1953, under Contract No. 53/I/012. All these aircraft were powered by Bristol Centaurus 18 engines with five-blade Rotol propellers).

The Hawker Pakistani Sea Fury Mark 60. Total of 93 single-seat fighters and fighter-bombers: 50 aircraft, *L900* to *L949,* built and delivered during 1950 under Contract No. 2795/49. One aircraft, *K857*, (previously F.2/43 Fury prototype, *NX802*) sold under Contract No. 3279/ PR.2259 dated 31 March 1949. 24 single-seaters delivered during 1951 under Contract No. A.1439/PR.8533 dated 23 January 1949, and 13 single-seaters delivered during 1951-52 under Contract No. A.1782/PR.9210 dated 21 February 1951. Five Sea Fury conversions delivered during 1953-54 under Contract No. A.3904/PRE.1434 dated 8 August 1951 (covered by Works Order No. 013304).

The Hawker Pakistani Sea Fury T. Mark 61. Total of 5 two-seat trainers. One aircraft, *K850*, transferred from Iraqi Contract and delivered under Contract No. 2795/49. Four aircraft, *K851-K854*, new-build, also delivered under this Contract.

The Hawker Egyptian Sea Fury. Twelve single-seat fighters delivered during 1950-51 under Contract No. 17/49/U.S.S. One further aircraft, formerly the F.2/43 Fury prototype, *NX798*, was also sold to Egypt.

The Hawker Burmese Sea Fury F.B. and T.T. Mark 11. Eighteen aircraft, selected from machines re-purchased by Hawker Aircraft Ltd. from the M.O.S. in 1957, reconditioned and sold to the Government of the Union of Burma under Contract HAL/57/B./030. *UB454-UB471*. Three of these aircraft were modified to tow targets (hook only, no winch). These aircraft were previously *VR928, VR929. VW566, VW667, VW694, VW717, VX628, VX656, VX693, WE720, WF615, WH585, WH613, WH619, WJ232, WJ280, WM488, WN486.*

The Hawker Burmese Sea Fury T. Mark 20. Three two-seat aircraft, selected from machines re-purchased by Hawker Aircraft Ltd. from the M.O.S. in 1957, reconditioned and sold under Contract HAL/57/B./030. *UB451-UB453.* Previously *VZ368, VZ292* and *VZ354* respectively.

The Hawker Cuban Sea Fury F.B. Mark 11 and T. Mark 20. Fifteen Mark 11s and two Mark 20s, selected from aircraft re-purchased from the M.O.S. in 1957, reconditioned and delivered without serial numbers by sea to Cuba during 1958 under Contract HAL/58/C./039.

The Hawker German Sea Fury T.T. Mark 20. Ten aircraft, selected from aircraft re-purchased from the M.O.S. in 1957-58, reconditioned and sold to *Deutsche Luftfahrt Beratungsdienst* during 1958-60, as follows: *ES.8501*, reg. *D-FIBO* (ex. *G-9-45*); *ES.8502*, reg. *D-AFMI* (ex. *G-9-49*); *ES.8503*, reg. *D-FATA* (ex. *G-9-37*); *ES.8504*, reg. *D-FOTE, ES.8505*, reg. *D-COCO* (ex. *G-9-59*); *ES.8506*, reg. *D-CEDO* (ex. *G-9-56*); *ES.8507*, reg. *D-CABU* (ex. *G-9-54*); *ES.8508*, reg. *D-CADA* (ex. *G-9-55*); *ES.8509*, reg. *D-CAFO* (ex. *G-9-57*) and *ES.8510*, reg. *D-CAME* (ex. *G-9-50*). Aircraft further modified in Germany for target-towing duties with a Swiss-designed target winch and gear. (Trial installation carried out by Hawker Aircraft Ltd. on Sea Fury T. Mark 20, *G-9-50*).

The Hawker P.1040. One prototype, *VP401*, designed and developed as a Private Venture during 1944 and 1945, eventually covered by Contract No. 6/Aircraft/234/CB.9b, and built during 1946-47 by Hawker Aircraft Ltd., Kingston, under Works Order No. 599190, dated 13 October 1945. Rolls-Royce Nene I (No. 30) turbojet. Component assembly at Kingston; final assembly at Langley and first flight at Boscombe Down on 2 September 1947.

The Hawker N.7/46. Two prototypes, *VP413* and *VP422*, designed to Naval Specification N.7/46, ordered under Contract No. 6/Aircraft/234/CB.9b from Hawker Aircraft Ltd., Kingston, and built under Works Order Nos. 599217 and 599221 respectively. Rolls-Royce Nene II (No. 136 in *VP413* and No. 210 in *VP422*). First flights: *VP413*, 3 September 1948; *VP422*, 17 October 1949.

The Hawker P.1052. Two research prototypes, *VX272* and *VX279*, designed to Air Ministry Specification E.38/46, ordered under Contract No. 6/Aircraft/1156/CB.9b, from Hawker Aircraft Ltd. and built during 1947-48 under Works Order Nos. 599297 dated 21-11-46, and No. 599330 dated 9-4-47 respectively. Rolls-Royce Nene IIs (No. 137 in *VX272*, and No. 143 in *VX279*). First flights: *VX272*, 19 November 1948; *VX279*, 13 April 1949. *VX272* later fitted with swept tailplane under Contract No. 4190.

The Hawker P.1072. One prototype, *VP401*, (originally P.1040, see above) modified to accommodate an Armstrong Siddeley Snarler liquid-fuel rocket in the tail. Contract No. 2688, and Works Order No. 010623, dated 18 January 1949. First flight, 16 November 1949 (without use of rocket); 20 November 1949 (using rocket).

The Hawker P.1081. One prototype, *VX279* (originally the second P.1052 prototype), modified as a Private Venture under Works Order No. 011900, dated 26 January 1950, to incorporate straight-through tail-pipe. Rolls-Royce Nene II (No. 143) turbojet. First flight, 9 June 1950. Crashed and struck off Company charge, 3 April 1951.

The Hawker Sea Hawk F. Mark 1. Production batch of 35 aircraft, designed to Naval Specification N.7/46 and built by Hawker Aircraft Ltd., Kingston, under Contract No. SP.6/Aircraft/3142/CB.7b, dated 22 November 1949. *WF143-WF161; WF167/WF177; WM901-WM905.* Rolls-Royce Nene RN.4 turbojet engines. [Made subject of "Super-Priority" order in 1951.]
  No. 804 Sqn.: *WF175; WF177; WM903; WM904.*
  No. 806 Sqn.: *WF169; WF171; WF173; WF902.*
  No. 898 Sqn.: *WF170; WF176; WM904.*
  Other Units and duties, etc.: *WF143* (fuel system and RATOG trials at R.A.E. and A. & A.E.E.); *WF144* (C.S.(A) aircraft, H.A.L., Dunsfold); *WF145* (miscellaneous radio trials, R.A.E.); *WF146* (generator cooling trials and trials with drop tanks at A. & A.E.E.); *WF147* (prototype **Sea Hawk Mark 2**; power-assisted aileron trials at Dunsfold); *WF148* (winterisation trials at C.E.P.E., Canada); *WF149* (gun firing trials at A. & A.E.E.; crashed due to faulty wing locking); *WF150* (trials with Rolls-Royce Ltd.); *WF157* (prototype **Sea Hawk Mark 3**; pressurised aircraft used for bombing trials with A. & A.E.E.); *WF161* (refrigeration trials at A. & A.E.E.); *WM901* (gun heating trials at A. & A.E.E.).

The Hawker Sea Hawk F. Mark 1. First production batch of 60 aircraft built by Sir W.G. Armstrong Whitworth Aircraft Ltd., Coventry, under Contract No. SP.6/Aircraft/9601/CB.5b. Rolls-Royce Nene RN.4 Mark 101 turbojets. *WF162-WF166; WF178-WF192; WF196-WF235.* Fighter version with provision for underwing drop tanks.
  No. 804 Sqn.: *WF200; WF202; WF207; WF208; WF210; WF211; WF212.*
  No. 806 Sqn.: *WF163; WF187; WF191; WF199.*
  No. 898 Sqn.: *WF183-WF195; WF187; WF192; WF213.*
  Other Units and duties, etc.: *WF164* (Naval Fighter School, Lossiemouth); *WF180* (N.A.E., Bedford); *WF196* (trial installation aircraft, Bitteswell); *WF218* (second Sea Hawk Mark 3 prototype).

The Hawker Sea Hawk F. Mark 2. Second production batch of 40 aircraft built by Sir W.G. Armstrong-Whitworth Aircraft Ltd., Coventry. *WF240-WF279.* Aircraft similar to Mark 1s but with fully-powered ailerons and spring-feel with centring.
  Allocation of test and other aircraft: *WF240* (handling and performance trials, A.W.A., Bitteswell, A. & A.E.E. and R.A.E.); *WF243* (N.A.E., Bedford; became prototype **Sea Hawk Mark 5** with Rolls-Royce Nene Mark 103 turbojet; trials at Bitteswell and A. & A.E.E.); *WF277* (Naval Fighter School, Lossiemouth).

The Hawker Sea Hawk F.B. Mark 3. Third production batch of 116 aircraft built by Sir W.G. Armstrong Whitworth Aircraft Ltd., Coventry. *WF280-WF289; WF293-WF303; WM906-WM945; WM960-WM999; WN105-WN119.* Engine and controls as for F. Mark 2, but provision made to carry two 500 lb. bombs or mines, or Phenolic-asbestos drop tanks under the wings.

No. 700 Sqn., T.R.U., Ford: *WF294; WF303; WM912.*

No. 736 Sqn.: *WF301; WM975; WN105.*

No. 800 Sqn.: *WM909; WN109; WN111; WN112; WN117.*

No. 801 Sqn.: *WF301; WF302; WM990; WM999; WN112; WN115; WN117.*

No. 806 Sqn.: *WM911; WM916; WM932; WM937; WM942; WN119.*

No. 897 Sqn.: *WF300; WM916; WM935; WM991; WN111.*

No. 898 Sqn.: *WM929; WM961; WM968; WM970; WM971; WM993.*

Other Units and duties, etc.: *WF299, WM982* (Naval Fighter School, Lossiemouth); *WM907* (radio trials, N.A.E., Bedford); *WM914* (F-94 camera trials, A. & A.E.E.); *WF280* (trial installations, Bitteswell); *WM992* (control system trials, Bitteswell and N.A.E., Bedford).

The Hawker Sea Hawk F.G.A. Mark 4. Fourth production batch of 97 aircraft built by Sir W.G. Armstrong Whitworth Aircraft Ltd., Coventry. *WV792-WV807; WV824-WV871; WV902-WV922; XE327-XE338.* Similar to Mark 2 but with provision to carry stores on four underwing pylons, or rocket projectiles and drop tanks. Rolls-Royce Nene Mark 101 turbojet.

No. 736 Sqn.: *WV803; WV830; WV805; WV919; XE328.*

No. 803 Sqn.: *WV836; WV842; WV851; WV893; WV854; WV857.*

No. 804 Sqn.: *WV802; WV827; WV833; WV852; WV865; WV914.*

No. 810 Sqn.: *XE329; XE331; XE337.*

No. 897 Sqn.: *WV920; WV922; XE330; XE338.*

Other Units and duties, etc.: *XE327* (N.A.F.D.U., West Raynham); *WV825* (trials with CATRAT and powered elevators); *WV840* (trials with flight refuelling probes on the underwing drop tanks); *XE327* (armament trials at A. & A.E.E.).

The Hawker Sea Hawk F.B. Mark 5. Conversion by Sir W.G. Armstrong Whitworth Aircraft Ltd. of Mark 3 aircraft to incorporate Rolls-Royce Nene Mark 103 turbojets (uprated to produce 5,200 lb. thrust). No new aircraft produced.

The Hawker Sea Hawk F.G.A. Mark 6. Production batch of 86 aircraft built by Sir W.G. Armstrong Whitworth Aircraft Ltd., Coventry. *XE339-XE344; XE362-XE411; XE435-XE463; XE490.* Equivalent to Mark 4s but with Rolls-Royce Nene Mark 103 engines.

No. 800 Sqn.: *XE339; XE341; XE371; XE372; XE376.*

No. 897 Sqn.: *XE343; XE365; XE368; XE379; XE381; XE399.*

No. 898 Sqn.: *XE344; XE375; XE377; XE380; XE384; XE390; XE405; XE436; XE460.*

No. 899 Sqn.: *XE364; XE382; XE383; XE388; XE402; XE411; XE444; XE462.*

Other aircraft: *XE369* (trial installations for Dutch Sea Hawk Mark 50); *XE456* (trial installations for German Sea Hawk Marks 100 and 101).

The Hawker Dutch Sea Hawk Mark 50. Production batch of 32 aircraft, similar to Sea Hawk Mark 6, built by Sir W.G. Armstrong Whitworth Aircraft Ltd., Coventry, during 1957-58. Rolls-Royce Nene Mark 103 turbojets. Included Phillips UHF radio.

The Hawker German Sea Hawk Mark 100 and 101. Production batch of 64 aircraft, developed from the Sea Hawk Mark 6, built by Sir W.G. Armstrong Whitworth Aircraft Ltd., Coventry, during 1957-59. The first 32 aircraft were interceptor fighters (Mark 100s) with gyro gunsights; the remaining 32 (Mark 101s) were all-weather fighters with EKCO search radar carried in a large underwing pod which necessitated increasing the fin and rudder area.

The Hawker Indian Sea Hawk. Production batch of 24 aircraft, similar to the F.G.A. Mark 6, built by Sir W.G. Armstrong Whitworth Aircraft Ltd., Coventry, in 1959-60. (The production line had been dismantled and this order necessitated re-assembly of the jigs.) Approximately 12 further aircraft (reconditioned F.A.A. Mark 4s and 6s) were supplied later in the 1960s, together with 28 ex-German Navy Mark 100s/101s. These Sea Hawks continued to serve on No. 300 Sqn., embarked in the INS *Vikrant*, until the late 1970s.

The Hawker P.1067 Hunter. Designed to Air Ministry Specification F.3/48, three prototypes, *WB188, WB195* and *WB202*, ordered from Hawker Aircraft Ltd., Kingston and Dunsfold, under Contract dated 25 June 1948. *WB188*, powered by Rolls-Royce Avon Ra.2, was unarmed. First flight, 20 July 1951, Sqn. Ldr. N.F. Duke, DSO, OBE, DFC, AFC. Performance and handling trials, Dunsfold and A. & A.E.E. to 1952. Fitted with Avon RA.7R turbojet with re-heat for attack on World Absolute Air Speed Record, September 1953. Became Ground Instruction Machine at No. 1 S. of T.T., Halton. *WB195* was armed prototype with four 30-mm Aden guns in detachable pack in nose. First flight, 5 May 1952. Employed in airbrake development and initial spinning trials. Became Ground Instruction Machine, *7284M*, at No. 1 S. of T.T., 3-59. *WB202* was prototype of Hunter Mark 2, powered by Armstrong Siddeley Sapphire axial-flow turbojet. First flight, 30 November 1952; full gun armament. Employed in early airbrake development and drop tank trials at Dunsfold. Later fitted with four dummy Firestreak AAMs.

The Hawker Hunter F. Mark 1. First production batch of 113 aircraft, designed to Specification F.3/48 (as amended), and built by Hawker Aircraft Ltd., Kingston and Dunsfold, under Contract No. SP/6/Aircraft/5910/CB.7a dated 14 March 1951. Instruction to Proceed received on 20 October 1950. *WT555-WT595; WT611-WT660; WT679-WT700*. First flight by *WT555*, 16 May 1953, by Frank Murphy. First few aircraft were completed without airbrakes, pending their development; all subsequently modified.

No. 43 (F) Sqn., Leuchars: *WT580; WT581* ("*S*"); *WT582-WT585; WT587; WT590; WT594* ("*N*"); *WT595; WT613* ("*R*"); *WT619; WT619; WT622* ("*G*"); *WT623; WT630; WT637; WT641* ("*T*"); *WT642-WT644; WT649* ("*N*").

No. 54 (F) Sqn., Odiham: *WT558* ("*T*"); *WT592; WT640; WT659* ("*U*"); *WT681; WT682; WT685-WT687; WT692* ("*S*"); *WT693; WT694; WT696; WT698.*

No. 222 (F) Sqn., Leuchars: *WT619* ("*B*"); *WT630* ("*T*"); *WT634; WT637* ("*G*"); *WT646-WT650; WT651* ("*C*").

No. 229 Operational Conversion Unit: *WT575; WT579; WT584; WT586; WT624-WT626; WT631; WT637; WT640; WT642; WT653; WT654; WT657; WT679; WT682; WT685; WT688; WT689* (crashed, 2-9-55); *WT691; WT695; WT696; WT699; WT700.*

No. 233 Operational Conversion Unit: *WT592; WT615; WT619; WT620; WT625; WT630; WT634-WT636; WT638; WT643; WT655; WT657; WT691; WT695.*

Air Fighting Development Sqn.: *WT576-WT578; WT588.*

Day Fighter Leaders' School: *WT591; WT593; WT613; WT617; WT627; WT629; WT639; WT641; WT645; WT652; WT658; WT660; WT683; WT684; WT690; WT692; WT694.*

Other Units and duties, etc.: H.A.L. trials aircraft: *WT555* (handling); *WT558* (gun-firing); *WT561* (T.I.s); *WT562* (one-third-span flaps); *WT563* (interim flying tail); *WT566* (airbrake development); *WT569, WT570* (full-power ailerons); *WT656* (flap-blowing); *WT697* (demonstration aircraft). A. & A.E.E. trials aircraft: *WT556* (familiarisation); *WT557* (radio trials); *WT559* (hood jettison trials); *WT564* (interception target aircraft); *WT567* (gun-firing); *WT568* (extended leading edge); *WT611, WT612* (trials with Avon 115); *WT616* (engine handling). R.A.E. trials aircraft: *WT571* ("area-ruled" Hunter); *WT572, WT633* (miscellaneous trials). Rolls-Royce test beds: *WT560; WT565; WT573* (Avon 119). Other aircraft: *WT615* (Fighter Weapons School); *WT621, WT628* (Empire Test Pilots' School); *WT680* (West Raynham Stn. Flt.); *WT632* (crashed at Kemble, 8-12-55).

The Hawker Hunter F. Mark 1. First production batch of 26 aircraft, built by Hawker Aircraft (Blackpool) Ltd., Blackpool. Contract No. SP/6/Aircraft/8435/CB.7(a), dated 15 August 1953. *WW599-WW610; WW632-WW645.* All aircraft completed with airbrakes from the outset.

No. 43 (F) Sqn., Leuchars: *WW599* ("*B*"); *WW600* ("*U*").

No. 54 (F) Sqn., Odiham: *WW610* ("*A*"); *WW636; WW640* ("*C*"); *WW641* ("*B*").

No. 222 (F) Sqn., Leuchars: *WW606.*

No. 247 (F) Sqn., Odiham: *WW638* ("*J*").

No. 229 Operational Conversion Unit: *WW602; WW606; WW607; WW632; WW634; WW636; WW637; WW643; WW644.*

No. 233 Operational Conversion Unit: *WW604; WW605; WW609; WW637.*

Day Fighter Leaders' School: *WW600; WW601; WW603; WW608; WW633; WW635* (crashed, 8-2-55); *WW638; WW639; WW641; WW645.*

Other Units: *WW610* (Fighter Weapons School); *WW642* (Air Fighting Development Squadron).

The Hawker Hunter F. Mark 2. Single production batch of 45 aircraft built by Sir W.G. Armstrong Whitworth Aircraft Ltd., Coventry. Contract No. SP/6/Aircraft/6315/CB.7a. *WN888-WN921; WN943-WN953.* 8,000 lb. thrust Armstrong Siddeley Sapphire 101 turbojet. First flight by *WN888,* 14 October 1953.

No. 257 (F) Sqn., Wattisham: *WN898* ("*A*"); *WN901* ("*B*"); *WN902* ("*D*"); *WN903; WN904* ("*Q*"); *WN907* ("*H*"); *WN909* ("*S*"); *WN914* ("*V*"); *WN915* ("*T*"); *WN917* ("*E*"); *WN918* ("*W*"); *WN919* ("*Q*"); *WN945* ("*M*"); *WN947* ("*W*"); *WN948* ("*R*"); *WN949* ("*M*"); *WN950* ("*F*"); *WN951; WN952* ("*G*"); *WN953* ("*C*").

No. 263 (F) Sqn., Wattisham: *WN897-WN899; WN900* ("*U*"); *WN903* ("*B*"); *WN908; WN912; WN913; WN915* ("*L*"); *WN919* ("*F*"); *WN921* ("*S*"); *WN944* ("*H*"); *WN946* ("*N*"); *WN947* ("*R*"); *WN948; WN951.*

Air Fighting Development Squadron: *WN895; WN906; WN911; WN912; WN916; WN920; WN921; WN945; WN946.*

No. 1 (F) Sqn. (temporary establishment): *WN898* ("*A*"); *WN918; WN919.*

Other Units and duties, etc.: *WN888* (CA aircraft, A.W.A.; to Dunsfold, 3-11-53); *WN889-WN894* (CA aircraft, A.W.A., A. & A.E.E., R.A.E., H.A.L.); *WN889* (trials with Sapphire ASSa.12 engine); *WN890* (de-tuner trials, A. & A.E.E., 11-62); *WN891* (to C.E.P.E., Canada, for winterisation trials); *WN896* (crashed and S.O.C., 1954); *WN899* (became Ground Instruction Machine, *7542M,* Henlow); *WN905* (crashed, 1955, and S.O.C.); *WN907* (R.A.F. Colerne, 8-68); *WN910* (R.A.F. Halton, 1964); *WN915* (Fire Fighting School, Sutton-on-Hull).

The Hawker Hunter Mark 3. (Company designation). P.1067, first prototype *WB188,* modified for trials with Rolls-Royce Avon RA.7R with reheat (in preparation for Hawker P.1083, see below) and side-mounted airbrakes. Established World Absolute Air Speed Records, 1953, flown by Sqn. Ldr. N.F. Duke.

The Hawker Hunter F. Mark 4. First production batch of 85 aircraft built by Hawker Aircraft Ltd., Kingston and Dunsfold, under Contract No. SP/6/5910/CB.7a (Second Part). *WT701-WT723; WT8734-WT780; WT795-WT811.* Rolls-Royce RA.7 Avon (Mark 113 or 115) turbojets. First flight by WT701, 20 October 1954, by Frank Murphy. Aircraft progressively modified with ammunition case collector fairings and extended wing leading edges (three aircraft only).

No. 4 (F) Sqn., Jever, Germany: *WT737; WT777* ("*U*"); *WT799; WT801* (wing leading edge extensions).

No. 14 (F) Sqn., Oldenburg, Germany: *WT711* ("*A*"); *WT714* (collided with *WT807,* 18-8-55, and crashed near Bremen); *WT723* ("*T*"); *WT745; WT749* ("*P*"); *WT755; WT761;*

WT767; WT797; WT806; WT807 (collided with *WT714*, 18-8-55, near Bremen; pilot ejected safely).

No. 26 (F) Sqn., Oldenburg, Germany: *WT722* ("*S*"); *WT763* ("*F*"); *WT769* ("*B*"); *WT778* ("*W*").

No. 43 (F) Sqn., Leuchars: *WT719*.

No. 54 (F) Sqn.: Odiham: *WT708* ("*F*"); *WT709* (crashed at Slinfold, Sussex, in bad weather, 3-11-55; pilot ejected safely); *WT710-WT712; WT721-WT723; WT740; WT764* ("*G*"); *WT800; WT810*.

No. 66 (F) Sqn., Linton-on-Ouse: *WT809* ("*G*").

No. 74 (F) Sqn., Horsham St. Faith: *WT720* ("*B*"); *WT764* ("*J*").

No. 92 (F) Sqn., Linton-on-Ouse: *WT719*.

No. 98 (F) Sqn., Jever, Germany: *WT742* ("*A*"); *WT747* ("*B*"); *WT761; WT777* ("*F*"); *WT802*.

No. 111 (F) Sqn., North Weald: *WT710* ("*N*"); *WT713-WT716; WT718; WT719; WT739; WT759* ("*B*"); *WT764; WT771; WT797; WT799; WT808* ("*G*"); *WT811* ("*H*").

No. 118 (F) Sqn.: Jever, Germany: *WT719; WT737* ("*N*"); *WT738* (collided with *WT757* near Hamburg, 20-10-55, and crashed); *WT741* ("*Q*"); *WT743* ("*R*"); *WT748* ("*S*"); *WT751; WT752* ("*D*"); *WT753* ("*E*"); *WT754; WT757* (collided with *WT738* near Hamburg, 20-10-55, and crashed); *WT760; WT768* ("*C*").

No. 130 (F) Sqn., Bruggen, Germany: *WT805* ("*X*").

No. 222 (F) Sqn., Leuchars: *WT737; WT771* ("*C*"); *WT808* ("*G*"); *WT811* ("*D*").

No. 247 (F) Sqn., Odiham: *WT750-WT753; WT762; WT764; WT768* ("*G*"); *WT775* ("*Q*"; S.O.C. after accident, 26-3-56); *WT795* ("*A*"); *WT802; WT804* ("*R*"); *WT810* ("*W*").

Converted to Hunter T. Mark 7 (see also below): *WT701*.

Converted to Hunter T. Mark 8 (see also below): *WT702; WT722; WT723; WT744; WT745; WT755* (see also **Kenyan Hunter T. Mark 81** below); *WT772; WT799*.

Converted to Hunter G.A. Mark 11 (see also below): *WT711; WT718; WT741* (see also **Singaporean Hunter T. Mark 75A** below); *WT744; WT804-WT806; WT808-WT810*.

Converted to Hunter P.R. Mark 11 (see also below): *WT721*.

Sold to Peru (see also **Peruvian Hunter Mark 52** and **T. Mark 62** below): *WT706; WT717; WT734; WT756; WT758; WT759; WT765; WT766; WT768; WT773; WT774; WT776; WT779; WT796; WT800; WT803*.

Converted to Swiss Hunter Mark 58A (see also below): *WT797*.

Converted to Chilean Hunter Mark 71 (see also below): *WT801*.

Other Units and duties, etc.: Trials with H.A.L., Dunsfold: *WT701, WT702* (CA aircraft; radio trials); *WT703* (CA aircraft; external stores); *WT704* (CA aircraft); *WT705* (CA aircraft; gunnery trials); *WT706* (CA aircraft); *WT735* (radio trials with American equipment); *WT751* (trials with 230-gallon drop tanks); *WT772* (TI with extended tailplane); *WT780* (TIs included five-camera nose; used to make film *High Flight* (Warwick Films); tail hook; drag chute development; ram-air turbine, etc). Trials with A. & A.E.E.: *WT701, WT702* (radio trials); *WT705* (gunnery trials; collided with banner target and damaged, 16-10-57; broken up, 11-64); *WT751* (jettison trials with empty 230-gallon drop tanks). Other aircraft: *WT770* (sold to Sweden for evaluation as *34001* and not flown in U.K.; became first **Swedish Hunter Mark 50**; see also below). WT708 (Fighter Weapons School); WT717 (North Weald Stn. Flt.); WT809 (Linton-on-Ouse Stn. Flt.).

The Hawker Hunter F. Mark 4. Second production batch of 100 aircraft built by Hawker Aircraft Ltd., Kingston and Dunsfold, under Contract No. SP/6/Aircraft/6867/CB.7a dated 9 May 1951. *WV253-WV281; WV314-WV334; WV363-WV412*. Rolls-Royce Avon RA.7 (Marks 115 and 119) turbojets. Provision for underwing l00-gallon drop tanks.

No. 4 (F) Sqn., Jever, Germany: *WV253; WV263; WV266* ("*T*"); *WV271* (crashed during beatup of Oldenburg airfield, 23-10-55); *WV274; WV275; WV279; WV316; WV321* ("*B*").

No. 14 (F) Sqn., Oldenburg, Germany: *WV259; WV277* ("*K*"); *WV318; WV377*.

No. 20 (F) Sqn., Gutersloh, Germany: *WV390; WV391; WV394* ("*E*"); *WV395* ("*W*"); *WV396-WV398; WV401; WV407; WV408; WV410* ("*X*"); *WV411* ("*D*").

No. 26 (F) Sqn., Oldenburg, Germany: *WV255* ("*X*"); *WV256; WV257* ("*E*"); *WV260; WV261; WV265* ("*V*"); *WV268* ("*T*"); *WV270* ("*Z*"); *WV318; WV364; WV369; WV377; WV390; WV398.*

No. 43 (F) Sqn., Leuchars: *WV314; WV315* ("*J*"); *WV324* ("*U*"); *WV333* ("*A*"); *WV366* ("*T*"); *WV378* ("*H*"); *WV387* ("*Q*").

No. 54 (F) Sqn., Odiham: *WV258; WV269; WV270; WV272; WV281* ("*M*"); *WV317; WV326; WV329* ("*D*"); *WV334* ("*C*"); *WV365; WV370; WV371; WV375* ("*A*"); *WV404.*

No. 66 (F) Sqn., Linton-on-Ouse: *WV278* ("*H*"); *WV314; WV315; WV385* ("*L*"); *WV389; WV392* (crashed during air firing sortie, 17-7-56); *WV400; WV409* ("*N*").

No. 67 (F) Sqn., Bruggen, Germany: *WV266* ("*B*"); *WV273* ("*D*"); *WV332* ("*X*"); *WV367* ("*X*"); *WV374* ("*T*"); *WV382* ("*C*"); *WV387; WV403* ("*T*").

No. 71 (F) Sqn., Bruggen Germany: *WV384* (crashed on landing, 5-4-57); *WV387.*

No. 74 (F) Sqn., Horsham St. Faith: *WV262* ("*T*"); *WV269* ("*H*"); *WV272* ("*L*"); *WV276* ("*P*"); *WV281* ("*Q*"); *WV314* ("*BH*"); *WV324* ("*C*"); *WV326; WV334* ("*E*"); *WV370* ("*M*"); *WV371* ("*N*").

No. 92 (F) Sqn., Linton-on-Ouse: *WV314* ("*B*").

No. 93 (F) Sqn., Jever, Germany: *WV267* ("*R*"); *WV268; WV277; WV318* (wing leading edge extensions); *WV364* ("*S*"); *WV368; WV377* ("*V*").

No. 98 (F) Sqn., Jever, Germany: *WV267; WV316; WV364; WV368; WV373; WV389.*

No. 111 (F) Sqn., North Weald: *WV258* ("*T*"); *WV264* ("*A*"); *WV275; WV277; WV321* ("*E*"); *WV327* ("*U*"); *WV379* ("*V*").

No. 112 (F) Sqn., Bruggen, Germany: *WV412* ("*A*"; crashed after engine flamed-out in landing circuit; pilot safe; 13-9-56).

No. 118 (F) Sqn., Jever, Germany: *WV263; WV274* (damaged during landing, 16-7-57; not repaired and S.O.C., 11-57); *WV364; WV368; WV373.*

No. 222 (F) Sqn., Leuchars: *WV314* ("*J*"); *WV320* ("*S*"); *WV321; WV327* ("*U*"); *WV372* ("*H*"); *WV376* ("*W*"); *WV378; WV381* ("*Q*"); *WV386* ("*G*"); *WV388* ("*R*"; crashed into sea during night landing approach, 25-3-57); *WV389; WV399* ("*B*"); *WV405* ("*A*"); *WV406* ("*F*").

No. 234 (F) Sqn., Geilenkirchen, Germany: *WV266* ("*B*"); *WV332* ("*P*"); *WV363* ("*K*"); *WV367* ("*J*"); *WV409* ("*K*").

No. 245 (F) Sqn., Stradishall: *WV330* ("*D*").

No. 247 (F) Sqn., Odiham: *WV254; WV262* ("*D*"); *WV267; WV317* ("*S*"); *WV328* (burnt and destroyed by fire after starter explosion, 25-1-56); *WV365; WV389; WV404* ("*T*").

No. 229 Operational Conversion Unit: *WV254; WV256; WV275; WV277; WV279; WV330; WV385; WV386; WV389; WV391* (crashed while landing, 5-6-58); *WV394; WV396-WV399; WV400* (Iraqi student pilot omitted to lower wheels for landing at Chivenor, 6-3-59); *WV401; WV402; WV404-WV406; WV408; WV409* ("*ES-K*"; aircraft jumped chocks on starting, collided with Hunter 6 *XG210* and destroyed, 3-61); *WV410* (Iraqi pilot accidentally landed on the bed of the River Taw at Chivenor, 20-3-59; same pilot as in *WV400* above); *WV411.*

R.A.F. Flying College, Manby: *WV280; WV380; WV383; WV390; WV407.*

Central Fighter Establishment (A.F.D.S., D.F.L.S., etc.): *WV385; WV400.*

Fighter Weapons School: *WV264; WV376* ("*J*"); *WV381* ("*F*").

Central Flying School: *WV318; WV319; WV325.*

Converted to Hunter T. Mark 7 (see also below): *WV253* (T.Mk.7 Special); *WV318* (later T.Mk.7A); *WV372.*

Converted to Hunter T. Mark 8 (see also below): *WV319; WV322; WV363; WV396* (T.Mk.8C); *WV397* (T.Mk.8C).

Converted to Hunter G.A. Mark 11 (see also below): *WV256; WV257; WV267; WV374; WV380.*

582

Converted to Swiss Hunter Mark 58A (see also below): *WV257; WV261; WV266; WV329; WV380; WV393; WV404; WV405; WV411.*

Converted to Swiss Hunter T. Mark 68 (see also below): *WV332; WV398.*

Converted to Chilean Hunter Mark 71 (see also below): *WV326* (FR. Mk.71A).

Converted to Jordanian Hunter Mark 73 (see also below): *WV325* (Mark 73A); *WV407* (Mark 73A); *WV408* (Mark 73A).

Converted to Singaporean Hunter Mark 74 (see also below): *WV257* (Mark 74B); *WV331* (Mark 74B); *WV364* (Mark 74B); *WV366* (Mark 74B).

Converted to Singaporean Hunter T. Mark 75 (see also below): *WV272* (T.Mk. 75A); *WV386* (T.Mk. 75A).

Converted to Abu Dhabian Hunter Mark 76 (see also below): *WV389* (FGA Mk. 76); *WV400* (FR.Mk.76A).

Ground Instruction Machines (B.B.O.C. and returned to H.A.L. for restoration to flying condition and re-sale): *WV258* (*7779M*); *WV261* (*7780M*); *WV272* (*7782M*); *WV326* (*7669M*); *WV329* (*7671M*); *WV331* (*7783M*); *WV332* (*7673M*); *WV364* (*7674M*); *WV366; WV404* (*7768M*).

Other Units and duties, etc.: *WV276* (A. & A.E.E.: trials with Rolls-Royce Avon 121 engine); *WV278* (Paris Air Show, 6-55); *WV374* (R.A.E.); *WV385* (H.A.L. trials with Avon 115 engine; to No. 3 C.A.A.C.U., Exeter, 5-60); *WV405, WV411* (transferred to Admiralty charge; HMS *Condor*, Arbroath, 1-66); *WV406* (No. 3 C.A.A.C.U., Exeter).

The Hawker Hunter F. Mark 4. Third production batch of three aircraft, *WW589-WW591*, built by Hawker Aircraft Ltd., Kingston and Dunsfold, in 1955 under Contract No. SP/6/7144/CB.7a dated 19 July 1951. Instruction to Proceed received 12-7-51. (Remainder of this production batch transferred to Hawker Aircraft (Blackpool) Ltd.; see Contract No. 8435). First flight by *WW589*, 6-10-55, by David Lockspeiser.

No. 20 (F) Sqn.: Gutersloh, Germany: *WW589; WW590.*

No. 229 Operational Conversion Unit: *WW589; WW590.*

Converted to Swiss Hunter Mark 58A (see also below): *WW589; WW590.*

Ground Instruction Machine (B.B.O.C., and returned to H.A.L. for restoration to flying condition and re-sale): *WW589* (*7943M*).

Other Aircraft: *WW591* (ff. 4-10-55; sold to Denmark as first **Danish Hunter Mark 51**, 2-11-55).

The Hawker Hunter F. Mark 4. First production batch of 20 aircraft, *WW646-WW665*, built by Hawker Aircraft (Blackpool) Ltd., Blackpool, during 1954-55 under Contract No. SP/6/Aircraft/8435/CB.7a dated 15 August 1952. Rolls-Royce Avon Mark 115 turbojets. First flight by *WW646*, 20-1-55.

No. 14 (F) Sqn., Oldenburg, Germany: *WW663* ("*H*").

No. 26 (F) Sqn.: Oldenburg, Germany: *WW664* ("*C*").

No. 98 (F) Sqn., Jever, Germany: *WW647* ("*C*"); *WW648* ("*D*"); *WW649* ("*E*"); *WW650* ("*F*"); *WW651; WW652* ("*G*"); *WW653; WW654* ("*L*"); *WW655* ("*M*"); *WW656* ("*N*"); *WW658* ("*O*"); *WW661.*

No. 111 (F) Sqn., North Weald: *WW646* ("*P*"); *WW651* ("*F*").

No. 118 (F) Sqn., Jever, Germany: *WW567* ("*G*"); *WW660* ("*B*").

No. 222 (F) Sqn., Leuchars: *WW650* ("*R*"); *WW651; WW652* ("*H*").

No. 245 (F) Sqn., Stradishall: *WW665.*

No. 247 (F) Sqn.: Odiham: *WW646* ("*P*"); *WW647* ("*A*"); *WW648* ("*C*"); *WW652; WW659* ("*V*"); *WW665* ("*E*").

No. 229 Operational Conversion Unit: *WW648; WW654; WW658* ("*RS-5*"); *WW660.*

Converted to Hunter T. Mark 8 (see also below): *WW664* (T.Mk. 8B prototype).

Converted to Hunter G.A. Mark 11 (see also below): *WW654; WW659.*

Converted to Peruvian Hunter Mark 52 (see also below): *WW662.*

Converted to Swiss Hunter Mark 58 (see also below): *WW659* (Mk. 58A).
Converted to Chilean Hunter Mark 71 (see also below): *WW653* (FGA Mk. 71).
Converted to Singaporean Hunter T. Mark 75 (see also below): *WW664.*
Ground Instruction Machines (B.B.O.C., and returned to H.A.L. for restoration to flying condition and re-sale): *WW653 (7784M).*
Other Aircraft: *WW646* (A. & A.E.E.; check on manufacturing standards).

The Hawker Hunter F. Mark 4. Second production batch of 100 aircraft built by Hawker Aircraft (Blackpool) Ltd., Blackpool, during 1955-56 under Contract No. SP/6/Aircraft/9817/CB.7a dated 24 August 1953. *XE657-XE689; XE702-XE718; XF289-XF324; XF357-XF370.* Rolls-Royce Avon 115 turbojets (many later changed to Avon 121 engines). First flight by *XE657*, 3 May 1955.

No. 3 (F) Sqn., Geilenkirchen, Germany: *XE715 ("L"); XF359; XF360; XF363.*

No. 4 (F) Sqn., Jever, Germany: *XE663 ("V"); XE666 ("X"); XE667 ("Z"); XE668 ("X"); XE677 ("M"); XE684; XE703 ("J"); XF315; XF367; XF368 ("N"); XF370.*

No. 14 (F) Sqn., Oldenburg, Germany: *XE657 ("Y"); XE708; XE710 ("R").*

No. 26 (F) Sqn., Oldenburg, Germany: *XE668 ("G"); XE670; XE675 ("H"; wing leading edge extensions); XF312.*

No. 43 (F) Sqn., Leuchars: *XE663 ("V"); XE664 ("F"); XE702 ("B"); XE705 ("P"); XE706 ("P"); XE709 ("Q"); XE712 ("U"); XF299 ("O"); XF301 ("L"); XF302 ("S"); XF314 ("N"); XF315.*

No. 54 (F) Sqn., Odiham: *XE658 ("R"); XE659; XE661 ("B"); XE671 ("K"; crashed after flame-out, 1-5-56); XE683 ("S").*

No. 66 (F) Sqn., Linton-on-Ouse: *XE659; XE681 ("J"); XE713 ("E"); XF303 ("A"); XF304 ("B"); XF319 ("F").*

No. 67 (F) Sqn., Bruggen, Germany: *XE689 ("W"); XE713; XE716 ("A"); XE717 ("G"); XF289-XF291; XF296 ("Z"); XF305* (destroyed by fire at Sylt following simultaneous firing of two starter cartridges, 28-11-56); *XF317 ("U").*

No. 71 (F) Sqn., Bruggen, Germany: *XE715; XF312; XF313 ("G"); XF316; XF365-XF368.*

No. 74 (F) Sqn., Horsham St. Faith: *XE658; XE661 ("F"); XE662 ("S";* aircraft crashed on landing at Horsham St. Faith, 25-5-57); *XE683 ("G"); XE688 ("A").*

No. 92 (F) Sqn., Linton-on-Ouse: *XE659 ("J"); XE702 ("E"); XE705 ("F"); XE706 ("L"); XF324 ("D").*

No. 93 (F) Sqn., Jever, Germany: *XE670 ("D"); XE675 ("E"); XE677 ("Q"); XE684; XE685; XE687 ("C"); XE703 ("P"); XE707; XE718 ("A"); XF315.*

No. 98 (F) Sqn., Jever, Germany: *XE669* (aircraft crashed following explosion shortly after take-off, 4-12-56); *XE684; XE685; XE687; XE718 ("A").*

No. 111 (F) Sqn., North Weald: *XE666; XE675; XE677; XE679 ("B"); XE684; XE705.*

No. 112 (F) Sqn., Bruggen, Germany: *XE672 ("B"); XE673 ("C"); XE674 ("D"); XE704 ("S"); XE714; XF293 ("N"); XF298; XF306 ("E"); XF307 ("F"); XF309 ("C"); XF312 ("T"); XF313; XF316 ("R"); XF322; XF358 ("P"); XF362 ("Q"); XF366 ("R").*

No. 118 (F) Sqn., Jever, Germany: *XE665 ("A"); XE682; XE687 ("F"); XE703 ("B"); XE707; XF318 ("Z"); XF368 ("N"); XF370.*

No. 130 (F) Sqn., Bruggen, Germany: *XE680 ("Y"); XE715; XF292 ("A"); XF294 ("B"); XF295 ("C"); XF297; XF298 ("G"); XF300 ("W"); XF308 ("F"); XF311 ("V"); XF318 ("Z"); XF321("G"); XF357; XF359-XF361; XF364.*

No. 222 (F) Sqn., Leuchars: *XE676 ("U"); XE678 ("X"); XE679 ("Y"); XE688; XE709 ("D"); XE712 ("E"); XF324 ("K").*

No. 234 (F) Sqn., Geilenkirchen, Germany: *XE673; XE680 ("L"); XE689; XE714; XE717 ("G"); XF293 ("N"); XF296 ("H"); XF297 ("D"); XF300 ("P"); XF360; XF363; XF364; XF369 ("M").*

No. 245 (F) Sqn., Stradishall: *XE666 ("R"); XE686 ("O").*

No. 247 (F) Sqn., Odiham: *XE660 ("H";* aircraft crashed from formation flying between Alton and Lasham, 5-12-56); *XE662* ("*Z*"); *XE686* ("*H*"); *XF320* ("*R*").

No. 229 Operational Conversion Unit: *XE659* ("*RS-23*"); *XE666* ("*ES-D*"); *XE675; XE677; XE684; XE686* ("*ES-C*"); *XE708; XE710; XF314* ("*RS-24*"); *XF320* ("*RS-4*"); *XF360* ("*ES-K*"); *XF361* ("*RS-22*"); *XF363-XF366; XF368.*

Converted to Hunter T. Mark 7 (see also below): *XF310; XF321.*

Converted to Hunter T. Mark 8 (see also below): *XE664; XE665; XF289; XF322; XF357* (later to T.Mk.8C); *XF358.*

Converted to Hunter G.A. Mark 11 (see also below): *XE673; XE674; XE680; XE682; XE685; XE689; XE716; XE717; XF291; XF297; XF300; XF301; XF368.*

Converted to Swiss Hunter Mark 58A (see also below): *XE659; XE674; XE678; XE717; XF303; XF306; XF308; XF312; XF316; XF318; XF361; XF365; XF370.*

Converted to Swiss Hunter T. Mark 68 (see also below): *XE702.*

Converted to Chilean Hunter Mark 71 (see also below): *XF302* (FGA Mk.71); *XF317* (FR Mk.71A); *XF323* (FGA Mk.71).

Converted to Chilean Hunter T. Mark 72 (see also below): *XE704.*

Converted to Jordanian Hunter FGA Mark 73A (see also below): *XF364.*

Converted to Singaporean Hunter Mark 74 (see also below): *XE679* (Mk. 74B); *XF360* (FR Mk. 74B); *XF369* (FR Mk. 74B).

Converted to Singaporean Hunter T. Mark 75 (see also below): *XE664.*

Converted to Abu Dhabian Hunter FGA Mark 76 (see also below): *XF362; XF367.*

Converted to Kenyan Hunter Mark 80 (see also below): *XF309.*

Ground Instruction Machines (B.B.O.C. and returned to H.A.L. for restoration to flying condition and re-sale): *XE659* (*7785M*); *XE678; XE679* (*7787M*); *XE702* (*7794M*); *XE704* (*7788M*); *XF302* (*7774M*); *XF303* (*A2565*); *XF306* (*7776M*); *XF308* (*7777M*); *XF309* (*7771M*); *XF311* (*A2566*; supplied in non-flying condition as Ground Instruction Machine to Singapore, 31-1-70); *XF316* (*7778M*): *XF317* (*7773M*); *XF318* (*A2567*); *XF369* (*7941M*); *XF370* (*7772M*).

Other Units and duties, etc.: *XE665, XF315* (Jever Stn. Flt.); *XE676* (Fighter Weapons School); *XE677* (refurbished and present to Loughborough College, 11-61); *XE686* (Air Fighting Development Sqn.); *XE702* (trials at A. & A.E.E. with various external stores); *XE711, XF323, XF367, XF369* (R.A.F. Flying College, Manby); *XE714* (Bruggen Stn. Flt.); *XF295* (F.T.U., Benson); *XF303, XF311, XF318* (transferred to Admiralty charge; HMS *Condor*, Arbroath); *XF304* (Turnhouse Stn. Flt., "*MR*"); *XF310* (Fairey Aviation Ltd., experimental Fairey Fireflash AAM installation); *XF370* (Sylt Stn. Flt.; R.A.F. Staff College, Strubby).

The Hawker Hunter F. Mark 4. Third production batch of 57 aircraft built by Hawker Aircraft (Blackpool) Ltd., Blackpool, during 1956 under Contract No. SP/6/Aircraft/10344/CB.7a. *XF932-XF953; XF967-XF999; XG341* and *XG342.* Rolls-Royce Avon 121 turbojets. First flight by *XF932* (and *XF933*), 23-3-56.

No. 3 (F) Sqn., Geilenkirchen, Germany: *XF947* ("*S*"); *XF948* ("*J*"); *XF949* ("*C*"; aircraft burned after two starter cartridges fired simultaneously, 13-1-57); *XF950* ("*M*"); *XF951* ("*P*"); *XF967* ("*Z*"); *XF968* ("*R*"); *XF969* ("*D*"); *XF971* ("*K*"); *XF972* ("*V*"); *XF974* ("*G*"); *XF975* ("*W*"); *XF976; XF990* ("*K*").

No. 4 (F) Sqn., Jever, Germany: *XF984.*

No. 14 (F) Sqn., Oldenburg, Germany: *XF936; XF972.*

No. 20 (F) Sqn., Gutersloh, Germany: *XF978; XF983.*

No. 26 (F) Sqn., Oldenburg, Germany: *XF970; XF972; XF978; XF983; XF989* ("*A*").

No. 43 (F) Sqn., Leuchars: *XF982* ("*D*"); *XF992* ("*C*"); *XF993; XF997* (pilot overshot landing trying to avoid flock of birds and crashed, 28-6-56); *XG341* ("*H*").

No. 54 (F) Sqn., Odiham: *XF998* ("*A*").

No. 66 (F) Sqn., Linton-on-Ouse: *XF973; XF994; XG342.*

No. 71 (F) Sqn.: Bruggen, Germany: *XF937; XF938* ("*D*"); *XF939-XF942; XF972; XF973;*

XF984; XF985.

No. 74 (F) Sqn.: Horsham St. Faith: *XF940* ("*F*"); *XF993* (engine seized during ground run and destroyed aircraft, 1960).

No. 93 (F) Sqn.: Jever, Germany: *XF987.*

No. 98 (F) Sqn., Jever, Germany: *XF996.*

No. 111 (F) Sqn., North Weald: *XF951; XF976; XF990; XG342* ("*A*").

No. 112 (F) Sqn., Bruggen, Germany: *XF937* ("*K*"); *XF986* ("*A*").

No. 118 (F) Sqn., Jever, Germany: *XF977* ("*A*"); *XF987.*

No. 130 (F) Sqn., Bruggen, Germany: *XF970.*

No. 222 (F) Sqn., Leuchars: *XG342* ("*W*").

No. 234 (F) Sqn., Geilenkirchen, Germany: *XF932* ("*A*"; crashed on take-off at Kleim-Brogel following engine failure, 22-9-56); *XF934* ("*C*"); *XF935* ("*D*"); *XF936* ("*E*"); *XF937; XF943* ("*F*"); *XF944* ("*G*"); *XF945* ("*H*"; crashed at night following flame-out at 20,000 ft., 20-11-56); *XF946* ("*L*"); *XF952; XF970; XF986; XF991* ("*A*").

No. 245 (F) Sqn., Stradishall: *XF998.*

No. 247 (F) Sqn., Odiham: *XF995; XF996; XG342.*

No. 229 Operational Conversion Unit: *XF938; XF939; XF941; XF942; XF947; XF948* (aircraft crashed into sea off Lundy Isle after take-off, 7-11-57); *XF951; XF952; XF968; XF970; XF972; XF974; XF975* ("*RS-27*"); *XF976* ("*RS-15*"); *XF982* ("*RS-23*"); *XF983; XF984* ("*ES-55*"); *XF986* (crashed at Milton Damerel, Devon, 7-8-59); *XF987; XF989; XF990* ("*RS-16*"); *XF991; XF993-XF995; XF996* (ailerons jammed in landing circuit and aircraft crashed at Saunton Sands, 6-5-59); *XF998; XG342.*

Central Flying School: *XF934; XF943; XF944; XF999.*

R.A.F. Flying College, Manby: *XF979* ("*A*"); *XF980* (collided with Gloster Javelin, 24-8-56, and crashed); *XF981; XF988; XG341.*

Converted to Hunter T. Mark 8 (see also below); *XF938* (T. Mk.8B); *XF939* (T. Mk.8B); *XF942* (T. Mk.8C); *XF967* (T. Mk.8C); *XF978* (T. Mk.8B); *XF983* (T. Mk.8C); *XF985* (T. Mk.8C); *XF991* (T. Mk.8B); *XF992* (T. Mk.8B); *XF994* (T. Mk.8B); *XF995* (T. Mk.8C).

Converted to Hunter G.A. Mark 11 (see also below). *XF977.*

Converted to Swiss Hunter Mark 58A (see also below); *XF933; XF937; XF941; XF944; XF947; XF973; XF976; XF981; XF984; XF990; XF998.*

Converted to Swiss Hunter T. Mark 68 (see also below); *XF951.*

Converted to Chilean FR Mark 71A (see also below); *XF982.*

Converted to Jordanian Hunter Mark 73 (see also below); *XF936* (FGA Mk.73A); *XF952* (FGA Mk.73A); *XF968* (FGA Mk.73A); *XF979* (FGA Mk.73B); *XF987* (FGA Mk.73A).

Converted to Singaporean Hunter FR. Mark 74B (see also below): *XF969.*

Converted to Singaporean Hunter T. Mark 75A (see also below): *XF950; XF970.*

Converted to Abu Dhabian Hunter Mark 76 (see also below); *XF935* (FGA Mk.76); *XF971* (FR Mk.76A); *XG341* (FGA Mk.76).

Converted to Kenyan Hunter FGA Mark 80 (see also below): *XF972; XF975.*

Ground Instruction Machines (B.B.O.C. and returned to H.A.L. for restoration to flying condition and re-sale): *XF941* (*8006M*); *XF947* (*A2568*); *XF972* (*7948M*); *XF975* (*7945M*); *XF984* (*A2570*).

Other Units and duties, etc.: *XF940;* (Empire Test Pilots' School; crashed near Farnborough after running out of fuel, 13-10-61); *XF947, XF984* (transferred to Admiralty charge, HMS *Condor*, Arbroath); XF950 (Geilenkirchen Stn. Flt.); *XF969* (Empire Test Pilots' School); *XF970* (A. & A.E.E., tropical trials, Idris, 18-6-56); *XF977* (Sylt Stn. Flt.); *XF979* (Staff College, Strubby); *XF987* (No. 3 C.A.A.C.U., Exeter); *XF994* (A.F.D.S., C.F.E.).

The Hawker Hunter F. Mark 5. One production batch of 105 aircraft built by Sir W.G. Armstrong Whitworth Aircraft Ltd., Coventry, under Contract No. SP/6/Aircraft/6315/

CB.7a during 1954-55. *WN954-WN992; WP101-WP150; WP179-WP194.* Armstrong Siddeley Sapphire Mark 101 turbojet. First flight by *WN954,* 19 October 1954. Provision made to carry underwing drop tanks.

No. 1 (F) Sqn., Tangmere: *WN956* ("*P*"); *WN959* ("*A*"); *WN962* ("*N*"); *WN973* ("*B*"); *WN974* ("*H*"); *WN975* ("*C*"); *WN977* ("*P*"; collided with *WP137,* 5-5-58, and SOC); *WN978* ("*F*"); *WN980* ("*F*"); *WN982; WN986* ("*P*"); *WN988* ("*A*"); *WP103* ("*C*"); *WP105* ("*R*"); *WP112* ("*D*"); *WP113* ("*Q*"); *WP116* ("*D*"); *WP117* ("*R*"); *WP118* ("*S*"); *WP119* ("*T*"); *WP120* ("*R*"); *WP121* ("*W*"); *WP126; WP127* ("*G*"); *WP131* ("*V*"); *WP137* ("*S*"; crashed after collision with *WN977,* 5-5-58); *WP138; WP141* ("*GRC*"); *WP143; WP144* ("*PJS*"); *WP146* ("*H*"); *WP147* ("*G*"); *WP180* ("*F*"); *WP182* ("*V*"); *WP188* ("*X*"); *WP190* ("*K*"); *WP191* ("*Z*").

No. 34 (F) Sqn., Nicosia, Cyprus and Tangmere: *WN963; WN967; WN970* ("*L*"); *WN978* ("*B*"); *WP111* ("*M*"); *WP112* ("*E*"); *WP113* ("*V*"); *WP124; WP126* ("*R*"); *WP127* ("*O*"); *WP130* ("*S*"); *WP132* ("*T*"); *WP133* ("*L*"); *WP136* ("*N*"); *WP139* ("*J*"); *WP140* ("*R*"); *WP142* ("*L*", later "*W*"); *WP144* ("*JRG*"); *WP145* ("*X*"); *WP149* ("*H*"); *WP182* ("*C*"); *WP184* ("*A*"); *WP185* ("*E*"); *WP191; WP192* ("*D*"; crashed, 9-57); *WP193.*

No. 41 (F) Sqn., Biggin Hill: *WN956* ("*G*"); *WN961* ("*G*"); *WN962; WN963* ("*F*"); *WN964* ("*C*"); *WN965* ("*P*"); *WN966* ("*M*"); *WN967* ("*A*"); *WM968; WN969* ("*N*"); *WN972* ("*U*"); *WN983* ("*T*"); *WN984* ("*C*"); *WN985* ("*P*"); *WN986* ("*M*"); *WN988* ("*H*"); *WP103; WP108* ("*S*"); *WP112; WP117* ("*N*"); *WP119* ("*L*"); *WP122* ("*A*"); *WP123* ("*O*"); *WP128* ("*C*"; crashed and SOC); *WP129* ("*J*"); *WP133* ("*D*"); *WP134; WP135* ("*E*"; crashed Anglesey, 5-5-56); *WP141* ("*B*"); *WP147* ("*L*"); *WP148* ("*K*"); *WP180* ("*H*"); *WP181* ("*P*"); *WP187* ("*R*"); *WP190; WP194.*

No. 56 (F) Sqn., Waterbeach: *WN968* ("*P*"); *WN970* ("*M*"); *WN971* ("*T*"); *WN976* ("*P*"); *WN979* ("*E*"); *WN982* ("*H*"); *WN984* ("*O*"); *WN986* ("*H*"); *WN987* ("*C*"); *WN990* ("*U*"); *WN992* ("*U*"); *WN101* ("*N*"); *WP102* ("*Q*"); *WP103* ("*J*"); *WP104* ("*A*"); *WP106* ("*F*"); *WP109* ("*B*"); *WP110* ("*M*"); *WP115* ("*G*"); *WP116* ("*W*"); *WP120* ("*S*"); *WP123* ("*B*"); *WP125* ("*R*"); *WP136* ("*D*"); *WP139* ("*O*"); *WP148* ("*G*"); *WP149* ("*H*"); *WP183* ("*V*"); *WP186* ("*AW*"); *WP194* ("*H*").

No. 257 (F) Sqn., Wattisham: *WN961; WN963* ("*T*"); *WP102; WP118* ("*W*"); *WP143* ("*M*"; crashed and SOC, 1956).

No. 263 (F) Sqn., Wattisham: *WN972; WN975; WN976* ("*P*"); *WN980; WN981* ("*V*"); *WN983; WN989* (crashed and SOC); *WN990* ("*F*"); *WP102; WP103; WP105; WP107* ("*A*"; crashed near Wymeswold, 25-11-56); *WP108* ("*T*"); *WP134; WP179* ("*W*"); *WP181.*

Other Units and duties, etc.: *WN954* (A. & A.E.E.; handling and performance trials; later target towing); *WN955, WP114* (to Armstrong Siddeley Motors Ltd.; flight trials with Sapphire ASSa.7 engines); *WN956* (A. & A.E.E., fuel system trials); *WN957, WN961* (R.A.E., miscellaneous trials); *WN958* (A. & A.E.E, external store trials); *WN967; WP119, WP120* (fatigue tested to destruction by H.A.L., 3-62); *WN976, WN990* (Wattisham Stn. Flt); *WN985, WN991* (A.F.D.S.; tactical evaluation trials); *WP143* (miscellaneous trials at A. & A.E.E. and R.A.E.); *WP150* (miscellaneous trials at A.W.A. and A. & A.E.E.); *WP185* (became Ground Instruction Machine, *7583M*); *WP189* (Metropolitan Sector Cdr's aircraft).

The Hawker P.1083. One prototype, *WN470,* ordered under Contract No. 6/Aircraft/6296/CB.7b from Hawker Aircraft Ltd., Kingston. Manufacture covered by Works Order Nos. 013021 to 013034. Design directly developed from the Hunter but employed 50-degree swept wing and Rolls-Royce Avon RA.14R with reheat. Prototype was approximately 70 per cent completed, but was cancelled on 9 July 1953.

The Hawker P.1099 Hunter Mark 6. Prototype Hunter Mark 6, *XF833.* Aircraft used front and centre fuselage components of cancelled P.1083 (see above). Ordered from Hawker Aircraft

Ltd., Kingston, under Contract No. 6/Aircraft/10032/CB.7b. First flight, 22 January 1954, by Sqn. Ldr. N.F. Duke. Extensive flying trials at Dunsfold and A. &. A.E.E., 1954-56. Delivered to Miles Aircraft Ltd., Shoreham, 5-6-56, to be fitted with Rolls-Royce thrust-reversal system.

The Hawker Hunter F. Mark 6. First production batch of seven pilot production (development) aircraft (employing Pre-Mod. 228 Mark 4 wings), built by Hawker Aircraft Ltd., Kingston, and Dunsfold, under Contract No. 6/Aircraft/7144/CB.8a (Part 2), during 1955. *WW592-WW598.* First flight by *WW592*, 23 May 1955, by A.W. Bedford.

WW592 ff. 23-5-55. Performance trials, H.A.L. and A.&.A.E.E., 1955-56. Repurchased by H.S.A., 1968. Converted to **Abu Dhabian Hunter FR Mark 76A** (see also below); crashed and SOC, 1971.

WW593 ff. 19-8-55, Frank Bullen. Miscellaneous TIs, H.A.L. and A. & A.E.E. Returned to H.A.L., 1960. Converted to **Hunter FR Mark 10.**

WW594 ff. 23-9-55, Frank Bullen. Was modified by H.A.L. to become **P.1109A**; aerodynamic test aircraft for de Havilland Firestreak AAM installation; missiles not fitted. Refurbished to standard, then converted to **Hunter FR Mark 10**, 1961. Repurchased by H.S.A., 7-74, and converted to **Lebanese FGA Mark 70A** (see also below).

WW595 ff. 29-9-55, Hugh Merewether. To H.A.L. (Blackpool) for TIs. To H.A.L., Dunsfold 13-10-59. Converted to **Hunter FR Mark 10.** Written off at Gutersloh, 24-1-67.

WW596 ff. 10-10-55, Frank Bullen. CA aircraft. TIs at Blackpool. Day Fighter Conversion School. Returned to H.S.A., 14-10-59. Converted to **Hunter F.R. Mark 10.** Repurchased by H.S.A., 2-3-71. Converted to **Indian Hunter T. Mark 66E.**

WW597 ff. 10-10-55, Duncan Simpson. Stored, 1955-58. Returned to H.S.A., 1958. Converted to **Jordanian Hunter Mark 6.**

WW598 ff. 31-12-55, Frank Bullen. TIs at Dunsfold. To R.A.E., Farnborough and Bedford, High Speed Flight. Converted to **P.1109A** standard (see *WW594*) and employed on tropical low-altitude gust investigation. Repurchased by H.S.A., 14-5-74, as *G-9-424* (with 1,291 flying hours). Converted to **Lebanese Hunter FGA Mark 70A.**

The Hawker Hunter F. Mark 6. Second production batch of 100 aircraft built by Hawker Aircraft Ltd., Kingston and Dunsfold, during 1955-56. *XE526-XE561; XE579-XE628; XE643-XE656.* Aircraft not completed with wing leading edge extensions, but later modified, together with gun blast deflectors. Seven aircraft returned to H.A.L. and sold to India as Hunter Mark 56s; twelve aircraft returned to H.A.L. from Maintenance Units for sale to Switzerland as Mark 58s. First flight by *XE526*, 11 October 1955, by Hugh Merewether.

No. 1 (F) Sqn., Stradishall: *XE561; XE604* ("*Z*"); *XE622* ("*E*"); *XE627; XE650* ("*U*").

No. 4 (F) Sqn., Jever, Germany: *XE548* ("*H*"); *XE590* (crashed after bird strikes, 10-11-60).

No. 19 (F) Sqn., Leconfield: *XE557* ("*O*"); *XE583* ("*Z*"); *XE583* ("*D*"; crashed off the Danish coast, 12-9-61); *XE590* ("*R*"); *XE603* ("*R*").

No. 20 (F) Sqn., Gutersloh, Germany: *XE535.*

No. 26 (F) Sqn., Gutersloh, Germany: *XE530* ("*A*"); *XE535* ("*F*"); *XE546* ("*M*").

No. 43 (F) Sqn., Leuchars: *XE560* ("*E*"); *XE561* ("*D*"); *XE592; XE611* ("*Q*"); *XE653.*

No. 54 (F) Sqn., Odiham: *XE561; XE606; XE609* ("*R*"); *XE627* ("*D*").

No. 56 (F) Sqn., Waterbeach and Wattisham: *XE594* ("*N*"); *XE602* ("*G*"); *XE621; XE645* ("*B*"); *XE647* ("*E*"); *XE648* ("*H*"); *XE651; XE655.*

No. 63 (F) Sqn., Waterbeach: *XE596; XE597* ("*A*"); *XE602; XE643; XE648; XE651* ("*R*"); *XE655.*

No. 65 (F) Sqn., Duxford: *XE552; XE560; XE591; XE593* ("*P*"; aircraft destroyed in starter explosion, Duxford, 23-1-61); *XE594* ("*J*"); *XE595* (crashed on take-off, 26-7-57); *XE617; XE627* ("*T*"); *XE644* ("*B*"); *XE654* ("*G*"); *XE656* ("*R*").

No. 66 (F) Sqn., Acklington: *XE544* ("*V*"); *XE582* ("*J*"); *XE595; XE596; XE618; XE643; XE648; XE651; XE652.*

No. 74 (F) Sqn., Horsham St. Faith and Coltishall: *XE559* ("*D*"); *XE589; XE591* ("*G*"); *XE610* ("*J*"); *XE612* ("*M*"; crashed while landing due to brake failure, Horsham, 17-5-60); *XE613* ("*C*").

No. 92 (F) Sqn., Thornaby, Middle St. George and Leconfield: *XE532* ("*L*"); *XE602; XE617* ("*D*"); *XE621; XE627; XE644; XE645; XE647; XE654; XE655; XE656* ("*B*").

No. 93 (F) Sqn., Jever, Germany: *XE546* ("*Z*"); *XE550* ("*R*"); *XE590*.

No.111 (F) Sqn, North Weald, North Luffenham and Wattisham: *XE561; XE592* ("*P*"); *XE620; XE621; XE628; XE653* ("*S*").

No. 208 (F) Sqn., Tangmere, Nicosia and Akrotiri: *XE556* ("*B*"); *XE579* ("*A*"); *XE599* ("*C*"); *XE611*.

No. 247 (F) Sqn., Odiham: *XE581* ("*T*"); *XE582*.

No. 263 (F) Sqn., Stradishall: *XE552; XE557* ("*I*"); *XE584* ("*W*"); *XE586* (crashed from spin, 2-8-57; pilot ejected); *XE590; XE604* ("*D*"); *XE607; XE614* ("*R*"); *XE615* ("*A*"); *XE616* ("*E*"); *XE619* "*S*"; written off at Honington, 2-3-59); *XE620; XE622; XE623* ("*G*"); *XE624; XE625; XE626* ("*P*"); *XE628; XE646; XE650*.

No. 229 Operational Conversion Unit: *XE561; XE591; XE594* (collided with *XF433* during formation aerobatics, 7-3-63); *XE602* ("*41*"); crashed while landing due to screwdriver jammed in throttle, 8-3-61); *XE606; XE627; XE644; XE653* ("*1*" and "*28*"); *XE656* .

Sold to India as Hunter Mark 56 (see also below): *XE537-XE540; XE547; XE549; XE600* (later deleted from Contract and returned to H.A.L.).

Sold to Switzerland as Hunter Mark 58 (see also below): *XE526-XE529; XE533; XE536; XE541; XE542; XE545; XE553-XE555*.

Converted to Lebanese Hunter Mark 6: *XE534; XE598*.

Converted to Jordanian Hunter Mark 6: *XE543; XE551; XE558*.

Converted to Hunter F Mark 6A: *XE606*.

Converted to Hunter F.G.A. Mark 9 (see also below): *XE530-XE532; XE535; XE544; XE546; XE550; XE552; XE581; XE582; XE584* (Interim Mark 9); *XE592; XE604* (Interim Mark 9); *XE607; XE609-XE611; XE615; XE616 (Interim Mark 9); XE617; XE618; XE620; XE622-XE624; XE628; XE643; XE645-XE647; XE649-XE652; XE6564; XE655*.

Converted to Rhodesian Hunter FGA Mark 9: *XE548; XE559; XE560; XE613*.

Converted to Hunter FR Mark 10 (see also below): *XE556; XE579; XE580; XE585; XE589; XE596; XE599; XE605; XE614; XE621; XE625; XE626*.

Converted to Hunter Mark 12: *XE531*.

Converted to Indian Hunter Mark 56A (see also below): *XE620*.

Converted to Swiss Hunter Mark 58A (see also below): *XE611*.

Converted to Saudi Hunter F Mark 60 (see also below): *XE591*.

Converted to Indian Hunter T. Mark 66E (see also below): *XE556; XE585*.

Converted to Kuwaiti Hunter T. Mark 67 (see also below): *XE530*.

Converted to Chilean Hunter FGA Mark 71 (see also below): *XE557; XE561; XE625; XE644*.

Converted to Jordanian Hunter FGA Mark 73 (see also below): *XE603; XE645; XE655*.

Converted to Singaporean Hunter Mark 74 (see also below): : *XE599* (Mark 74B); *XE605* (FR Mk. 74B); *XE614* (FR Mk. 74B): *XE615* (FGA Mk.74); *XE652* (FGA Mk.74).

Converted to Abu Dhabian Hunter FGA Mark 76 (see also below); *XE589*.

Converted to Kenyan Hunter FGA Mark 80 (see also below): *XE626*.

Other Units and duties, etc.: *XE530, XE531, XE532* (CA aircraft, Rolls-Royce Ltd; tropical trials, 1956); *XE543* (A. & A.E.E. for armament trials); *XE550* (transferred to the Kuwaiti Air Force, 12-67); *XE551* (A. & A.E.E., miscellaneous trials, 1956-57); *XE558* (A. & A.E.E., air firing trials, 1956-57); *XE560* (CA aircraft, H.A.L.; TIs); *XE584* (D.F.L.S., "*G*"); *XE585* (D.F.L.S., "*Q*"); *XE587* (demonstrations in Switzerland; development of tail parachute; E.T.P.S., 1971); *XE588* (demonstrations in Switzerland; spinning trials, H.A.L. and A. & A.E.E.; crashed, 9-11-57); *XE598* (development of gun blast deflectors,

589

H.A.L. and A. & A.E.E.); *XE599* (A. & A.E.E., intensive gun firing trials; trials with wing leading edge extensions, H.A.L. and A. & A.E.E.); *XE600* (trials with nosewheel brake, H.S.A.); *XE601* (prototype F.G.A. Mark 9, though not designated as such); *XE603* (D.F.L.S. and A.F.D.S.); *XE605* (H.A.L. and A. & A.E.E., TIs); *XE608* (D.F.L.S. and A.F.D.S.; transferred to Admiralty Charge, 10-76; R.N.A.S. Brawdy, 10-76); *XE611* (D.F.C.S.); *XE618* (Church Fenton Stn. Flt.); *XF652, XE656* (D.F.L.S.; No. 1 TWU/No. 63 Sqn., 1978).

The Hawker Hunter F. Mark 6. Third production batch of 110 aircraft built by Hawker Aircraft Ltd., Kingston and Dunsfold, and Sir W.G. Armstrong Whitworth Aircraft Ltd., during 1956. Built by Hawker: *XG127-XG137; XG169-XG172; XG185-XG211; XG225-XG239; XG251-XG274; XG289-XG298.* Sub-contracted by A.W.A.: *XG150-XG168.* All aircraft subsequently retrospectively modified with wing leading edge extensions and gun blast deflectors. First flight by *XG127,* 18-7-56, by Fg. Off W.D.E. Eggleton (seconded test pilot).

No. 1 (F) Sqn., Stradishall: *XG157* ("*Y*"); *XG195* ("*C*"); *XG207* ("*F*").

No. 2 (FR) Sqn., Gutersloh, Germany: *XG294* ("*W*").

No. 4 (FR) Sqn., Jever, Germany: *XG262; XG263; XG267-XG269; XG293* ("*V*"); *XG297* ("*Y*"); *XG298* ("*X*").

No. 14 (F) Sqn., Ahlhorn, Gutersloh and Jever, Germany: *XG131* ("*N*"); *XG166; XG209; XG210; XG274* ("*P*"); *XG291; XG292* ("*R*"); *XG295* ("*S*").

No. 19 (F) Sqn., Church Fenton, Leconfield and Gutersloh: *XG133; XG135; XG152* ("*X*"); *XG159; XG167* ("*F*"); *XG169* ("*Q*"); *XG172* ("*B*"); *XG185* ("*T*"); *XG186; XG187; XG188* (suffered air collision, 15-5-61; pilot ejected); *XG191* ("*E*"); *XG195* ("*V*"); *XG196* ("*U*"); *XG199* ("*J*").

No. 20 (F) Sqn., Gutersloh, Germany: *XG128* ("*Y*"); *XG225* ("*P*"); *XG272; XG293* ("*D*").

No. 26 (F) Sqn., Gutersloh, Germany: *XG208* (crashed after flame-out during aerobatic display, 24-3-59; pilot ejected); *XG292* ("*D*").

No. 43 (F) Sqn., Leuchars: *XG129; XG160; XG170; XG171; XG190; XG193; XG194; XG200; XG201; XG203; XG205* ("*E*"); *XG261* ("*G*").

No. 54 (F) Sqn., Odiham and Stradishall: *XG151* ("*H*"); *XG155* ("*T*"); *XG156; XG157* ("*H*"); *XG254* ("*A*"); *XG259* ("*G*"); *XG260; XG261* ("*C*"); *XG271* ("*F*"); *XG273* ("*L*").

No. 56 (F) Sqn., Waterbeach and Wattisham: *XG159* ("*P*"); *XG187* ("*V*"); *XG229* ("*M*"); *XG235* ("*O*").

No. 63 (F) Sqn., Waterbeach: *XG127; XG130* ("*J*"); *XG134.*

No. 65 (F) Sqn., Duxford: *XG128* ("*S*"); *XG158* ("*O*").

No. 66 (F) Sqn., Acklington: *XG127; XG130; XG153* ("*L*"); *XG154* ("*T*"); *XG186; XG187; XG202* (crashed near Morpeth while landing, 13-2-57, pilot ejected); *XG210; XG226* ("*B*"); *XG233* (crashed in Famagusta Bay, Cyprus, 20-8-58); *XG236* (crashed near Scottish border, 14-2-58); *XG237* ("*C*"); *XG251; XG252* ("*D*"); *XG253* ("*A*"); *XG255; XG256* ("*K*"); *XG257* ("*H*"); *XG265* ("*P*"); *XG266* ("*R*"); *XG273* ("*E*"); *XG274.*

No. 74 (F) Sqn., Horsham St. Faith and Coltishall: *XG164* ("*H*"); *XG198* ("*Q*"); *XG225; XG229; XG231; XG234; XG235; XG238.*

No. 92 (F) Sqn., Thornaby, Middle St. George and Leconfield: *XG137* ("*E*"); *XG153; XG186* ("*J*"); *XG189; XG194* ("*P*"); *XG201* ("*B*"); *XG211* ("*H*"); *XG225* ("*M*"); *XG227* ("*B*"); *XG228* ("*C*"); *XG229* ("*F*"); *XG230* (crashed, probably with icing, 15-11-56; pilot ejected); *XG231* ("*A*"); *XG232* ("*G*"); *XG234* ("*E*"); *XG235* ("*R*"); *XG238* ("*F*"; crashed into sea off Cyprus, 5-5-61); *XG239* (crashed on take-off, 11-1-58).

No. 93 (F) Sqn., Jever, Germany: *XG207; XG208; XG257; XG258* (crashed during aerobatics at Spangdahlan, 17-5-57); *XG272; XG274* (crashed on take-off at Sylt, 29-10-57); *XG294* ("*A*"); *XG296* ("*X*").

No. 111 (F) Sqn., North Weald, North Luffenham and Wattisham: *XG129* ("*F*"); *XG160* ("*U*"); *XG164; XG170* ("*G*"); *XG171; XG189* ("*D*"); *XG190* ("*C*"); *XG193* ("*A*"; collided with *XG200,* 10-6-60, during aerobatic practice); *XG194; XG198; XG200* ("*Q*"); *XG201*

("*B*"); *XG203* ("*H*", crashed 30-4-57); *XG209; XG211; XG231; XG264.*

No. 208 (F) Sqn., Tangmere, Nicosia and Akrotiri: *XG152; XG165* ("*GW*"); *XG168.*

No. 234 (F) Sqn., Geilenkirchen, Germany: *XG204* ("*B*").

No. 247 (F) Sqn., Odiham: *XG205* ("*Y*");

No. 263 (F) Sqn., Stradishall: *XG133* (crashed on take-off at Duxford, 7-9-58); *XG135; XG159; XG172; XG191; XG198.*

No. 229 Operational Conversion Unit: *XG131; XG157* (crashed in bad weather, 16-6-66); *XG159; XG160; XG162; XG166* (crashed into sea, 17-2-64); *XG191; XG196; XG199; XG205; XG229* (crashed, 3-9-71; pilot ejected); *XG274.*

Transferred to the Royal Jordanian Air Force, 1962: *XG257; XG263; XG267-XG269; XG298.*

Converted to Jordanian Hunter Mark 6: *XG187; XG231.*

Converted to Lebanese Hunter Mark 6: *XG167.*

Converted to Hunter FGA Mark 9 (see also below): *XG128; XG130; XG134-XG136; XG151; XG153; XG155; XG156* (Interim Mark 9); *XG169; XG194; XG195; XG205; XG207; XG228; XG237; XG251; XG255; XG256; XG260; XG261; XG264-XG266; XG271; XG272; XG273* (Interim Mark 9); *XG291-XG293; XG297; XG298.*

Converted to Rhodesian FGA Mark 9 (see also below): *XG294; XG295.*

Converted to Hunter FR Mark 10 (see also below): *XG127.*

Converted to Jordanian Hunter FR Mark 10: *XG262.*

Converted to Indian Hunter Mark 56A (see also below): *XG129; XG150* (Mark 56); *XG163* (Mark 56); *XG170; XG186; XG189; XG190; XG201; XG211.*

Converted to Swiss Hunter Mark 58A (see also below): *XG127; XG272.*

Converted to Chilean Hunter FGA Mark 71 (see also below): *XG199; XG232.*

Converted to Jordanian Hunter FGA Mark 73 (see also below): *XG137; XG159; XG234* (FGA Mk.73A); *XG237* (FGA Mk.73A); *XG255.*

Converted to Singaporean Hunter Mark 74 (see also below): *XG153* (FR Mk.74B); *XG205* (Mark 74A); *XG251; XG260; XG266* (FR Mk.74B); *XG292* (FR Mk.74A); *XG296.*

Other Units and duties, etc.: *XG152, XG186* (D.F.L.S.); *XG158* (Tactical Weapons Unit, "*21*", 1979); *XG160* (transferred to Admiralty charge; R.N.A.S. Brawdy; TWU/No. 79 Sqn., "*22*"); *XG161* (A.F.D.S.; D.F.L.S., "*P*"); *XG162* (D.F.L.S., "*W*"; crashed at West Raynham, 7-11-57); *XG164* (West Raynham Stn. Flt.; transferred to Admiralty charge; R.N.A.S. Brawdy, 10-76; TWU, "*36*", 1978); *XG165* (Middleton St. George Stn. Flt.; crashed after flame-out, 18-4-58; pilot ejected); *XG185* (No. 4 Flying Training School); *XG192* (D.F.L.S., "*F*"; F.T.U., Benson); *XG197* (D.F.L.S., "*A*"; D.F.C.S., "*A*"; R.N.A.S. Brawdy, 10-76); *XG198* (aircraft allocated to Eastern Sector Commander, 19-1-58); *XG204* (D.F.L.S., "*B*"; No. 4 F.T.S.; crashed, 15-9-69); *XG206* (D.F.L.S.; D.F.C.S, crashed into sea, 2-6-65); *XG209* (D.F.L.S.; D.F.C.S.; No. 4 F.T.S.); *XG226* (R.N.A.S. Brawdy, 10-76); *XG232* (A.& A.E.E., 1964); *XG270* (while with No. 5 M.U., force landed on Isle of Baltrum, 28-6-57, and swamped by rising tide before salvaging); *XG290* (Miscellaneous trials with A.& A.E.E.).

The Hawker Hunter F. Mark 6. Fourth production batch of 45 aircraft built by Hawker Aircraft Ltd., Kingston and Dunsfold, during 1956-57. *XJ632-XJ646; XJ673-XJ695; XJ712-XJ718.* These were the first aircraft completed at manufacture with wing leading edge extensions incorporated; gun blast deflectors fitted retrospectively. First flight by *XJ633* (first of the batch to fly), 4-12-56, by David Lockspeiser.

No. 1 (F) Sqn., Stradishall: *XJ636* ("*D*"); *XJ712; XJ713; XJ717.*

No. 2 (FR) Sqn., Gutersloh, Germany: *XJ637; XJ676.*

No. 4 (FR) Sqn., Jever, Germany: *XJ636; XJ637; XJ638* ("*D*"); *XJ639; XJ640; XJ674.*

No. 14 (F) Sqn., Ahlhorn, Gutersloh and Jever, Germany: *XJ642* ("*A*"); *XJ643; XJ644; XJ646* ("*D*"); *XJ673* ("*E*"); *XJ689; XJ690* ("*H*"); *XJ691; XJ695; XJ712; XJ713.*

No. 20 (F) Sqn., Gutersloh, Germany: *XJ680* ("*A*"); *XJ684* ("*B*"); *XJ685* ("*C*"); *XJ686* ("*D*");

XJ688 ("E"); XJ692; XJ693 ("X"; crashed while landing at Gutersloh, 3-10-60); XJ695 ("U"); XJ712; XJ713; XJ716 ("T"); XJ717.

No. 26 (F) Sqn., Gutersloh, Germany: XJ632 ("H"); XJ636 ("K"); XJ674 ("L"); XJ717.

No. 54 (F) Sqn., Odiham and Stradishall: XJ642 ("L"); XJ717.

No. 65 (F) Sqn., Duxford: XJ633 ("Z");

No. 66 (F) Sqn., Acklington: XJ673; XJ687 ("H"); XJ689; XJ691.

No. 93 (F) Sqn., Jever, Germany: XJ632 ("H"); XJ633; XJ634 ("V"); XJ635 ("F"); XJ641 (aircraft lost off Dutch coast, 11-11-59); XJ645; XJ675 (crashed on take-off after flame-out, 8-1-60; pilot ejected); XJ676; XJ683 ("D"); XJ718 ("B").

No. 111 (F) Sqn., North Weald and North Luffenham: XJ715 ("H").

No. 118 (F) Sqn., Jever, Germany: XJ718.

No. 208 (F) Sqn., Tangmere, Nicosia and Akrotiri: XJ694 ("D"); XJ714 ("B").

No. 229 Operational Conversion Unit: XJ637; XJ639; XJ715.

Presented to Iraq by H.M. Government: XJ677 (as "394")' XJ678 (as "395"); XJ679 (as "396"); XJ681 (as "397"); XJ882 (as "398").

Converted to Hunter FGA Mark 9 (see also below): XJ632; XJ635; XJ640; XJ642-XJ646; XJ673; XJ674; XJ680; XJ683-XJ692; XJ695.

Converted to Rhodesian Hunter FGA Mark 9 (see also below): XJ638.

Converted to Hunter FR Mark 10 (see also below): XJ633; XJ694.

Converted to Indian Hunter Mark 56A (see also below): XJ646; XJ692.

Converted to Indian Hunter T. Mark 66E (see also below): XJ694.

Converted to Lebanese Hunter FGA Mark 70A (see also below): XJ640; XJ644.

Converted to Jordanian Hunter FGA Mark 73A (see also below): XJ645.

Converted to Singaporean Hunter Mark 74 (see also below): XJ632 (FGA Mk.74); XJ633 (FR Mk.74B); XJ642 (FGA Mk.74); XJ643 (FGA Mk.74); XJ680 (FGA Mk.74); XJ684 (FGA Mk.74); XJ685 (FGA Mk.74); XJ689 (FR Mk.74A).

The Hawker Hunter F. Mark 6. Fifth production batch of 53 aircraft built by Hawker Aircraft Ltd., Kingston and Dunsfold, during 1957. The original Contract was for 153 aircraft, but the last 100 aircraft were cancelled by H.M. Government. Completed: XK136-XK176 and XK213-XK224 (of which only XK136-XK156 were delivered to the R.A.F.). Cancelled: XK225-XK241, XK257-XK306 and XK323-XK355. Five of the aircraft completed for the R.A.F. were presented to Iraq by H.M. Goverment, and 32 other aircraft were completed as Mark 56s and sold to India.

No. 1 (F) Sqn., Stradishall: XK149.

No. 14 (F) Sqn., Ahlhorn, Gutersloh and Jever, Germany: XK138 ("Y").

No. 20 (F) Sqn.: Gutersloh, Germany: XK137; XK138.

No. 54 (F) Sqn., Odiham and Stradishall: XK149.

No. 66 (F) Sqn., Acklington: XK139 ("G").

No. 74 (F) Sqn., Horsham St. Faith and Coltishall: XK136; XK140; XK141; XK142 ("L").

No. 229 Operational Conversion Unit: XK141; XK149.

Converted to Hunter FGA Mark 9 (see also below): XK136; XK137; XK139; XK140; XK142; XK150; XK151.

Converted to Chilean Hunter FR Mark 71A (see also below): XK148.

Converted to Singaporean FR Mark 74B (see also below): XK142.

Presented to Iraq by H.M. Government, 12-57: XK143-XK147 (as "400" to "404" respectively).

Completed as Indian Hunter Mark 56 (see also below): XK157-XK176 and XK213-XK224 (as BA201-BA232 respectively).

Other Units and duties, etc.: XK141 (R.N.A.S. Brawdy, 10-76); XK148 (A. & A.E.E., miscellaneous trials); XK149 (A.F.D.S., tactical evaluation, 1958); XK150 (A.F.D.S.; operational trials, Aden, 1958; transferred to the Royal Jordanian Air Force, 1968); XK151 (A.F.D.S.; operational trials, Aden, 1958).

The Hawker Hunter F. Mark 6. Single production batch of 100 aircraft built by Sir W.G. Armstrong Whitworth Aircraft Ltd., Coventry, during 1956, under Contract No. SP/6/ Aircraft/9818/CB.7a. *XF373-XF389; XF414-XF463; XF495-XF527.* Wing leading edge extensions and gun blast deflectors fitted retrospectively. Production and delivery completed, 31-12-56.

No. 1 (F) Sqn., Stradishall: *XF383; XF439; XF445* ("*Z*").

No. 19 (F) Sqn., Church Fenton and Leconfield: *XF439; XF449; XF525* ("*O*"); *XF527* ("*J*").

No. 26 (F) Sqn., Gutersloh, Germany: *XF415; XF417.*

No. 43 (F) Sqn., Leuchars: *XF416; XF424; XF430; XF431; XF434* (crashed into the sea off Akrotiri, Cyprus, 11-4-60); *XF435* ("*P*"); *XF437; XF439; XF440* ("*U*"); *XF442; XF454; XF455; XF456* ("*A*"); *XF514; XF515* ("*R*").

No. 54 (F) Sqn., Odiham and Stradishall: *XF420; XF421* ("*P*"); *XF427* (crashed on the Isle of Wight, 13-3-57); *XF431* ("*D*"); *XF439; XF453; XF508; XF509* ("*M*"); *XF513* (crashed on landing, 1-9-58); *XF517; XF523* ("*N*"); *XF524* ("*S*"; crashed in Cyprus, 5-11-57).

No. 56 (F) Sqn., Waterbeach: *XF389; XF414* ("*P*"); *XF516* ("*E*"); *XF526* ("*C*").

No. 63 (F) Sqn., Waterbeach: *XF387* ("*D*"); *XF414* ("*P*"); *XF526* ("*C*").

No. 65 (F) Sqn., Duxford: *XF382* ("*Q*"); *XF383* ("*V*"); *XF385* ("*M*"); *XF386* ("*C*"); *XF388; XF433* ("*G*"); *XF443* ("*E*"); *XF447* ("*H*"); *XF507* ("*A*").

No. 66 (F) Sqn., Acklington: *XF462; XF518; XF519; XF521* ("*E*"); *XF527* ("*S*").

No. 74 (F) Sqn., Horsham St. Faith and Coltishall: *XF419* ("*C*"); *XF425* (collided with *XF502* near Norwich at night and crashed, 26-8-59); *XF448* (crashed into sea, 21-8-58); *XF450; XF502* ("*K*"; collided with *XF425* near Norwich at night, 26-8-59); *XF504* ("*B*"); *XF511* ("*P*").

No. 92 (F) Sqn., Thornaby, Middleton St. George and Leconfield: *XF382; XF384; XF385; XF389; XF443; XF447; XF449* ("*S*"); *XF512* ("*MH*", later "*RD*"); *XF516* ("*N*"); *XF517* ("*L*"); *XF518; XF520* ("*K*"); *XF521* ("*X*"); *XF522.*

No. 93 (F) Sqn., Jever, Germany: *XF423.*

No. 111 (F) Sqn., North Weald and North Luffenham: *XF384; XF416* ("*T*"); *XF424; XF430; XF446* ("*R*"); *XF506* ("*X*"); *XF508; XF511; XF517; XF524; XF525* (crashed during aerobatic rehearsal at North Weald, 7-6-57); *XF526; XF527* ("*F*").

No. 208 (F) Sqn., Tangmere, Nicosia and Akrotiri: *XF422* ("*X*"); *XF426* ("*Y*"); *XF428* ("*S*"); *XF438* ("*H*"); *XF441* ("*P*"); *XF457* ("*V*"); *XF458* ("*Z*"); *XF460* ("*T*").

No. 247 (F) Sqn., Odiham: *XF424* ("*V*"); *XF434; XF435; XF437* ("*A*"); *XF439; XF440* ("*D*"); *XF442* ("*Z*"); *XF451; XF453; XF454; XF455* ("*B*"); *XF456; XF514* ("*P*"); *XF515* ("*W*").

No. 263 (F) Sqn., Stradishall: *XF383* ("*F*"); *XF433; XF445; XF449; XF506; XF525.*

No. 229 Operational Conversion Unit: *XF383* ("*14*"); *XF384; XF386; XF387; XF389; XF433* (collided with *XE594* during formation aerobatics, 7-3-63; pilot ejected); *XF439* ("*3*"); *XF443* (crashed on night landing approach at Chivenor, 3-8-67; pilot ejected); *XF450; XF451; XF516; XF526* ("*9*").

No. 4 Flying Training School: *XF383; XF384* and *XF387* (collided at Valley and crashed, 10-8-72); *XF509* ("*73*"); *XF526* ("*78*"); *XF527* ("*70*").

Supplied as Jordanian Hunter Mark 6 (under US Offshore Payment): *XF373* (as "*703*"); *XF379* (as "*709*"); *XF380* (as "*710*"); *XF381* (as "*711*"); *XF444* (as "*705*"); *XF452* (as "*708*"); *XF496* (as "*706*"); *XF498* (as "*704*").

Supplied as Lebanese Hunter Mark 6 (under US Offshore Payment): *XF377* (as "*L.173*"); *XF461* (as "*L.171*"); *XF495* (as "*L.175*").

Converted to Hunter FGA Mark 9 (see also below): *XF376; XF382; XF388; XF414; XF416; XF419; XF421; XF424; XF430; XF431; XF435; XF437; XF440; XF442; XF445; XF446; XF454-XF456; XF462; XF504; XF508; XF511; XF517; XF519; XF523.*

Converted to Rhodesian Hunter FGA Mark 9: (see also below): *XF374; XF504; XF506.*

Converted to Hunter FR Mark 10 (see also below): *XF422; XF426; XF428; XF429* (prototype conversion); *XF432; XF436; XF438; XF441; XF457-XF460.*

Converted to Indian Hunter Mark 56 (in 1957-58): *XF463* (as *BA241*); *XF497* (as *BA242*);

XF499 (as *BA243*); *XF500* (as *BA240*); *XF501* (as *BA244*); *XF503* (as *BA245*); *XF505* (as *BA246*).

Converted to Indian Hunter Mark 56A (see also below): *XF446; XF521.*

Converted to Swiss Hunter Mark 58A (see also below): *XF429; XF436; XF438; XF462.*

Converted to Saudi Hunter F. Mark 60 (see also below): *XF450.*

Converted to Indian Hunter T. Mark 66E (see also below): *XF459.*

Converted to Lebanese Hunter FGA Mark 70A (see also below): *XF430; XF457.*

Converted to Chilean Hunter Mark 71 (see also below): *XF453* (FR Mk.71A); *XF512* (FGA Mk.71).

Converted to Jordanian Hunter Mark 73 (see also below): *XF389* (FGA Mk.73A); *XF520* (FGA Mk.73).

Converted to Singaporean Hunter Mark 74 (see also below): *XF422* (FR Mk.74B); *XF428* (FR Mk.74B); *XF432* (FR Mk.74B); *XF437* (FR Mk.74A); *XF441* (FR Mk.74B); *XF456* (FGA Mk.74); *XF458* (FR Mk.74B); *XF460* (FR Mk.74B).

Transferred to Royal Jordanian Air Force, 1962: *XF415; XF417; XF423; XF454* (1968); *XF514* (1968); *XF518.*

Presented to Jordan by H.M. Government: *XF426* (later passed to Oman, 1976).

Other Units and duties, etc.: *XF373, XF388* (CA aircraft; Rolls-Royce Ltd., Wymeswold); *XF374* (CA aircraft, H.A.L., Dunsfold; fuel system and handling trials with early 230-gallon dop tanks); *XF375, XF377, XF452* (CA aircraft; A.W.A. Wymeswold and Bitteswell); *XF376, XF452* (trials at A. & A.E.E.); *XF378* (CA aircraft, H.A.L. Dunsfold; modified to P.1109B standard with full de Havilland Firestreak AAM system; firing trials at Hatfield and Valley, 1957); *XF379* (CA aircraft, H.A.L., Dunsfold; development of lateral fuselage-mounted airbrakes for proposed Hunter night/all-weather fighter, 1957); *XF380* (CA aircraft, H.A.L.); *XF381* (trials at A. & A.E.E.); *XF418, XF420, XF508, XF527* (A.F.D.S.; D.F.L.S.); *XF418, XF435, XF515* (transferred to Admiralty charge; R.N.A.S. Brawdy, 10-76); *XF450, XF453* (D.F.C.S.); *XF510* (North Weald Stn. Flt.; crashed while landing at North Weald, 13-7-57).

[Note: A production batch of 50 Hunter F. Mark 6s was to have been built by Hawker Aircraft (Blackpool) Ltd., Blackpool, under Contract No. SP/6/Aircraft/13132/CB.7a, dated 22 April 1955. This Contract was cancelled by H.M. Government in February 1957. Aircraft allocated under this Contract were *XJ945-XJ959; XJ971-XJ997; XK103-XK111.*]

The Hawker P.1101 Hunter. Two two-seat trainer prototypes, *XJ615* and *XJ627*, designed to Air Ministry Specification T.157D, and built during 1956-57 under Contract No. 6/Aircraft/11595/CB.7a. *XJ615*, based on the Hunter Mark 4 was powered by a Rolls-Royce Avon RA.21-series engine; *XJ627*, based on the Hunter Mark 6, was powered by an Avon 200-series engine. *XJ615*: ff. 8 July 1955. Prototype **Hunter T. Mark 7.** Employed on cockpit canopy profile development; drag parachute development; spinning and gun-firing trials (first with twin 30-mm Aden guns, later reduced to single gun); delivered to the R.A.E., 1-5-59. *XJ627*: ff. 17 November 1956; used as prototype for "large Avon" Hunter trainers. Retained twin Aden gun armament. To Martin-Baker Ltd., for prolonged ejection seat development, 19-11-58. Re-purchased by H.A.L., 27-9-68, as *G-9-296.* Converted to Chilean T. Mark 72, and delivered to Chile as "*721*", 19-5-71.

The Hawker Hunter T. Mark 7. Production batch of 45 aircraft built under Contract No. 6/Aircraft/12626/CB.9c, originally placed with Hawker Aircraft (Blackpool) Ltd., but sub-contracted to Kingston. Rolls-Royce Avon 121A or 122 turbojets. (Original Contract called for 55 aircraft, but ten were transferred to Admiralty charge during manufacture as Hunter T. Mark 8s, see below). *XL563-XL579; XL583; XL586; XL587; XL591-XL597; XL600; XL601; XL605; XL609-XL623.* First flight by *XL563*, 11 October 1957, by Frank Bullen.

No. 229 Operational Conversion Unit, Chivenor: *XL567; XL569* ("*ES-85*"); *XL570* (crashed into sea after take-off, 29-8-58); *XL571* ("*ES-87*"); *XL572* ("*ES-83*"); *XL573*; *XL575* ("*ES-88*"); *XL576* ("*ES-81*"); *XL577* ("*ES-82*"); *XL578* ("*ES-89*"); *XL579* ("*ES-92*"); *XL583* ("*ES-84*"); *XL586* ("*ES-90*"); *XL587* ("*ES-91*"); *XL592* ("*ES-93*"); *XL605* (re-registered as *XX467*, see below); *XL617; XL618; XL620* (re-registered as *XX466*, see below).

Instrument Rating Squadron: *XL571* ("*X*"); *XL575* ("*Y*"); *XL586; XL594.*

No. 4 Flying Training School, Valley: *XL566* ("*86*"); *XL567* ("*84*"); *XL573* ("*97*"); *XL591* ("*82*"); *XL596* ("*90*"); *XL597* ("*87*"); *XL600* ("*83*"); *XL601* ("*88*"); *XL609* ("*80*"); *XL621* ("*87*"); *XL622* ("*81*").

Aircraft on Operational Squadrons: *XL565* (No. 208 (F) Sqn., "*Y*"; No. 8 (F) Sqn., "*Y*"); *XL566* (No. 208 (F) Sqn., "*Y*"); *XL568* (No. 74 (F) Sqn., "*X*"); *XL571* (No. 92 (F) Sqn.); *XL587* (No. 208 (F) Sqn., 1981); *XL594* (No. 19 (F) Sqn., 1959; No. 1 (F) Sqn., 1961); *XL596* (No. 54 (F) Sqn., "*LIV*"); *XL597* (No. 66 (F) Sqn.; No. 208 (F) Sqn., "*Y*"); *XL600* (No. 65 (F) Sqn.; No. 16 Sqn., "*83*", 1981); *XL601* (No. 1 (F) Sqn.; No. 19 (F) Sqn.); *XL605* (No. 92 (F) Sqn., "*T*"; No. 66 (F) Sqn.); *XL609* (No. 56 (F) Sqn., 1959; No. 216 Sqn., 1980); *XL610* (No. 111 (F) Sqn., "*Z*"); *XL611* (No. 43 (F) Sqn.); *XL612* (No. 43 (F) Sqn.); *XL613* (No. 43 (F) Sqn.; No. 8 (F) Sqn.; No. 208 (F) Sqn., "*Z*"); *XL615* (No. 8 (F) Sqn.; aircraft crashed at night near Khormaksar, Aden, 1-6-60); *XL619* (No. 20 (F) Sqn.); *XL620* (No. 66 (F) Sqn.; No. 74 (F) Sqn.); *XL623* (No. 65 (F) Sqn.; No. 208 (F) Sqn.; No. 92 (F) Sqn.; No. 43 (F) Sqn.; No. 1 (F) Sqn.; No. 19 (F) Sqn.; No. 74 (F) Sqn.).

Converted to Hunter T. Mark 7A: *XL568; XL611; XL614; XL616.*

Converted to Saudi Hunter "T. Mark 70" (unofficial designation): *XL605* (deld, 7-6-66, as *70/617*; returned to UK, 7-74, and re-entered R.A.F. service as *XX467*, 1976); *XL620* (deld, 2-5-66, as *70/616*; returned to UK, 7-74, and re-entered R.A.F. service as *XX466*, 1976).

Transferred to Admiralty charge (remaining T. Mark 7): *XL571, XL576-XL578, XL583, XL586, XL587, XL592, XL595, XL618; XL623* (all aircraft to R.N.A.S. Brawdy, 10-76; returned to R.A.F. charge, 1978).

Air fighting Development Squadron, and Day Fighter Leaders' School, C.F.E.: *XL573* ("*L*"); *XL591* ("*M*"); *XL593* ("*N*"); *XL595* ("*O*").

No. 1 Tactical Weapons Unit: *XL571* ("*99*"); *XL572* ("*02*"); *XL576* ("*81*"); *XL578* ("*83*"); *XL583* ("*91*"); *XL587* ("*86*"); *XL592* ("*87*"); *XL593* (crashed following engine failure, 5-8-82; both pilots ejected); *XL595; XL605* ("*92*"); *XL616* ("*94*"); *XL617* ("*89*").

No. 2 Tactical Weapons Unit: *XL583* ("*84*"; aircraft crashed while landing at Brawdy, 1-12-81); *XL619* ("*06*"); *XL620* (as *XX466*, "*79*"); *XL623* ("*90*").

Other Units and duties, etc.: *XL563* (CA aircraft; trials at H.A.L. and A. & A.E.E.; later to R.A.E. as chase plane for Bristol Type 188 aircraft, 1976); *XL564* (trials at A. & A.E.E.; UHF trials, 5-10-61; Empire Test Pilots' School, 1983); *XL565* (CA aircraft, Rolls-Royce Ltd.; No. 1417 Flt.); *XL566* (A. & A.E.E., tropical trials, Bahrein, 20-6-58); *XL574* (CA aircraft, H.S.L. and A. & A.E.E.; windscreen rain dispersal and de-icing trials; fatigue tested to destruction, H.A.L., 11-61); *XL579* (Empire Test Pilots' School; fitted with nose boom/probe); *XL600*, (Wattisham Stn. Flt.); *XL610* (Wattisham Stn. Flt.; aircraft crashed, 7-6-62); *XL611* (A. & A.E.E.; crashed on take-off at Boscombe Down, 14-5-68); *XL612, XL616* (Weapons Training Station, Sylt; Empire Test Pilots' School, 1983); *XL613* (Khormaksar Stn. Flt., Aden; R.A.F., Germany, 1980); *XL617, XL622* (Jever Stn. Flt.); *XL618, XL621* (Gutersloh and Jever Stn. Flts.); *XL619* (Gutersloh Stn. Flt.).

The Hawker Hunter T. Mark 7 (Conversions from Mark 4s). Six aircraft converted to two-seaters by Hawker Aircraft Ltd., Kingston, and Sir W.G. Armstrong Whitworth Aircraft Ltd., Coventry, during 1958-59. *WV253, XV372, XV318, XV383, XF310* and *XF321.*

WV253 (**T.Mark 7 (Special)**; spinning trials with E.T.P.S., Farnborough); *WV372* (deld, 7-5-59; Jever Stn. Flt.; Gutersloh Stn. Flt.; No. 2 (FR) Sqn., "*R*"; No. 4 F.T.S., "*85*", 1977); *XV318* (later **T. Mark 7A**; No. 15 (B) Sqn., C.F.S., 1964; Laarbruch Stn. Flt., 1970; No.

237 O.C.U., 1980); *XV383* (deld, 3-7-59; Gutersloh Stn. Flt.; Jever Stn. Flt.; No. 28 (F) Sqn., Kai Tak, 1964; R.A.E., Farnborough, 7-77); *XF310* (deld, 24-4-59; No. 20 (F) Sqn., "*T*"; No. 2 T.W.U., "*01*", 1980); *XF321* (No. 56 (F) Sqn.; No. 43 (F) Sqn.; R.A.E., Farnborough, 1976).

The Hawker Hunter T. Mark 8. Production batch of 10 new-build aircraft built by Hawker Aircraft Ltd., Kingston and Dunsfold, during 1958. Transferred from Contract No. 12626 during manufacture to Admiralty charge. Rolls-Royce Avon 122 turbojets. Single Aden 30-mm gun, airfield arrester hook, tail parachute and naval radio. *XL580-XL582; XL584, XL585; XL598; XL599; XL602-XL604.* First flight by *XL580*, 30 May 1958, by David Lockspeiser (*XL581* flown the same day).

No. 700 Sqn., F.A.A.: *XL585.*
No. 738 Sqn., F.A.A.: *XL582* (aircraft crashed on take-off after engine failure, 26-1-68); *XL585; XL598.*
No. 759 Sqn., F.A.A.: *XL602* (8-64); *XL603; XL604.*
No. 764 Sqn., F.A.A.: *XL580; XL584; XL585; XL598; XL599; XL602; XL604.*
Converted to Hunter T. Mark 8C: *XL604* (deld, 22-11-63).
Converted to Hunter T. Mark 8M (Blue Fox radar trainers): *XL580; XL602; XL603.*
Converted to Kenyan Hunter T. Mark 81 (see also below): *XL604.*
Other Units and duties, etc.: *XL580, XL584* (Flag Officer, Flying Training, R.N.A.S. Yeovilton); *XL581* (R.N.A.S., Lossiemouth; crashed on Lossiemouth airfield during aerobatics, 6-5-58); *XL584* (F.R.A.D.U.. "*874*"); *XL585* (R.A.E., Bedford); *XL598* (F.R.A.D.U., "*870*").

The Hawker Hunter T. Mark 8. (Conversion from Mark 4s). First order for 18 aircraft to be brought up to T. Mark 8 standard by Hawker Aircraft Ltd., Kingston, and Sir W.G. Armstrong Whitworth Aircraft Ltd., Coventry, during 1958-59. Prototype conversion, *WW664*, and *WT701, WT702, WT722, WT745, WT755, WT772, WT799, WV319, WV322, WV363, WW661, XE664, XE665, XF289, XF322, XF357* and *XF358.*

WW664 (first as prototype T. Mark 8 was CA aircraft, H.A.L.; served with No. 764 Sqn.; returned to H.A.L., and converted to prototype **Hunter T. Mark 8B** with TACAN equipment); *WT701* (No. 764 Sqn., F.A.A.; collided with Hunter T.8 XL599, 23-8-61); *WT702* (No. 703 Sqn., F.A.A.; No. 759 Sqn., F.A.A., "*BY806*"; F.R.A.D.T.U., "*877*"); *WT722* (deld, 10-4-59. No. 703 Sqn., F.A.A.; No. 764 Sqn., F.A.A., "*LM972*"; F.R.A.D.T.U., "*VL742*", 1973; F.R.A.D.U., "*VL873*"; Yeovilton, 1984-85; on 21-3-85 had flown 6,925.35 flying hours—believed to be the highest number achieved by any Hunter by that date); *WT745* (Yeovilton Instrument Flt.; No. 764 Sqn., F.A.A.); *WT755* (R.N.A.S. Lossiemouth; R.N.A.S. Brawdy, 8-64); *WT722* (No. 764 Sqn., F.A.A.; No. 759 Sqn., F.A.A., "*BY808*"; F.R.A.D.U., "*VL874*", 1980); *WT799* (R.N.A.S. Lossiemouth; R.A.E., Bedford; No. 759 Sqn., F.A.A.; F.R.A.D.U., "*VL879*", 1980). *WV319, WV322, WV363, WW661, XE664, XE665, XF289, XF322* (No. 764 Sqn., F.A.A.); *XE665* (No. 237 O.C.U., 1983); *XF357* (converted to **Hunter T. Mark 8C** with "partial" TACAN system; F.R.A.D.U., "*VL877*", 1983); *XF358* (R.N.A.S. Lossiemouth, 1965).

The Hawker Hunter T. Mark 8B (Conversion from Mark 4s and 7s). Second order for four aircraft to be brought up to T. Mark 8B standard with full TACAN system. Prototype conversion (T. Mark 7/8, *WW664*, see above), and *XF967, XF978* and *XF994.*
XF967 (R.N.A.M.U., Changi, Singapore, 1-66; No. 237 O.C.U., 1971-79); *XF978* (R.N.A.S., Lossiemouth, "*LM110*", 10-64); *XF994* (No. 759 Sqn., F.A.A.; N.F.S.F., "*VL718*").

The Hawker Hunter T. Mark 8C (Conversion from Mark 4s and 7s). Third order for 11 aircraft to be brought up to T. Mark 8C standard with "partial" TACAN system. *WV396, WV398, XF938, XF939, XF942, XF983, XF985, XF991, XF992, XF995* and *XL604.*

WV396 (R.N.A.S. Brawdy, 1-66); *WV397* (No. 759 Sqn., F.A.A.; aircraft abandoned over the sea after fire warning light came on, 23-11-65; one pilot ejected safely, the other drowned); *XF983* (No. 759 Sqn., F.A.A.; crashed at Brawdy, 29-9-66); *XF985* (F.R.A.D.U., 1983); *XF995* (No. 764 Sqn., F.A.A.; No. 237 O.C.U., 8-72); *XL604* (No. 759 Sqn., F.A.A.).

The Hawker Hunter F.G.A. Mark 9. First conversion order to modify 40 Hunter F. Mark 6s to full F.G.A. Mark 9 standard placed with Hawker Siddeley Aviation, Kingston and Dunsfold, in 1958. This involved the installation of Avon 207 turbojets, tail parachutes and provision to mount 230-gallon drop tanks; aircraft progressively made compatible with requirements for service in the tropics. *XE544, XE552, XE581, XE592, XE597, XE600, XE607, XE609, XE617, XE618, XE620, XE623, XE643, XE645, XE647, XE649, XE651, XE654, XE655; XF376, XF388, XF419, XF421, XF424, XF442, XF454, XF455, XF462; XG128, XG130, XG134-XG136, XG169; XJ643, XJ687; XK139, XK140, XK150 and XK151.*

No. 1 (F) Sqn., Stradishall: *XE597* ("*A*"); *XE651* ("*L*"); *XF419* ("*Q*"); *XF442* ("*H*"); *XG130* ("*E*"); *XK139* ("*X*").

No. 8 (F) Sqn., Khormaksar, Aden: *XE581* (crashed following full tail trim runaway, 22-11-61); *XE592* (crashed into the sea, 16-10-64); *XE609* ("*A*"); *XF424; XF442* ("*H*"); *XG128; XG169* ("*B*"); *XK150.*

No. 20 (F) Sqn., Tengah, Singapore: *XG136* (crashed from spin, 19-10-64; pilot ejected).

No. 28 (F) Sqn., Kai Tak, Hong Kong: *XJ643.*

No. 43 (F) Sqn., Nicosia and Khormaksar: *XE655; XF454; XF455.*

No. 45 (F) Sqn., Wittering: *XG130*, 1973.

No. 54 (F) Sqn., Waterbeach and West Raynham: *XE552* ("*M*"); *XE592* ("*Y*").

No. 208 (F) Sqn., Khormaksar and Muharraq: *XE597* ("*G*"); *XE607* ("*F*"; crashed, 30-3-62); *XE609* ("*E*"); *XE618* ("*L*"); *XE623* ("*C*"; crashed, 11-8-64); *XE643* ("*K*"); *XE645* ("*M*"); *XE647* (crashed, 30-6-64); *XF376* ("*J*"); *XF388* ("*B*"); *XF421* ("*H*"); *XF454; XG134* ("*A*"; crashed in Kuwait during local crisis, 16-7-61); *XG135* ("*A*"); *XG169* ("*K*"); *XJ643* ("*J*"); *XJ687* ("*B*"); *XK150.*

Other Units and duties, etc.: *XE552* (No. 2 T.W.U., "*R*"); *XE597* (transferred to Admiralty charge; R.N.A.S. Brawdy, 10-76); *XE600* (crashed, 25-6-62); *XE617* (S.O.C. at Aden, 5-66); *XE618* (transferred to the Kuwaiti Air Force, 12-67); *XE649* (transferred to Admiralty charge, 1976, R.N.A.S. Brawdy; No. 1 T.W.U.; crashed following turbine failure, 13-5-82); *XE651, XF376, XK151* (R.N.A.S. Brawdy, 10-76); *XE654* (crashed, 20-11-67); *XF419* (No. 1 T.W.U.); *XF442, XK151* (No. 2 T.W.U.).

The Hawker Hunter F.G.A. Interim Mark 9. Second conversion order to modify 36 Hunter F. Mark 6s to ground attack standard; wing stressing and wiring for ground attack stores; tropicalisation kits and tail parachute; Avon 201 engines temporarily retained but replaced later by Avon 207s. *XE584, XE604, XE611, XE615, XE616, XE622, XE624, XE628, XE646, XE650; XF431, XF435, XF440, XF455, XF456, XF517, XF519, XF523; XG151, XG154-XG156, XG195, XG205, XG207, XG237, XG252, XG253-XG256, XG260, XG261, XG264, XG271 and XG273.*

No. 1 (F) Sqn., Stradishall: *XE604* ("*Z*"; crashed into sea during rocket firing, 2-3-61); *XE615* ("*A*"); *XE616* ("*E*"); *XE624* ("*B*"); *XE628* ("*G*"; crashed at El Adem, 24-4-63); *XE646* ("*V*"; crashed in Leconfield village, 30-12-66; pilot ejected); *XF519* ("*Q*").

No. 8 (F) Sqn., Khormaksar, Aden: *XE584; XE650* ("*A*"); *XF435* ("*E*"); *XG154* ("*H*").

No. 20 (F) Sqn., Tengah, Singapore: *XF455* (crashed into sea off Singapore, 19-9-64).

No. 28 (F) Sqn., Kai Tak, Hong Kong: *XE622* ("*A*"; destroyed after starter explosion, 12-7-66).

No. 43 (F) Sqn., Nicosia and Khormaksar: *XE611; XF431; XF456; XG154* ("*B*"); *XG237* ("*C*"); *XG253* ("*A*"); *XG256* ("*G*"); *XG261* ("*G*").

No. 54 (F) Sqn., Wittering: *XF517* ("*V*"); *XF523* (crashed, 24-6-63); *XG151; XG156; XG205*

("E"); *XG207* ("C"); *XG254* ("A"); *XG260* ("B"); *XG264* ("D"); *XF273* ("U"; collided with Hunter *XF446* near El Adem and crashed into the sea; date not known).

No. 208 (F) Sqn., Khormaksar and Muharraq: *XE650; XG195* ("K").

Other Units and duties, etc.: *XE624, XF435, XG154, XG252* (R.N.A.S. Brawdy, 10-76); *XE624, XG155* (No. 2 T.W.U.); *XF431, XF435, XG154, XG252* (No. 1 T.W.U.) *XG151, XG207* (No.2 T.W.U.; crashed at Lossiemouth, 3-4-81; pilot ejected); *XG156, XG253* (No. 229 O.C.U.); *XG271* (crashed and burned on take-off at Sylt, 25-7-61).

The Hawker Hunter F.G.A. Mark 9. Four conversion orders to modify a total of 52 Hunter F. Mark 6s to full tropicalised ground attack standard; wing leading edge extensions, gun blast deflectors, strengthened inboard wing pylons, jettison guns on outboard wing pylons, tail parachutes and Rolls-Royce Avon 207 turbojets. 1st order, placed in 1960, covered the following 31 aircraft: *XE530, XE535, XE546, XE550, XE582, XE610, XE652; XF414, XF508; XG153, XG265, XG266, XG272, XG292, XG293, XG296, XG297, XG298; XJ632, XJ673; XJ680, XJ683-XJ686, XJ688; XJ692; XK136-XK138* and *XK142*. 2nd order, placed in 1964, covered the following six aircraft: *XE532; XG291; XJ689, XJ690, XJ691* and *XJ695*. 3rd order, placed in 1965, covered the following six aircraft: *XF430; XF446; XG251; XJ635, XJ640* and *XJ674*. 4th order, also placed in 1965, covered the following nine aircraft: *XF416, XF437, XF511; XG194, XG228; XJ642* and *XJ644-XJ646*.

No. 1 (F) Sqn., Stradishall: *XG194* ("Q"); *XJ640* ("F").

No. 8 (F) Sqn., Khormaksar, Aden: *XE532; XF511*.

No. 20 (F) Sqn., Tengah, Singapore: *XE582* ("J"); *XE610* ("C"); *XE652* ("A"); *XF414* ("E"; crashed near Tengah, 20-2-67); *XF508* ("D"); *XG153* ("L"); *XG265* ("K"; crashed in Labuan, Borneo after fire in the air, 1-3-64); *XG266* ("N"); *XG297* ("Y"); *XJ673* ("XX"); *XJ690* ("G"); *XK136* ("O"; crashed from spin, 19-10-64; pilot ejected); *XK138; XK142* ("P").

No. 28 (F) Sqn., Kai Tak, Hong Kong: *XE535* ("C"; crashed 28-12-62); *XG297* ("B").

No. 43 (F) Sqn., Nicosia and Khormaksar: *XE546* ("B"); *XE550* ("X"); *XG296* ("A"); *XG298* ("J"); *XJ683* ("L"); *XJ684* ("D"); *XK137* ("P").

No. 54 (F) Sqn., Wittering: *XK137* ("E"); *XJ644* ("K").

No. 208 (F) Sqn., Khormaksar and Muharraq: *XJ632* ("K"); *XJ691* (Missing; believed to have crashed at sea, 4-67).

Other Units and duties, etc.: *XE546, XF416, XF511, XG194, XG228, XG291, XJ695* (R.N.A.S. Brawdy, 10-76); *XE550* (transferred to the Kuwaiti Air Force, 12-67); *XE582* (No. 2 T.W.U.).

The Hawker Hunter F.R. Mark 10. Conversion order to modify 33 Hunter F. Mark 6s to Mark 10 reconnaissance fighter standard with three cameras forward of frame 3 in the fuselage nose. Order placed in 1959 and conversions completed during 1960-61. Rolls-Royce Avon 207 turbojets. *WW593-WW596; XE556, XE579, XE580, XE585, XE589, XE596, XE599, XE605, XE614, XE621, XE625, XE626; XF422, XF428, XF429* (prototype); *XF432, XF436, XF438, XF441, XF457-XF460; XG127, XG168; XJ633, XJ694* and *XJ714*. First flight by *XF429* (prototype), 7 November 1958.

No. 2 (FR) Sqn., Gutersloh, Germany: *WW593; XE621* (crashed at Gutersloh, 30-1-62); *XF457* ("A"); *XF458* ("W"); *XG168* ("N"); *XJ633; XJ694*.

No. 4 (FR) Sqn., Gutersloh, Germany: *WW594; XE580* ("D"); *XE585* ("A"); *XE625* ("E"); *XE626* ("E"); *XF438* ("E").

No. 8 (F) Sqn., Khormaksar, Aden: *XE556; XE579* (crashed near Zinjibah, East Aden Protectorate, 8-8-61); *XE589*.

No. 79 (FR) Sqn., Gutersloh, Germany: *WW595; XE621*.

Other Units and duties, etc.: *XE589* (No. 1417 Flt.); *XE596* (No. 229 O.C.U.); *XF429* (A. & A.E.E., 1959; camera trials).

The Hawker Hunter G.A. Mark 11. Conversion order to modify 40 Hunter F. Mark 4s placed with Hawker Aircraft Ltd., Kingston and Dunsfold, in 1961 and completed during 1962-63. Admiralty Specification for single-seat weapon trainers equipped with TACAN navigation system for the Fleet Air Arm; Aden cannon removed (most weapon training to involve use of underwing rocket batteries), and airfield arrester hook added; aircraft painted in grey/white epoxy finish. *WT711-WT714, WT718, WT721, WT723, WT741, WT744, WT804-WT806, WT808-WT810; WV256, WV257, WV267, WV374, WV380-WV382; WW654, WV659; XE668, XE673, XE674, XE680, XE682, XE685, XE689, XE707, XE712, XE716, XE717; XF291, XF297, XF300, XF301, XF368* and *XF977.*

   No. 738 Sqn., F.A.A., R.N.A.S. Brawdy: *WT711* ("*BY783*"); *WT744; WT805* (crashed at St. Bride's Bay, Brawdy, 22-3-67); *WT809; WV256; WV257; WV267; WV374; WV380; WW659; XE668; XE673; XE674; XE682* ("*BY786*"); *XE685; XE707; XE712* ("*BY785*"); *XE717; XF297* ("*BY781*"); *XF300; XF301* ("*BY791*").

   No. 764 Sqn., F.A.A., R.N.A.S. Lossiemouth: *WT721* ("*LM694*"); *WT723; WT744* ("*LM691*"); *WT809; WV256* ("*LM690*"); *WV381* ("*LM693*"); *XE685* ("*LM694*"); *XE689* ("*LM695*"); *XE707; XF368* ("*LM695*"); *XF977* ("*LM696*").

   Fleet Requirements and Direction Unit, R.N.A.S. Yeovilton: *WT723* ("*VL866*"); *WT744* ("*VL868*"); *WT804* ("*VL879*"; Blue Herons); *WT806* ("*VL838*"; Blue Herons); *WT809* ("*VL867*", 1978); *WV256* ("*VL862*"); *WV267* ("*VL836*"; Blue Herons); *WW654* ("*VL833*"; Blue Herons); *XE668* ("*VL832*"); *XE682* ("*VL835*"); *XE689* ("*VL684*"); *XE707* ("*VL865*"); *XE716* ("*VL834*"); *XF300* ("*VL860*"); *XF368.*

   Fleet Requirements and Direction Training Unit, R.N.A.S. Yeovilton: *WT809* ("*VL737*", 1973); *WV256* ("*VL732*"); *XF977.*

   Other Units and duties, etc.: *WT712* (collided with *WT810*, 1965); *WT721* (converted to P.R. Mark 11, 1965); *WT808* (A. & A.E.E., 1966); *WT810* (collided with *WT712*, 1965); *XE685, XE712* (Yeovilton Stn. Flt., both aircraft "*VL708*").

The Hawker Hunter Mark 12. One two-seat aircraft, *XE531*, ordered by the Ministry of Supply on behalf of the R.A.E., Farnborough, to be converted from F. Mark 6 to feature two-seat cockpit with head-up display and vertical nose camera; Rolls-Royce Avon 208 engine. Delivered to the R.A.E., 8-3-63. Crashed on take-off at Farnborough, 17-3-82.

EXPORTED AND LICENCE-BUILT HAWKER HUNTERS

1. New-Build, United Kingdom.

The Hawker Dutch Hunter T. Mark 7. Production batch of 20 aircraft built by Hawker Aircraft Ltd., Kingston and Dunsfold. First ten aircraft, numbered *N-301* to *N-310*, ordered under Contract No. HAL/55N/022; the remainder, numbered *N-311* to *N-320* were diverted from cancelled Ministry of Supply batch *XM117-XM126*. Rolls-Royce Avon 121A turbojets, single Aden gun and tail parachute. First flight by *N-301*, 19 March 1958, by Frank Bullen. First aircraft delivered, 18-7-58; last delivered, 4-2-59.

   Repurchased by H.S.A., 1965-69, for refurbising and sale abroad: *N-301* (became **Abu Dhabian T. Mark 77**, *712*); *N-303* (became **Singaporean T. Mark 75**, *500*); *N-304* (became **Singaporean T. Mark 75**, *504*); *N-312* (became **Abu Dhabian T. Mark 77**, *711*); *N-313* (became **Swiss Mark 58A**, *J-4127*); *N-316* (became **Qatari T. Mark 79**, *QA13*); *N-318* (became **Swiss Mark 58A**, *J-4128*); *N-319* (became **Singaporean T. Mark 75**, *514*).

   Note. Two other aircraft (Dutch numbers not known) were sold to Demark where they were numbered *ET-273* and *ET-274*; they were subsequently purchased by H.S.A. as *G-9-431* and *G-9-432* and ultimately disposed of to the Imperial War Museum and a museum at Elstree).

The Hawker Swedish Hunter Mark 50. Production batch of 120 aircraft, based on the Hunter F. Mark 4, numbered *34001* to *34120*. Aircraft *34001* to *34024* built by Hawker Aircraft Ltd., Kingston and Dunsfold; the remainder built by Hawker Aircraft (Blackpool) Ltd., Blackpool. Contract, dated 29 June 1954, No. HAL/54/S.016. First flight by *34001*, 24 June 1955, by Frank Bullen. First aircraft delivered, 26-8-55.

> **Repurchased by H.S.A., 1970, for refurbishing and sale abroad:** *34017* (became **Swiss Hunter T. Mark 68,** *J-4207*); *34072* (became **Swiss Hunter T. Mark 68,** *J-4206*); *34080* (became **Swiss Hunter T. Mark 68,** *J-4208*); *34086* (became **Swiss Hunter T. Mark 68,** *J-4205*).

The Hawker Danish Hunter Mark 51. Production batch of 30 aircraft, based on Hunter F. Mark 4, numbered *401* to *430*, built by Hawker Aircraft Ltd., Kingston and Dunsfold, during 1955-56. Contract No. HAL/54/D.017, dated 3 July 1954. Aircraft served with ESK-724 of the Danish Air Force. First flight by *401*, 15-12-55, by David Lockspeiser. Last aircraft delivered to Demark, 18-8-56.

> Repurchased by H.S.A., 1975-76, for disposal: *402* (returned to U.K. as *G-9-433*; sold to Mr. John Lee); *403* (returned to U.K. as *G-9-434*; sold to Mr. Letcher, U.S.A.); *407* (returned to U.K. as *G-9-435*; to Loughborough Aircraft Preservation Society, 12-79); *408* (returned to U.K. as *G-9-436*; to RAF/RNAS Brawdy, 2-78); *409* (returned to U.K. as *G-9-437*; to South Wales Aircraft Preservation Society, Rhoos Airport); *410* (returned to U.K. as *G-9-438*; to Aviodrome National Aerospace Museum, Schiphol, Amsterdam, 7-79); *412* (returned to U.K. as *G-9-439*); *418* (returned to U.K. as *G-9-440*; to Elstree Museum; remained airworthy as *G-HUNT*); *419* (returned to U.K. as *G-9-441*; to NE Vintage and Veteran Aircraft Association, Sunderland Airport, 2-77); *420* (returned to U.K. as *G-9-442*); *421* (returned to U.K. as *G-9-443*; to Kingston Apprentices School); *423* (returned to U.K. as *G-9-444*; to Bitteswell Apprentices School); *424* (returned to U.K. as *G-9-445*; to Mr. Peter Warren, Biggin Hill); *425* (returned to U.K. as *G-9-446*; to Midland Air Museum, Coventry); *427* (returned to U.K. as *G-9-447*; disposed of to Brough Apprentices School); *430* (returned to U.K. as *G-9-448*; to Thorpe Park Leisure Centre).

The Hawker Danish Hunter T. Mark 53. Two aircraft, initially numbered *35-271* and *35-272* (and later *EP-271* and *EP272*), built under Contract Nos. HAL/56/D.026 and HAL/57/K.024 by Hawker Aircraft Ltd., Kingston and Dunsfold. Wing leading edge extensions not fitted. First flights: *35-271*, 17-10-58 (Frank Bullen); *35-272* (Duncan Simpson). Both aircraft served with ESK-724 of the Danish Air Force. Aircraft repurchased by H.S.A. in 12-75 as *G-9-429* and *G-9-430* respectively, and disposed of to the Duxford Aviation Museum in 1976.

The Hawker Indian Hunter Mark 56. Order for 160 aircraft, based on the Hunter F. Mark 6 and F.G.A. Mark 9, of which the first 32 were diverted from cancelled Ministry of Supply Hunter F. Mark 6s (see R.A.F. F. Mark 6s *XK157-XK224*, re-numbered *BA201* to *BA232*), and the next 16 were ex-R.A.F. aircraft (see under R.A.F. Hunter F. Mark 6s *XE537-XE540, XE547, XE549, XE600; XF463, XF497, XF499-XF501, XF503, XF505; XG150* and *XG163*, re-numbered *BA233* to *BA248*). The remainder, *BA249-BA360*, were new-build aircraft built by Hawker Aircraft Ltd., Kingston and Dunsfold, in 1957-1960 under Contract No. HAL/57/I.034. All Mark 6 modifications, plus tail parachutes and punka louvres; aircraft later given 230-gallon drop tank facility with increased oxygen supply.

> **Notes on Aircraft and Indian Service:** First flight by a new-build aircraft (*BA250*), 26-6-58, David Lockspeiser; first new-build aircraft delivered (*BA249, BA252* and *BA253*), 8-8-58. Aircraft served with Nos. 7, 17, 20 and 27 Sqns., I.A.F. Final deliveries in 11-60. None of this batch of aircraft was repurchased by H.S.A. (Note: *BA360* was the last new-build single-seat Hunter to be manufactured in the United Kingdom; its first flight was on 5 October 1960, flown by Don Lucey.)

The Hawker Swiss Hunter Mark 58. Order for 100 aircraft, based on the Hunter F. Mark 6, of which the first 12 were ex-R.A.F. aircraft (see under R.A.F. Hunter F. Mark 6s *XE526-XE529, XE533, XE536, XE541, XE542, XE545* and *XE553-XE555*, re-numbered *J-4001* to *J-4012*); the remainder were new-build and numbered *J-4013* to *J-4100*), built by Hawker Aircraft Ltd., Kingston and Dunsfold, during *1958-60*; these were equipped with tail parachutes but were otherwise similar to the R.A.F. Mark 6. First flight by a new-build aircraft (*J-4014*), 6-12-58, Duncan Simpson. First delivery of a new-build aircraft (*J-4014*, to Dubendorf), 15-1-59. Last delivery of a new-build aircraft (*J-4093*, to Kloten), 6-4-60. None of this batch of aircraft was repurchased by H.S.A.

The Hawker Indian Hunter T. Mark 66. Production order for 22 new-build two-seat Hunters, based on the second prototype P.1101 Hunter trainer, powered by Avon 200-series turbojet and with twin-Aden gun armament. Built by Hawker Aircraft Ltd., Kingston and Dunsfold, during 1958-59 under Contract No. HAL/57/I.034. The original order was for 16 aircraft, numbered *BS361-BS376*, but this was increased by a further six aircraft, *BS485-BS490*.
  Notes on Aircraft and Indian Service: First flight by a new-build aircraft (*BS361*), 6-8-58, Hugh Merewether; first new-build aircraft (*BS363*), 13-4-59. Aircraft served with Nos. 7, 14, 17, 20 and 27 Sqns., I.A.F. *BS366* attended the Paris Air Show, 6-59, and participated in the Paris-to-London Air Race, 7-59. Final aircraft delivered to India (*BS490*), 11-60. None of this batch of aircraft was repurchased by H.S.A. (Note: *BS490* was the last new-build Hunter to be manufactured in the United Kingdom; its first flight was on 21 October 1960, flown by Don Lucey.)

The Hawker Jordanian Hunter T. Mark 66B. One new-build aircraft, numbered *714*, based on Avon 200-series powered P.1101 Hunter two-seater prototype, built by Hawker Aircraft Ltd., Kingston and Dunsfold. (See also Jordanian T. Mark 66B under "Converted Aircraft" below). First flight by *714*, 24 May 1960 (by David Lockspeiser); delivered 4-7-60; crashed and written off, 15-8-65.

2. Licence New-Build Production, Holland and Belgium.

The Hawker Dutch Hunter Mark 4. Licence production of 96 aircraft, similar to R.A.F. Hunter F. Mark 4s, undertaken by Fokker-Aviolanda, Amsterdam, during 1955-56. Numbered *N-101* onwards. Served with the *Koninklijke Luchtmacht* on Nos. 324 and 325 Squadrons at Leeuwarden, and on No. 327 Squadron, Soesterberg. None of these aircraft purchased by H.S.A.

The Hawker Belgian Hunter Mark 4. Licence production of 112 aircraft, similar to R.A.F. Hunter F. Mark 4s, undertaken by Avions Fairey, Brussels, and S.A.B.C.A., during 1955-56. Numbered *ID-1* onwards. Served with the *Force Aérienne Belge/Belgische Luchtmacht* with Nos. 1, 7 and 9 Wings at Beauvechain, Chièvres and Bierset respectively. None of these aircraft purchased by H.S.A.

The Hawker Dutch Hunter Mark 6. Licence production of 93 aircraft, similar to R.A.F. Hunter F. Mark 6s, undertaken by Fokker-Aviolanda, Amsterdam, during 1956-58. Number *N-201* onwards. Served with the *Koninklijke Luchtmacht* between 1957 and 1963. A total of 47 of these aircraft was purchased by H.S.A. between February 1964 and August 1968 for refurbishing and re-sale abroad:
  Converted to Indian Hunter Mark 56A: *N-209* (purchased as *G-9-188*; became *A4930*; *N-213* (purchased as *G-9-281*; became *A1014*); *N-216* (purchased as *G-9-282*; became *A1015*); *N-252* (purchased as *G-9-280*; became *A1013*); *N-271* (purchased as *G-9-278*; became *A1011*); *N-274* (purchased as *G-9-279*; became *A1012*).

Converted to Iraqi Hunter F.G.A. Mark 59, 59A and 59B: *N-205* (purchased as *G-9-166*; became Mark 59B, *663*); *N-221* (purchased as *G-9-169*; became Mark 59B, *662*); *N-234* (purchased as *G-9-172*; became Mark 59, *632*); *N-253* (purchased as *G-9-175*; became Mark 59A, *657*); *N-255* (purchased as *G-9-176*; became Mark 59A, *658*); *N-259* (purchased as *G-9-177*; became Mark 59B, *664*); *N-263* (purchased as *G-9-179*; became Mark 59B, *665*).

Converted to Jordanian Hunter T. Mark 66B: *N-249* (purchased as *G-9-174*; became *716*); *N-283* (purchased as *G-9-231*; became *801*).

Converted to Indian Hunter T. Mark 66D: *N-203* (purchased as *G-9-165*; became *S.577*); *N-204* (purchased as *G-9-182*; became *S.572*); *N-208* (purchased as *G-9-167*; became *S.571*); *N-212* (purchased as *G-9-183*; became *S.573*); *N-214* (purchased as *G-9-168*; became *S.578*); *N-218* (purchased as *G-9-184*; became *S.580*); *N-223* (purchased as *G-9-170*; became *S.579*); *N-230* (purchased as *G-9-171*; became *S.574*); N-250 (purchased as G-9-185; became S.581); N-261 (purchased as *G-9-178*; became *S.575*); *N-265* (purchased as *G-9-180*; became *S.576*); *N-269* (purchased as *G-9-181*; became *S.570*).

Converted to Kuwaiti Hunter T. Mark 67: *N-257* (purchased as *G-9-266*; became *219*); *N-282* (purchased as *G-9-236*; became *218*).

Converted to Chilean Hunter F.G.A. Mark 71: *N-201* (purchased as *G-9-217*; became *J-708*); *N-210* (purchased as *G-9-227*; became *J-704*); *N-220* (purchased as *G-9-226*; became *J-705*); *N-232* (purchased as *G-9-221*; became *J-712*); *N-262* (purchased as *G-9-220*; became *J-707*); *N-266* (purchased as *G-9-228*; became *J-709*); *N-270* (purchased as *G-9-219*; became *J-710*); *N-273* (purchased as *G-9-222*; became *J-713*); *N-276* (purchased as *G-9-224*; became *J-706*); *N-277* (purchased as *G-9-225*; became *J-711*).

Converted to Chilean Hunter T. Mark 72: *N-202* (purchased as *G-9-223*; became *J-720*); *N-224* (purchased as *G-9-218*; became *J-719*).

Converted to Jordanian Hunter F.G.A. Mark 73A: *N-264* (purchased as *G-9-285*; became *840*).

Converted to Jordanian Hunter F.G.A. Mark 73B: *N-279* (purchased as *G-9-287*; became *841*).

Converted to Qatari Hunter F.G.A. Mark 78: *N-219* (purchased as *G-9-283*; became *QA11*); *N-268* (purchased as *G-9-286*; became *QA10*).

The Hawker Belgian Hunter Mark 6. Licence production of 144 Hawker Hunter Mark 6s undertaken by Avions Fairey, Brussels, and S.A.B.C.A. during 1956-58. Numbered *IF-1* onwards. Served with the *Force Aérienne Belge/Belgische Luchtmacht*. A total of 96 of these aircraft was purchased by H.S.A. between 1962 and 1966 for re-furbishing and re-sale abroad:

Converted to Indian Hunter Mark 56A: *IF-1* (purchased as *G-9-187*; became *A482*); *IF-3* (purchased as *G-9-107*; became *A484*); *IF-4* (purchased as *G-9-124*; became *A460*); *IF-7* (purchased as *G-9-154*; became *A474*); *IF-13* (purchased as *G-9-128*; became *A463*); *IF-16* (purchased as *G-9-123*; became *A462*); *IF-17* (purchased as *G-9-158*; became *A476*); *IF-18* (purchased as *G-9-148*; became *A472*); *IF-36* (purchased as *G-9-141*; became *A492*); *IF-43* (purchased as *G-9-117*; became *A 488*); *IF-50* (purchased as *G-9-134*; became *A465*); *IF-62* (purchased as *G-9-146*; became *A469*); *IF-64* (purchased as *G-9-142*; became *A479*); *IF-66* (purchased as *G-9-138*; became *A491*); *IF-77* (purchased as *G-9-118*; became *A461*); *IF-78* (purchased as *G-9-163*; became *A478*); *IF-85* (purchased as *G-9-139*; became *A467*); *IF-89* (purchased as *G-9-161*; became *A477*); *IF-91* (purchased as *G-9-122*; became *A459*); *IF-98* (purchased as *G-9-137*; became *A490*); *IF-104* (purchased as *G-9-130*; became *A464*); *IF-110* (purchased as *G-9-147*; became *A471*); *IF-113* (purchased as *G-9-115*; became *A487*); *IF-115* (purchased as *G-9-152*; became *A473*); *IF-116* (purchased as *G-9-140*; became *A468*); *IF-117* (purchased as *G-9-143*; became *A494*); *IF-120* (purchased as *G-9-136*; became *A466*); *IF-123* (purchased as *G-9-144*; became *A470*); *IF-124* (purchased as *G-9-113*; became *A480*); *IF-127* (purchased as *G-9-157*; became *A475*); *IF-128* (purchased as *G-9-131*; became *A483*); *IF-131* (purchased as *G-9-111*; became *A485*); *IF-132* (purchased as *G-9-132*; became *A489*); *IF-137* (purchased as *G-9-156*; became *A481*); *IF-144* (purchased as *G-9-112*; became *A486*).

Converted to Iraqi Hunter F.G.A. Mark 59: *IF-6* (purchased as *G-9-70*; became *570*); *IF-10* (purchased as *G-9-71*; became *584*); *IF-11* (purchased as *G-9-97*; became *631*); *IF-14* (purchased as *G-9-72*; became *572*); *IF-21* (purchased as *G-9-74*; became *574*); *IF-24* (purchased as *G-9-75*; became *577*); *IF-27* (purchased as *G-9-77*; became *575*); *IF-28* (purchased as *G-9-78*; became *573*); *IF-32* (purchased as *G-9-100*; became *583*); *IF-48* (purchased as *G-9-81*; became *571*); *IF-51* (purchased as *G-9-82*; became *581*); *IF-75* (purchased as *G-9-84*; became *587*); *IF-79* (purchased as *G-9-85*; became *628*); *IF-80* (purchased as *G-9-86*; became *630*); *IF-88* (purchased as *G-9-88*; became *578*); *IF-94* (purchased as *G-9-98*; became *629*); *IF-107* (purchased as *G-9-90*; became *580*); *IF-114* (purchased as *G-9-91*; became *586*); *IF-122* (purchased as *G-9-92*; became *579*); *IF-126* (purchased as *G-9-93*; became *585*); *IF-140* (purchased as *G-9-94*; became *576*); *IF-142* (purchased as *G-9-95*; became *582*).

Converted to Iraqi Hunter F.G.A. Mark 59A: *IF-8* (purchased as *G-9-127*; became *660*); *IF-9* (purchased as *G-9-133*; became *661*); *IF-22* (purchased as *G-9-108*; became *659*); *IF-25* (purchased as *G-9-162*; became *693*); *IF-31* (purchased as *G-9-120*; became *696*); *IF-49* (purchased as *G-9-159*; became *702*); *IF-54* (purchased as *G-9-116*; became *692*); *IF-59* (purchased as *G-9-125*; became *697*); *IF-71* (purchased as *G-9-151*; became *668*); *IF-72* (purchased as *G-9-150*; became *700*); *IF-74* (purchased as *G-9-109*; became *695*); *IF-87* (purchased as *G-9-149*; became *691*); *IF-93* (purchased as *G-9-126*; became *698*); *IF-99* (purchased as *G-9-135*; became *699*); *IF-135* (purchased as *G-9-153*; became *694*); *IF-138* (purchased as *G-9-155*; became *701*).

Converted to Hawker Hunter Mark 66A. *IF-19* (purchased by H.A.L. in 1958 and components used to build the two-seat Hunter demonstrator *G-APUX*; aircraft leased to air forces in the Middle East and later converted and sold as **Chilean Hunter T. Mark 72**, *J-718*; see below).

Converted to Lebanese Hunter T. Mark 66C: *IF-34* (purchased as *G-9-96*; became *L.282*); *IF-60* (purchased as *G-9-145*; became *L.280*); *IF-112* (purchased as *G-9-119*; became *L.281*).

Converted to Kuwaiti Hunter T. Mark 67: *IF-37* (purchased as *G-9-79*; became *211*); *IF-56* (purchased as *G-9-101*; became *210*).

Converted to Iraqi Hunter T. Mark 69: *IF-20* (purchased as *G-9-73*; became *627*); *IF-68* (purchased as *G-9-83*; became *568*); *IF-84* (purchased as *G-9-87*; became *567*); *IF-97* (purchased as *G-9-89*; became *626*); *IF-143* (purchased as *G-9-99*; became *569*).

Converted to Lebanese Hunter F.G.A. Mark 70: *IF-86* (purchased as *G-9-110*; became *L.176*); *IF-96* (purchased as *G-9-121*; became *L.177*); *IF-101* (purchased as *G-9-114*; became *L.179*); *IF-129* (purchased as *G-9-102*; became *L.178*).

Converted to Chilean Hunter F.G.A. Mark 71: *IF-44* (purchased as *G-9-106*; became *J-703*); *IF-106* (purchased as *G-9-104*; became *J-701*); *IF-108* (purchased as *G-9-105*; became *J-702*); *IF-141* (purchased as *G-9-103*; became *J-700*).

3. Conversion of Hawker Hunters for Export

The Hawker Rhodesian Hunter F.G.A. Mark 9. Order for 12 ex-R.A.F. Hunter F. Mark 6s to be brought up to full F.G.A. Mark 9 standard by Hawker Aircraft Ltd., Kingston and Dunsfold, during 1963. Aircraft selected were *XE548, XE559, XE560, XE613; XF374, XF504, XF506; XG294, XG295; XJ638, XJ716;* and *XK718.*

The Hawker Peruvian Hunter Mark 52. Order for 16 ex-R.A.F. Hunter F. Mark 4s to be prepared by Hawker Aircraft Ltd., Kingston and Dunsfold, for sale to Peru during 1956, numbered *630-645*. Aircraft selected were *WT717, WT734, WT756, WT758, WT759, WT765, WT766, WT768, WT773, WT774, WT776, WT779, WT796, WT800, WT803* and *WW662*.

The Hawker Indian Hunter Mark 56. *First order* for 160 aircraft, of which 16 were converted from R.A.F. Hunter F. Mark 6s (*BA232-BA248*) by Hawker Aircraft Ltd., Kingston and Dunsfold, during 1957 under Contract No. HAL/57/I./034; aircraft selected were *XE537-XE540, XE547, XE549, XE600* (later removed from Contract); *XF463, XF497, XF499-XF501, XF503, XF505; XG150* and *XG163*.

The Hawker Indian Hunter Mark 56A. *Second conversion order*, Contract No. HSA/65/I/061, for 36 Hunter 6s to be brought to full F.G.A. Mark 9 standard by Hawker Siddeley Aviation Ltd., Kingston and Dunsfold, and delivered between June 1966 and July 1967. Conversions were of 35 ex-Belgian Mark 6s (*IF-1, IF-3, IF-4, IF-7, IF-13, IF-16 to IF-18, IF-36, IF-43, IF-50, IF-62, IF-64, IF-66, IF-77, IF-78, IF-85, IF-89, IF-91, IF-98, IF-104, IF-110, IF-113, IF-115 to IF-117, IF-120, IF-123, IF-124, IF-127, IF-128, IF-131, IF-132, IF-137* and *IF-144*) and one ex-Dutch Mark 6 (*N-209*). Aircraft numbered *A459-A494. Third conversion order*, Contract No. HSA/65/I/00 Part 1, for eight ex-R.A.F. Hunter F. Mark 6s to be brought up to full F.G.A. Mark 9 standard by Hawker Siddeley Aviation Ltd., Kingston and Dunsfold, and delivered between November 1968 and April 1969. Aircraft selected were R.A.F. Hunters *XF521; XG129, XG170, XG186, XG189, XG190, XG201* and *XG211*. Aircraft numbered *A936-A943. Fourth conversion order*, Contract No. HSA/65/I/00 Part 2, for three ex-R.A.F. Hunter F. Mark 6s to be brought to full F.G.A. Mark 9 standard and delivered between July and September 1969. Aircraft were *XE620, XJ646* and *XJ692*. Aircraft numbered *A967-A969. Fifth conversion order*, Contract No. HSAL/68/I/077, for six Hunter 6s to be brought to full F.G.A. Mark 9 standard by Hawker Siddeley Aviation Ltd., Kingston and Dunsfold, and delivered between September 1969 and March 1970. Aircraft were ex-R.A.F. Hunter F. Mark 6 *XF446*, and ex-Dutch Hunter 6s *N-213, N-216, N-252, N-271* and *N-274*. Aircraft numbered *A1010-A1015*.

The Hawker Kuwaiti Hunter F.G.A. Mark 57. Conversion order for four ex-Belgian Hunter Mark 6s to be brought to full F.G.A. Mark 9 standard by Hawker Siddeley Aviation Ltd., and delivered to Kuwait between February 1965 and February 1966. Aircraft selected were ex-Belgian Hunter 6s *IF-26, IF-41, IF-69* and *IF-70*. Aircraft re-numbered *212-215*.

The Hawker Swiss Hunter Mark 58. Order for 100 aircraft, of which the first 12 were converted from ex-R.A.F. Hunter F. Mark 6s by Hawker Aircraft Ltd., Kingston and Dunsfold, during 1958. Aircraft selected were Hunter 6s *XE526-XE529, XE533, XE536, XE541, XE542, XE545* and *XE553-XE555*. Aircraft re-numbered *J-4001* to *J-4012*.

The Hawker Swiss Hunter Mark 58A. *First conversion order* for 30 ex-R.A.F. Hunter F. Mark 4s (and ex-F.A.A. Mark 11s), ex-R.A.F. Mark 6s and two ex-Dutch T. Mark 7s to full F.G.A. Mark 9 standard by Hawker Siddeley Aviation, for delivery between December 1971 and April 1973. Aircraft were ex-R.A.F. Mark 4s/11s: *WT713, WT808, WV257, WV374, WV380, WV405, WV411, WW589, WW659, XE674, XE717, XF291, XF303, XF318, XF361, XF365, XF937, XF947, XF976, XF981, XF984* and *XF992*; R.A.F. Hunter 6s: *XE611, XF436, XF438, XF462, XG127* and *XG272*; ex-Dutch Hunter T. Mark 7s: *N-313* and *N-318*. Aircraft re-numbered *J-4101* to *J-4130. Second conversion order* for 22 aircraft to be converted from ex-R.A.F. Hunter Mark 4s and a Mark 6 to full F.G.A. Mark 9 standard by Hawker Siddeley Aviation for delivery to Switzerland between January 1974 and April 1975. R.A.F. Hunter Mark 4s: *WT716, WT797, WV261, WV266, WV329, WV393, WV404, WW590, XE659, XE678, XF306, XF308, XF312, XF316, XF370, XF933, XF941, XF944, XF973, XF990* and *XF998*; and Hunter Mark 6 *XF429*. Aircraft re-numbered *J-4131* to *J-4152*.

The Hawker Iraqi Hunter F.G.A. Mark 59. Conversion order for 24 aircraft to be converted from ex-Belgian and ex-Dutch Hunter F. Mark 6s to full F.G.A. Mark 9 standard by Hawker Siddeley Aviation Ltd., Kingston and Dunsfold, for delivery to Iraq between March 1964 and May 1965. Ex-Belgian aircraft were *IF-6, IF-10, IF-11, IF-14, IF-20, IF-21, IF-24, IF-27, IF-28, IF-32, IF-48, IF-75, IF-79, IF-80, IF-88, IF-94, IF-107, IF-114, IF-122, IF-126, IF-140* and *IF-142*. Ex-Dutch aircraft, *N-234* and *N-247*. Aircraft re-numbered *570-587* and *628-633*.

The Hawker Iraqi Hunter F.G.A. Mark 59A. Conversion order for 18 aircraft to be converted from ex-Belgian and ex-Dutch Hunter Mark 6s to full F.G.A. Mark 9 standard by Hawker Siddeley Aviation Ltd., under Contract Nos. HSAL/65/I/060, HSAL/65/I/062 and HSAL/65/I/O62A, for delivery to Iraq between November 1965 and May 1967. Ex-Dutch aircraft were *N-253* and *N-255*; ex-Belgian aircraft were *IF-8, IF-9, IF-22, IF-25, IF-29, IF-31, IF-54, IF-59, IF-71, IF-72, IF-74, IF-87, IF-93, IF-99, IF-135* and *IF138*. Aircraft re-numbered *657-661* and *690-702*.

The Hawker Iraqi Hunter F.G.A. Mark 59B. Conversion order for four ex-Dutch Hunter Mark 6s to be converted to full F.G.A. Mark 9 standard by Hawker Siddeley Aviation under Contract No. HSAL/65/I/060 (Part 2), for delivery to Iraq between May and September 1966. Ex-Dutch aircraft were *N-205, N-221, N-259* and *N-263*. Aircraft re-numbered *662-665*.

The Hawker Saudi Hunter F. Mark 60. Conversion order for four ex-R.A.F. Hunter F. Mark 6s to be prepared for the Royal Saudi Air Force by Hawker Siddeley Aviation Ltd., under Contract No. HSAL/66/S/064, dated 28 March 1966, for delivery to Saudi Arabia in May 1966. R.A.F. Hunter F. Mark 6s were *XE591, XF450, XJ712* and *XJ715*. Aircraft re-numbered *60/601* to *60/604*. One aircraft lost in action against the Egyptian Air Force in 1967, and the remaining aircraft were presented to the Royal Jordanian Air Force the following year.

The Hawker Peruvian Hunter T. Mark 62. Conversion order for one ex-R.A.F. Hunter F. Mark 4, *WT706*, to be brought to modified T. Mark 7 standard by Hawker Aircraft Ltd., Kingston and Dunsfold, and delivered to Peru in February 1960. Re-numbered *681*.

The Hawker Hunter Mark 66A. Aircraft originally prepared as Manufacturer's Hunter demonstrator as a private venture and registered as *G-APUX*; it was constructed using the centre and rear fuselage of ex-Belgian Hunter Mark 6 *IF-19*, but also included the two-seat front fuselage and cockpit of a ground display unit (originally intended for sale to India), the wings, fin and rudder of *IF-67* and the engine and gearbox from ex-R.A.F. Hunter 6 XE378. It was flown in numerous displays at home and abroad, was the first Hunter to carry 230-gallon drop tanks and UHF radio, and was fitted with nosewheel braking. In May 1963 it was leased to Iraq, Jordan and Lebanon for general training purposes and, in 1965, was returned to Hawker Siddeley Aviation for conversion and sale as a **Chilean Hunter T. Mark 72**, numbered *J-718*, and delivered to Chile on 9 August 1967.

The Hawker Jordanian Hunter T. Mark 66B. Two conversion orders, Contract Nos. HSAL/65/J/063 and HSAL/67/070, each for single ex-Dutch Hunter Mark 6s, *N-249* and *N-283*, to be converted to two-seaters based on the Hawker P.1101 (second prototype) with Rolls-Royce Avon 207 torbojet and twin-Aden gun armament. Delivered in October 1966 and February 1969, re-numbered *716* and *810* respectively.

The Hawker Lebanese T. Mark 66C. Conversion order for three ex-Belgian Hunter Mark 6s to be converted to two-seat trainers (similar to the new-build Indian T. Mark 66) by Hawker Siddeley Aviation Ltd., Kingston and Dunsfold, under Contract No. HSA/64/L/059 for delivery between November 1965 and July 1966. Aircraft were ex-Belgian Hunter 6s *IF-34*, *IF-60* and *IF-112*; re-numbered *L.280* to *L282*.

The Hawker Indian Hunter T. Mark 66D. Conversion order for 12 ex-Dutch Hunter Mark 6s to be converted to two-seat trainers (of a standard similar to that of the new-build Indian Hunter T. Mark 66) by Hawker Siddeley Aviation Ltd., Kingston and Dunsfold, under Contract No. HSA/66/I/067 dated 10 March 1966, for delivery to India between May 1966 and September 1967. Ex-Dutch Hunter 6s were *N-203, N-204, N-208, N-212, N-214, N-218, N-223, N-230, N-250, N-261, N-265* and *N-269*. Aircraft re-numbered *S.570* to *S.281*.

The Hawker Indian Hunter T. Mark 66E. Conversion order for five ex-R.A.F. Hunter F. Mark 6s to be modified to full Indian two-seat trainer standard (T. Mark 66 with new equipment introduced) by Hawker Siddeley Aviation Ltd., Kingston and Dunsfold, for delivery to India between June and December 1973. Ex-R.A.F. Hunter F. Mark 6s were *WW596, XE556, XE585, XF459* and *XJ694*. Aircraft re-numbered *S.1389* to *S.1393*.

The Hawker Kuwaiti Hunter T. Mark 67. *First conversion order* for two ex-Belgian Hunter Mark 6s to be brought to two-seat trainer standard by Hawker Aircraft Ltd., Kingston and Dunsfold, under Contract No. HAL/63/K/050 for delivery to Kuwait during February 1965. Ex-Belgian aircraft were *IF-37* and *IF-56*. Re-numbered *211* and *210* respectively.
Second conversion order for two ex-Dutch and one ex-R.A.F. Hunter 6s to be brought to two-seat trainer standard by Hawker Siddeley Aviation Ltd., Kingston and Dunsfold, under Contract No. HSA/67/K/069 for delivery to Kuwait during May 1969. Ex-Dutch aircraft were *N-257* and *N-282*; R.A.F. Hunter 6 was *XE530*. Aircraft re-numbered *218-220*.

The Hawker Swiss Hunter T. Mark 68. Conversion order for four ex-R.A.F. Hunter F. Mark 4s and four ex-Swedish Hunter Mark 50s to be brought to two-seat trainer standard with Rolls-Royce Avon 207 turbojets by Hawker Siddeley Aviation Ltd., Kingston and Dunsfold, for delivery to Switzerland between August 1974 and June 1975. Ex-R.A.F. Hunter 4s were *WV332, WV398, XE702* and *XF951*; Ex-Swedish Hunter 50s were *34017, 34072, 34080* and *34086*. Aircraft re-numbered *J-4201* to *J-4208*.

The Hawker Iraqi Hunter T. Mark 69. *First conversion order* for three ex-Belgian Hunter Mark 6s to be brought to two-seat trainer standard (with Rolls-Royce Avon 207 turbojets) by Hawker Siddeley Aviation Ltd., Kingston and Dunsfold, under Contract No. HSA/63/I/054, for delivery to Iraq during 1964. Ex-Belgian Hunter 6s were *IF-68, IF-84, IF-143*. Aircraft were re-numbered *567-569*.
Second conversion order for two ex-Belgian Hunter Mark 6s (*IF-20* and *IF-97*) to be brought to two-seat trainer standard (with Rolls-Royce Avon 207 turbojets) by Hawker Siddeley Aviation Ltd., Kingston and Dunsfold, under Contract No. HSA/64/I/056, for delivery to Iraq early in 1965. Aircraft re-numbered *626* and *627*.

The Hawker Saudi Hunter T. Mark 7 (unofficially T. Mark 70). Conversion order for two ex-R.A.F. Hunter T. Mark 7s to be prepared for the Royal Saudi Air Force by Hawker Siddeley Aviation Ltd., under "Magic Carpet" package air defence Contract, No. HSAL/66/S/064 dated 28 March 1966 for delivery in May 1966. Formerly R.A.F. Hunter T. Mark 7s, *XL605* and *XL620*. Aircraft re-numbered *70/616* and *70/617*; presented to the Royal Jordanian Air Force by Saudi Arabia in 1968. Returned to the U.K. in 1974 and re-issued to the R.A.F., 7-74, re-registered as *XX467* and *XX466* respectively.

The Hawker Lebanese Hunter F.G.A. Mark 70. Conversion order for four ex-Belgain Hunter Mark 6s to be brought to full F.G.A. Mark 9 standard by Hawker Siddeley Aviation Ltd., Kingston and Dunsfold, under Contract No. HSA/64/L/o59, for delivery to Lebanon between September 1965 and September 1966. Ex-Belgian Mark 6s were *IF-86, IF-96, IF-101* and *IF-128*. Aircraft re-numbered *L.176* to *L.179*.

The Hawker Chilean Hunter F.G.A. Mark 71. *First conversion order* for 15 ex-Belgian and ex-Dutch Hunter Mark 6s and one ex-R.A.F. F. Mark 6 to be brought up to full F.G.A. Mark 9 standard by Hawker Siddeley Aviation Ltd., Kingston and Dunsfold, under Contract No. HSAL/66/C/066 dated 26th October 1966, for delivery to Chile between September 1966 and June 1968. Ex-R.A.F. Hunter 6 was *XG232*; ex-Belgian Mark 6s were *IF-44, IF-106, IF-108* and *IF-141*; ex-Belgian Mark 6s were *N-201, N-210, N-220, N-232, N-262, N-266, N-270, N-273, N-276* and *N-277*. Aircraft re-numbered *J-700* to *J-714*.

Second conversion order for 9 ex-R.A.F. Hunter F. Mark 6s to be brought to full F.G.A. Mark 9 standard by Hawker Siddeley Aviation Ltd., under Contract No. HSAL/69/C/084 dated 10 September 1969 for delivery to Chile between December 1970 and September 1971. Ex-R.A.F. aircraft were *XE557, XE561, XE580, XE625, XE644, XF447, XF512, XG199* and *XJ713*. Aircraft re-numbered *J-722* to *J-730*.

Third conversion order for four ex-R.A.F. Hunter F. Mark 4s to be breought up to full F.G.A. Mark 9 standard (with Rolls-Royce Avon 207s) by Hawker Siddeley Aviation Ltd., for delivery to Chile between September 1973 and January 1974. Ex-R.A.F. Mark 4s were *WT801, WW653, XF302* and *XF323*; aircraft re-numbered *J-731* to *J-733*, and *J-737*.

The Hawker Chilean Hunter T. Mark 72. *First conversion order* for three aircraft to be brought to full P.1101 (second prototype) two-seat trainer standard by Hawker Siddeley Aviation Ltd., for delivery to Chile between August 1967 and January 1968. Aircraft were formerly the Hunter Mark 66 *G-APUX*/Belgian Mark 6 *IF-19*, and ex-Dutch Hunter Mark 6s *N-202* and *N-224*; re-numbered *J-718* to *J-720*.

Second conversion order for three aircraft (extended by a fourth later), selected from various redundant Hunters, to be brought to full Avon 200-series two-seat trainer standard by Hawker Siddeley Aviation Ltd.; first three aircraft delivered to Chile during 1970-71, the fourth in 1974. The aircraft were formerly the P.1101 (second prototype, *XJ627*) Hunter F. Mark 4 *XE704*, and Hunter Mark 6s *XF447* and *XJ713*; re-numbered *J-721* to *J-723*, and *J-736*.

The Hawker Jordanian Hunter F.G.A. Mark 73. Conversion order for two ex-R.A.F. Hunter F. Mark 6s (*XE603* and *XF520*) to be brought up to full F.G.A. Mark 9 standard by Hawker Siddeley Aviation Ltd., Kingston and Dunsfold, under Contract No. HSAL/68/J/075, for delivery to Jordan during June 1968. Aircraft re-numbered *814* and *832*.

The Hawker Jordanian Hunter F.G.A. Mark 73A. *First conversion order* for four ex-R.A.F. Hunter Mark 6/9s (*XF389, XG234, XG237* and *XJ645*) to be brought to full F.G.A. Mark 9 standard by Hawker Siddeley Aviation Ltd., under Contract No. HSAL/68/J/076, for delivery to Jordan between May and July 1969; aircraft re-numbered *828-831*.

Second conversion order for nine aircraft to be brought to full F.G.A. Mark 9 standard by Hawker Siddeley Aviation Ltd., for delivery to Jordan between June and December 1971. The aircraft were formerly Dutch Hunter Mark 6 *N-264*, and ex-R.A.F. Hunter Mark 4s *WV325, WV407, WV408, XF364, XF936, XF952, XF968* and *XF987*. Re-numbered *840* and *842-849*.

The Hawker Jordanian Hunter F.G.A. Mark 73B. Conversion order for three aircraft to be brought to F.G.A. Mark 9 standard by Hawker Siddeley Aviation Ltd., Kingston and Dunsfold, for delivery to Jordan between June and November 1971. The aircraft were formerly the Dutch Hunter Mark 6 *N-279* and R.A.F. Hunter F. Mark 4s *WV401* and *XF979*; they were re-numbered *841, 850* and *851*.

The Hawker Singaporean Hunter F.G.A. Mark 74. Conversion order for 12 ex-R.A.F. Hunter F. Mark 6s to be re-furbished and brought to full F.G.A. Mark 9 standard by Hawker Siddeley Aviation Ltd., Kingston and Dunsfold, under Contract No. HSAL/68/SG/078, for delivery to Singapore between November 1970 and May 1971. The following aircraft were selected (Singaporean serial numbers in brackets): *XE615 (508)*; *XE652 (519)*; *XG251 (507)*; *XG260 (501)*; *XG296 (510)*; *XJ632 (505)*; *XJ642 (518)*; *XJ643 (515)*; *XJ680 (511)*; *XJ684 (513)*; *XJ685 (502)*; *XF456 (509)*. Several aircraft held temporarily in the U.K. in 1971 for training purposes.

The Hawker Singaporean Hunter F.R. Mark 74A. Conversion order for four ex-R.A.F. Hunter F. Mark 6s to be brought to full F.G.A. Mark 10 standard by Hawker Siddeley Aviation Ltd., Kingston and Dunsfold, under Contract No. HSAL/68/SG/078, for delivery to Singapore between June and August 1971. The following aircraft were selected (Singaporean serial numbers in brackets): *XF437 (503)*; *XG205 (506)*; *XG292 (512)*; *XJ689 (517)*.

The Hawker Singaporean Hunter F.R. Mark 74B. Conversion order for eight ex-R.A.F. Hunter F. Mark 4s and 14 ex-R.A.F. Hunter F. Mark 6s to be brought to full F.R. Mark 10 (modified) standard by Hawker Siddeley Aviation Ltd., for delivery to Singapore between June 1972 and October 1973. The following aircraft were selected for conversion (Singaporean serial numbers in brackets): Hunter F. Mark 4s: *WV258 (539)*; *WV331 (543)*; *WV364 (530)*; *WV366 (537)*; *XE679 (541)*; *XF360 (542)*; *XF369 (538)*; *XF969 (529)*; Hunter F. Mark 6s: *XE599 (535)*; *XE605 (523)*; *XE614 (533)*; *XF422 (524)*; *XF428 (525)*; *XF432 (526)*; *XF441 (545)*; *XF458 (527)*; *XF460 (546)*; *XG153 (520)*; *XG266 (521)*; *XJ633 (534)*; *XJ714 (531)*; *XK142 (522)*.

The Hawker Singaporean Hunter T. Mark 75. Conversion order for four Hunters to be refurbished and brought to full T. Mark 7 standard (Avon 121A turbojets) by Hawker Siddeley Aviation Ltd., Kingston and Dunsfold, under Contract No. HSAL/68/SG/078 for delivery to Singapore between December 1969 and September 1970. Aircraft selected were ex-R.A.F. Hunter T. Mark 7 *WW664*, ex-Admiralty Hunter T. Mark 8 *XE664*, and Dutch Hunter T. Mark 7s *N-303* and *N-304*; re-numbered *500, 504, 514* and *516*.

The Hawker Singaporean Hunter T. Mark 75A. Conversion order for five ex-R.A.F. Hunter F. Mark 4s/11s to be brought up to full two-seat T. Mark 7 standard by Hawker Siddeley Aviation Ltd., for delivery to Singapore between November 1972 and October 1973. Selected aircraft (with Singaporean serial numbers in brackets) were formerly *WT741 (541)*, *WV272 (540)*, *WV386 (532)*, *XF950 (536)*, and *XF970 (528)*.

The Hawker Abu Dhabian Hunter F.G.A. Mark 76. Conversion order for seven ex-R.A.F. Hunter F. Mark 4s to be modified and brought up to F.G.A. Mark 9 standard by Hawker Siddeley Aviation Ltd., Kingston and Dunsfold, under Contract No. HSA/69/AD/082, dated 28 February 1969 for delivery to Abu Dhabi between March 1970 and January 1971. Aircraft selected were formerly *WV389, WV402, XE589, XF362, XF367, XF935* and *XG341*. Re-numbered *701-707*.

The Hawker Abu Dhabian Hunter F.R. Mark 76A. Conversion order for three ex-R.A.F. Hunters to be modified and brought to full F.R. Mark 10 standard by Hawker Siddeley Aviation Ltd., under Contract No. HSAL/69/AD/082 for delivery to Abu Dhabi during January 1971. The aircraft were formerly Hunter Mark 4s *WV400* and *XF971*, and Mark 6 *WW592*; re-numbered *708-710*.

The Hawker Abu Dhabian Hunter T. Mark 77. Conversion order for two ex-Dutch Hunter T. Mark 7s to be refurbished and brought up to latest standard of preparation by Hawker

Siddeley Aviation Ltd., under Contract No. HSAL/69/AD/082 for delivery during May 1970. Aircraft were formerly Dutch Hunter T. Mark 7s *N-301* and *N-312*; re-numbered *711* and *712*.

The Hawker Qatari Hunter F.G.A. Mark 78. Conversion order for three ex-Dutch Hunter Mark 6s to be brought to full F.G.A. Mark 9 standard by Hawker Siddeley Aviation Ltd., under Contract No. HSAL/69/Q/083 for delivery to Qatar in December 1971. Aircraft were formerly Dutch Hunter Mark 6s *N-219*, *N-222* and *N-268*; re-numbered *QA-10* to *QA-12*.

The Hawker Qatari Hunter T. Mark 79. Conversion order to refurbish the ex-Dutch Hunter T. Mark 7 *N-316* by Hawker Siddeley Aviation Ltd., under Contract No. HSAL/69/Q/083 for delivery to Qatar in December 1971. Re-numbered *QA-13*.

The Hawker Kenyan Hunter F.G.A. Mark 80. Conversion order for four ex-R.A.F. Hunters to be brought to full F.G.A. Mark 9 standard by Hawker Siddeley Aviation Ltd. for delivery to Kenya between June 1974 and January 1975. Aircraft were formerly Hunter F. Mark 4s *XF309*, *XF972* and *XF975*, and Hunter F. Mark 6 *XE626*; re-numbered *803* to *806*.

The Hawker Kenyan Hunter T. Mark 81. Conversion order for two ex-R.A.F. Hunters to be refurbished and brought to latest T. Mark 7 standard by Hawker Siddeley Aviation Ltd., for delivery to Kenya in June 1974. Aircraft were formerly Hunter Mk. 4/8 *WT577* and T. Mark 8 *XL604*; aircraft re-numbered *801* and *802* respectively.

The Hawker P.1127. Two prototypes, *XP831* and *XP836*, designed and built as private ventures during 1958-60, but eventually purchased under Government Contract. *XP831*: commenced hovering trials at Dunsfold, 21-10-60, flown by A.W. Bedford, OBE; first untethered hovering flight, 19-11-63. Damaged in Paris Air Show, 16-6-63. Repaired and returned to Dunsfold, 9-64. Preserved at R.A.F. Museum (Sir Sydney Camm Memorial Hall), Hendon, from 1973. *XP836*: First flown 7-7-61; used to "close the gap" between horizontal and vertical flight, 7-61 until 11-62, flown by A.W. Bedford and H. Merewether. Crashed and destroyed at Yeovilton, 14-12-61, after cold nozzle became detached in flight; A.W. Bedford ejected safely at 200 ft.

The Hawker P.1127. Four further prototypes, *XP972*, *XP976*, *XP980* and *XP984*, purchased under H.M. Government Contract for aerodynamic and powerplant research. *XP972*: First flight, 5-4-62. Aircraft suffered engine failure following bearing seizure and blade fouling in high-g turn, 30-10-62; force landed at Tangmere, suffered titanium fire and was extensively damaged following undercarriage failure. Hugh Merewether escaped unhurt. *XP976*: First flight, 12-7-62. Aircraft introduced inflatable intake lips and fin-mounted pitot head. Used for radio aerial trials at R.A.E. Scrapped at R.A.E., c.1970. *XP980*: First flight, 5-63. Aircraft introduced anhedral tailplane and streamwise wing tip fairings. Taxying trials and undercarriage load measurements, R.A.F. Gaydon, 1972-73. Aircraft preserved. *XP984*: First flight, 10-63. Aircraft introduced swept wing, wing leading edge extensions and cold steel nozzles. Force landed, Thorney Island, 19-3-65; aircraft damaged but repaired. Crashed and destroyed in landing at R.A.E., Bedford, 31-10-75.

The Hawker Siddeley Kestrel FGA Mark 1. Nine evaluation aircraft, *XS688-XS696*, ordered for Tripartite evaluation trials at the C.F.E., West Raynham, Norfolk, during 1964-65. Aircraft introduced fully swept wing, nose camera, taller fin, bulged and slightly longer fuselage for 15,000 lb. thrust Bristol Siddeley Pegasus, and (later) slightly extended tailplane. Six aircraft shipped to U.S.A. as XV-6A for Tri-Service Trials at Patuxent River, and aboard USS *Raleigh* and USS *Independence*. USAF trials at Edwards AFB, and flown by USAF, Army, Navy and Marine Corps pilots. *XS688*: First flown, 7-3-64; short tailplane. Evaluation No.

8. S.B.A.C. Display, 9-64. Shipped to U.S.A., with U.S. fin No. *64-18262*. (Fitted with extended tailplane, 7-64). Displayed at USAF Museum, Wright Patterson AFB. *XS689*: First flown, 28-5-64; extended tailplane. Evaluation No. *9*. Shipped to U.S.A., with U.S. fin No. *64-18263*. To Edwards AFB carrying NASA No. *521*. *XS690*: First flown, 5-8-64. Evaluation No. *0*. Shipped to U.S.A., with U.S. fin No. *64-18264*. Tri-Service trials; trials from USS *Guam*, 1968. Dumped in Virginia river at completion of trials. *XS691*: First flown, 5-9-64. Evaluation No. *1*. Shipped to U.S.A., with fin No. *64-18265* for Tri-Service Trials; to Edwards AFB, 5-67, carrying New Trials No. *5*; scrapped after completion of trials. *XS692*: First flown, 7-11-64. Evaluation No. *2*. Shipped to U.S.A., with U.S. fin No. *64-18266* for Tri-Service Trials; later cannibalised for spares. *XS693*: First flown, 15-11-64. Evaluation No. *3*. Performed first night VTO, 1-2-65, and was first to be delivered to C.F.E., 8-2-65. Retained in U.K. after Tripartite evaluation. Fitted with Pegasus 6 engine at Brough; first flight 10-6-67. Crashed at Filton, 21-9-67; pilot, Sqn. Ldr. H. Rigg, escaped safely. *XS694*: First flown, 10-12-64. Evaluation No. *4*. Shipped to U.S.A. with U.S. fin No. *64-18267* for Tri-Service Trials; ground looped, extensively damaged and scrapped. *XS695*: First flown 17-2-65. Evaluation No. *5*. Crashed at A. & A.E.E., Boscombe Down, but later delivered to R.A.E., Farnborough. *XS696*: First flown, 5-3-65. Evaluation No. *6*. Crashed at West Raynham following ground loop during take-off. Pilot rescued.

The Hawker Siddeley Harrier GR Mark 1 (DB). Pre-production development batch of 6 aircraft, *XV276-XV281*, ordered under Ministry of Defence Contract in 1965. 19,000 lb.-thrust Bristol Siddeley Pegasus 6 (Mark 101) vectored-thrust turbofans. *XV276*: First flown, 31-8-66., A.W. Bedford. Flight trials, H.S.A., Dunsfold, 1966-73. Engine flamed out and aircraft crashed, Dunsfold, 10-4-73, with throttle stop out of adjustment; pilot ejected safely. *XV277*: First flown, 9-11-66, H. Merewether. Performance and handling trials. Later employed on store clearance trials. *XV278*: First flown, 31-12-66, A.W. Bedford. Store TIs, and preliminary installation of LRMTS nose profile, 1972. *XV279*: First flown, 4-3-67, A.W. Bedford. Employed on engine handling and performance trials, Dunsfold and Filton, 1967-70. *XV280*: First flown, 29-4-67, A.W. Bedford. Miscellaneous trials by H.S.A., Rolls-Royce (Bristol), A. & A.E.E. and R.A.E., etc. *XV281*: First flown, 14-7-67, D.M.S. Simpson. Trials at Dunsfold and Filton, 1967-68. To R.A.E. for all-weather trials. Ski-ramp launch trials, c.1977, Boscombe Down and elsewhere, 1981.

The Hawker Siddeley Harrier GR Mark 1. First production batch of 60 aircraft, *XV738-XV762*, *XV776-XV810*, ordered in 1966 to meet Air Staff Requirement 384. Bristol Siddeley Pegasus (Mark 101) vectored-thrust turbofan, rated at 19,000 lb. thrust with water injection.

XV738 ff. 28-12-67; employed on engine trials by Rolls-Royce Bristol from 16-4-68; deld to No. 3 Sqn., 10-75, "*B*"; 4-82 "*AB*". No. 1 Sqn., 7-83, "*15*". No. 4 Sqn., 3-84, "*B*"; 1988.

XV739 ff. 21-4-68; trials at Boscombe Down from 16-4-68; deld to No. 1 Sqn., Wittering, 15-3-73, "*V*"; crashed in Cyprus following pitch-down in vertical climb from hover; pilot ejected but broke his leg, 24-9-73.

XV740 ff. 3-7-68; trials at Boscombe Down from 22-7-68; deld to No. 4 Sqn., Wildenrath, 1-75, "*CA*"; 4-84, "*A*".

XV741 ff. 5-8-68; trials at Boscombe Down from 16-8-68; deld to No. 4 Sqn., Wildenrath, 7-72. No. 3 Sqn., 9-72. Converted to **GR Mark 3**. No. 3 Sqn., 1977, "*A*"; 4-82 "*AA*". No. 233 OCU, 1987, "C".

XV742 ff. 13-9-68; retained by HSA for trials and TIs; temporarily painted in US Marine Corps markings for demonstrations.

XV743 ff. 19-12-68; crashed at Dunsfold, 27-1-69. Aircraft entered uncontrollable roll during turn in transition following VTO; US Marine Corps pilot killed.

XV744 ff. 5-3-69, John Farley. Deld to No. 1 Sqn. at Boscombe Down preparatory for Trans-Atlantic Air Race. Harrier Conversion Unit, Wittering, 9-70. No. 1 Sqn., "*26*". No. 233 OCU, 11-70; 1981, "*D*".

XV745 ff. 25-3-69. Deld No. 1 Sqn., Wittering, 3-70. Harrier Conversion Unit, Wittering, 9-70. No. 233 O.C.U., Wittering, 11-70. Converted to **GR Mark 3**. Written off after collision with *XV754* at Wittering, 19-1-76; pilot did not eject and was killed.

XV746 ff. 3-4-69. Deld No. 1 Sqn., Wittering, 18-4-69. No. 233 O.C.U., Wittering, 12-75. Aircraft crashed into mountainside near Tromso, Norway, 12-3-76; pilot believed to have ejected but was killed.

XV747 ff. Tony Hawkes. Deld Harrier Conversion Unit, Wittering, 3-70. No. 233 O.C.U., 11-70. No. 4 Sqn., 4-75, "*G*". No. 233 OCU, 2-85, "*G*".

XV748 ff. Tony Hawkes. Deld Harrier Conversion Unit, Wittering, 3-70. No. 1 Sqn., 9-72. Taken on temporary loan by HSA for Lugano Air Show, 19-6-73 to 16-6-73. No. 233 OCU, "*B*". Converted to **GR Mark 3**.

XV749 ff. 17-4-69. Deld No. 1 Sqn., 3-70; aircraft crashed while flying over the Wash, following bird-strike, 26-4-72; pilot ejected safely.

XV750 ff. 13-5-69. Deld to R.A.F.; to No. 1 Sqn., Wittering, 3-70; aircraft damaged by bird-strike during STO at Wittering, 6-4-70. Repaired and deld to No. 20 Sqn., Wildenrath, 4-72. Aircraft crashed in Holland, 6-9-73, following engine failure; pilot ejected safely with minor injuries.

XV751 ff. 28-5-69, John Farley. Deld to R.A.F., 2-7-69. Suffered Cat.4 damage at West Raynham, 5-8-69; aircraft entered rapid descent in decelerating transition and crashed inverted in cabbage patch. Repaired by HSA. ff. 22-10-70, Andy Jones. No. 233 OCU, 4-71, "*51*". Converted to **GR Mark 3**, 3-73. No. 20 Sqn., 4-73, "*V*". No. 3 Sqn., 2-77, "*M*". No. 1 Sqn., 2-79.

XV752 ff. 30-5-69, Duncan Simpson. Harrier Conversion Unit, Wittering, 3-70. No. 1 Sqn., 11-72. Converted to **GR Mark 3**. No. 1 Sqn., 11-73, "*03*". No. 233 OCU, 2-77, "*M*". No. 1 Sqn., 6-83, "*04*". No. 3 Sqn., 1988, "G".

XV753 ff. 1-7-69, Tony Hawkes. No. 1 Sqn., Wittering, 3-70. No. 233 OCU, 9-72. Converted to **GR Mark 3**. No. 233 OCU, 11-73, "*C*". No. 1 Sqn., 4-76. No. 233 OCU, 8-77. No. 1 Sqn., 6-85, "*06*".

XV754 ff. 4-7-69. No. 1 Sqn., 3-70. Converted to **GR Mark 3**. Written off after mid-air collision with *XV745* at Wittering, 19-1-76; pilot did not eject and was killed.

XV755 ff. 15-8-69, Don Riches. No. 233 OCU, 1970. No. 1 Sqn., 8-72. Converted to **GR Mark 3**. No. 233 OCU, 1975, "*55*". No. 1 Sqn., 1977, "*20*". No. 233 OCU, 1987, "M".

XV756 ff. 20-8-69, Don Riches. No. 233 OCU, 1970, "*D*". No. 1 Sqn., 10-73. Converted to **GR Mark 3**. No. 233 OCU, 1976, "*34*". No. 1 Sqn., 9-79, "*26*".

XV757 ff. 29-8-69, Barry Tonkinson. No. 233 OCU, 1970. No. 1 Sqn., c.1972. Converted to **GR Mark 3**. No. 1 Sqn., 4-78, "*12*".

XV758 ff. 6-9-69, Don Riches. Demonstrated aboard HMS *Bulwark*, 17/18-9-69. No. 233 OCU, 1970. Converted to **GR Mark 1A**. No. 3 Sqn., Wildenrath, 6-74; aircraft damaged Cat.4 after striking runway at Wildenrath following loss of power at 30 ft., 3-10-74. Repaired at Bitteswell. ff. 20-10-77, Don Riches. Converted to **GR Mark 3**. No. 3 Sqn., 1-2-77, "*AV*". No. 233 OCU, 5-85, "*J*". No. 3 Sqn., 1988, "V".

XV759 ff. 20-9-69, Barry Tonkinson. Deld to R.A.F., 12-3-70. Converted to **GR Mark 1A** and later to **GR Mark 3**. No. 233 OCU. No. 1 Sqn. No. 233 OCU, 8-83, "*E*".

XV760 ff. 25-9-69, Barry Tonkinson. Deld to R.A.F., 30-1-70. Converted to **GR. Mark 1A**. No. 233 OCU, 1977, "*42*"; 1979, "*F*".

XV761 ff. 14-2-70, Tony Hawkes. No. 233 OCU, 1970. Converted to **GR Mark 1A**. No. 3 Sqn., Wildenrath, 1-73. No. 4 Sqn., 2-74. Converted to **GR Mark 3**. No. 4 Sqn., 4-78, "*B*".

VX762 ff. 8-10-69, Tony Hawkes. No. 233 OCU, 1970. Converted to **GR Mark 1A** and later to **GR Mark 3**. No. 1 Sqn., Wittering, 4-76. No. 233 OCU, 6-76, "*44*". On loan to BAe, Dunsfold, for demonstration to Chinese delegation, Dunsfold, 12-78. No. 233 OCU, 1979, "*G*".

XV776 ff. 26-2-70. Deld to R.A.F., 3-4-70. No. 1 Sqn., 4-70. Converted to **GR Mark 1A** and later to **GR Mark 3**. Aircraft crashed while flying from Wittering at 33,000ft. following main engine bearing failure, 9-4-75; pilot ejected safely.

XV777 ff. 13-3-70. Deld to R.A.F., 1-5-70. No. 1 Sqn., 5-70, "*W*". Aircraft crashed at Wittering during decelerating transition to vertical landing, 1-5-72; pilot ejected safely.

XV778 ff. 16-3-70, Tony Hawkes. Aircraft demonstrated at Hanover Air Show, 24-4-70. No. 1 Sqn., 1970, "*E*". Converted to **GR Mark 1A** and later to **GR Mark 3.** No. 1 Sqn., 6-83; 1987, "08".

XV779 ff. 26-3-70, Don Riches. No. 1 Sqn., 5-70. No. 4 Sqn., 7-70. No. 20 Sqn., 8-72. Converted to **GR Mark 1A** and later to **GR Mark 3.** No. 3 Sqn., Wildenrath, 2-77, "*P*"; 4-81 "*AP*"; 6-85, "*AB*".

XV780 ff. 26-3-70. No. 1 Sqn., 5-70. No. 4 Sqn., Wildenrath, 7-70. Aircraft crashed in Germany following bird-strike, 27-6-72; pilot ejected safely.

XV781 ff. 18-4-70, John Farley. No. 1 Sqn., 5-70. No. 4 Sqn., Wildenrath, 7-70. No. 20 Sqn., 8-72. Converted to **GR Mark 1A**. No. 3 Sqn., 5-73. Converted to **GR Mark 3**.

XV782 ff. 19-5-70, Tony Hawkes. No. 1 Sqn., 7-70. No. 4 Sqn., 8-70. Converted to **GR Mark 1A** and later to **GR Mark 3.**

XV783 ff. 9-6-70, Tony Hawkes. No. 4 Sqn., 8-70. Converted to **GR Mark 1A.** No. 20 Sqn., 4-74. Converted to **GR Mark 3.** No. 4 Sqn., 2-77, "*C*". No. 3 Sqn., 1981, "*AK*". No. 233 OCU, 1987, "*N*".

XV784 ff. 2-7-70, Barry Tonkinson. No. 4 Sqn., 8-70. Converted to **GR Mark 1A** and later to **GR Mark 3.** No. 4 Sqn., 5-81, "*CD*"; 3-84, "*D*".

XV785 ff. 29-7-70. No. 233 OCU, 9-70. No. 20 Sqn., 11-70. No. 3 Sqn., 7-72. No. 4 Sqn., 9-72. Converted to **GR Mark 1A** and later to **GR Mark 3**.

XV786 ff. 20-8-70, Tony Hawkes. No. 233 OCU, 9-70. No. 20 Sqn., Wildenrath, 12-70. Converted to **GR Mark 1A.** No. 4 Sqn., 4-74. Converted to **GR Mark 3.** No. 1 Sqn., 10-77; to Belize, 10-78; 8-82, "*V*";

XV787 ff. 9-9-70, Tony Hawkes. No. 1 Sqn., 11-70. Converted to **GR Mark 1A** and later to **GR Mark 3**. No. 1 Sqn., 1977, "*02*".

XV788 ff. 7-4-70. No. 1 Sqn., 11-70. Converted to **GR Mark 3**. Aircraft crashed at Belize, 1-12-75, after pilot experienced engine surge at 450 knots at 1,000 ft; pilot ejected safely.

XV789 ff. 7-4-70. No. 1 Sqn., 6-70. No. 4 Sqn., Wildenrath, 8-70. Converted to **GR Mark 3**. Taken on loan by HSA for 1978 SBAC Display, Farnborough. No. 4 Sqn., 1977, "*F*".

XV790 ff. 4-6-70, Don Riches. No. 4 Sqn., 8-70. No. 20 Sqn., 8-72. Converted to **GR Mark 3.** No. 4 Sqn., 2-77. No. 3 Sqn., 1987, "AP".

XV791 ff. 13-5-70. No. 1 Sqn., 6-70. No. 4 Sqn., 7-70. No. 20 Sqn., 8-72. Aircraft crashed at Wildenrath, 9-7-73, following bird-strike; pilot ejected safely.

XV792 ff. 22-5-70, Tony Hawkes. No. 1 Sqn., 6-70. Aircraft crashed at Gardemoen, Oslo, 21-11-71, and suffered Cat. 4 damage; pilot suffered loss of directional control during landing on snow and aircraft overturned. To HSA, 31-12-71, for repair. ff. 16-8-73, Duncan Simpson. No. 3 Sqn., 2-11-73, as **GR Mark 1A.** No. 4 Sqn., 9-77. No. 3 Sqn., 10-77; 6-79, "*N*".

XV793 ff. 2-7-70, Barry Tonkinson. No. 233 OCU, 1970. Converted to **GR Mark 1A** and later to **GR Mark 3.** No. 20 Sqn., 3-73, "*N*". No. 3 Sqn., 2-77. No. 1 Sqn., 8-78. No. 4 Sqn., 10-78 (Belize).

XV794 ff. 12-6-70. No. 4 Sqn., 8-70. Aircraft crashed at Wildenrath, 4-5-72, following bird-strikes and ingestion; pilot ejected safely.

XV795 ff. 24-7-70, Duncan Simpson. No. 1 Sqn., 9-70, "*DS*". Converted to **GR Mark 1A** and later to **GR Mark 3**. No. 233 OCU. No. 1 Sqn., 8-78. No. 4 Sqn., Belize, 10-78. No. 3 Sqn., 2-79.

XV796 ff. 6-8-70. No. 1 Sqn., 9-70. Aircraft crashed at Ouston, Northumberland, after flame-out, 6-10-70; pilot ejected safely.

XV797 ff. 3-9-70. No. 233 OCU, 11-70. No. 20 Sqn., 12-70. No. 4 Sqn., 8-72. Converted to **GR**

Mark 1A. Aircraft crashed in Holland in uncontrollable dive, 23-1-74; pilot ejected but killed following parachute harness failure.

XV798 ff. 15-9-70. No. 20 Sqn., 1970. Aircraft crashed during approach to vertical landing at Wildenrath, 23-4-71; pilot ejected safely through trees.

XV799 ff. 17-9-70. No. 233 OCU, 11-70. Pilot flew into high ground in Scotland, 13-9-72, and was killed; aircraft destroyed.

XV800 ff. 28-9-70. No. 20 Sqn., 1-71. Converted to **GR Mark 1A** and later to **GR Mark 3**. No. 4 Sqn., 4-74. Aircraft crashed after flame-out at 50 ft. after take-off at Wildenrath, 16-5-75; pilot ejected safely.

XV801 ff. 20-11-70, Andy Jones. (First Harrier delivered direct to Germany). No. 20 Sqn., 11-1-71. Converted to **GR Mark 1A** and later to **GR Mark 3**. No. 4 Sqn., 3-73. No. 20 Sqn., 4-74. No. 3 Sqn., 2-77.

XV802 ff. 25-11-70. No. 20 Sqn., 1-71. Aircraft flew into wooded area and crashed, Stadtoldendorf, 21-3-72; pilot killed.

XV803 ff. 12-5-71. No. 1 Sqn., 7-71. Aircraft crashed at Wittering following nozzle runaway, 3-8-71. USAF pilot killed as seat rocket pins had not been removed.

XV804 ff. 13-11-70. No. 233 OCU, 2-71. Converted to **GR Mark 1A** and later to **GR Mark 3**. No. 233 OCU, 1976, "*45*"; 1977 "*J*"; 9-82, "*O*". No. 3 Sqn., 4-84, "*03*".

XV805 ff. 11-5-71. No. 20 Sqn., 22-6-71. Converted to **GR Mark 1A**. Aircraft crashed at Wildenrath after bird-strike, 30-7-73; pilot, Major Gibson, USMC, ejected safely at 500 ft.

XV806 ff. 21-4-71. No. 20 Sqn., 15-6-71. Converted to **GR Mark 1A** and later to **GR Mark 3**. No. 4 Sqn., 4-74, "*H*"; 4-83, "*B*". No. 3 Sqn., 1988, "*N*".

XV807 ff. 16-9-71. Deld No. 233 OCU, 20-10-71. Converted to **GR Mark 1A** and later to **GR Mark 3**. No. 3 Sqn., 7-75. No. 233 OCU, 7-77, "*L*".

XV808 ff. 23-1-71. Deld No. 4 Sqn., 26-3-71. No. 20 Sqn., 7-72. Converted to **GR Mark 1A** and later to **GR Mark 3**. No. 3 Sqn., 2-77. No. 233 OCU, 1987, "*L*".

XV809 ff. 9-3-71. Deld No. 20 Sqn., 2-4-71; No. 4 Sqn., 8-72, "*J*". Converted to **GR Mark 1A** and later to **GR Mark 3**. No. 4 Sqn., 5-78, "*J*". No. 3 Sqn., 3-84, "*AF*"; 1988, "*F*".

XV810 ff. 25-3-71. Deld No. 20 Sqn., 26-4-71. Converted to **GR Mark 1A** and later to **GR Mark 3**. No. 4 Sqn., 2-77, "*C*". No. 233 OCU, 1987, "*A*".

The Hawker Siddeley Harrier GR Mark 1. One replacement aircraft, *XW630*, built in 1970-71. Standard of preparation as in the first production batch.

XW630 ff. 10-6-71. Deld No. 20 Sqn., 6-71. No. 4 Sqn., 8-72. Converted to **GR Mark 1A** and later to **GR Mark 3**. No. 20 Sqn., 6-74; No. 3 Sqn., 2-77; 8-82, "*AG*".

The Hawker Siddeley Harrier GR Mark 1. Second production batch of 17 aircraft, *XW916-XW924, XW763-XW770* (batch flown in this order). Rolls-Royce (Bristol) Pegasus 6 (Mark 101) vectored-thrust turbofans.

XW916 ff. 11-6-71. Deld No. 20 Sqn., 11-71. No. 3 Sqn., 1-72. Converted to **GR Mark 1A** and later to **GR Mark 3**. No. 20 Sqn., 8-73. No. 4 Sqn., 2-77, "*H*"; 4-83, "*W*".

XW917 ff. 30-6-71. No. 4 Sqn., 8-71. No. 3 Sqn., 2-77, "*L*". Converted to **GR Mark 1A** and later to **GR Mark 3**. No. 3 Sqn., 3-84, "*AL*".

XW918 ff. 10-7-71. No. 4 Sqn., 7-71. No. 3 Sqn., 1-72; aircraft struck farm building and crashed during demonstration at Wildenrath, 12-1-72; pilot killed.

XW919 ff. 23-7-71. No. 233 OCU, 9-71. No. 1 Sqn., 11-72. Aircraft badly damaged in accident at Lyneham, 28-6-73, but repaired and converted to **GR Mark 3**. No. 1 Sqn., 4-76, "*09*". No. 4 Sqn., Belize, 10-78. No. 1 Sqn., 4-84, "*03*".

XW920 ff. 2-9-71. No. 20 Sqn., 10-71. No. 3 Sqn., 1-72. Aircraft crashed in Sardinia, 21-6-72, following fuel system failure due to shearing of low-pressure governor shaft; pilot ejected safely.

XW921 ff. 17-9-71. No. 20 Sqn., 10-71. No. 3 Sqn., 1-72. No. 4 Sqn., 7-72. Converted to **GR**

Mark 1A and later to **GR Mark 3.** No. 4 Sqn., Belize, 1-79, "*K*".

XW922 ff. 26-8-71. No. 1 Sqn., 10-71. No. 233 OCU, 11-72. Converted to **GR Mark 1A** and later to **GR Mark 3.** No. 1 Sqn., 5-76. No. 233 OCU, 6-76, "*49*"; 5-80, "*K*".

XW923 ff. 8-9-71. No. 1 Sqn., 10-71. Converted to **GR Mark 1A** and later to **GR Mark 3.** No. 233 OCU. No. 1 Sqn., 12-76, "*F*".

XW924 ff. 15-9-71. No. 20 Sqn., 10-71. No. 4 Sqn., 8-72. Converted to **GR Mark 1A** and later to **GR Mark 3.** No. 4 Sqn., Belize, 4-79. No. 1 Sqn., 4-83, "*01*". No. 4 Sqn., 1987.

XW763 ff. 30-9-71. No. 4 Sqn., 11-71. No. 3 Sqn., 9-73. Converted to **GR Mark 1A** and later to **GR Mark 3.** No. 3 Sqn., 1977, "*K*".

XW764 ff. 14-10-71. No. 4 Sqn., 11-71. No. 3 Sqn., 1-72, "*C*". Aircraft damaged (Cat. 3); repaired and converted to **GR Mark 3.** No. 3 Sqn., 1977, "*C*"; 5-81, "*AC*".

XW765 ff. 1-11-71. No. 20 Sqn., 12-71. No. 3 Sqn., 2-72. Converted to **GR Mark 1A** and later to **GR Mark 3.**

XW766 ff. 1-11-71. No. 20 Sqn., 12-71. No. 3 Sqn., 2-72, "*E*". Aircraft damaged (Cat. 3, 10-72) but repaired and converted to **GR Mark 1A,** and later to **GR Mark 3.**

XW767 ff. 24-11-71. No. 20 Sqn., 12-71. No. 3 Sqn., 2-72. Converted to **GR Mark 1A** and later to **GR Mark 3.** No. 1 Sqn. No. 233 OCU, 2-76.

XW768 ff. 9-12-71. No. 3 Sqn., 4-72. No. 20 Sqn., 9-72. Converted to **GR Mark 1A** and later to **GR Mark 3.** No. 4 Sqn., 2-77, "*O*".

XW769 ff. 10-1-72. No. 3 Sqn., 3-72. Converted to **GR Mark 1A** and later to **GR Mark 3.** No. 20 Sqn., "*F*". No. 1 Sqn., "*24*". No. 233 OCU, 10-76.

XW770 ff. 4-1-72. Stored until 9-6-72. No. 3 Sqn., 1-73. Converted to **GR Mark 3.** Aircraft crashed after flame-out at 600 ft. at Wildenrath, 6-7-76; pilot ejected safely.

The Hawker Siddeley Harrier T Mark 2. Two development two-seat aircraft, *XW174* and *XW175*, ordered in 1967 to conform to Air Staff Requirement 386. Rolls-Royce (Bristol) Pegasus 6 (Mark 101) engines, rated at 19,000 lb. thrust with water injection.

XW174 ff. 24-4-69, Duncan Simpson. Retained for development flight trials, HSA, Dunsfold. Aircraft crashed, 4-6-69, at Larkhill following fuel system fault. Pilot, Duncan Simpson, ejected but injured.

XW175 ff. 14-7-69. Aircraft retained for development flight trials (eg, weathercock stability, etc.), HSA, Dunsfold. R.A.E., Bedford, 1989.

The Hawker Siddeley Harrier T Mark 2 and 2A. First production batch of 12 two-seat aircraft, *XW264-XW272, XW925-XW927,* ordered in 1967 to conform to Air Staff Requirement 386. Rolls-Royce (Bristol) Mark 101 engines rated at 19,000 lb. thrust. First ten aircraft delivered as T Mark 2s, remaining two as T Mark 2As.

XW264 ff. 3-10-69. Not delivered to the R.A.F. but retained by HSA for store and weapon clearance. Aircraft written off after forced landing at Boscombe Down, 11-7-70, following fuel system fault; aircraft burned but pilot, Barry Tonkinson, safe.

XW265 ff. 28-2-70. Retained for CA Release clearance trials. Accepted by MoD, 21-5-70.

XW 266 ff. 1-2-70. Harrier Converson Unit, Wittering, 28-7-70. No. 233 OCU, 11-70. Converted to **T. Mark 2A** and later to **T. Mark 4.** No. 1 Sqn., 6-77. No. 233 OCU, 8-77, "*S*".

XW267 ff. 3-7-70. Harrier Conversion Unit, Wittering, 28-7-70. No. 233 OCU., 11-70, "*52*"; 7-72, "*67*". Converted to **T. Mark 2A** and later to **T. Mark 4.** No. 233 OCU, 1977, "*T*".

XW268 ff. 5-11-70. No. 233 OCU, 7-1-71. Converted to T. Mark 2A and later to **T. Mark 4.** No. 1 Sqn., 5-77. No. 233 OCU, 7-77, "*54*"; 8-77, "*U*". No. 4 Sqn., c.10-77, "*B*".

XW269 ff. 12-2-71. Deld No. 4 Sqn., 1-4-71. Converted to **T. Mark 2A** and later **T. Mark 4.** S.A.O.E.U., Boscombe Down, 1989, for Night Bird trials.

XW270 ff. 24-11-70. Deld No. 233 OCU, 10-3-71. Converted to **T. Mark 2A** and later to

T. Mark 4. No. 1 Sqn., 8-76. No. 233 OCU, 9-76, "56"; 1977 "*V*". No. 1 Sqn., 10-83, "*12*".
XW271 ff. 26-5-71. Deld No. 1 Sqn., 20-7-71, "*T*". Converted to **T. Mark 2A** and later to
  T. Mark 4A. No. 1 Sqn., "*17*". No. 233 OCU, "*R*". No. 3 Sqn., 1988, "*Z*".
XW272 ff. 4-5-71. Deld No. 20 Sqn., 10-6-71. Converted to **T. Mark 2A** and later to **T. Mark**
  4. No. 4 Sqn., 2-77, "*Z*"; aircraft crashed at Bergen Hohne tactical range, Germany,
  29-2-82; pilot attempted short take-off without flaps, hit trees and was killed.

XW925 ff. 26-8-71. Deld No. 233 OCU, 1-10-71. Converted to **T. Mark 2A** and later to
  T. Mark 4. No. 1 Sqn., 5-76. No. 233 OCU, 10-76, "*57*". No. 1 Sqn., 6-83, "*12*".
XW926 ff. 6-4-72. Delivered as the first **T. Mark 2A.** No. 3 Sqn., 11-5-72. Converted to
  T. Mark 4. No. 233 OCU, 10-75, "58"; 1977, "*X*".
XW927 ff. 8-6-72. Second Harrier **T. Mark 2A.** No. 233 OCU, 28-7-72. Converted to **T. Mark**
  4. No. 233 OCU, 1-77, "59". Loaned to Royal Navy, 1980, "*Y*". No. 4 Sqn., 4-84, "*S*".

The Hawker Siddeley A V-8A Harrier Mark 50. First production batch of 12 aircraft (US Nos.
  158384 to *158395*) purchased by U.S. Navy Department for U.S. Marine Corps. Funding
  voted during 1970 for FY 1971. Aircraft delivered with Rolls-Royce (Bristol) Pegasus Mark
  102 engines, but ten aircraft retrospectively fitted with Mark 103 engines.
158384 ff. 20-11-70; deld, 19-1-71. VMA-513. NATC, 1976.
158385 ff. 24-12-70; deld, 5-2-71. VMA-513. VMA-231.
158386 ff. 3-2-71; deld, 15-3-71. VMA-513; aircraft failed to recover from dive attack,
  Chesapeake Bay, 18-6-71; pilot killed.
158387 ff. 16-2-71; deld, 12-3-71. VMA-513.
158388 ff. 16-4-71; deld, 11-5-71. VMA-513; aircraft crashed at Beaufort after bird-strike,
  27-3-73; pilot ejected safely.
158389 ff. 7-4-71; deld, 30-4-71. VMA-513.
158390 ff. 20-5-71; deld, 30-4-71. VMA-513. VMA-231.
158391 ff. 7-5-71; deld, 28-5-71. VMA-513.
158392 ff. 19-6-71; deld, 13-7-71. VMA-513. VMA-231, 1980, "*CE-10*".
158393 ff. 28-10-71; deld, 29-11-71. VMA-513; crashed, 26-8-82.
158394 ff. 23-12-71; deld, 31-1-72. Aircraft modified to become the first McDonnell-Douglas
  YAV-8B, 1974-75. NATC, 1979.
158395 ff. 18-2-72; deld (airlifted), 21-3-72. Aircraft modified to become the second
  McDonnell-Douglas **YAV-8B.** NATC, 1979; crashed 15-11-79 (pilot ejected safely).

The Hawker Siddeley A V-8A Harrier Mark 50. Second production batch of 18 aircraft (US
  Nos. *158694* to *158711*), purchased by U.S. Navy Department for U.S. Marine Corps.
  Funding voted during 1971 for FY 1972. All aircraft delivered with Roll-Royce (Bristol)
  Pegasus Mark 103 engines. Aircraft retained Ferranti 541 inertial nav-attack system.
158694 ff. 12-4-72; deld, 4-5-72. VMA-513.
158695 ff. 11-5-72; deld, 31-5-72. VMA-513. VMA-542, 1980, "*WH-02*".
158696 ff. 6-6-72; deld, 13-7-72. VMA-513. VMA-231, 1980, "*CG-12*".
158697 ff. 23-6-72; deld, 10-7-72. VMA-513, "*WF-01*".
158698 ff. 18-7-72; deld, 19-9-72. VMA-513 aboard USS *Guam* (LPH-9). VMA-231, 1980,
  "*CG-08*".
158699 ff. 22-8-72; deld, 22-9-72. VMA-513, "WF-04" aboard USS *Guam* (LPH-9). VMA-
  231, 1980, "*CG-13*".
158700 ff. 8-8-72; deld, 6-9-72. VMA-513. Converted to **AV-8C.** VMA-542, 1982, "*WH-09*".
158701 ff. 8-8-72; deld (airlifted), 7-9-72. VMA-513. VMA-542, 1982, "*WH-09*".
158702 ff. 18-9-72; deld, 11-10-72. VMA-513. VMA-231, 1980, "*CG-00*".
158703 ff. 21-9-72; deld, 6-10-72. Crashed 26-6-81.
158704 ff. 20-10-72; deld, 11-12-72. VMA-542.

158705 ff. 6-10-72; deld (airlifted), 26-10-72. VMA-542.

158706 ff. 16-10-72; deld, 7-12-72. VMA-513 aboard USS *Guam* (LPH-9). Converted to **AV-8C**. VMA-542, 1982, *"WH-03"*.

158707 ff. 27-10-72; deld (airlifted), 29-11-72. VMA-542.

158708 ff. 17-11-72; deld 28-12-72. VMA-542. VMA-231; aircraft crashed after engine failure at night off Kadena, Okinawa, 29-11-77; pilot ejected safely.

158709 ff. 18-11-72. VMA-513. VMA-542; aircraft crashed during landing at Jacksonville, 10-1-76; pilot ejected safely.

158710 ff. 22-11-72; deld, 2-1-73. VMA-513 aboard USS *Guam* (LPH-9). VMA-231, 1982, *"CG-06"*.

158711 ff. 27-11-72. VMA-542, *"WH-5"*. VMA-231, 1982, *"CG-02"*.

The Hawker Siddeley AV-8A Harrier Mark 50. Third production batch of 30 aircraft (U.S. Nos. *158948* to *158977*), purchased by U.S. Navy Department for U.S. Marine Corps. Funding voted during 1972 for FY 1973. All aircraft delivered with Rolls-Royce (Bristol) Pegasus Mark 103 engines. First 29 aircraft retained Ferranti 541 inertial nav-attack system; 30th aircraft with Baseline system.

158948 ff. 29-12-72; deld, 2-2-73. VMA-542; aircraft crashed on landing, 5-6-74; pilot ejected but was killed.

158949 ff. 28-12-72; deld, 21-1-73. VMA-542, *"WH-09"*. Converted to **AV-8C**. VMA-542, 1982, *"WH-14"*.

158950 ff. 17-1-73; deld, 20-2-73. VMA-542, *"WH-10"*.

158951 ff. 13-2-73; deld, 13-3-73. VMA-542.

158952 ff. 6-2-73; deld, 8-3-73. VMA-542; aircraft crashed, 3-2-78, following engine failure; pilot ejected but slightly hurt.

158953 ff. 6-3-73; deld, 27-3-73. VMA-542, *"WH-12"*; aircraft crashed off Cherry Point, 27-7-77; pilot killed.

158954 ff. 13-3-73; deld, 6-4-73. VMA-542. Converted to **AV-8C**. VMA-542, 1982 *"WH-01"*.

158955 ff. 28-3-73; deld, 17-4-73. VMA-542; crashed, 1-12-82.

158956 ff. 18-4-73; deld, 18-4-73. VMA-542. Converted to **AV-8C**. Crashed 4-3-82.

158957 ff. 18-5-73; deld, 9-7-73. VMA-542, *"WH-16'"*; crashed at Cherry Point, 27-8-76, following engine failure; pilot ejected safely.

158958 ff. 11-5-73; deld, 28-6-73. VMA-542. VMA-513, 1978, *"WF-20"*.

158959 ff. 25-5-73; deld, 5-7-73. VMA-542, *"WH-11"*.

158960 ff. 13-6-73; deld, 17-7-73. VMA-542.

158961 ff. 2-7-73; deld, 27-7-73. VMA-542. VMA-513, 1980, *"WF-06"*.

158962 ff. 3-7-73; deld, 31-7-73. VMA-542. Converted to **AV-8C**. Aircraft crashed 24-9-82.

158963 ff. 24-7-73; deld, 30-8-73. VMA-542. VMA-513, 1980.

158964 ff. 27-7-73; deld, 9-7-73. VMA-542. Converted to **AV-8C**. VMA-542, 1982 *"WH-08"*.

158965 ff. 7-8-73; deld, 30-8-73. VMA-513, 1978, *"WF-00"*.

158966 ff. 23-8-73; deld, 21-9-73. VMA-513, 1978, *"WF-04"*.

158967 ff. 18-9-73; deld, 4-10-73. VMA-542; engine failed at high altitude and failed to re-light, 11-2-77; aircraft crashed but pilot ejected safely.

158968 ff. 21-9-73; deld, 2-11-73. VMA-513. Crashed, 26-1-82.

158969 ff. 26-9-73; deld, 26-10-73. VMA-513. VMA-231, 1980, *"CG-04"*.

158970 ff. 1-11-73; deld, 30-11-73. VMA-513; crashed into mountainside near Las Vegas during dive bombing, 6-9-77; pilot killed.

158971 ff. 22-10-73; deld, 9-11-73. VMA-513; aircraft crashed from hover during demonstration, Beaufort, 27-7-74; pilot injured.

158972 ff. 7-11-73; deld, 28-11-73. VMA-513. Converted to **AV-8C**. VMA-542, 1982 *"WH-10"*.

158973 ff. 16-11-73; deld, 7-12-73. VMA-513 . Converted to **AV-8C**. VMA-542, 1982 *"WH-02"*.

158974 ff. 21-11-73; deld, 20-12-73. VMA-513. Aircraft ran out of fuel and crashed, Iwakuni, 30-8-76; pilot ejected safely.

158975 ff. 11-12-73; deld, 22-1-74. VMA-513. VMA-231, 1980, *"CG-15"*.

158976 ff. 7-12-73; deld, 4-1-74. VMA-513, 1980, *"WF-11"*.

158977 ff. 7-12-73; deld, 7-2-74, after Baseline trials. Trials also at Patuxent River. 1974. Converted to **AV-8C**. VMA-542, 1982, *"WH-05"*.

The Hawker Siddeley AV-8A Harrier Mark 50. Fourth production batch of 30 aircraft, (U.S. Nos. *159230-159259*), purchased by the U.S. Navy Department for the U.S. Marine Corps. Funding voted during 1973 for FY 1974. All aircraft delivered with Rolls-Royce (Bristol) Pegasus 103 engine, and all equipped with Baseline system.

159230 ff. 2-1-74; deld 25-1-74. VMA-513; crashed into sea off Iwakuni, 6-12-76; pilot killed.

159231 ff. 19-12-73; deld, 25-1-74. VMA-513,*"WF-02"*.

159232 ff. 11-1-74; deld, 13-2-74. VMA-513. Converted to **AV-8C**. VMA-542, 1982.

159233 ff. 20-3-74; deld, 5-4-74.

159234 ff. 20-3-74; deld, 5-6-74.

159235 ff. 21-3-74; deld, 21-6-74. VMA-231; crashed during vertical landing, Cherry Point, 13-2-75; pilot killed.

159236 ff. 22-3-74; deld, 19-6-74. VMA-231; aircraft crashed near Beaufort, 4-7-75; pilot did not eject and was killed.

159237 ff. 3-4-74; deld 10-7-74. VMA-531; crashed into the sea off Mayport after engine failure at 600 feet, 16-6-76; pilot ejected safely.

159238 ff. 3-4-74; deld 26-6-74. VMA-231, *"CG-17"* and *"CG-01"*.

159239 ff. 11-4-74; deld 30-7-74. VMA-231. VMA-542, 1980, *"WH-00"*.

159240 ff. 26-4-74; deld, 23-7-74. VMA-231, *"CG-10"*.

159241 ff. 3-5-74; deld, 29-8-74. VMA-231, *"CG-03"*.

159242 ff. 24-5-74; deld, 15-8-74. VMA-231.

159243 ff. 19-6-74; deld, 13-9-74. VMA-231. Converted to **AV-8C**. VMA-542, 1982.

159244 ff. 26-6-74; deld, 20-9-74. VMA-231, *"CG-30"*; crashed after engine failure at low level, Beaufort, 4-7-75; pilot ejected safely.

159245 ff. 16-7-74; deld, 7-8-74. VMA231 crashed during landing at Cherry Point, 9-10-74.

159246 ff. 23-7-74; deld, 22-8-74. VMA-231, *"NM-05"*. VMA-542, 1980, *"WH-17"*.

159247 ff. 25-7-74; deld, 5-9-74. VMA-231. Converted to **AV-8C**. VMA-542, 1984 *"WH-01"*.

159248 ff. 21-8-74; deld, 27-9-74. VMA-231.

159249 ff. 10-9-74; deld, 4-10-74. VMA-231, *"CG-04"*.

159250 ff. 23-9-74; deld, 22-10-74. VMA-231; crashed at sea during rocket attack while flying from USS *Saratoga* off Cape Hatteras, North Carolina, 12-7-77; pilot killed.

159251 ff. 8-10-74; deld, 6-11-74. VMA-231. VMA-513, 1976, *"WF-03"*; crashed, 13-8-80.

159252 ff. 25-10-74; deld, 18-11-74. VMA-231. VMA(T)-203, 1978, *"KD-00"*.

159253 ff. 8-11-74; deld, 18-12-74. VMA-231, "CG-00", 1976.

159254 ff. 27-11-74; deld, 23-12-74. VMA-513, 1978, "WF-24". Converted to **AV-8C**. VMA-542, *"WH-15"*.

159255 ff. 13-12-74; deld, 13-1-75. VMA-231, USS *Roosevelt*, 1976, *"NM-614"*. NATC. SATD, 1978.

159256 ff. 4-12-74; deld, 6-1-75. VMA(T)-203, *"KD-29"*.

159257 ff. 19-12-74; deld, 20-1-75. VMA(T)-203. VMA-542, *"WH-01"*.

159258 ff. 7-1-75; deld, 30-6-76. Converted to **AV-8C**. VMA-542, *"WH-11"*.

159259 ff. 24-1-75; deld, 3-3-75. Crashed 27-11-77.

The Hawker Siddeley AV-8A Harrier Mark 50. Fifth production batch of 12 aircraft (U.S. Nos. *159366* to *159377*), purchased by U.S. Navy Department for U.S. Marine Corps under Contract No. K/A10a/15. Funding voted during 1974 for FY 1975. All aircraft delivered with Rolls-Royce (Bristol) Pegasus 103 engines and all equipped with Baseline system.

159366 ff. 25-3-75; deld, 20-6-75. VMA(T)-203, *"KD-17"*.

159367 ff. 25-4-75; deld, 27-6-75. VMA(T)-203, *"KD-16"*.

159368 ff. 13-5-75; deld, 30-6-75; crashed, 19-1-81.

159369 ff. 24-6-75; deld, 25-7-75.

159370 ff. 5-8-75. VMA(T)-203. Converted to **AV-8C**. VMA-542, *"WH-07"*.

159371 ff. 20-8-75; deld, 17-10-75. VMA(T)-203, *"KD-15"*.

159372 ff. 12-9-75; deld, 28-10-75. VMA(T)-203; crashed during landing transition, 6-4-77; pilot killed.

159373 ff. 2-7-76; deld, 4-8-76. VMA(T)-203, *"KD-14"*.

159374 ff. 24-8-76; deld, 8-10-76. VMA(T)-203, *"KD-12"*.

159375 ff. 6-11-75; deld, 5-1-76. VMA(T)-203; 1982, *"KD-11"*.

159376 First flight and delivery dates not known. VMA(T)-203, *"KD-10"*.

159377 ff. 12-12-75; deld, 29-1-76. VMA(T)-203, *"KD-15"*; crashed during pilot's first transition, 19-3-77; pilot ejected safely.

The Hawker Siddeley Harrier T. Mark 52. Single two-seat demonstration aircraft, *G-VTOL/ ZA250*, built as private venture and owned by manufacturers. ff. 16-9-71. Demonstration flights at home and overseas. Powered in turn by Rolls-Royce (Bristol) Pegasus 102 and 103 engines. Also used to demonstrate Sky Hook proposal.

The Hawker Siddeley Harrier T. Mark 4. Two production two-seat trainers for the Royal Air Force, *XW933* and *XW934*, ordered in 1972 and delivered in 1973 with Rolls-Royce (Bristol) Pegasus 103 engines.

XW933 ff. 4-5-73; deld to No. 20 Sqn., 22-8-73. No. 3 Sqn., 1-75, *"Q"*; 4-84, *"AQ"*.

XW934 ff. 16-10-73; deld, 21-12-73, to No. 1 Sqn. To A. & A.E.E., Boscombe Down, 4-74. No. 1 Sqn., *"06"*, and No. 233 OCU, from 7-74.

The Hawker Siddeley TAV-8A Harrier T. Mark 54. Production batch of eight two-seaters (U.S. Nos. *159378* to *159385*), purchased by the U.S. Navy Department for the U.S. Marine Corps under Contract No. K/A10a/15. Funding voted during 1975 for FY 1975-76. Rolls-Royce (Bristol) Pegasus Mark 103 engines.

159378 ff. 16-7-75; deld, 1-10-75. VMA(T)-203, 1976, *"KD-00"*; 1978, *"KD-06"*.

159379 ff. 17-10-75; deld, 16-1-76. VMA(T)-203, 1976, *"KD-01"*.

159380 ff. 12-12-75; deld, 16-1-76. VMA(T)-203, 1976, *"KD-02"*.

159381 ff. 19-3-76; deld, 12-4-76. VMA(T)-203, 1976, *"KD-07"*; aircraft crashed during landing transition and overturned, 19-4-77; both pilots unhurt.

159382 ff. 10-8-76; deld, 16-9-76. VMA(T)-203, 1977, *"KD-04"*.

159383 ff. 4-5-76; deld, 28-6-76. VMA(T)-203, 1977, *"KD-05"*.

159384 First flight and delivery details not known. Crashed, 1-8-80.

159385 ff. 7-10-76; delivery date not known. VMA(T)-203, 1977, *"KD-03"*.

The Hawker Siddeley Harrier GR Mark 3. First production batch of 12 aircraft, *XZ128-XZ139*, ordered during 1974 under Contract No. KA/9a/31 for delivery during 1975-76. Powered by Rolls-Royce (Bristol) Pegasus 11 (Mark 103) engines rated at 21,500 lb. thrust.

XZ128 ff. 9-1-76; deld No. 233 OCU, Wittering, 15-3-76. No. 1 Sqn., 5-76, *"15"*; to Belize, 4-78. (Was the first Harrier to be built and delivered as a GR Mark 3).

XZ129 ff. 24-2-76; deld No. 233 OCU, 6-4-76. No. 1 Sqn., 6-76, *"29"*; 6-83, *"06"*.

XZ130 ff. 24-2-76; deld No. 3 Sqn., Wildenrath, 7-4-76. No. 20 Sqn., 6-76. No. 3 Sqn., 1-77. No. 4 Sqn., 2-77. No. 1 Sqn., 7-78.

XZ131 ff. 5-4-76; deld No. 4 Sqn., Wildenrath, 30-4-76, *"M"*. No. 1 Sqn., 5-85, *"07"*.

XZ132 ff. 15-4-76; deld No. 3 Sqn., Wildenrath, 14-5-76. No. 1 Sqn., 8-78. No. 233 OCU, 10-78.

XZ133 ff. 21-5-76; deld No. 233 OCU, 9-7-76, *"32"*. No. 1 Sqn., 2-77. No. 233 OCU, 8-77,

"*A*". No. 1 Sqn., 4-84, "*10*".

XZ134 ff. 2-7-76; deld No. 3 Sqn., Wildenrath, 29-7-76, "*J*"; 5-82, "*AJ*"; crashed at Stormede, 3-5-83, following failure of engine combustion chamber outer casing; pilot ejected but injured.

XZ135 ff. 25-8-76; deld No. 20 Sqn., Wildenrath, 2-11-76, "*P*". No. 3 Sqn., 1-77. No. 4 Sqn., 3-77, "*P*".

XZ136 ff. 9-9-76; deld No. 1 Sqn., 5-11-76.

XZ137 ff. not known. Deld, No. 4 Sqn., Wildenrath, 6-1-77, "*E*".

XZ138 ff. not known. Deld, No. 3 Sqn., Wildenrath, 22-3-77, "*Z*".

The Hawker Siddeley Harrier T. Mark 4 and 4A. Production batch of four two-seat trainers, *XZ145-XZ147* and *XZ445*, ordered for the R.A.F. during 1975 for delivery in 1976. Rolls-Royce (Bristol) Pegasus 103 engines.

XZ145 ff. 20-1-76; deld, No. 3 Sqn., Wildenrath, 8-3-76, "*T*"; 4-82, "*AT*". (Laser nose). No. 233 OCU, 19887, "*T*".

XZ146 ff. 4-8-76; deld, No. 1 Sqn., Wittering. No. 4 Sqn., Wildenrath, 4-83, "*Y*". No. 233 OCU, 2-85, "*W*". (Laser nose).

XZ147 ff. not known. No. 1 Sqn. No. 233 OCU, 1977-82. (Laser nose); 1988, "*Z*".

XZ445 ff. not known. No. 233 OCU, 1979, "*Q*". Designated T. Mark 4A. (No laser in nose).

The Hawker Siddeley AV-8S Matador (Harrier Mark 55). Also referred to as AV-8A Matador (Harrier Mark 50). Six single-seat aircraft ordered by the Spanish government via the U.S.A. during 1973. Aircraft were added to the end of the U.S. Navy AV-8A Contract and therefore carried the U.S. Nos. *159557-159562*. Aircraft built at Kingston, shipped to the U.S.A., and thence to Spain aboard the Spanish aircraft carrier *Dédalo*.

159557 ff. 26-6-76; deld, 1-4-76. Served on *Escuadrilla 008* at Rota and aboard carrier PH-01 *Dédalo*, Spanish Naval Air Arm, from 1977, "*008-1*".

159558 ff. 14-4-76; deld, 10-5-76. Served on *Escuadrilla 008* at Rota and aboard carrier PH-01 *Dédalo*, Spanish Naval Air Arm, from 1977, "*008-2*".

159559 ff. 11-6-76; deld, 7-7-76. Served on *Escuadrilla 008* at Rota and aboard carrier PH-01 *Dédalo*, Spanish Naval Air Arm, from 1977, "*008-3*".

159560 ff. 18-9-75; deld, 7-11-75. Served on *Escuadrilla 008* at Rota and aboard carrier PH-01 *Dédalo*, Spanish Naval Air Arm, from 1977, "*008-4*".

159561 ff. 24-10-75; deld, 12-12-75. Aircraft crashed during training period at Whiteman, U.S.A., 11-6-76; aircraft pitched up during short take-off; pilot ejected safely (Stencel ejection seat).

159562 ff. 3-12-75; deld, 22-1-76. Served on *Escuadrilla 008* at Rota and aboard carrier PH-01 *Dédalo*, Spanish Naval Air Arm, from 1977, "*008-6*".

The Hawker Siddeley AV-8S (Harrier Mark 55). Second production batch of five single-seat aircraft, U.S. Nos. *161174-161178*, ordered by the Spanish government, via the U.S.A., in 1977. Aircraft built at Kingston and shipped direct to Spain. Carried Nos. *008-9* to *008-12* and *008-14* in service. The last was a replacement for *159561*. Served at Rota and aboard the carrier PH-01 *Dédalo*.

The Hawker Siddeley TAV-8S Matador (Harrier Mark 58). Two two-seat trainers ordered by the Spanish government via the U.S.A. during 1973; aircraft , built at Kingston, carried U.S. Nos. *159563* and *159564* and were shipped to the U.S.A., thence to Spain aboard the Spanish carrier PH-01 *Dédalo*.

159563 ff. 21-1-76; deld, 25-2-76. Served with *Escuadrilla 008* at Rota as "*008-7*".

159564 ff. 28-5-76; deld, 5-7-76. Served with *Escuadrilla 008* at Rota as "*008-8*".

The Hawker Siddeley Sea Harrier. Three development (pre-production) aircraft, *XZ438-XZ440*, ordered from Hawker Siddeley Aviation Ltd., Kingston-upon-Thames, in 1975, powered by 21,500 lb. thrust Rolls-Royce (Bristol) Pegasus 104 vectored-thrust turbofans.

XZ438 ff. 30-12-78, Mike Snelling. Retained by H.S.A. at Dunsfold, 1978-81, for performance and handling trials.

XZ439 ff. 30-3-79, Mike Snelling. Store trials at Dunsfold and A. & A.E.E., Boscombe Down. Sea trials, HMS *Hermes*, 1979. Brought up to production standard, 1981. No. 899 Sqn., 7-82, "Z". Became 2nd **Sea Harrier F.R.S. Mk. 2** prototype; ff., 8-3-89, Paul Hopkins.

XZ440 ff. 6-6-79, Mike Snelling. Handling and performance trials, Dunsfold, Boscombe Down, R.A.E., and Rolls-Royce (Bristol). Sea trials, HMS *Hermes*, 1979.

The British Aerospace (Kingston) Sea Harrier FRS Mark 1. Production batch of 31 aircraft, *XZ450-XZ460, XZ491-XZ500, ZA174-ZA177* and *ZA190-ZA195*, ordered from Hawker Siddeley Aviation Ltd., Kingston-upon-Thames, in 1975, powered by 21,500 lb. thrust Rolls-Royce (Bristol) Pegasus 104 vectored-thrust turbofans.

XZ450 ff. 20-8-78, J.F. Farley (was the first Sea Harrier to fly on account of low instrumentation; S.B.A.C. Display, Farnborough, September 1978). Retained for trials at Dunsfold, 1978-81. No. 800 Sqn., F.A.A. Shot down by ground fire over Goose Green, Falkland Is., 4-5-82; pilot killed.

XZ451 ff. 25-5-79, H. Frick. Deld No. 700A Sqn., F.A.A., Yeovilton, 18-6-79, "*VL-100*". No. 899 Sqn.: To Falkland Is., HMS *Invincible*, 5-82. No. 801 Sqn., 9-83, "*N-000*".

XZ452 ff. 17-8-79, M.H.B. Snelling; deld No. 700A Sqn., F.A.A., Yeovilton, 12-10-79, "*VL-101*". No. 899 Sqn.; suffered Cat. 3 damage, 5-3-80. Collided with *XZ453* off Falkland Is., 6-5-82, in bad weather; pilot killed.

XZ453 ff. 5-12-79, J.F. Farley; deld No. 700A Sqn., F.A.A., Yeovilton, 31-1-80, "*VL-105*". No. 899 Sqn., "*715*". Collided with *XZ452* off Falkland Is., 6-5-82, in bad weather; pilot killed.

XZ454 ff. 12-12-79, H. Frick; deld No. 800 Sqn., F.A.A., Yeovilton, 15-2-80, "*N-250*"; crashed into English Channel and lost, 1-12-80; pilot ejected safely.

XZ455 ff. 9-10-79, H. Frick; deld No. 700A Sqn., F.A.A., Yeovilton, 9-11-79, "*VL-102*". No. 899 Sqn.; to Falkland Is., HMS *Hermes*, 5-82. No. 800 Sqn., 9-83, "*127*".

XZ456 ff. 9-11-79, H. Frick; deld, No. 700A Sqn., F.A.A., Yeovilton, 4-1-80, "*103*". No. 899 Sqn., "*VL-733*". Hit and damaged by ground fire near Port Stanley, Falkland Is., 28-5-82; pilot ejected and rescued.

XZ457 ff. 15-12-79, John Farley; deld No. 700A Sqn., F.A.A., Yeovilton, 31-1-80, "*104*". No. 899 Sqn., "*715*"; to Falkland Is., HMS *Hermes*, 5-82; destroyed two Mirage IIIs and one Skyhawk. No. 809 Sqn., 9-82. No. 899 Sqn., 7-84.

XZ458 ff. 10-1-80, H. Frick; deld No. 800 Sqn., Yeovilton, 22-2-80, "*N-251*". No. 809 Sqn.; to South Atlantic by air, 30-4-82. No. 899 Sqn., 5-83, "*715*". No. 800 Sqn., 10-84, "*L-125*".

XZ459 ff. 21-3-80, H. Frick; deld No. 800 Sqn., Yeovilton, 15-5-80, "*N-252*"; to Falkland Is., HMS *Hermes*, 5-82. No. 899 Sqn., 7-83, "*716*"; 10-84, "*713*". No. 801 Sqn., 1-85, "*N-001*".

XZ460 ff. 10-4-80, T. Scott; deld No. 800 Sqn., Yeovilton, 29-5-80, "*N-253*"; to Falkland Is., HMS *Hermes*, 5-82. No. 899 Sqn., 7-83, "*26*"; 5-83, "*710*"; 10-85, "*714*".

XZ491 ff. 20-6-80, H. Frick; deld A. & A.E.E., Boscombe Down, 18-8-80, for Service trials. Returned to Dunsfold, 6-11-80, for manufacturers' trials. To South Atlantic by air, No. 899 Sqn., 30-4-82; No. 899 Sqn., 7-83, "*N-711*".

XZ492 ff. 25-10-80, John Farley; deld No. 800 Sqn., Yeovilton, 29-12-80, "*H-123*"; later "*VL-254*". To Falkland Is., HMS *Hermes*; destroyed one Skyhawk. No. 809 Sqn., 9-82, "*23*". No. 899 Sqn., 10-84, "*714*". No. 800 Sqn., 4-85, "*L-125*".

XZ493 ff. 26-11-80, John Farley; deld, No. 801 Sqn., Yeovilton, 6-1-81, "*N-001*"; to Falkland

Is., HMS *Invincible*, 5-82. No. 800 Sqn., 1984, "*L-123*". No. 801 Sqn., 1-85. No. 899 Sqn., 8-85, "*713*".

XZ494 ff. 24-10-84, John Farley; deld, No. 899 Sqn., Yeovilton, 5-12-80, "*106*". To Falkland Is., HMS *Hermes*, 5-82. No. 899 Sqn., 9-83, "*714*"; 7-84, "*716*".

XZ495 ff. 1-81. To Falkland Is., HMS *Invincible*, with No. 801 Sqn., 5-82, "*N-003*". No. 899 Sqn., 5-84.

XZ496 ff. 9-12-80, T. Scott; deld, No. 801 Sqn., Yeovilton, 1-81, "*002*". To Falkland Is., HMS *Hermes*, with No. 800 Sqn.; destroyed one Skyhawk, 5-82.

XZ497 ff. 2-5-82, T. Scott; No. 899 Sqn., 7-82, "*4*".

XZ498 ff. 20-2-81, T. Scott. To Falkland Is., HMS *Invincible*, with No. 801 Sqn., 5-82, "*N-005*". No. 800 Sqn., 9-83, "*L-124*".

XZ499 ff. 12-6-81, T. Scott. To South Atlantic by air with No. 809 Sqn., 30-4-82; destroyed one Mirage III. No. 801 Sqn., 7-82, "*255*"; 9-84, "*002*".

XZ500 ff. 28-5-81, T. Scott. To Falkland Is., HMS *Hermes*, with No. 800 Sqn., 5-82; destroyed one Skyhawk.

ZA174 ff. 15-9-81, H. Frick; deld No. 899 Sqn., F.A.A. To Falkland Is., 5-82; hit by ground fire, 28-5-82; pilot ejected and rescued.

ZA175 ff. 28-10-81, John Farley; to Falkland Is., HMS *Invincible*, with No. 801 Sqn., 5-82. No. 800 Sqn., 9-83, "*L-124*" , later "*L-125*". No. 899 Sqn., 5-84, "*710*".

ZA176 ff. 25-11-81, H. Frick; to South Atlantic by air with No. 809 Sqn., 30-4-82; destroyed one Mirage III.

ZA177 ff. 5-12-81, Mike Snelling; to South Atlantic by air with No. 809 Sqn., 30-4-82; destroyed two Mirage IIIs.

ZA190 ff. 5-11-81, John Farley; to South Atlantic by air with No. 809 Sqn., 30-4-82. No. 800 Sqn., 10-84, "*L-126*".

ZA191 ff. 4-12-81, H. Frick; to Falkland Is., 5-82 with No. 899 Sqn.; No. 800 Sqn., 4-85, "*L-123*". Aircraft lost in English Channel, 4-10-89, after clipping mast of HMS *Ark Royal*; pilot ejected safely.

ZA192 ff. 29-1-82, John Farley; to Falkland Is. as reserve aircraft, 5-82; crashed on take-off from HMS *Hermes*, South Atlantic, 24-5-82; Lt.-Cdr. G.W. Batt, DSC, killed.

ZA193 ff. 13-1-81, John Farley; to Falkland Is. as reserve aircraft, 5-82; destroyed one Mirage III. No 801 Sqn., 7-82, "*254*"; 1-85, "*N-004*".

ZA194 ff. 23-4-82, Mike Snelling; to South Atlantic by air with No. 809 Sqn., 30-4-82; destroyed one Mirage III. No. 801 Sqn., 7-82, "*251*".

ZA195 ff. not known. No. 899 Sqn., 5-84; 5-85, "*710*". Trials with Sea Eagle ASM, 1986. Became the first **Sea Harrier F.R.S. Mark 2** development aircraft; first flight, 19 September 1988. See below.

The British Aerospace (Kingston) Harrier GR Mark 3. Second production batch of 24 aircraft, XZ963-XZ973 and XZ987-XZ999, ordered from British Aerospace PLC in 1978 and built at Kingston and Dunsfold in 1980 and 1981. Full modification standard with Rolls-Royce (Bristol) Pegasus 103 turbofans, LRMTS/FE541 and RWR equipment.

XZ963 ff. 26-3-80, T. Scott; deld No. 1 Sqn., Wittering, 8-5-80. Shot down by SAM, Goose Green, Falkland Is., 21-5-82; pilot wounded.

XZ964 ff. 14-3-80, T. Scott; deld No. 1 Sqn., Wittering, 22-4-80, "*09*". No. 233 OCU, 8-84, "*P*".

XZ965 ff. 27-6-80, T. Scott; deld to R.A.F. Germany, 28-8-80.

XZ966 ff. 18-7-80, T. Scott; deld No. 1 Sqn., Wittering, 4-9-80. No. 233 OCU, 6-83, "*C*".

XZ967 ff. 17-7-80, H. Frick; deld No. 233 OCU, Wittering, 3-9-80.

XZ968 ff. 31-10-80, H. Frick; deld to R.A.F. Germany, 19-12-80. No. 4 Sqn., Wildenrath, 4-83, "*K*".

XZ969 ff. 13-11-80, Mike Snelling; deld to R.A.F. Germany, 15-12-80.

XZ970 ff. 5-12-80, T. Scott; deld to R.A.F. Germany, 13-1-81. No. 3 Sqn., Wildenrath, 4-81, "*AR*".

XZ971 ff. 20-2-81, H. Frick; deld to No. 233 OCU, Wittering; 8-84, "*N*".

XZ972 ff. 5-6-81, T. Scott; No. 1 Sqn., Wittering; hit by ground fire, Falkland Is., 30-5-82; pilot, Sqn. Ldr. J.J. Pook DFC, ejected and rescued.

XZ973 ff. 14-8-81, John Farley. Written off in fatal accident following systems failure over North Wales, 12-2-82.

XZ987 ff. 9-9-81, T. Scott. No. 3 Sqn., Wildenrath, 4-82, "*AX*".

XZ988 ff. 28-8-81, H. Frick.

XZ989 ff. 3-10-81, T. Scott. No. 1 Sqn., Wittering, 1981-82; hit by ground fire, Falkland Is., and damaged in crash landing, 9-6-82; Wg. Cdr. Squire unhurt.

XZ990 ff. 4-11-81, John Farley. No. 4 Sqn., Wildenrath, 8-82, "*H*"; 1987, "*L*"

XZ991 ff. 28-11-81, John Farley. No. 3 Sqn., Wildenrath, 7-82, "*AD*". No. 1 Sqn., 4-84, "*07*".

XZ992 ff. 27-11-81, John Farley. No. 1 Sqn., Wittering, 6-83, "*05*".

XZ993 ff. 14-12-81, Mike Snelling. No. 3 Sqn., Wildenrath, 4-82, "*AU*". No. 1 Sqn., 1987, "*11*".

XZ994 ff. 18-12-81, H. Frick. No. 233 OCU, Wittering, 2-85, "*F*".

XZ995 ff. 22-2-82, Mike Snelling. No. 3 Sqn., Wildenrath, 6-82, "*AO*".

XZ996 ff. 13-1-82, T. Scott; deld, Wittering, 3-82. No. 233 OCU, 5-85, "*C*".

XZ997 ff. 21-1-82, Mike Snelling. No. 4 Sqn., Wildenrath, 12-83, "*AR*".

XZ988 ff. 14-4-82, T. Scott. No. 1 Sqn., Wittering, 4-82; hit by ground fire, Falkland Is., 27-5-82; Sqn. Ldr R.D. Iveson ejected and evaded capture.

XZ999 ff. 25-5-82, H. Frick. No. 4 Sqn., Wildenrath, 8-82, "*T*".

The British Aerospace (Kingston) Harrier T. Mark 4. Production batch of four two-seat trainers, *ZB600-ZB603*, to fully-modified standard; Rolls-Royce (Bristol) Pegasus 103 turbofans, LRMTS/FE541 and RWR. First flight details not known.

ZB600 No. 4 Sqn., Wildenrath, 4-83, "*R*".

ZB601 No. 233 OCU, Wittering, 6-83, "*X*".

ZB602 No. 233 OCU, Wittering, 11-84, "*Y*".

The British Aerospace (Kingston) Harrier T. Mark 4N. Production batch of three two-seat trainers, *ZB604-ZB606*, to naval standard of preparation, without LRMTS/FE541. Rolls-Royce (Bristol) Pegasus 103 turbofans. First flight details not known.

ZB604 No. 899 Sqn., Yeovilton, 8-85, "*717*".

ZB605 No. 899 Sqn., Yeovilton, 5-84, "*718*".

ZB606 No. 899 Sqn., Yeovilton, 5-84.

The British Aerospace (Kingston) Sea Harrier FRS Mark 1. Second production batch of 14 aircraft, *ZD578-ZD582* and *ZD607-ZD615*, ordered in 1982 for delivery from 1985 onwards. Built at Kingston at standard of preparation similar to first production batch, plus post-Falklands modifications. Some aircraft scheduled to be completed as or modified as Sea Harrier Mark 2s.

ZD578 No. 899 Sqn., Yeovilton, 10-85, "*711*".

ZD579 Paris Air Show, 7-85, "*200*". No. 899 Sqn., Yeovilton, 10-85, "*710*".

The British Aerospace (Kingston) Indian Sea Harrier FRS Mark 51. Production batch of six single-seat naval fighters for the Indian Navy, *IN601-IN606*, ordered in 1979 for delivery in

1983. Built at Kingston and Dunsfold. Rolls-Royce (Bristol) Pegasus 11 (Mark 104) vectored-thrust turbofans. Gaseous oxygen system and provision for MATRA Magic AAMs.

IN601 ff. 6-8-82, H. Frick. Carried temporary markings *G-9-478* at S.B.A.C. Display, Farnborough, 9-82. Deld to INTU, Yeovilton, 21-12-82. Deld to India, 13-12-83. No. 300 Sqn., INS *Hansa*, Goa-Dabolim, 1984.

IN602 Deld to INTU, Yeovilton, 1983. Deld to India, 13-12-83. No. 300 Sqn., INS *Hansa*, Goa-Dabolim, 1984.

IN603 Deld to INTU, Yeovilton, 1983. Deld to India, 13-12-83. No. 300 Sqn., INS *Hansa*, Goa-Dabolim, 1984.

IN604 Deld to INTU, Yeovilton, 1983. Deld to India, 3-84. No. 300 Sqn., INS *Hansa*, Goa-Dabolim, 1984.

IN605 Deld to INTU, Yeovilton, 1983. Deld to India, 3-84. No. 300 Sqn., INS *Hansa*, Goa-Dabolim, 1984.

IN606 Deld to INTU, Yeovilton, 1983. Deld to India, 3-84. No. 300 Sqn., INS *Hansa*, Goa-Dabolim, 1984.

The British Aerospace (Kingston) Indian Sea Harrier FRS Mark 51. Second production batch of seven single-seat naval fighters for the Indian Navy ordered late in 1985.

The British Aerospace (Kingston) Indian Harrier T. Mark 60. One two-seat trainer ordered for the Indian Navy late in 1985. (Note: The Indian Government has intimated that a third order, for both single- and two-seat aircraft, will be placed, bringing the total number delivered to approximately 25 aircraft.)

The British Aerospace (Kingston) Sea Harrier F.R.S. Mark 2. Two development aircraft (modified from production F.R.S. Mark 1s). *ZA195* was aerodynamic test aircraft for modifications to be introduced, including Ferranti Blue Vixen multi-mode fire-control radar, AIM-120 AMRAAM and BAe Sea Eagle ASM. First flight by *ZA195*, 19 September 1988. *XZ439* was 2nd prototype; first flight, 8-3-89. *XZ497* was first production conversion.

The British Aerospace (Kingston) Harrier G.R. Mark 5. Two "development batch" aircraft, *ZD318* and *ZD319*, included in initial Memorandum of Understanding, signed in August 1982, which set down agreement with McDonnell Douglas to share the production of "Harrier II" aircraft required for service by the Royal Air Force and the United States Marine Corps. The MOU covered the manufacture in the U.K. of up to 100 Harrier IIs. Of these 62 (including the two "development batch" aircraft) were immediately taken up by the Ministry of Defence. First flight by *ZD318*, 30-4-85, flown by Mike Snelling. First flight by *ZD319*, 31-7-85.

The British Aerospace (Kingston) Harrier G.R. Mark 5. Production batch of 41 aircraft, *ZD320-ZD330*, *ZD345-ZD355*, *ZD375-ZD380* and *ZD400-ZD412*, powered by 21,750 lb. thrust Rolls-Royce Pegasus 11, Mark 105, vectored-thrust turbofan. Gun armament, two 25-mm ROF cannon. First aircraft, *ZD323*, delivered to R.A.F. (Wittering), 29-5-87. Representative unit allocations:

No. 1 Sqn.: *ZD378* (*"01"*); *ZD404* (*"07"*).
No. 3 Sqn.: *ZD401* (*"AA"*); *ZD406*; *ZD407*.
No. 233 O.C.U.: *ZD324* (*"B"*); *ZD326*; *ZD327* (*"D"*); *ZD349* (*"H"*).
A. & A.E.E., Boscombe Down): *ZD322*.
Strike/Attack Operational Evaluation Unit, Boscombe Down: *ZD328*, *ZD330*.
R.A.F., Germany (familiarisation, Gütersloh): *ZD376* (7-12-88).
Ground Instruction Airframe, Wittering: *ZD355*.
Other aircraft: *ZD325* (lost during flight test, 22-10-87; ejection seat drogue deployed, pulling

pilot, Taylor Scott, from the cockpit; aircraft crashed at sea). *ZD402* (Rolls-Royce Ltd.; test bed for 23,800 lb. thrust Pegasus 11-61; first flight with this engine, 9-6-89; set four new F.A.I. (Class H —Jet Lift) Time to Height World Records, 14-8-89.)

The British Aerospace (Kingston) Harrier G.R. Mark 5A. Production batch of 19 aircraft, *ZD430-ZD438* and *ZD461-ZD470.* Aircraft incorporating GEC sensors FLIR blister on nose. First aircraft flown in 1989.

The British Aerospace (Kingston) Harrier G.R. Mark 7. Production batch of 34 aircraft (Serial numbers not yet known), to be built during 1990-1991. GEC Avionics FLIR, Computing Devices ACCS-2500, night-goggle compatible instruments, GEC Digital Colour Map Unit and HUD equipment.

[Note: At the time of writing, the designations Harrier T. Mark 6, T Mark 8 and T. Mark 10 had been mentioned as two-seat versions of the aircraft being considered. The first two, if they materialise, are likely to be conversions of in-service T. Mark 4s, probably incorporating equipment up-grading to Harrier G.R. Mark 7 and Sea Harrier F.R.S. Mark 2 respectively. The Harrier T. Mark 10 is to be an R.A.F. version of the American TAV-8B Harrier II two-seat trainer (see below) with British equipment.]

British Aerospace/McDonnell Douglas AV-8B Harrier II. Four full-scale development aircraft (FSD), ordered in 1978, incorporating supercritical wing of revised planform and composite materials in structure. U.S. Navy Nos. *161396-161399.* Rolls-Royce Pegasus 11 F402-RR-404 vectored-thrust turbofans.
- *161396* ff. 5-11-81. Nose instrumentation boom, no LERX. General handling, performance and flutter trials, NATC, 1982-83. Development of revised intakes, 1983. In-flight refuelling trials, 1984.
- *161397* ff. 7-4-82. Nose instrumentation boom; LERX fitted. Flight load measurements, store trials and engine handling, NATC, 1982-83. Development of revised intakes. Repainted in black, white, red and gold colour scheme. In-flight refuelling trials, Patuxent River, 1984-85.
- *161398* ff. 9-4-82. No nose boom; LERX fitted. Handling with stores, and avionics integration trials, NATC, 1982-83. NPE, Patuxent River from 6-63.
- *161399* ff. 4-6-83. Representative of subsequent production aircraft. Acceptance criteria development, 1983. GAU-12 gun firing trials, NATC, 1984.

British Aerospace/McDonnell Douglas AV-8B Harrier II. Pilot production batch of 12 aircraft, ordered in 1982 for U.S. Marine Corps (U.S. Nos. *161573-161584*). Rolls-Royce Pegasus 11 F402-RR-404A turbofans in early aircraft, later -406 engines. Component manufacture shared between the U.K. (Kingston) and the U.S.A.
- *161573* ff. 29-8-83. VMA(T)-203, Cherry Point, *"KD-21"*.
- *161574* ff. 1983. VMA(T)-203, Cherry Point, *"KD-22"*.
- *161575* ff. 1983. VMA(T)-203, Cherry Point, *"KD-23"*.
- *161576* ff. 1984. VMA(T)-203, Cherry Point, *"KD-24"*.
- *161577* ff. 1984. VMA(T)-203, Cherry Point, *"KD-25"*.
- *161578* ff. 1984. VMA(T)-203, Cherry Point.
- *161579* ff. 1984. VMA(T)-203, Cherry Point.
- *161580* ff. 1984. VMA(T)-203, Cherry Point.
- *161581* ff. 1984. VMA(T)-203, Cherry Point.
- *161582* ff. 1984. VMA(T)-203, Cherry Point.
- *161583* ff. 1984. VMA(T)-203, Cherry Point.
- *161584* ff. 1984. VMA(T)-204, Cherry Point.

British Aerospace/McDonnell Douglas AV-8B Harrier II. Production of 300 single-seat aircraft, authorised in 1983 and commencing with No. *162068.* Delivery planned as 27 aircraft in 1985, 31 in 1986, 51 in 1987, 70 in 1988, 72 in 1989, and the remainder thereafter. However, delivery rates were allowed to slip in 1986-87, with the result that production is likely to run out in 1992. Rolls-Royce Pegasus 11 F-402-RR-406 turbofans.

162068 VMA-331, Cherry Point, *"VL-01"*.
162069 VMA-331, Cherry Point, *"VL-02"*.
162070 VMA-331, Cherry Point, *"VL-03"*.
162071 VMA-331, Cherry Point, *"VL-04"*.

British Aerospace/McDonnell Douglas TAV-8B Harrier II. Production batch of 28 two-seat trainers for U.S. Marine Corps. Introduced into service in 1987. (Aircraft No. *162747* attended the 1988 S.B.A.C. Display.)

British Aerospace/McDonnell Douglas EAV-8B Matador. Twelve aircraft ordered in 1983 for the Spanish Navy. First three aircraft delivered by air from St. Louis, Missouri, to Rota, Spain, on 6-10-87; three more on 2-12-87, and the remainder in 1988. Deployed aboard Spanish Navy's ski-deck carrier *Principe de Asturias,* 1989.

The Hawker Siddeley (British Aerospace, Kingston) Hawk T. Mark 1. Hawker P.1182 design to Air Staff Requirement 397, selected 1-10-71. Contract for one pre-production aircraft, *XX154*, and 175 production aircraft. Original allocation was *XX156-XX205, XX217-XX266; XX278-XX327* and *XX339-XX363*; this was later changed by deleting *XX354-XX363* and inserting *XX329-XX338*. Rolls-Royce/Turboméca Adour 151 engines. (Dates given below do not necessarily indicate the dates of delivery but those on which the aircraft was known to be flying with the Unit.)

No. 4 Flying Training School: *XX161; XX162* (1983); *XX163; XX167-XX171; XX172* (1983); *XX173, XX174, XX176-XX180; XX181* (1980); *XX182-XX185, XX223* (1980); *XX225; XX226; XX231-XX233; XX235-XX237; XX238* (1985); *XX239-XX242; XX244; XX245; XX249; XX250; XX290; XX291; XX293-XX299; XX307-XX309; XX313; XX314; XX338; XX347; XX349.*

Central Flying School: *XX162* (1977); *XX163* (1978); *XX165* (1980); *XX172* (1987); *XX175* (1977); *XX181* (1983); *XX224* (1984); *XX234* (1983); *XX238* (1987); *XX310* (1987); *XX312* (1983).

No. 1 Tactical Weapons Unit (No. 79 Squadron): *XX191* (1988); *XX301* (1984); *XX172* (1987)

No. 1 Tactical Weapons Unit (No. 234 Squadron): *XX159* (1985); *XX188* (1984); *XX193* (1983); *XX196; XX197; XX220* (1983); *XX302* (1983); *XX323* (1984); *XX324* (1983); *XX339; XX350* (1983); *XX351* (1987).

[The following Hawk T.1s were flown by No. 1 T.W.U., but their squadron affiliation is not known: *XX157; XX190; XX192; XX198-XX200; XX221; XX254; XX258; XX261; XX279; XX281; XX284; XX286; XX287; XX300; XX303; XX315-XX318; XX321, XX348* (1983).]

No. 2 Tactical Weapons Unit (No. 63 Squadron): *XX158* (1986); *XX186* (1983); *XX189* (1983); *XX195* (1983); *XX201-XX205* (1983); *XX217-XX219* (1983); *XX230* (1983); *XX238* (1987); *XX246-XX248; XX255; XX256; XX263; XX278-XX280* (1983); *XX282* (1983); *XX283; XX287; XX288* (1980); *XX289* (1984); *XX352* (1983).

No. 2 Tactical Weapons Unit (No. 151 Squadron): *XX187* ("*L*", 1983); *XX228* ("*Q*", 1982; *XX265* ("*U*", 1985); *XX285* ("*R*", 1983); *XX320* ("*V*", 1983); *XX322* ("*W*", 1984); *XX326* ("*A*", 1984); *XX327* ("*B*", 1987); *XX329* ("*C*", 1985); *XX330* ("*D*", 1986); *XX331* ("*E*", 1983); *XX332* ("*F*", 1981); *XX333* ("*G*", 1985); *XX334* ("*H*", 1984); *XX335* ("*I*", 1981); *XX336* ("*J*", 1983); *XX337* ("*K*", 1985); *XX340* ("*Z*", 1983); *XX345* ("*Y*", 1983); *XX346* ("*T*", 1983); *XX348* ("*M*", 1982); *XX353* ("*M*", 1983).

Empire Test Pilots' School: *XX341* ("*1*", 1983); *XX342* ("*2*", 1983); *XX343* ("*3*", 1984; converted to Advanced Systems Training Aircraft, ASTRA, by the College of Aeronautics, 1984-1985).

"The Red Arrows": *XX227* (1980); *XX243* (1984); *XX251* (1984); *XX252* (1980); *XX257* (1980, 1984); *XX259* (1980); *XX266* (1980); *XX297* (1984); *XX304* (1980); *XX306* (1984).

Systems development, handling trials and evaluation: *XX156-XX160, XX164, XX166* (BAe, Rolls-Royce Ltd., A. & A.E.E., R.A.E., etc, 1976-1980).

The British Aerospace (Kingston) Hawk T. Mark 1A. Conversion Contract issued, 31-1-83, by the Ministry of Defence for 88 Hawk T. Mark Is to be modified to carry AIM-9 Sidewinder AAMs for second-line interceptor rôle.

No. 1 Tactical Weapons Unit: *XX187* (No. 79 Sqn., 1987); *XX196* (No. 234 Sqn., 1987); *XX197* (6-84); *XX201* (No. 79 Sqn., 1987); *XX218* (No. 234 Sqn., 1987); *XX221* (1985); *XX286* (No. 79 Sqn., 1987); *XX302* (No. 234 Sqn., 1986); *XX315* (No. 234 Sqn., 1987); *XX318* (No. 79 Sqn., 1987); *XX319* (No. 79 Sqn., 1987); *XX339* (No. 234 Sqn., 1987); *XX350* (No. 234 Sqn., 1987).

No. 2 Tactical Weapons Unit: *XX159* (No. 151 Sqn., "*J*", 1986); *XX200* (1984); *XX219* (No. 63 Sqn., 1986); *XX229* (No. 151 Sqn., 1985); *XX230* (No. 151 Sqn., "*M*", 1987); *XX254* (No. 63 Sqn., 1988); *XX255* (No. 63 Sqn., 1986); *XX282* (No. 63 Sqn., 1986); *XX283* (No. 63 Sqn., 1986); *XX285* (No. 151 Sqn., "*R*", 1986); *XX288* (No. 63 Sqn., 1986); *XX289* (No. 151 Sqn., 1987); *XX301* (No. 151 Sqn., "*L*", 1986); *XX322* (No. 151 Sqn., 1987); *XX326* (No. 151 Sqn., 1985, 1987); *XX327* (No. 151 Sqn., "*K*", 1988); *XX334* (No. 63 Sqn., 1987); *XX337* (No. 151 Sqn., "*K*", 1986); *XX345* (No. 151 Sqn., "*Y*", 1986); *XX346* (No. 63 Sqn., 1987).

Other Units, etc.: *XX156* (A. &.A.E.E., 1987); *XX237* (The Red Arrows, 1987).

The Hawker Siddeley Hawk Mark 50 Demonstrator. One aircraft, *ZA101/G-HAWK*, first flown on 17 May 1976, built to demonstrate proposed export version with Rolls-Royce Adour 851 engine, five store pylons and enhanced equipment standard (including UHF, VHF, TACAN, VOR, ADF, ILS, IFF, twin-gyro attitude and heading reference system, angle-of-attack indicator and modified Martin Baker Mark 10B ejection seats. Also flown with TI of laser nose profile, optional tail parachute, combat wing, combat flap, RWR, chaff and flare dispenser, etc.

The British Aerospace (Kingston) Finnish Hawk Mark 51. Production of 50 aircraft (50-series standard) for the Finnish Air Force. Contract signed on 30 December 1977. Four aircraft, *HW302, HW303, HW305* and *HW306*, to be completed by British Aerospace (Kingston), and 46 (*HW301, HW304, HW307-HW350*) to be assembled—with some component manufacture—by Valmet OY, Finland. First flight, 16 October 1980. First two aircraft delivered to Finland, 16 December 1980.

The British Aerospace (Kingston) Kenyan Hawk Mark 52. Production order for 12 aircraft (50-series standard), *1001-1012*, for the Kenyan Air Force, signed on 9 February 1978. First production Hawks with braking parachute. First flight, 3 December 1979; first deliveries, 11 April 1980.

The British Aerospace (Kingston) Indonesian Hawk Mark 53. Total of 20 aircraft, *LL-5301* to *LL-5320*, for advanced flying/weapon training by the Indonesian Air Force (TNI-AU). First eight aircraft (*LL-5301* to *LL-5308*) ordered, 4 April 1978; four (*LL-5309* to *LL-5312*) ordered, 18 May 1981; five (*LL-5313* to *LL-5317*) ordered, 30 October 1981; three (*LL-5318* to *LL-5320*) ordered, 30 November 1982. First flight, 6 June 1980; first two aircraft ferried to Jogjakarta, Indonesia, 1 September 1980.

The British Aerospace (Kingston) Zimbabwean Hawk Mark 60. Production order for for 8 aircraft, *600-607*, for the Air Force of Zimbabwe; contract signed 9 April 1981. Aircraft to Series-60 standard with Rolls-Royce/Turboméca Adour 861. First flight, 1 April 1982; first four aircraft delivered, 27 April 1982. (Three aircraft damaged in terrorist attack on the ground in 1982, of which one was written off and two were repaired by British Aerospace and returned to service.)

The British Aerspace (Kingston) Dubai Hawk Mark 61. Production order for 8 aircraft, *501-508*, placed by the United Arab Emirates on 30 June 1981, for the Dubai Air Wing. Aircraft to Series-60 standard with Rolls-Royce/Turboméca Adour 861 engine. First flight, 11 November 1982; first aircraft delivered to Dubai, 29 March 1983.

The British Aerospace (Kingston) Venezuelan Hawk Mark 62. Contract signed for undisclosed number of "ground attack enhanced" aircraft, but subsequently cancelled.

The British Aerospace (Kingston) Abu Dhabi Hawk Mark 63. Production order for 16 aircraft placed by the United Arab Emirates on 2 January 1963 for the Abu Dhabi Air Force for advanced flying/weapons training. Aircraft to Series-60 standard with Rolls-Royce/Turboméca Adour 861 engine.

The British Aerospace (Kingston) Kuwaiti Hawk Mark 64. Production order for 12 aircraft placed by the Kuwaiti Air Force on 31 October 1983 for advanced flying/weapons training. Aircraft to Series-60 standard with Rolls-Royce/Turboméca Adour 861 engine.

The British Aerospace (Kingston) Saudi Arabian Hawk Mark 65. Production order placed for 30 aircraft for service with the Royal Saudi Air Force in the advanced flying/weapons training rôle. Aircraft to Series-60 standard with Rolls-Royce/Turboméca Adour 861.

The British Aerospace (Kingston) Swiss Hawk Mark 66. Order for 20 aircraft to Series-60 standard, signed on 20-10-87, with Rolls-Royce/Turboméca Adour 861 engine. One aircraft assembled in Britain, and first flown on 7-4-89 by Paul Hopkins (and delivered to G.R.D. Switzerland, 8-11-89, with Swiss registration *U-1251*), and 19 to be assembled in Switzerland. Deliveries from the Swiss assembly line due to start in 1990. (Note: The first Swiss aircraft carried the British serial number *ZG974* for armament range and flight test purposes in the U.K. during 1989.)

The British Aerospace (Kingston) Hawk 200. One private venture prototype, *ZG200*. Single-seat aircraft with full combat potential, powered by Rolls-Royce/Turboméca Adour 871. First flight, 19 May 1986, flown by Mike Snelling. Destroyed in accident at Dunsfold, 2-7-86; pilot, Jim Hawkins, killed.

The British Aerospace (Kingston) Hawk 200. One private venture pre-production development aircraft, *ZH200*. 7,845 lb.-thrust Rolls-Royce/Turboméca Adour 781 engine; equipment included Singer-Kearfott inertial navigator, Smiths HUD-WAC, HOTAS, UFC and PDU. First flight, 24-4-87, flown by Chris Roberts. Possesses optional radar fit facility for Westinghouse AN/AGP-66H radar.

The British Aerospace/McDonnell Douglas T-45A Goshawk. Two pre-production aircraft, and 12 pilot-production (Lot 1) naval two-seat trainers (developed directly from the BAe Hawk), assembled at McDonnell Douglas Air Force Plant No. 42, Palmdale, California. First pre-production aircraft, BuNo. *162787*, flown at Long Beach, California, on 16-4-88, flown by Fred Hamilton of Douglas Aircraft Company. Lot 1 aircraft financed by FY 1988 funding planned to start delivery to NAS, Kingsville, Texas, in October 1989. Lot II (24 limited-production aircraft) funded in FY 1989 budget. 5,700-lb. thrust Rolls-Royce/Turboméca Adour (861) F105-RR-400L turbofan. Aircraft stressed for deck landing and equipped with arrester hook. (Ultimate U.S. Navy requirement is said to be for up to 300 aircraft.)

The British Aerospace (Kingston) Hawk 100. Order placed by United Arab Emirates in 1989, said to be for 12 aircraft to serve with one Squadron of the Abu Dhabi Air Force.

GLOSSARY

A.A.C.U.	Anti-Aircraft Co-operation Unit	B.B.O.C.	Brought back on Charge
A.A.F.	Auxiliary Air Force	B.D.U.	Bombing Development Unit
A. & A.E.E.	Aeroplane and Armament Experimental Establishment	B.G.S.	Bombing and Gunnery School
		B.P.	Boulton-Paul Aircraft Ltd.
A.A.M.	Air-to-Air missile	B.U.	Broken up
A.A.P.C.	Anti-Aircraft Practice Camp	B.V.R.	Beyond Visual Range
A.A.S.	Air Armament School		
A.A.S.F.	Advanced Air Striking Force	(C)	(Communications)
A.C.D.U.	Army Co-operation Development Unit	CA and C(A)	Controller (Air)
		C.A.A.C.U.	Civilian Anti-Aircraft Co-operation Unit
A.D.G.B.	Air Defence of Great Britain		
A.E.A.F.	Allied Expeditionary Air Force	C.A.A.D.	Coastal Area Aircraft Depot
A.F.B.	Air Force Base (American)	C.A.C.F.	Coast Artillery Co-operation Flight
A.F.D.U. (S)	Air Fighting Development Unit (Squadron)		
		C.A.F.	Canadian Air Force
A.F.E.E.	Airborne Forces Experimental Establishment	Cal.	Calibration
		C.A.P.	Combat Air Patrol
A.G.M.E.	Aircraft Gun Mounting Establishment	C.A.S.	Chief of the Air Staff
		C.C.D.U.	Coastal Command Development Unit
A.G.S.	Air Gunners' School		
A.I.	Airborne Interception	C.C.F.	Canadian Car & Foundry Corporation Ltd.
A.M.	Air Ministry		
A.M.E.S.	Air Ministry Experimental Station	C.D.	Coastal Defence
		C.F.	Communications Flight
AMRAAM	Advanced Medium-range Air-to-Air Missile.	C.F.E.	Central Fighter Establishment
		C.F.S.	Central Flying School
A.N.S.	Air Navigation School	C.G.S.	Central Gunnery School
A.O.C.	Air Officer Commanding	C.L.	Crash landed
A.O.C.-in-C.	Air Officer Commanding-in-Chief	C.L.E.	Central Landing Establishment
		C.L.S.	Central Landing School
A.O.N.S.	Air Observers' Navigation School	C.N.S.	Central Navigation School
A.O.S.	Air Observers' School	C.R.O.	Civilian Repair Organisation
A.P.C. (S)	Armament Practice Camp (Station)	C.S.	Communications Squadron
		C.S.(A)	Controller of Supplies (Air)
A.S.M.	Air-to-Surface missile	C.T.O.L.	Conventional Take-off and Landing
A.S.M.	Armstrong Siddeley Motors Ltd.		
A.S.R.	Air-Sea Rescue	C.T.P.	Chief Test Pilot
A.S.R.	Air Staff Requirement	C.U.	Conversion Unit (with number)
A.S.T.	Air Staff Target	C.U.	Communications Unit
A.S.T.O.V.L.	Advanced Short Take-off and Vertical Landing	C.U.A.S.	Cambridge University Air Squadron
ASTRA	Advanced Systems TRaining Aircraft		
		D.B.	Development Batch
A.T.A.	Air Transport Auxiliary	D.B.F.	Destroyed by Fire
A.T.C. (S)	Armament Training Camp (Station)	D.B.R.	Damaged beyond (economic) repair
A.T.D.U.	Air Torpedo Development Unit	Deld.	Delivered (and date following)
A.T.U.	Armament Training Unit (India)	D.F.L.S.	Day Fighter Leaders' School
A.W.A.	Sir W.G. Armstrong Whitworth Aircraft Ltd.	D.T.D.	Director (or Directorate) of Technical Development
		D.W.I.	Direction Wireless Installation
(B)	(Bomber)		
B.A.C.	British Aircraft Corporation	E.A.A.S.	Empire Air Armament School
BAe	British Aerospace PLC.	E.A.N.S.	Empire Air Navigation School
B.A.F.O.	British Air Forces of Occupation	E.C.F.S.	Empire Central Flying School

E.F.S.	Empire Flying School	H.A.L.	Hawker Aircraft Ltd.
E.F.T.S.	Elementary Flying Training School	H.C.C.S.	Home Command Communications Squadron
E.R.F.T.S.	Elementary & Reserve Flying Training School	H.C.F.	Home Communications Flight
		H.C.U.	Heavy Conversion Unit
E.R.S.	Empire Radio School	H.G.H.E.L.	H.G. Hawker Engineering Co., Ltd.
E.T.P.S.	Empire Test Pilots' School		
E.W.S.	Electrical & Wireless School	H.O.T.A.S.	Hands on Throttle and Stick
		H.S.(A).L.	Hawker Siddeley (Aviation) Ltd.
(F)	(Fighter)	H.U.D.	Head-up Display
F.A.A.	Fleet Air Arm		
F.A.B.	*Force Aérienne Belge*	I.A.F.	Indian Air Force
F.C.C.S.	Fighter Command Communications Squadron	I.N.S.	Indian Navy Ship
		I.N.T.U.	Indian Navy Training Unit
ff.	First flight (and date following)	I.R.S.	Instrument Rating Squadron
F.F.S.	Fire Fighting School		
F.G.A.	Fighter Ground Attack	L.C.F.	Levant Communications Flight
Fg. Off. (F/O)	Flying Officer	L.E.R.X.	Leading Edge Root Extension
F.I.S.	Flying Instructors' School	L.G.	Landing Ground
F.I.U.	Fighter Interception Unit	L.I.D.	Lift Improvement Device
F.L.	Force landed	L.R.M.T.S.	Laser Ranging and Marked Target System
F.L.I.R.	Forward-looking Infra-red		
F.L.S.	Fighter Leaders' School		
Flt.	Flight	M.A.E.E.	Marine Aircraft Experimental Establishment
Flt. Lt. (F/L)	Flight Lieutenant		
F.P.	Ferry Pool	M.A.P.	Ministry of Aircraft Production
F.P.P.	Ferry Pilots' Pool	M.C.A.	Ministry of Civil Aviation
(FR)	(Fighter Reconnaissance)	M.C.S.	Metropolitan Communications Squadron
F.R.A.D.U.	Fleet Requirements and Development Unit		
		M.E.C.S.	Middle East Communications Squadron
F.R.A.D.T.U.	Fleet Requirements and Development Training Unit		
		M.I.A.	Missing In Action
F.R.L.	Flight Refuelling Ltd.	M.o.D.	Ministry of Defence
F.R.U.	Fleet Requirements Unit	M.o.S.	Ministry of Supply
F/Sgt.	Flight Sergeant	M.S.F.U.	Merchant Ship Fighter Unit
F.T.S.	Flying Training School	M.U.	Maintenance Unit
F.T.U.	Ferry Training Unit		
F.W.S.	Fighter Weapons School	N.A.E.	Naval Aircraft Establishment
F.Y.	Financial (or Fiscal) Year	N.A.S.	Naval Air Station (U.S. Navy)
		N.A.T.C.	Naval Air Test Center (U.S.N.)
G.A.	Ground Attack	N.B.M.R.	Nato Basic Military Requirement
G.A.C.	Gloster Aircraft Co. Ltd.	N.F.F.	Night Flying Flight
G.C.F.	Gunnery Co-operation Flight	N.T.P.	New Types Park
G.D.G.S.	Ground Defence Gunners' School	N.T.U.	Navigation Training Unit
G.G.S.	Ground Gunners' School		
G.G.S.	Gyro Gunsight	O.A.D.U. (F)	Overseas Aircraft Delivery Unit (Flight)
G.I.S.	Glider Instructors' School		
G.O.T.U.	Glider Operational Training Unit	O.A.F.U.	Observers' Advanced Flying Unit
(GP)	(General Purpose)	O.C.U.	Operational Conversion Unit
Gp.	Group	O.F.U.	Overseas Ferry Unit
Gp. Capt. (G/C)	Group Captain	O.T.S.	Officers Training School
G.P.E.U.	Glider Pilots' Exercise Unit	O.T.U.	Operational Training Unit
G.T.F.	Gunnery Training Flight	O.U.A.S.	Oxford University Air Squadron
G.T.S.	Glider Training School (with number)		
		P.A.F.U.	Pilots' Advanced Flying Unit
G.T.S.	Glider Training Squadron (without number)	P.A.P.	Pilots & Aircrew Pool (Kenya)
		P.C.B.	Plenum Chamber Burning
		P.D.	Packing Depot
H.A.D.	Home Aircraft Depot	P.D.U.	Photographic Development Unit

Plt. Off. (P/O)	Pilot Officer	S.T.S.	Seaplane Training Squadron
P.R.U.	Photographic Reconnaissance Unit	S. of T.T.	School of Technical Training
P.T.S.	Parachute Training School	(T)	(Training)
P.V.	Private Venture	TACAN	TACtical Air Navigation
		T.A.F.	Tactical Air Force
Q.F.I.	Qualified Flying Instructor	Tac R	Tactical Reconnaissance
		T.B.	Torpedo Bomber
R.A.A.F.	Royal Australian Air Force	T.C.D.U. (F)	Transport Command Development Unit (Flight)
R.Aux.A.F.	Royal Auxiliary Air Force		
R.A.E.	Royal Aircraft Establishment	T.D.U.	Torpedo Development Unit
R.A.F.C.	Royal Air Force College, Cranwell	T.E.U.	Tactical Exercise Unit
		T.F.	Training Flight
R.A.F.F.C.	Royal Air Force Flying College	T.F.U.	Telecommunications Flying Unit
R.A.F.G.	Royal Air Force, Germany	T.I.	Trial installations
R.C.A.F.	Royal Canadian Air Force	T.O.C.	Taken on Charge
R.F.S.	Reserve Flying School	T.R.E.	Telecommunications Research Establishment
R.I.A.F.	Royal Indian Air Force		
R.N.A.S.	Royal Naval Air Station	T.S.T.	Tri-Service Trials (U.S.A.)
R.N.Z.A.F.	Royal New Zealand Air Force	T.T.	Target Towing
R.P.W.	Runway Penetration Weapon	T.T.C.C.F.	Technical Training Command Communications Flight
R.R.	Rolls-Royce Ltd.		
R.S.	Radio School	T.T.F.	Target Towing Flight
R.S.U.	Repair and Servicing (or Salvage) Unit	T.T.U.	Torpedo Training Flight
		T.U.R.P.	Training Unit and Reserve Pool (Middle East)
R.W.R.	Radar Warning Receiver		
		T.W.U.	Tactical Weapons Unit
S.A.A.F.	South African Air Force		
S.A.C.	School of Army Co-operation	U.A.E.	United Arab Emirates
S.A.N.	School of Air Navigation	U.A.S.	University Air Squadron
S.B.A.C.	Society of British Aircraft (or Aerospace) Constructors	U.L.A.S.	University of London Air Squadron
S.D.	Special Duties	U.S.A.A.F.	United States Army Air Force
S.F.	Station Flight	U.S.A.F.	United States Air Force
S.F.C.	School of Flying Control	U.S.M.C.	United States Marine Corps
S.F.P.P.	Service Ferry Pilots' Pool	U.S.M.C.S.	United States Marine Corps Station
S.F.T.S.	Service Flying Training School		
S.F.T.S.(I)	Service Flying Training School	U.S.N.	United States Navy
Sgt.	Sergeant		
S.N.C.	School of Naval Co-operation	V.A.	Vickers-Armstrongs
S.O.C.	Struck off Charge	V./S.T.O.L.	Vertical/ Short Take-off and Landing
S. of P.	School of Photography		
S.P.	Super-Priority	V.T.O.	Vertical Take-off
Spec.	Specification	V.T.O.L	Vertical Take-off and Landing
Sqn. Ldr. (S/L)	Squadron Leader		
S.R.A.A.M.	Short Range Air-toAir Missile	W.D.C.F. (U)	Western Desert Communications Flight (Unit)
S.R.A.F.	Southern Rhodesian Air Force		
S.S.	Signals School	W.D.U.	Wireless Development Unit
S.S.V.A.F.	Straits Settlements Volunteer Air Force	W.E.E.	Wireless Experimental Establishment
Stn. Flt.	Station Flight	Wg.	Wing
S.T.O.V.L.	Short Take-off and Vertical Landing	Wg. Cdr. (W/C)	Wing Commander
		W/Off (W/O)	Warrant Officer

UNBUILT AND UNFINISHED PROJECTS

Prior to 1939 no Company Project Designation system existed, each project being referred to by the Air Ministry Specification to which it was designed. In many cases, however, design studies were initiated when no official requirement existed and these designs were usually referred to simply by their duty and engine, for example "Hawker Corps Reconnaissance Monoplane (Jaguar)". There is no complete record of the early projects and the following is the most comprehensive available from the Company records.

Name/Designation.	Date.	Remarks.
Hawker Humpback Fleet Spotter.	1920	Schemed only.
Hawker Skua Scout Fighter.	1921	Schemed only.
Racing Biplane (Jupiter).	1922	Design incomplete.
Metal-wing Duiker.	1923	Manufacture incomplete.
Hawker Cantilever Monoplane Fighter (Jupiter).	1925	Schemed only.
Middle-East Transport Biplane.	1927	Project drawings only.
Night Bombing Landplane to Spec. B.19/27.	1928	Project drawings only.
Two-seat Torpedo Ship-plane to Spec. M.5/28.	1928	Reached detail design.
3-seat Fleet Spotter Recce. to Spec. S.9/30.	1930	Project drawings only.
2-seat Day Bomber to P.27/32.	1932	Tendered, 1933.
Single-seat Fighter to F.5/34.	1934	Became F.36/34 Hurricane.
2-seat Fleet Fighter to Spec. O.27/34.	1934	Tendered, 1934.
2-seat Army Co-operation Biplane to Spec. A.39/34.	1934	Tendered, 1934.
Single-seat Fighter to Spec. F.35/35.	1935	Tendered, 21/2/36.
Day and Night Fighter to Spec. F.37/35.	1935	Tendered, 23/4/36.
Medium Bomber (2 Vultures) to Spec. P.13/36.	1936	Tendered, 1/1/37.
2-engine 2-seat Turret Fighter to Spec. F.11/37.	1937	Tendered, 1937.
Torpedo Bomber Recce. to Spec. S.24/37.	1937	Tendered, 1938.
Fleet Fighter with fixed guns to Spec. N.8/39.	1939	Detail design. Tendered.
Fleet Fighter with turret guns to Spec. N.9/39.	1939	Project tendered.
Single-seat Fighter (Griffon) with two 40-mm guns.	1939	Only schemed.
Tornado with Bristol Centaurus.	1939	Preliminary scheme only.
P.1000. Single-engine shaft-drive Fighter (Sabre with 2 propellers).	1940	Only schemed.
Tornado with Duplex Cyclone.	1940–1	Preliminary scheme only.
Tornado with Fairey Monarch.	1940	Preliminary scheme only.

Typhoon with 6-cannon wing.	1940	Set of wings built.
P.1001. Close Support Bomber based on Henley to B.7/40.	1940	Only schemed.
P.1002. Installation of 20-mm cannon in Hurricane.	1940	Became Hurricane IIC.
Henley Long-range two-seat Fighter.	1940	Only bomb-bay tanks designed.
P.1003. Henley Escort Fighter conversion.	1940	Only schemed.
P.1004. 2-seat High Altitude Fighter to F.7/40.	1940	Tendered, 1941.
P.1005. High Speed Bomber with two Sabres.	1940	Spec. B.11/41 later framed round this design.
P.1006 Henley Close Support Bomber to B.20/40.	1940	Tendered, 1940.
P.1007. Single-seat High Altitude Fighter.	1940	Tendered, 1941.
P.1008. Night Fighter to Spec. F.18/40.	1940	Tendered, 1940.
Hurricane Floatplane.	1940	Conversion cancelled.
Hurricane with Griffon.	1940	Abandoned in 1941.
Hurricane/Liberator Composite aircraft.	1941	Designed with Short & Harland Ltd.
Towed Hurricane Project.	1941	With Flight Refuelling Ltd.
P.1009 Typhoon Fleet Fighter to Spec. N.11/40.	1941	Tendered, 1941.
P.1010. Typhoon with Turbo-Supercharger.	1941	Schemed only.
P.1011. P.1005 with Power Jet engines.	1941	Schemed only.
P.1012. Typhoon II with leading edge radiators.	1941	Became Tempest Mk. I.
P.1013. P.1005 with remotely operated guns.	1941	Schemed only.
P.1014. Single-seat Fighter with one Power Jet engine.	1941	Schemed only.
Hurricane with Hercules.	1941	Schemed only.
Hurricane with Merlin XXX.	1942	Schemed only.
P.1015. P.1005 with Centaurus engines.	1942	Schemed only.
P.1016. Typhoon II with Griffon.	1942	Became Tempest III and IV.
P.1017. Single-seat Fighter with Griffon.	1942	Based on Typhoon wings.
P.1018. Hawker Light Fighter with Sabre IV.	1942	Formed basis of Fury.
P.1019. Hawker Light Fighter with Griffon 61.	1942	Formed basis of Fury.
P.1020. Hawker Light Fighter with Centaurus IV.	1942	Formed basis of Fury.
Tempest with 0.50-in guns.	1942	Schemed only.
P.1021. Tempest with Centaurus.	1942	Formed basis of F.6/43.
P.1022. Naval Fighter to N.7/43.	1943	Became Sea Fury X.
P.1023. Sabre IV in Tempest I.	1943	Tendered, 1943.

P.1024. Tempest development with Sabre.	1943	Not tendered.
P.1025. Light Fighter with Griffon.	1943	Tendered, 1943.
P.1026. F.2/43 with Griffon.	1943	Built: *LA610*.
P.1027. Tempest with R.R.46.	1943	Not tendered.
P.1028. Tail-less Fighter.	1943	Schemed only. Not tendered.
P.1029. Tail-first aircraft.	1943	Schemed only. Not tendered.
P.1030. Fighter with 4,000 h.p. engine.	1943	Not tendered.
P.1031. Fighter with Rolls-Royce B.40 jet engine.	1944	Schemed only.
P.1032. P.1026 with Rolls-Royce Eagle engine.	1944	Schemed only.
P.1033. P.1005 with two Eagles.	1944	Schemed only.
P.1034. P.1005 with two Rolls-Royce B.41 engines.	1944	Schemed only.
P.1035. P.1026 with one Rolls-Royce B.41 engine.	1944	Schemed only
P.1036. P.1026 with Sabre V.	1944	Private venture scheme.
P.1037. Twin-boom Fighter with two Griffons.	1944	Not tendered.
P. 1038. P.1034 with Rolls-Royce B.41 engine.	1944	Schemed only.
P.1039. P.1034 with two B.41s in fuselage.	1945	Schemed only.
P.1040 P.1035 with one B.41 in fuselage.	1945	Tendered, Feb 1945; became Sea Hawk.
P.1041. Design investigation into Mosquito Replacement.	1945	—
P.1042. Variation of P.1040.	1945	Schemed only.
P.1043. P.1040 without undercarriage.	1945	Led to trials later.
P.1044. Naval Fighter-Bomber.	1945	Schemed only.
P.1045. Naval version of P.1040.	1945	Schemed only.
P.1046. Naval version of P.1040 with rocket boost.	1945	Schemed only.
P.1047. P.1046 with extreme sweep-back.	1945	Schemed only.
P.1048. Fighter with two Armstrong Siddeley AS.65.	1945	Tendered, November 1945.
P.1049. Fighter with one AS.65 and extreme sweep-back.	1945	Schemed only.
P.1050. Long-range High-Altitude tail-less Transport.	1946	Schemed only.
P.1051. Fleet Bomber with large missile.	1946	Schemed only.
P.1052. P.1050 with swept wings to Spec. E.38/46.	1946	Two built: *VX272 & VX279*.
P.1053. Various Rocket Fighters.	1946	Schemed only.
P.1054. Design to F.43/46 with AS.65s close to fuselage.	1946	Tendered, 1946.
P.1055. Eight-seat Commercial aircraft.	1946	Schemed only.

P.1056. Night Fighter with unswept wing to F.44/46.	1946	Reached detail design.
P.1057. Night Fighter with swept wing to F.44/46.	1946	Reached detail design.
P.1058. Four-five seat Private Owner/ Taxi aircraft.	1947	Project design only.
P.1059. Naval version of P.1056 with wing nacelles.	1947	Schemed only.
P.1060. Naval version of P.1056 with fuselage nacelles.	1947	Schemed only.
P.1061. P.1054 with straight wings.	1947	Schemed only.
P.1062. P.1052 with AS65 engine.	1947	Schemed only.
P.1063. To Spec. H.9/47.	1947	Schemed only.
P.1064. Research aircraft with 2 Avons on top of wing.	1948	Project design only.
P.1065. Fighter with one jet and one 2,000 lb rocket engine.	1948	Schemed only.
P.1066. Omitted.		
P.1067. Interceptor Fighter to F.3/48. Hunter.	1948	Three prototypes, *WB188, WB195* and *WB202.*
P.1068. P.1040 with Rolls-Royce R.B.66 engine.	1948	Project design only.
P.1069. Transonic Research aircraft.	1948	Project design only.
P.1070. Transonic Research aircraft.	1948	Project design only.
P.1071. Transonic Research aircraft.	1948	Project design only.
P.1072. P.1040 with Snarler.	1948	Conversion of *VP401.*
P.1073. Fighter aircraft.	1949	Schemed only.
P.1074. N.7/46 aircraft with modified wings.	1949	Schemed only.
P.1075. P.1062 with Nene engine.	1949	Schemed only.
P.1076. Investigation and design development of P.1067.	1949	—
P.1077. General Purpose Fighter with two Avons.	1949	Schemed only.
P.1078. P.1052 with Rocket.	1949	Schemed only.
P.1079. Not used.		
P.1080. P.1052 to Australian requirements.	1950	Later embodied in P.1081.
P.1081. Development of P.1052 with Nene or Tay.	1950	Australian requirements investigated.
P.1082. Fighter design to F.23/48.	1950	Not proceeded with.
P.1083. 50 degrees swept wing on Hunter.	1950–2	Manufacture incomplete.
P.1084. Design for delta wing investigations.	1951	Not proceeded with.
P.1085. Design for delta wing investigations.	1951	Not proceeded with.
P.1086. Not used (possible confusion with American F-86 fighter).		
P.1087. Naval version of P.1081.	1951	Project design only.

P.1088. Light Fighter with two 3,000-lb-thrust engines.	1951	Project design only.
P.1089. Rocket Fighter with one 5,000-lb-thrust engine.	1951	Project design only.
P.1090. Hunter with D.H. Gyron.	1951	Project design only.
P.1091. Hunter with delta wing.	1951	Design study in conjunction with Avros.
P.1092. 2-seat supersonic delta All-weather Fighter.	1951	Project design only.
P.1093. Single-seat supersonic delta All-weather Fighter.	1952	Project design only.
P.1094. P.1072 with thin wings.	1952	Schemed only.
P.1095. P.1083 with larger fuselage for Sapphire 4 or Avon R.A.14 & reheat.	1952	Project design only.
P.1096. Supersonic delta with Rolls-Royce R.B.106.	1953	Project design only.
P.1097. P.1083 with R.B.106.	1953	Schemed only.
P.1098. Medium Transport with two Alvis Leonides.	1953	Project design only.
P.1099. Hunter with Avon R.A.19 or R.A.28.	1953	Became Hunter Mk. 6.
P.1100. Supersonic Hunter with RA.24 and 2 Rockets.	1955	Project design only.
P.1101. Two-seat Hunter Trainer.	1953–5	Became Hunter T. Mk. 7.
P.1102. Thin-wing Hunter.	1954	Schemed only.
P.1103. Strike Fighter with D.H. Gyron.	1954	Prototype commenced.
P.1104. Mach 2 aircraft with 2 Rolls-Royce R.B.112s.	1954	Project design only.
P.1108. Naval Strike Fighter to Spec. M.148T.	1954	Tendered.
P.1109. Hunter 6 with Firestreak.	1954	Two aircraft built.
P.1114. All-weather Hunter. Avon.	1955	T.I.s commenced.
P.1115. All-weather Hunter. Sapphire.	1955	T.I.s commenced.
P.1120. Hunter Advanced Trainer.	1956	Reached detail design.
P.1121. Air Superiority Strike aircraft (several versions). From P.1103.	1956–8	Prototype half completed.
P.1122. P.1121 with steel wing.	1957	Project design only.
— Twin ASM air turbo-rocket Mach 3 to 4 research aircraft.	1956	Schemed only.
P.1126. VTO project undertaken as installation and configuration exercise.	1957	Project design only.
P.1127. PV V/STOL research aircraft; became HS Kestrel.	1957–62	Major research programme; six prototypes built.
P.1128. Hunter 6-seat high-speed transport.	1957	Project design only.
— V/STOL design with 4 deflected-thrust engines plus 2 cruise engines.	1957	Project design only.
P.1134. Mach 3 to 4 research aircraft with	1959	Project design only.

636

one Rolls-Royce RB.146 plus two ramjets.

P.1136. V/STOL design. 4 lift engines plus one cruise engine.	1959	Project design only.
P.1137. V/STOL design. 2 rotatable tip pods plus 2 cruise engines.	1959	Project design only.
P.1139. V/STOL design. 2 lift/1 cruise engine.	1960	Project design only.
P.1140. V/STOL design. 3 lift/1 cruise engine.	1960	Schemed only.
P.1143. V/STOL project. 4 rotatable tip pods plus 3 lift engines.	1960	Schemed only.
P.1149. V/STOL design. 6 lift/2 cruise engines.	1961	Schemed only.
P.1150. Supersonic V/STOL design. One BS. 100 VT turbofan with PCB.	1961	Submitted to M.o.D. P.1150/3 became P.1154.
P.1152. V/STOL project. 4 lift/1 cruise engine.	1961	Schemed only.
P.1154. Detail design for Mach 2 V/STOL RAF and RN fighter and strike aircraft. One 33,000 lb thrust VT turbo-fan or 2 VT Speys with PCB cf. P.1150/3.	1961–64	Won NBMR-3 design competition. Prototype construction advanced, but cancelled, 1964.
P.1179. STOVL project.	c.1967	Schemed only.
P.1182. Tandem two-seat dual-rôle trainer.	c.1967	Became HS/BAe Hawk T.1.
P.1185-9. STOVL project.	c.1969	Schemed only.
P.1205-11. STOVL project.	c.1974	Submitted to AST.403.
P.1214-3. STOVL project?	c.1976	Schemed only.

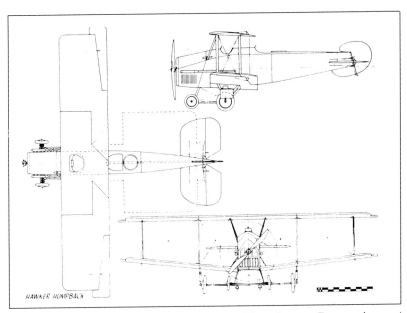

THE HAWKER HUMPBACK. Three-seat Fleet Spotter Reconnaissance/ General Purpose aircraft. Drawing No. A1, dated December 1920. First Hawker design.

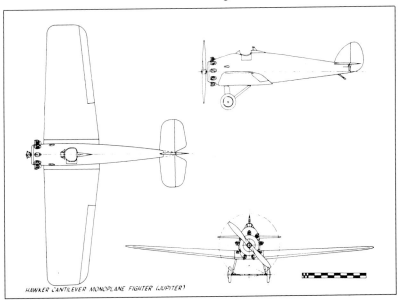

HAWKER MONOPLANE FIGHTER PROJECT. Drawing dated February 1925, signed by S. Camm. Bristol Jupiter engine, Twin Vickers gun armament.

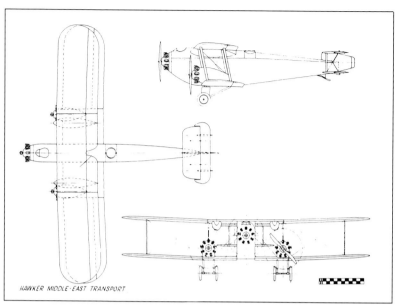

HAWKER MIDDLE-EAST TRANSPORT PROJECT. Drawing dated 1926. Three Bristol Jupiter engines. Also twin engine version.

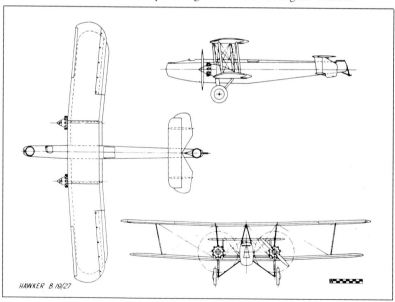

THE HAWKER B.19/27 HEAVY BOMBER. Drawings dated 1927–28. Two Bristol Jupiter engines. Crew of 4. Handley Page Heyford was successful tender to this Specification.

639

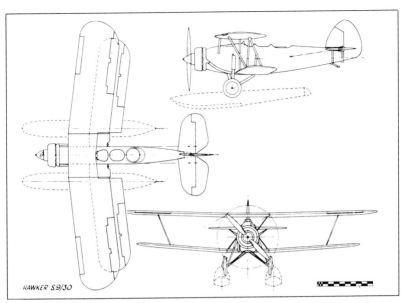

HAWKER S.9/30. Three-seat Torpedo Spotter Reconnaissance. Interchange-able wheel and float undercarriage. Armstrong Siddeley Panther engine.

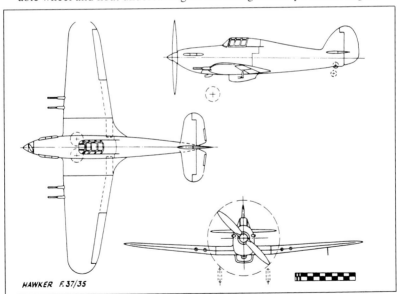

THE HAWKER F.37/35. Project tendered 23 April 1936. Hurricane with four 20-mm Oerlikon guns. Not accepted, as single engine not considered practical for the heavy armament. Westland Whirlwind was successful tender to this Specification.

640

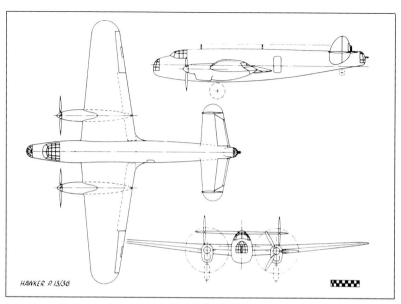

THE HAWKER P.13/36 MEDIUM BOMBER. Project tendered 1 January 1937. Powered by two Rolls-Royce Vulture engines. Avro Manchester was successful tender to this Specification.

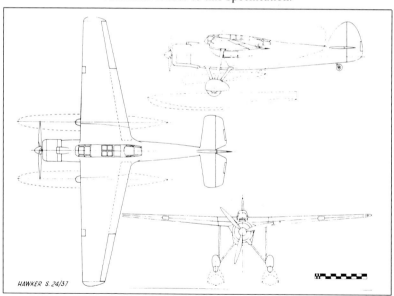

THE HAWKER S.24/37. Torpedo Spotter Reconnaissance monoplane. Bristol Taurus engine. Original requirement called for fixed undercarriage or floats. Fairey Barracuda was successful tender to this Specification.

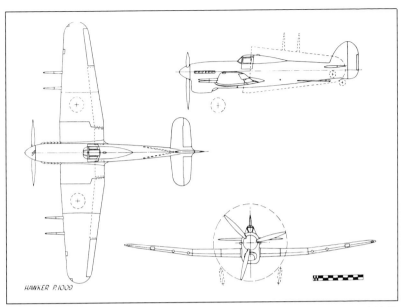

THE HAWKER P.1009. Naval Strike Fighter to Spec. N.11/40, tendered 1941. Development of Typhoon. Folding wings with additional fuel. Blackburn Firebrand was successful tender to this Specification.

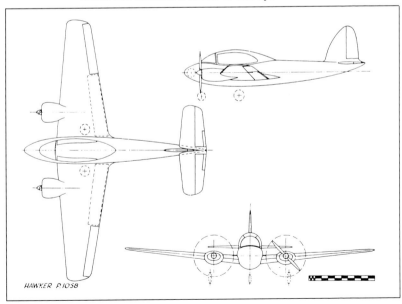

THE HAWKER P.1058. Private venture 4/5-seat private owner/taxi project. Two Lycoming/Continental engines. 1947

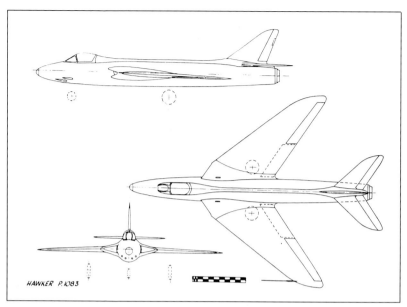

THE HAWKER P.1083. Supersonic development of the Hunter with 50 degrees swept wing. 1951–53. Rolls-Royce Avon R.A.14R turbojet with reheat. Construction of prototype commenced but abandoned in 1953.

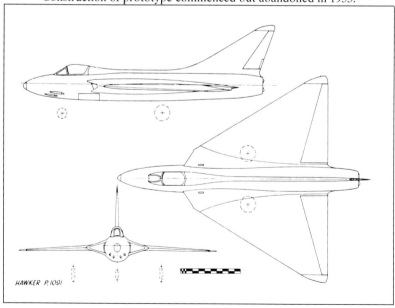

THE HAWKER P.1091. Delta-wing project design based on Hunter. Parallel with design proposals by A. V. Roe & Co. Ltd. Rolls-Royce Avon R.A.14R.

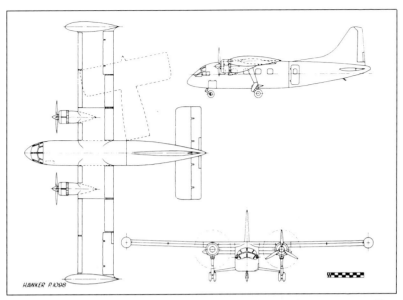

THE HAWKER P.1098. 15-16 seat Short-Haul Feederline Transport. Two Alvis Leonides engines. Swing-tail for freight loading. Project work undertaken in 1953.

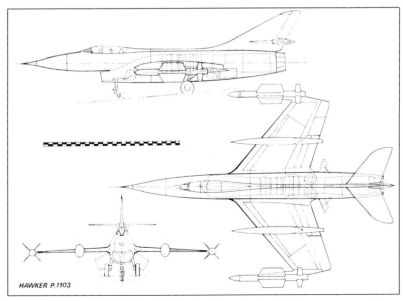

THE HAWKER P.1103. P.V. High altitude all-weather fighter to Spec. F.155T, 1955. D.H Gyron engine with rocket boosters. Shown with two Red Hebe AAMs.

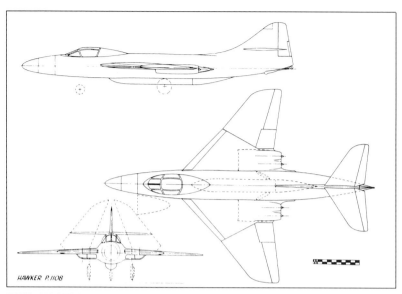

THE HAWKER P.1108. Two-seat Naval Strike aircraft to Spec. M.148T. Four small Rolls-Royce turbojets. Blackburn Buccaneer was successful tender to this Specification.

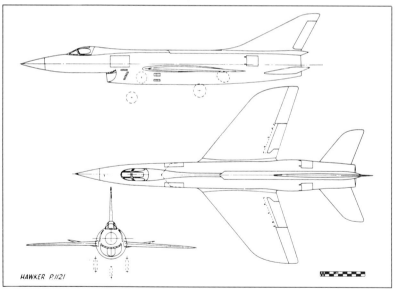

THE HAWKER P.1121. Private venture Air Superiority Strike aircraft. Mach 2.5 performance. De Havilland Gyron turbojet with reheat. Also two-seat version with Bristol Olympus or Rolls-Royce Conway engines. Prototype construction abandoned in 1958.

645

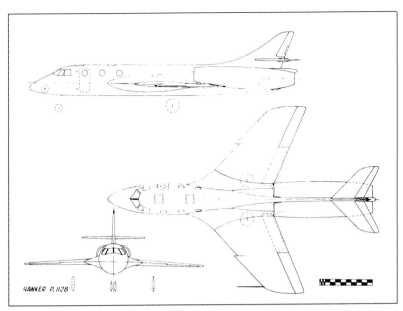

THE HAWKER P.1128. Private venture project, 1957. Six-seat High-Speed Transport based on Hunter. Two Bristol Orpheus turbojets.

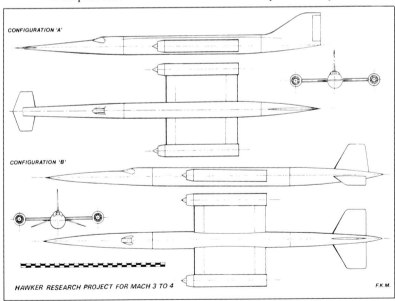

HAWKER MACH 3 TO 4 RESEARCH AIRCRAFT. To Spec. ER.161T., 1956. Alternative configurations. Two Armstrong Siddeley 30 in diameter air-turbo rockets.

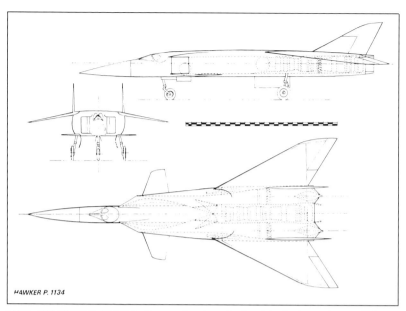

HAWKER P. 1134

THE HAWKER P.1134. Research aircraft for Mach 3 to 4, possibly to ER.180D. R.B.146 turbojet and two 8.4 sq ft ramjets. Span, 30 ft; length, 64.5 ft. T/c ratio, 3 per cent.

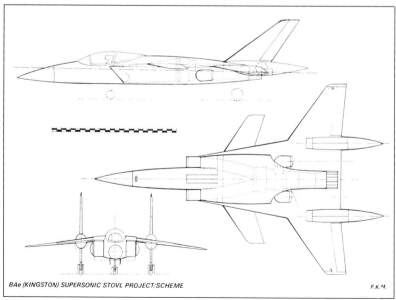

BAe (KINGSTON) SUPERSONIC STOVL PROJECT/SCHEME   F.K.M.

BRITISH AEROSPACE (KINGSTON) MACH 2+ STOVL PROJECT. c. 1976. Dimensions speculative. Modified Pegasus VT turbofan with reheat.

INDEX

649

655